Table of Atomic Masses*

	Symbol	Atomic Number	Atomic Mass		Symbol	Atomic Number	Atomic Mass
Actinium	Ac	89	(227)†	Mercury	Hg	80	200.6
Aluminum	Al	13	26.98	Molybdenum	Mo	42	95.94
Americium	Am	95	(243)	Neodymium	Nd	60	144.2
Antimony	Sb	51	121.8	Neon	Ne	10	20.18
Argon	Ar	18	39.95	Neptunium	Np	93	(237)
Arsenic	As	33	74.92	Nickel	Ni	28	58.70
Astatine	At	85	(210)	Niobium	Nb	41	92.91
Barium	Ba	56	137.3	Nitrogen	N	7	14.01
Berkelium	Bk	97	(247)	Nobelium	No	102	(259)
Beryllium	Be	4	9.012	Osmium	Os	76	190.2
Bismuth	Bi	83	209.0	Oxygen	O	8	16.00
Boron	B	5	10.81	Palladium	Pd	46	106.4
Bromine	Br	35	79.90	Phosphorus	P	15	30.97
Cadmium	Cd	48	112.4	Platinum	Pt	78	195.1
Calcium	Ca	20	40.08	Plutonium	Pu	94	(244)
Californium	Cf	98	(251)	Polonium	Po	84	(209)
Carbon	C	6	12.01	Potassium	K	19	39.10
Cerium	Ce	58	140.1	Praseodymium	Pr	59	140.9
Cesium	Cs	55	132.9	Promethium	Pm	61	(145)
Chlorine	Cl	17	35.45	Protactinium	Pa	91	(231)
Chromium	Cr	24	52.00	Radium	Ra	88	226.0
Cobalt	Co	27	58.93	Radon	Rn	86	(222)
Copper	Cu	29	63.55	Rhenium	Re	75	186.2
Curium	Cm	96	(247)	Rhodium	Rh	45	102.9
Dysprosium	Dy	66	162.5	Rubidium	Rb	37	85.47
Einsteinium	Es	99	(252)	Ruthenium	Ru	44	101.1
Erbium	Er	68	167.3	Samarium	Sm	62	150.4
Europium	Eu	63	152.0	Scandium	Sc	21	44.96
Fermium	Fm	100	(257)	Selenium	Se	34	78.96
Fluorine	F	9	19.00	Silicon	Si	14	28.09
Francium	Fr	87	(223)	Silver	Ag	47	107.9
Gadolinium	Gd	64	157.3	Sodium	Na	11	22.99
Gallium	Ga	31	69.72	Strontium	Sr	38	87.62
Germanium	Ge	32	72.59	Sulfur	S	16	32.06
Gold	Au	79	-197.0	Tantalum	Ta	73	180.9
Hafnium	Hf	72	178.5	Technetium	Tc	43	(98)
Helium	He	2	4.003	Tellurium	Te	52	127.6
Holmium	Ho	67	164.9	Terbium	Tb	65	158.9
Hydrogen	H	1	1.008	Thallium	Tl	81	204.4
Indium	In	49	114.8	Thorium	Th	90	232.0
Iodine	I	53	126.9	Thulium	Tm	69	168.9
Iridium	Ir	77	192.2	Tin	Sn	50	118.7
Iron	Fe	26	55.85	Titanium	Ti	22	47.90
Krypton	Kr	36	83.80	Tungsten	W	74	183.9
Lanthanum	La	57	138.9	Uranium	U	92	238.0
Lawrencium	Lr	103	(260)	Vanadium	V	23	50.94
Lead	Pb	82	207.2	Xenon	Xe	54	131.3
Lithium	Li	3	6.941	Ytterbium	Yb	70	173.0
Lutetium	Lu	71	175.0	Yttrium	Y	39	88.91
Magnesium	Mg	12	24.31	Zinc	Zn	30	65.38
Manganese	Mn	25	54.94	Zirconium	Zr	40	91.22
Mendelevium	Md	101	(258)				

*The values given here are to four significant figures. A table of more accurate atomic masses is given in Appendix F of the text.

†A value given in parentheses denotes the mass of the longest-lived isotope.

STUDY GUIDE · SOLUTIONS MANUAL TO ACCOMPANY

GENERAL CHEMISTRY

STUDY GUIDE · SOLUTIONS MANUAL TO ACCOMPANY

GENERAL CHEMISTRY

SECOND   EDITION

CAROLE H. McQUARRIE

DONALD A. McQUARRIE

UNIVERSITY OF CALIFORNIA, DAVIS

PETER A. ROCK

UNIVERSITY OF CALIFORNIA, DAVIS

W. H. FREEMAN AND COMPANY ▪ NEW YORK

CONTENTS

Acknowledgments ix

To the Student x

1 / Atoms and Molecules 1

2 / Chemical Reactions and the Periodic Table 23

3 / Chemical Calculations 40

4 / The Properties of Gases 69

5 / Thermochemistry 103

6 / The Quantum Theory and Atomic Structure 121

7 / Ionic Bonds and Compounds 148

8 / Lewis Formulas 162

9 / VSEPR Theory 182

10 / Covalent Bonding in Molecules 198

11 / Liquids and Solids 216

12 / Properties of Solutions 243

13 / Rates and Mechanisms of Chemical Reactions 268

14 / Chemical Equilibrium 296

15 / Acids and Bases, I 324

16 / Acids and Bases, II 356

17 / Solubility and Precipitation Reactions 386

18 / Oxidation-Reduction Reactions   409

19 / Entropy and Gibbs Free Energy   430

20 / Electrochemistry   456

21 / Nuclear and Radiochemistry   486

22 / Transition Metal Complexes   509

23 / Organic Chemistry   529

24 / Synthetic and Natural Polymers   551

Interchapters   563

Glossary   576

ACKNOWLEDGMENTS

We thank Barbara Brooks and Stephen Wagley of W. H. Freeman and Company for coordinating and directing the publication of this Manual in an expeditious and professional manner. We also thank Dr. Joseph Ledbetter for a careful and detailed review of the manuscript, Helene DeLorenzo for a first-rate copy editing job, and Elaine Rock for her prompt and accurate typing of the manuscript.

TO THE STUDENT

This Study Guide/Solutions Manual accompanies the text *General Chemistry*, by Donald A. McQuarrie and Peter A. Rock. For each chapter in the text, this Manual has sections entitled

A   Outline of the Chapter
B   Self-Test
C   Calculations You Should Know How to Do
D   Solutions to the Odd-Numbered Problems
E   Answers to the Self-Test

Because your instructor may not assign Interchapters in the order in which they appear in the textbook, we have grouped them together beginning on page 563, following Chapter 24. There is also a Glossary that is cross-referenced to the text.

The Outline (Section A) of each chapter lists the headings for each section of the text, together with a few concise sentences that describe the key contents of each section.

The Self-Test (Section B) consists of about 40 short questions such as true/false or fill-in-the-blank questions. The Self-Test questions will give you a good indication of your understanding of the material in each chapter of the text, and we recommend that you answer these questions before you go on to do the numerical problems. The Answers to the Self-Test questions are given in Section F.

Section C, Calculations You Should Know How to Do, outlines each type of calculation that is presented in the chapter. It tells you what calculations you are expected to be able to do and keys these calculations to the worked Examples in the chapter and to the Problems at the end of the chapter. If you understand each type of calculation outlined in this section, then you are ready to go on to the Problems.

Occasionally, Section C also contains a detailed review of mathematical topics that appear in the chapter. For example, Chapter 1 requires a knowledge of exponents and writing numbers in scientific notation. Consequently, we treat these topics in this manual and include a number of worked examples **and practice** Exercises (with Answers). Other mathematical topics that are discussed are the equation of a straight line and its use to plot data (Chapter 4) logarithms and antilogarithms (Chapter 11), and the quadratic equation (Chapter 14).

We feel that Section D, Solutions to the Odd-Numbered Problems, is an especially valuable part of this manual. Most general chemistry courses tend to emphasize numerical problems, and so we have included detailed solutions to all the odd-numbered problems. There is definitely a correct way and an incorrect way to use these problem solutions. When you are assigned a specific odd-numbered problem, you should do that problem first and compare your answer with the answer given in Appendix F of the text. If you are unable to get the correct answer, then you should refer to the detailed solution presented here in order to *understand* how to do the problem. Note that many problems in the text have been grouped and labeled according to topic, and so if you have difficulty with a particular topic, you should work on additional problems, using this manual as an aid. It is of little or no value for you to refer to the solutions given here before you make an honest, thoughtful attempt to do the problems yourself. Only by using the solutions as an aid to your understanding of how to do the problems will the solutions be of real value.

CAROLE H. McQUARRIE
DONALD A. McQUARRIE
PETER A. ROCK

September 1986

ATOMS AND MOLECULES

A OUTLINE OF CHAPTER 1

1-1 Why should you study chemistry?

1-2 Chemistry has an experimental basis.

Experiments are used to answer scientific questions. A scientific law or natural law is a concise summary of a large body of experimental results.

1-3 Elements are the simplest substances.

An element is a substance that consists of the same type of atoms.

A compound is a substance that can be broken down into simpler substances.

1-4 About three fourths of the elements are metals.

The elements are classified into metals, semimetals, and nonmetals.

Chemical symbols of some common metals and nonmetals are given in Tables 1-3 through 1-5.

Some nonmetals exist as diatomic molecules (Figure 1-1).

1-5 Antoine Lavoisier was the founder of modern chemistry.

A quantitative measurement is one in which the result is expressed as a number.

A qualitative observation is a notation of a particular characteristic such as color or taste.

The law of conservation of mass: In an ordinary chemical reaction, the total mass of the substances reacted is equal to the total mass of the products formed.

1-6 The law of constant composition states that the relative amount of each element in a compound is always the same.

The law of constant composition is based on the chemical analysis of compounds.

The mass percentage composition of a compound can be calculated from the chemical analysis of the compound (Example 1-1).

1-7   Dalton's atomic theory explains the law of constant composition.

The postulates of Dalton's atomic theory are given on page 9 of the text.

Atoms are the small, indivisible particles of which matter is composed.

A molecule is the particle that results when two or more atoms are joined together.

Atomic mass is the mass of one atom relative to that of another atom.

Atomic mass unit (amu) is a unit assigned to atomic masses.

1-8   Molecules are groups of atoms joined together.

A molecular picture of chemical reactions is introduced.

1-9   Compounds are named by an orderly system of chemical nomenclature.

If a compound is composed of a metal and a nonmetal, the metal is named first and then the nonmetal with the ending of the name of the nonmetal changed to -*ide* (Table 1-6).

Subscripts in a chemical formula of a compound indicate the relative numbers of each kind of atom in the compound.

If a compound is composed of two nonmetals, then the number of each element is indicated in the name of the compound by Greek prefixes (Table 1-7).

1-10   Molecular mass is the sum of the atomic masses of the atoms in a molecule.

The molecular mass of a compound can be calculated from its chemical formula, and from the atomic masses of the elements in the compound.

Mass percentage compositions are calculated using atomic masses and molecular masses (Example 1-4).

1-11   Most of the mass of an atom is concentrated in its nucleus.

An atom is composed of subatomic particles.

The electron was discovered in 1897 by Joseph J. Thomson.

An electron is a negatively charged particle with a mass $\frac{1}{1837}$ that of a hydrogen atom.

Radioactivity is the process in which certain nuclei spontaneously break apart.

Alpha particles, β-particles, and γ-rays are products of radioactive disintegrations (Table 1-8).

The nucleus was discovered by Rutherford and Marsden from the scattering of α-particles by a thin gold foil (Figure 1-7).

The proton was discovered in the early 1900s by Ernest Rutherford.

A proton is a positively charged particle with a mass almost the same as the mass of a hydrogen atom.

All the positive charge and essentially all of the mass of an atom are concentrated in the very small volume in the center of the atom, called the nucleus.

1-12 Atoms consist of protons, neutrons, and electrons.

The neutron was postulated to account for the mass of a nucleus and was discovered by James Chadwick in 1932.

A neutron is an uncharged particle with essentially the same mass as a proton.

Atomic number is the number of protons in an atom and is denoted by Z.

Mass number is the total number of protons and neutrons in an atom and is denoted by A.

1-13 Most elements occur in nature as mixtures of isotopes.

Isotopes are atoms that contain the same number of protons but different numbers of neutrons.

An isotope is denoted by $_Z^A X$.

The natural abundance of isotopes of an element can be measured (Table 1-9).

Calculations involving isotopic abundances and the atomic mass of an element are illustrated.

1-14 Isotopic masses are determined with a mass spectrometer.

Ions are atoms that have either more or fewer electrons than the neutral atom.

Positive ions are called cations.

Negative ions are called anions.

1-15 The precision of a measured quantity is indicated by the number of significant figures used to express the result.

There are uncertainties associated with measured quantities.

1-16 Calculated numbers should show the correct number of significant figures.

The result of multiplication and division can be no more accurate than the quantity with the fewest significant figures.

The result of addition and subtraction can be expressed to no more digits after the decimal point than the quantity with the fewest digits after the decimal point.

1-17 The metric system is used in scientific work.

The numerical value of a physical quantity depends on the units.

A physical quantity is converted from one unit to another by using a unit conversion factor.

Many physical quantities are expressed in compound units.

1-18 The Guggenheim notation is used to label table headings and figure axes.

Numbers are listed in tables of data without units.

The heading for tabulated data is given in the form, number/unit (Example 1-11).

The heading in a table of numerical values is treated as an algebraic quantity.

B   SELF-TEST

1   The way to answer a scientific question is to _____

_____..

2   A scientific law is _____

_____.

3   A scientific law is a concise explanation of experimental results. *True/False*

4   A theory can be used to make predictions that lead to new knowledge. *True/False*

5   Experiments may prove a theory incorrect. *True/False*

6   Scientific theories never change. *True/False*

7   A hypothesis precedes a theory. *True/False*

8   An element is a substance that consists of only one type of _____.

9   A pure substance that can be decomposed into simpler substances is called a

_____.

10   Three properties of a metal are (a) _____, (b) _____, and

(c) _____.

11   Most metals are solids at room temperature. *True/False*

12   Nonmetals are usually good conductors of electricity. *True/False*

13   Give the chemical symbol for the following metals: aluminum ____, calcium ____,

potassium ____, and zinc ____.

14   Name the element whose symbol is Ba _____, Cu _____,

Fe _____, and Na _____.

15   All nonmetals are gases at room temperature. *True/False*

16   Two examples of elements that exist as diatomic molecules are _____

and _____.

17   A quantitative measurement is one in which the result is expressed as

_____.

18   Explain how a qualitative result and a quantitative result differ.

19   In an ordinary chemical reaction, the total mass of substances that react is equal to
_____ .

20   The mass percentage of each element in a compound depends on how the compound is prepared. *True/False*

21   The law of constant composition states that the mass percentage of each element in a compound are equal. *True/False*

22   Chemical analysis of a compound is a determination of the _____
_____ .

23   State in your own words the postulates of Dalton's atomic theory.

(a)

(b)

(c)

(d)

(e)

24   Explain the meaning of the scale of atomic masses.

25   The unit of the atomic mass scale is called ————————.

26   The atomic mass of an element is the mass in grams of one atom of the element. *True/False*

27   Explain the law of constant composition in terms of Dalton's atomic theory.

28   In a chemical reaction, the atoms of the reacting compounds are ———————— to form the products.

29   The rules for naming binary compounds composed of a metal and a nonmetal are

(a)

(b)

30   The name of the compound CO_2 is ————————.

31   The molecular mass of a compound is the ————————

————————.

32   A beam of electrons passing between a voltage applied across electrodes will be deflected toward the ———————— charged electrode.

33   A beam of protons passing between the same voltage as in Question 32 will be deflected in the same direction as the beam of electrons. *True/False*

34   A beam of protons passing between a voltage will be deflected to *(the same, a greater, a lesser)* extent than a beam of electrons.

35   Compare the relative charges and masses of a proton, a neutron, and an electron.

36 A neutron has the same mass as an electron. *True/False*

37 Explain why some α-particles will be deflected through large angles when a beam of α-particles is directed at a thin gold foil.

38 Compare the mass of an atom to the mass of its nucleus.

39 The number of protons in a neutral atom is equal to the number of _____.

40 The atomic number of an atom indicates the number of neutrons in the atom. *True/False*

41 An element can be identified by its mass number. *True/False*

42 All isotopes of an element have the same atomic number. *True/False*

43 Isotopes of an element contain the same number of _____ but different numbers of _____.

44 The notation for one isotope of oxygen is $^{16}_{8}O$. The superscript designates the _____ of the isotope and the subscript designates the _____.

45 The isotopes chlorine-35 and chlorine-37 differ by _____.

46 Deuterium is a naturally occurring isotope of which element?

_____.

47 Why does naturally occurring chlorine have an atomic mass that is not close to a whole number?

_____.

48 Isotopes of an element can be separated in a mass spectrometer. *True/False*

49   A positively charged ion is an atom that has ———————————————— .

50   A negatively charged ion is an atom that has ———————————— .

51   The result of a measurement expressed as 251.43 g may have an uncertainty in the digit ————— .

52   The zeros in the result 0.0289 m are significant figures. *True/False*

53   The result of the calculation 8.436×2.09 should be expressed to ————— significant figures.

54   The result of the calculation $8.436 + 2.09$ should be expressed to ————— digits after the decimal point.

55   The statement that the mass of a substance is 0.0289 is meaningless. *True/False*

56   A physical quantity is converted from one unit to another by the use of a

———————————————————————— .

57   The preferred system of units in scientific work is the ———————— system, which uses ———————— units.

58   If data for the speed of an object are tabulated in the form, $\text{speed}/10^4 \, \text{m} \cdot \text{s}^{-1}$, then the value of the speed for the entry 1.46 is ———————————————— .

59   In the Guggenheim notation, the numbers on figure axes are unitless. *True/False*

C   CALCULATIONS YOU SHOULD KNOW HOW TO DO

1   Use the results of a quantitative chemical analysis to calculate the mass percentage of each element in a compound. See Example 1-1 and Problems 1-5 through 1-10.

2   Use a table of atomic masses to calculate the molecular mass of a compound. See page 14 and Problems 1-17 through 1-20.

3   Use a table of atomic masses to calculate the mass percentage of each element in a compound. See Example 1-4 and Problems 1-21 through 1-26.

4   Calculate the observed atomic mass of an element, given the masses of its isotopes and their percent abundances. See Example 1-6 and Problems 1-33 through 1-36.

5   Use unit conversion factors to convert a quantity from one unit to another. See Example 1-10 and Problems 1-53 through 1-58.

Scientific Notation and Calculations Using Exponents

The numbers encountered in chemistry are often extremely large (such as the number of atoms in a given quantity of substance) or extremely small (such as the mass of an electron in kilograms). To work with such numbers it is convenient to express them in scientific notation, whereby the number is written as a number between one and ten multiplied by 10 raised to the appropriate power. For example, the number 2831 is 2.831×1000, which is written 2.831×10^3 in scientific notation. Some other examples are

$$42500 = 4.25 \times 10^4$$

$$293100 = 2.931 \times 10^5$$

The zeros in these numbers are not regarded as significant figures and are dropped. Notice that in each case the power of 10 is the number of places that the decimal point is moved to the left.

$$42500 \qquad 293100$$

4 places   5 places

When numbers less than one are expressed in scientific notation, 10 is raised to a negative power. For example, 0.529 becomes 5.29×10^{-1}. Recall that a negative exponent is governed by the relation

$$10^{-n} = \frac{1}{10^n}$$

Some other examples are

$$0.006 = 6 \times 10^{-3}$$

$$0.000000742 = 7.42 \times 10^{-7}$$

Notice that the power of 10 in each case is the number of places that the decimal point is moved to the right.

$$0.006 \qquad 0.000000742$$

3 places   7 places

Example 1   Express the following numbers in scientific notation.
(a) 0.000126   (b) 7380000000

Solution   (a) We move the decimal point four places to the right to obtain 1.26×10^{-4}.
(b) We move the decimal point nine places to the left to obtain 7.38×10^9. Note that we do not retain the zeros following 8 because they are not significant figures.

It is necessary to be able to work with numbers in scientific notation. To add or subtract two or more numbers expressed in scientific notation, the power of 10 must be the same in each number. For example, consider the sum

$$1.711 \times 10^3 + 9.056 \times 10^2$$

We rewrite the first number to the power of 10^2:

$$1.711 \times 10^3 = 17.11 \times 10^2$$

Note that in having changed the 10^3 factor to 10^2, we have made the factor in front of 10^2 one power of 10 larger. Thus we have

$$1.711 \times 10^3 + 9.056 \times 10^2 = (17.11 + 9.056) \times 10^2$$
$$= 26.17 \times 10^2$$
$$= 2.617 \times 10^3$$

Similarly, we have

$$(6.287 \times 10^{-6}) - (1.562 \times 10^{-7}) = (6.287 - 0.1562) \times 10^{-6} = 6.131 \times 10^{-6}$$

When multiplying two numbers, we add the powers of 10 because of the relation

$$(10^x)(10^y) = 10^{x+y}$$

For example,

$$(2.00 \times 10^7)(6.00 \times 10^3) = (2.00)(6.00) \times 10^{10}$$
$$= 12.0 \times 10^{10}$$
$$= 1.20 \times 10^{11}$$

and

$$(5.014 \times 10^4)(7.143 \times 10^{-6}) = (5.014)(7.143) \times 10^{-2}$$
$$= 35.82 \times 10^{-2}$$
$$= 3.582 \times 10^{-1}$$

To divide, we subtract the power of 10 of the number in the denominator from the power of 10 of the number in the numerator because of the relation

$$\frac{10^x}{10^y} = 10^{x-y}$$

For example,

$$\frac{3.0 \times 10^{10}}{6.0 \times 10^{23}} = \left(\frac{3.0}{6.0}\right) \times 10^{10-23}$$
$$= 0.50 \times 10^{-13}$$
$$= 5.0 \times 10^{-14}$$

and

$$\frac{3.56 \times 10^{-6}}{8.73 \times 10^{-12}} = \left(\frac{3.56}{8.73}\right) \times 10^{-6+12}$$
$$= 0.408 \times 10^6$$
$$= 4.08 \times 10^5$$

Example 2 Evaluate

$$x = \frac{(3.076 \times 10^{-4})(1.38 \times 10^{12})}{(6.67 \times 10^{-32})(7.110 \times 10^{21})}$$

Solution We rewrite x as

$$x = \frac{(3.076)(1.38)}{(6.67)(7.110)} \times 10^{-4+12+32-21}$$
$$= 0.0895 \times 10^{19}$$
$$= 8.95 \times 10^{17}$$

Note that we express our answer to three significant figures.

To raise a number to a power, we use the relation

$$(10^x)^n = 10^{nx}$$

For example,

$$(3.141 \times 10^4)^3 = (3.141)^3 \times 10^{12}$$
$$= 30.99 \times 10^{12}$$
$$= 3.099 \times 10^{13}$$

To take a root of a number, we use the relation

$$\sqrt[n]{10^x} = (10^x)^{1/n} = 10^{x/n}$$

Thus the power of 10 must be written so that it is divisible by the root. For example, the cube root of 6.40×10^7 is

$$\sqrt[3]{6.40 \times 10^7} = (6.40 \times 10^7)^{1/3} = (64.0 \times 10^6)^{1/3}$$
$$= (64.0)^{1/3} \times 10^2 = 4.00 \times 10^2$$
$$\sqrt{4.60 \times 10^5} = (4.60 \times 10^5)^{1/2} = (46.0 \times 10^4)^{1/2}$$
$$= (46.0)^{1/2} \times 10^2 = 6.78 \times 10^2$$

These calculations can be carried out directly on scientific hand calculators with a y^x function key. For example, to find $(6.40 \times 10^7)^{1/3}$, enter 6.40×10^7, press the y^x key, enter 0.33333 . . . and press the equals sign (=) key to get 4.00×10^2.

Example 3   Evaluate

$$x = \left(\frac{4.16 \times 10^{-3}}{9.723 \times 10^{12}} \right)^{1/3}$$

Solution $x = \left(\frac{4.16}{9.723} \times 10^{-15} \right)^{1/3} = (0.428 \times 10^{-15})^{1/3}$

$$= (428 \times 10^{-18})^{1/3}$$
$$= (428)^{1/3} \times 10^{-6}$$
$$= 7.54 \times 10^{-6}$$

You should realize that you can carry out all these calculations directly on your hand calculator. You can enter numbers in exponential notation, multiply and divide them, take roots and powers, and so on. It is well worth the effort to learn how to do this on your own hand calculator. Use your calculator to do the following exercises.

Exercises

Evaluate

1 $(4.164 \times 10^{-16})(9.275 \times 10^{12})$

2 $\dfrac{1.00 \times 10^4}{7.25 \times 10^8}$

3 $(6.176 \times 10^7)^{1/2}$

4 $(5.60 \times 10^{-3})^5$

5 $\dfrac{(2.14 \times 10^6)(7.813 \times 10^{-12})}{(8.89 \times 10^{16})}$

6 $\dfrac{(0.0929)(1728)}{(6.626 \times 10^{14})}$

7 $\left[\dfrac{(4.49 \times 10^5)(7.071 \times 10^{29})}{(1.019 \times 10^{-6})(6.88 \times 10^8)} \right]^{1/4}$

8 $\left[\dfrac{(5.716 \times 10^{-6})(4.28)}{(14.67 \times 10^2)} \right]^{1/3}$

Answers

1 3.862×10^{-3}
2 1.38×10^{-5}
3 7.859×10^3
4 5.51×10^{-12}

5 1.88×10^{-22}
6 2.42×10^{-13}
7 1.46×10^8
8 2.55×10^{-3}

D   SOLUTIONS TO THE ODD-NUMBERED PROBLEMS

1-1   (a) Se   (b) In   (c) Mn   (d) Tm

(e) Hg   (f) Kr   (g) Pd   (h) Tl

(i) U   (j) W

See the alphabetical list of the elements on the inside front cover.

1-3   (a) germanium   (b) scandium   (c) iridium

(d) cesium   (e) strontium   (f) americium

(g) molybdenum   (h) indium   (i) plutonium

(j) xenon

See the alphabetical list of the elements on the inside front cover.

1-5   The mass percentage of sodium is given by

$$\text{mass \% of Na} = \frac{\text{mass of Na}}{\text{mass of compound}} \times 100$$

$$= \frac{0.978 \text{ g}}{1.659 \text{ g}} \times 100 = 59.0\%$$

The mass percentage of oxygen is given by

$$\text{mass \% of O} = \frac{\text{mass of O}}{\text{mass of compound}} \times 100$$

$$= \frac{0.681 \text{ g}}{1.659 \text{ g}} \times 100 = 41.0\%$$

1-7   The mass percentage of copper in the compound is given by

$$\text{mass \% of Cu} = \frac{\text{mass of Cu}}{\text{mass of compound}} \times 100$$

$$= \frac{1.28 \text{ g}}{1.60 \text{ g}} \times 100 = 80.0\%$$

The mass of sulfur in the compound is

$$\text{mass of S} = \text{mass of compound} - \text{mass of Cu}$$
$$= 1.60 \text{ g} - 1.28 \text{ g} = 0.32 \text{ g}$$

The mass percentage of sulfur in the compound is given by

$$\text{mass \% of S} = \frac{\text{mass of S}}{\text{mass of compound}} \times 100$$

$$= \frac{0.32 \text{ g}}{1.60 \text{ g}} \times 100 = 20\%$$

1-9   The respective mass percentages are

$$\text{mass \% of K} = \frac{\text{mass of K}}{\text{mass of potassium cyanide}} \times 100$$

$$= \frac{7.58 \text{ mg}}{12.63 \text{ mg}} \times 100 = 60.0\%$$

$$\text{mass \% of C} = \frac{\text{mass of C}}{\text{mass of potassium cyanide}} \times 100$$

$$= \frac{2.33 \text{ mg}}{12.63 \text{ mg}} \times 100 = 18.4\%$$

$$\text{mass \% of N} = \frac{\text{mass of N}}{\text{mass of potassium cyanide}} \times 100$$

$$= \frac{2.72 \text{ mg}}{12.63 \text{ mg}} \times 100 = 21.5\%$$

1-11 Using Table 1-6 and the list of the elements on the inside front cover, we have

(a) lithium sulfide   (b) barium oxide

(c) magnesium phosphide   (d) cesium bromide

1-13 (a) calcium carbide   (b) gallium phosphide

(c) aluminum oxide   (d) beryllium chloride

1-15 (a) chlorine trifluoride and chlorine pentafluoride

(b) sulfur tetrafluoride and sulfur hexafluoride

(c) krypton difluoride and krypton tetrafluoride

(d) bromine oxide and bromine dioxide

1-17 Refer to the inside front cover for the atomic masses.

(a) The molecular mass of TiO_2 is

$$\text{molecular mass} = (\text{atomic mass of Ti}) + (2 \times \text{atomic mass of O})$$
$$= (47.90) + (2 \times 16.00) = 79.90$$

(b) The molecular mass of Fe_2O_3 is

$$\text{molecular mass} = (2 \times \text{atomic mass of Fe}) + (3 \times \text{atomic mass of O})$$
$$= (2 \times 55.85) + (3 \times 16.00) = 159.70$$

(c) The molecular mass of V_2O_5 is

$$\text{molecular mass} = (2 \times \text{atomic mass of V}) + (5 \times \text{atomic mass of O})$$
$$= (2 \times 50.94) + (5 \times 16.00) = 181.88$$

(d) The molecular mass of P_4O_{10} is

$$\text{molecular mass} = (4 \times \text{atomic mass of P}) + (10 \times \text{atomic mass of O})$$
$$= (4 \times 30.97) + (10 \times 16.00) = 283.88$$

1-19 (a) molecular mass of BrN_3 = (atomic mass of Br) +
$$(3 \times \text{atomic mass of N})$$
$$= (79.90) + (3 \times 14.01)$$
$$= 121.93$$

(b) molecular mass of $NaIO_3$ = (atomic mass of Na) +
(atomic mass of I) +
(3 × atomic mass of O)
= (22.99) + (126.9) + (3 × 16.00)
= 197.9

(c) molecular mass of CCl_2F_2 = (atomic mass of C) +
(2 × atomic mass of Cl) +
(2 × atomic mass of F)
= (12.01) + (2 × 35.45) + (2 × 19.00)
= 120.91

(d) molecular mass of $C_{14}H_9Cl_6$ = (14 × atomic mass of C) +
(9 × atomic mass of H) +
(6 × atomic mass of Cl)
= (14 × 12.01) + (9 × 1.008) + (6 × 35.45)
= 389.91

1-21 molecular mass of BrF_5 = (79.90) + (5 × 19.00)
= 174.90

$$\text{mass \% of Br} = \frac{\text{atomic mass of Br}}{\text{molecular mass of } BrF_5} \times 100$$

$$= \frac{79.90}{174.90} \times 100 = 45.68\%$$

$$\text{mass \% of F} = \frac{5 \times \text{atomic mass of F}}{\text{molecular mass of } BrF_5} \times 100$$

$$= \frac{5 \times 19.00}{174.90} \times 100 = 54.32\%$$

1-23 molecular mass of $C_{12}H_{22}O_{11}$ = 342.30

$$\text{mass \% of C} = \frac{12 \times \text{atomic mass of C}}{\text{molecular mass of } C_{12}H_{22}O_{11}} \times 100$$

$$= \frac{12 \times 12.01}{342.30} \times 100 = 42.10\%$$

$$\text{mass \% of H} = \frac{22 \times \text{atomic mass of H}}{\text{molecular mass of } C_{12}H_{22}O_{11}} \times 100$$

$$= \frac{22 \times 1.008}{342.30} \times 100 = 6.479\%$$

$$\text{mass \% of O} = \frac{11 \times \text{atomic mass of O}}{\text{molecular mass of } C_{12}H_{22}O_{11}} \times 100$$

$$= \frac{11 \times 16.00}{342.30} \times 100 = 51.42\%$$

1-25   molecular mass of $XeF_4 = 207.3$

$$\text{mass \% of Xe} = \frac{131.3}{207.3} \times 100 = 63.34\%$$

$$\text{mass of Xe} = \frac{\text{mass \% of Xe}}{100} \times \text{mass of } XeF_4$$

$$= \frac{63.34}{100} \times 2.000 \text{ g} = 1.267 \text{ g}$$

1-27   From the atomic numbers, we find that

	Protons	Electrons	Neutrons
(a) iodine-131	53	53	$131 - 53 = 78$
(b) cobalt-60	27	27	$60 - 27 = 33$
(c) potassium-43	19	19	$43 - 19 = 24$
(d) indium-113	49	49	$113 - 49 = 64$

1-29   The atomic number determines the element. The mass number is the sum of the atomic number and the number of neutrons.

Symbol	Atomic number	Number of neutrons	Mass number
$^{14}_{6}C$	6	8	14
$^{241}_{95}Am$	95	146	241
$^{123}_{53}I$	53	70	123
$^{18}_{8}O$	8	10	18

1-31

Symbol	Atomic number	Number of neutrons	Mass number
$^{67}_{31}Ga$	31	36	67
$^{15}_{7}N$	7	8	15
$^{58}_{27}Co$	27	31	58
$^{133}_{54}Xe$	54	79	133

1-33   atomic mass of H $= (1.0078)\left(\dfrac{99.985}{100}\right) + (2.0141)\left(\dfrac{0.015}{100}\right)$

$= 1.0080$

1-35   atomic mass of Ne $= (19.99)\left(\dfrac{90.51}{100}\right) + (20.99)\left(\dfrac{0.27}{100}\right) + (21.99)\left(\dfrac{9.22}{100}\right)$

$= 20.18$

1-37   Let x be the percentage of bromine-79 in naturally occurring bromine. The percentage of bromine-81 must be $100 - x$. Now set up the equation

$$\text{atomic mass of Br} = 79.904 = (78.9183)\left(\frac{x}{100}\right) + (80.9163)\left(\frac{100 - x}{100}\right)$$

Multiply this equation through by 100 to obtain

$$7990.4 = 78.9183x + 8091.63 - 80.9163x$$

Collecting terms, we get

$$1.9980x = 101.2$$

or

$$x = 50.65\% = \% \text{ of bromine-79}$$

The percentage of bromine-81 is

$$\% \text{ bromine-81} = 100 - x = 49.35\%$$

1-39   Let x be the percentage of nitrogen-15 in naturally occurring nitrogen. The percentage of nitrogen-14 must be $100 - x$. Now set up the equation

$$\text{atomic mass of N} = 14.0067 = (14.0031)\left(\frac{100 - x}{100}\right) + (15.0001)\left(\frac{x}{100}\right)$$

Multiply through by 100 to obtain

$$1400.67 = 1400.31 - 14.0031x + 15.0001x$$

Collecting terms, we get

$$0.9970x = 0.36$$

or

$$x = 0.36\% = \% \text{ of nitrogen-15}$$

1-41   The number of electrons = atomic number − ionic charge

(a) 54   (b) 54   (c) 36   (d) 10

1-43 (a) 54   (b) 78   (c) 24   (d) 18

1-45 (a) Ca^{2+}, Cl^-, S^{2-} (b) Rb^+, Sr^{2+}, Br^-, Se^{2-}

(c) Na^+, Mg^{2+}, F^-, O^{2-} (d) Cs^+, Ba^{2+}, Te^{2-}

1-47 (a) 0.0390 has three significant figures: 3, 9, 0.

(b) 6.022×10^{23} has four significant figures: 6, 0, 2, 2.

(c) 3.652×10^{-5} has four significant figures: 3, 6, 5, 2.

(d) 226,000,000 has three significant figures: 2, 2, 6. The word "about" implies that the zeros serve only to position the decimal point.

(e) The integer 16 is an exact number; there is no uncertainty associated with an integer.

1-49 (a) molecular mass of $H_2O = (2 \times 1.0079) + (15.9994)$
$$= 18.0152$$

(b) molecular mass of $MgCl_2 = (24.305) + (2 \times 35.453)$
$$= 95.211$$

(c) molecular mass of $AlI_3 = (26.98154) + (3 \times 126.9045)$
$$= 407.6950$$

(d) molecular mass of $TcBr_2 = (98) + (2 \times 79.904)$
$$= 258$$

1-51 (a) 2 (The result cannot be more accurate than zero digits past the decimal point.)

(b) 20800 or 2.08×10^4 (The result cannot be expressed to more than three significant figures.)

(c) 2.8 (The result cannot be expressed to more than two significant figures.)

(d) 3.4×10^{22} (The result cannot be expressed to more than two significant figures.)

1-53 (a) $(1.00 \ \cancel{L})\left(\dfrac{1 \text{ qt}}{0.94633 \ \cancel{L}}\right) = 1.06$ qt

(b) $(186,000 \ \cancel{\text{mile}} \cdot s^{-1})\left(\dfrac{1.6093 \ \cancel{\text{km}}}{1 \ \cancel{\text{mile}}}\right)\left(\dfrac{10^3 \text{ m}}{1 \ \cancel{\text{km}}}\right) = 2.99 \times 10^8 \text{ m} \cdot s^{-1}$

(c) $(8.314 \ \cancel{J} \cdot K^{-1} \cdot mol^{-1})\left(\dfrac{0.23901 \text{ cal}}{1 \ \cancel{J}}\right) = 1.987 \text{ cal} \cdot K^{-1} \cdot mol^{-1}$

1-55 The distance is given by

$$\text{distance} = \text{speed} \times \text{time}$$
$$= (3.00 \times 10^8 \text{ m} \cdot \cancel{s^{-1}})(1 \ \cancel{yr})\left(\dfrac{365 \ \cancel{d}}{1 \ \cancel{yr}}\right)\left(\dfrac{24 \ \cancel{h}}{1 \ \cancel{d}}\right)\left(\dfrac{60 \ \cancel{\min}}{1 \ \cancel{h}}\right)\left(\dfrac{60 \ \cancel{s}}{1 \ \cancel{\min}}\right)$$
$$= 9.46 \times 10^{15} \text{ m}$$

The distance in miles is

$$\text{distance} = (9.46 \times 10^{15} \text{ m})\left(\frac{1 \text{ km}}{10^3 \text{ m}}\right)\left(\frac{1 \text{ mile}}{1.6093 \text{ km}}\right)$$

$$= 5.88 \times 10^{12} \text{ miles}$$

1-57 The total volume of soda in a six-pack is

$$\text{volume} = (6)(16 \text{ oz})\left(\frac{0.94633 \text{ L}}{32 \text{ oz}}\right) = 2.84 \text{ L}$$

The cost per liter of soda in the six-pack is

$$\text{cost per L} = \frac{\$3.50}{2.84 \text{ L}} = \$1.23 \text{ per L}$$

The cost per liter of soda in the 2-L bottle is

$$\text{cost per L} = \frac{\$1.49}{2.00 \text{ L}} = \$0.75 \text{ per L}$$

The 2-L bottle is the better buy.

1-59 If the diameter of the nucleus were 3 cm, then the diameter of the atom would be

$$\text{diameter atom} = (3 \text{ cm})(10^5) = 3 \times 10^5 \text{ cm}$$

$$= (3 \times 10^5 \text{ cm})\left(\frac{1 \text{ m}}{100 \text{ cm}}\right) = 3 \times 10^3 \text{ m}$$

Three thousand meters corresponds roughly to two miles.

1-61 (a) mass % of N in $N_2O_3 = \dfrac{2 \times 14.01}{(2 \times 14.01) + (3 \times 16.00)} \times 100 = 36.86\%$

(b) mass % of N in $HNO_3 = \dfrac{14.01}{(1.008) + (14.01) + (3 \times 16.00)} \times 100 = 22.23\%$

(c) mass % of N in $NH_3 = \dfrac{14.01}{(14.01) + (3 \times 1.008)} \times 100 = 82.27\%$

(d) mass % of N in $NH_4Cl = \dfrac{14.01}{(14.01) + (4 \times 1.008) + (35.45)} \times 100 = 26.19\%$

(e) mass % of N in $PbN_6 = \dfrac{6 \times 14.01}{(207.2) + (6 \times 14.01)} \times 100 = 28.86\%$

Ammonia (NH_3) has the highest mass percentage of nitrogen.

1-63 The mass of $MgCO_3$ in 1000 kg of dolomite is

$$\text{mass of } MgCO_3 = \left(\frac{11.2}{100}\right)(1000 \text{ kg}) = 112 \text{ kg}$$

The mass percentage of magnesium in $MgCO_3$ is

$$\text{mass \% of Mg} = \frac{24.31}{(24.31) + (12.01) + (3 \times 16.00)} \times 100$$
$$= 28.83\%$$

The mass of magnesium in 112 kg of $MgCO_3$ is

$$\text{mass of Mg} = \left(\frac{28.83}{100}\right)(112 \text{ kg}) = 32.3 \text{ kg} = 3.23 \times 10^4 \text{ g}$$

1-65   The volume occupied by 55 g of benzene is

$$\text{volume} = (55 \text{ g})\left(\frac{1 \text{ cm}^3}{0.879 \text{ g}}\right)\left(\frac{1 \text{ mL}}{1 \text{ cm}^3}\right)$$
$$= 63 \text{ mL}$$

1-67   Let x be the percentage of silicon-29 in naturally occurring silicon. The percentages of silicon-29 and silicon-30 must be equal to

$$\text{\% of silicon-29} + \text{\% of silicon-30} = \text{total \%} - \text{\% of silicon-28}$$
$$= 100.00 - 92.23$$
$$= 7.77$$

Because x is the percentage of silicon-29, the percentage of silicon-30 is

$$\text{\% of silicon-30} = 7.77 - x$$

Now set up the equation

$$\text{atomic mass of Si} = 28.0855 = (27.9769)\left(\frac{92.23}{100}\right)$$
$$+ (28.9765)\left(\frac{x}{100}\right) + (29.9738)\left(\frac{7.77 - x}{100}\right)$$

Multiply through by 100 and collect terms to get

$$x = \text{\% of silicon-29} = 4.67\%$$

The percentage of silicon-30 is

$$\text{\% of silicon-30} = 7.77 - 4.67 = 3.10\%$$

1-69   The mass of 10.0 mL of mercury is

$$\text{mass of mercury} = (10.0 \text{ mL})\left(\frac{1 \text{ cm}^3}{1 \text{ mL}}\right)\left(\frac{13.59 \text{ g}}{1 \text{ cm}^3}\right)$$
$$= 136 \text{ g}$$

The volume occupied by 136 g of acetone is

$$\text{volume of acetone} = (136 \, \cancel{g})\left(\frac{1 \, \cancel{cm^3}}{0.792 \, \cancel{g}}\right)\left(\frac{1 \, mL}{1 \, \cancel{cm^3}}\right)$$
$$= 172 \, mL$$

E   ANSWERS TO THE SELF-TEST

1   perform an experiment

2   a concise summary of a large body of experimental results

3   false

4   true

5   true

6   false

7   true

8   atom

9   compound

10   luster, malleability, conductivity of heat and electricity

11   true

12   false

13   Al, Ca, K, Zn

14   barium, copper, iron, sodium

15   false

16   H_2, N_2, O_2, F_2, Cl_2, Br_2, I_2

17   a number

18   Consult Section 1-5 of the text.

19   the total mass of the products (law of conservation of mass)

20   false

21   false

22   mass percentage of each element in the compound

23   Consult Section 1-7 of the text.

24   Consult Section 1-7 of the text.

25   atomic mass unit, amu

26   false

27   Consult Section 1-7 of the text.

28   rearranged

29   Consult Section 1-9 of the text.

30   carbon dioxide

31   sum of the atomic masses of the elements corresponding to all the atoms in the molecule

32   positively

33   false

34   lesser

35

	Relative mass	Relative charge
proton	1	+1
neutron	1	0
electron	$\frac{1}{1837}$	−1

36   false

37   Consult Section 1-11 of the text.

38   The protons and neutrons are located in the nucleus and the electrons are located outside the nucleus. Consequently, the mass of an atom is essentially equal to the mass of its nucleus.

39   electrons

40 false

41 false

42 true

43 protons, neutrons

44 mass number, atomic number

45 two neutrons

46 hydrogen

47 Naturally occurring chlorine is composed of more than one isotope.

48 true

49 lost one or more electrons

50 gained one or more electrons

51 3

52 false

53 three

54 two

55 true; no units are given

56 unit conversion factor

57 metric, SI

58 $1.46 \times 10^4 \text{ m} \cdot \text{s}^{-1}$

59 true

CHEMICAL REACTIONS AND THE PERIODIC TABLE

A OUTLINE OF CHAPTER 2

2-1   New substances are formed in chemical reactions.

Chemical reactions are represented by chemical equations.

The reactants are the substances that react with each other.

The products are the substances formed in the reaction.

The symbols (s), (l), and (g) denote that a substance is a solid, liquid, or gas, respectively.

2-2   A chemical equation must be balanced.

The conservation of atoms in chemical reactions means that individual atoms of various types are neither created nor destroyed.

Chemical equations are balanced by using balancing coefficients.

The method of balancing chemical equations by inspection is discussed (Example 2-1).

2-3   Elements can be grouped according to their chemical properties.

Representative reactions of the alkali metals are presented.

Representative reactions of the alkaline earth metals are presented.

Representative reactions of the halogens are presented.

The prediction of reaction products can be made using representative reactions.

2-4   The elements show a periodic pattern when listed in order of increasing atomic number.

The chemical properties of the elements exhibit periodic behavior (Mendeleev).

In a modern periodic table of the elements, the elements are ordered according to increasing atomic number (Figure 2-5).

2-5 Elements in the same column in the periodic table have similar chemical properties.

Groups or families of elements appear in the same column of the periodic table.

The extreme right-hand column contains the group of unreactive elements called the noble gases (Group 8).

Predictions of the products of reactions between elements or simple compounds can be made using the periodic table.

Mendeleev used periodicity to predict chemical and physical properties of undiscovered elements.

The more common versions of the periodic table have the lanthanide series and the actinide series placed at the bottom of the table (Figure 2-8).

The horizontal rows in the periodic table are called periods.

2-6 Elements are arranged as main-group elements, transition metals, and inner transition metals.

The periodic table organizes the elements into

- groups (columns)
- periods (rows)
- semimetals
- metals
- nonmetals
- main-group elements
- transition metals
- inner transition metals, the lanthanides ($Z = 57$ to $Z = 70$) and the actinides ($Z = 89$ to $Z = 102$)

Elements can be classified based on their positions in the periodic table (Figures 2-9 and 2-12 and Example 2-5).

2-7 The periodic table contains some irregularities.

Hydrogen does not fit readily into any group.

The first member of a group often reacts somewhat differently than the other members of the group.

2-8 Many atoms form ions that have a noble-gas electron arrangement.

The nuclear model of the atom is reviewed.

Noble-gas electron arrangements are unusually stable.

Ions are formed by loss or gain of electrons by atoms or molecules (Examples 2-6 and 2-7).

The charge on an ion is designated by a superscript following the symbol for the atom that has lost or gained electrons.

2-9   Ionic charges can be used to write chemical formulas.

Metal atoms lose electrons and form positive ions.

Ionic charges are positive or negative numbers assigned to elements and can be used to write correct chemical formulas.

An ionic compound has no net charge — the total positive charge equals the total negative charge.

The prediction of chemical formulas of ionic compounds is made using ionic charges:

Group	Ionic charge
1	$+1$
2	$+2$
3	$+3$
5	-3
6	-2
7	-1

Transition metal ions have more than one possible ionic charge.

Roman numerals in parentheses are used to denote the charge on transition metal ions (Table 2-3).

2-10   A combination reaction is the reaction of two substances to form a single product.

Combination reactions can involve a metal and a nonmetal or two nonmetals.

Electrons are transferred from a metal atom to the nonmetal atom, resulting in an ionic compound.

An atom is oxidized when it loses electrons (the charge on the atom becomes more positive).

Oxidation denotes a loss of electrons.

An atom is reduced when it gains electrons (the charge on the atom becomes more negative).

Reduction denotes a gain of electrons.

A reaction in which electrons are transferred from one element to another is an oxidation-reduction reaction.

Ionic compounds are composed of ions.

Combustion reactions involve the burning of a compound in oxygen.

Molecular compounds are composed of molecules.

Binary compounds may be formed in combination reactions.

The nomenclature of compounds containing polyatomic ions is similar to that for binary compounds.

A compound containing a polyatomic ion is named using the information in Table 2-4.

The formula of a compound containing a polyatomic ion can be written from its name using Table 2-4.

2-11   Soluble metal oxides yield bases and soluble nonmetal oxides yield acids when dissolved in water.

Bases yield hydroxide ions, $OH^-(aq)$, in water.

Basic anhydrides are oxides that yield bases when dissolved in water.

Water-soluble metal oxides are basic anhydrides (Figure 2-18).

Acids yield hydrogen ions, $H^+(aq)$, in water.

The hydronium ion, H_3O^+, is the dominant species of $H^+(aq)$.

Acidic anhydrides are nonmetal oxides that yield acids when dissolved in water.

Certain nonmetal oxides are acidic anhydrides.

Some common acids are listed in Tables 2-5 and 2-6.

2-12   In a decomposition reaction, a substance is broken down into two or more simpler substances.

There is usually only one reactant in a decomposition reaction.

Some decomposition reactions involve metal oxides, carbonates, nitrates, and chlorates.

2-13   In a single-replacement reaction, one element in a compound is replaced by another.

One metal may replace another metal in a compound.

A reactive metal replaces hydrogen in a dilute acid to produce hydrogen gas.

2-14   Metals can be ordered in terms of relative reactivity.

The metals can be ranked in order of their reactivity in a reactivity series of the metals (Table 2-7).

A more reactive metal will replace a less reactive metal in a compound.

Single-replacement reactions do not have to take place in solution.

The reaction of carbon and a metal oxide is an important type of single-replacement reaction.

2-15   The reactivity order of the halogens is $F_2 > Cl_2 > Br_2 > I_2$.

A halogen may replace a less reactive halogen in a compound.

2-16   In a double-replacement reaction, cations and anions exchange to form new compounds.

A precipitation reaction involves the formation of an insoluble product.

Precipitate formation is one type of driving force for chemical reactions that occur in solution.

Net ionic equations are used to describe double-replacement reactions.

Spectator ions are not directly involved in double-replacement reactions.

A neutralization reaction is the reaction between an acid and a base.

The formation of water is the driving force for neutralization reactions.

The net ionic equation of a neutralization reaction is

$$H^+(aq) + OH^-(aq) \longrightarrow H_2O(l)$$

A salt is an ionic compound formed in the reaction between an acid and a base.

Some properties of acids and bases are summarized in Table 2-8.

Litmus paper is used to test if a solution is acidic or basic.

B   SELF-TEST

1   Substances formed in chemical reactions have a combination of the properties of the substances from which they are produced. *True/False*

2   Sodium chloride has properties similar to those of sodium and chlorine. *True/False*

3   $H_2(g) + O_2(g) \rightarrow H_2O(l)$. The chemical equation is balanced as written. *True/False*

4   Balancing coefficients are placed _____ of the chemical formulas of the reactants and products of a chemical equation.

5   The total number of each kind of atom in all the reactants must _____ in the products of a balanced chemical equation.

6   The chemical formulas of the products of a chemical reaction can be changed to balance the equation. *True/False*

7   The chemical properties of lithium are similar to those of _____ and

   _____ .

8   Complete and balance the equations

   (a) $Li(s) + Cl_2(g) \rightarrow$

   (b) $Na(s) + H_2O(l) \rightarrow$

9   The chemical properties of magnesium are similar to those of

   _____ , _____ , and _____ .

10   Complete and balance the equations

   (a) $Mg(s) + O_2(g) \rightarrow$

   (b) $Ca(s) + H_2O(g) \rightarrow$

11   The halogens consist of the elements _____ , _____ ,

   _____ , _____ , and _____ .

12   Complete and balance the equations

(a) $Na(s) + F_2(g) \rightarrow$

(b) $H_2(g) + Br_2(l) \rightarrow$

13   Mendeleev arranged the elements in order of increasing _____.

14   In the modern periodic table, the elements are arranged in order of increasing

_____.

15   Elements with similar chemical properties appear in the same row of the periodic table. *True/False*

16   Elements that have similar chemical properties are placed in the same column of the periodic table. *True/False*

17   Group 1 metals are also called _____.

18   Group 2 metals are also called _____.

19   The halogens appear in column _____ of the periodic table.

20   The noble gases occur in column _____ of the periodic table.

21   The noble gases used to be called _____.

22   Silicon is a nonmetal. *True/False*

23   Some properties of semimetals are _____, _____,

and _____.

24   There are almost as many nonmetals as metals. *True/False*

25   Where are the main-group elements located in the periodic table?

_____.

26   The main group elements have many chemical properties in common. *True/False*

27   The transition metals are more similar in their properties than the main-group elements. *True/False*

28   The transition metals occur between _____ and _____ in the periodic table.

29   The inner transition metals occur in the series that begin with _____

and with _____.

30 The lanthanide series is also called _____.

31 Members of the lanthanide series have very similar chemical properties. *True/False*

32 One of the properties that the elements in the actinide series have in common is that they are _____.

33 Explain why the inner transition metal series are placed at the bottom of many versions of the periodic table.

34 Hydrogen is sometimes placed in Group 1 because it is an alkali metal. *True/False*

35 The first member of a main-group family is typical of the group and behaves identically to the other members. *True/False*

36 The electron arrangements of the noble gases seem to be exceptionally stable. *True/False*

37 The noble gases are reactive nonmetals. *True/False*

38 An element in Group 1 _____ one electron to attain the electron arrangement of a noble gas.

39 An element in Group 7 _____ one electron to attain the electron arrangement of a noble gas.

40 An ionic compound consists of _____ and _____.

41 The net charge on an ionic compound is _____.

42 The charge of a magnesium ion is _____; the charge of a bromide ion is _____. The chemical formula of magnesium bromide is _____.

43 All transition metals have only one possible ionic charge. *True/False*

44 The designation tin(IV) indicates that tin has an ionic charge of _____.

45 An element is oxidized when the charge on its atoms _____.

46 An oxidation-reduction reaction involves _____.

47 In an oxidation-reduction reaction, the number of electrons lost by the element that is oxidized is equal to _____.

48 The reaction $2Rb(s) + Br_2(l) \rightarrow 2RbBr(s)$ is an example of a _____ reaction.

49   The reaction between a metal and a nonmetal usually results in an *(ionic, molecular)* compound.

50   The reaction between sulfur and oxygen to produce SO_2 is an example of a _____ reaction.

51   Magnesium sulfate, $MgSO_4$, dissolved in water consists of _____ ions and _____ ions.

52   The carbonate ion is an example of a _____ ion.

53   All metal oxides are soluble in water. *True/False*

54   Metal oxides that dissolve in water yield _____ ions in solution.

55   A base is a compound that _____ when dissolved in water.

56   The compound $Na_2O(s)$ is an example of a _____ anhydride.

57   An acid is a compound that _____ when dissolved in water.

58   An acidic anhydride yields _____ when dissolved in water.

59   The compound SO_3 is an example of an _____ anhydride.

60   The hydrogen ion exists as H^+ in aqueous solution. *True/False*

61   An example of a sulfur oxyacid is _____.

62   Binary acids contain only two elements. *True/False*

63   Decomposition reactions involve *(one, two, three)* reactant(s).

64   Oxygen can be produced in the laboratory by heating _____.

65   Many metal carbonates decompose upon heating to produce _____ and _____ gas.

66   When a reactive metal is added to an aqueous solution of an acid, _____ gas is produced.

67   All metals react with acids to produce hydrogen gas. *True/False*

68   A metal will replace a less reactive metal from a compound. *True/False*

69   The _____ of the metals is an ordering of the metals with respect to their reactivity.

70   Any metal will replace any other metal that lies *(above, below)* it in the reactivity series of the metals.

71 Many metals can be produced from their oxides by heating the metal oxide with

_____.

72 Fluorine, F_2, will replace iodine in the compound sodium iodide, NaI. *True/False*

73 The most reactive halogen is _____.

74 A precipitate is an _____ product of a reaction that takes place in solution.

75 A double-replacement reaction is a reaction in which _____

_____.

76 Consider the equation

$$AgNO_3(aq) + NaCl(aq) \longrightarrow NaNO_3(aq) + AgCl(s)$$

(a) The spectator ions are _____ and _____.

(b) The precipitate is _____.

(c) The net ionic equation is _____.

77 The driving force for the chemical reaction between NaCl(aq) and $AgNO_3$(aq) is

_____.

78 Consider the equation

$$HNO_3(aq) + KOH(aq) \longrightarrow KNO_3(aq) + H_2O(l)$$

(a) The spectator ions are _____ and _____.

(b) The net ionic equation is _____.

79 The driving force for the chemical reaction between HNO_3(aq) and KOH(aq) is

_____.

80 The reaction between an acid and a base is called a _____ reaction.

81 An ionic compound formed in the reaction between an acid and a base is called a

_____.

82 An acidic solution tastes _____.

83 A basic solution tastes _____.

84   The color of litmus is ———————— in an acidic solution and ———————— in a basic solution.

C   CALCULATIONS YOU SHOULD KNOW HOW TO DO

1   Balance chemical equations by inspection. See Example 2-1 and Problems 2-1 through 2-6.

2   Predict the products of chemical reactions using representative reactions. See Examples 2-2, 2-3, and 2-4 and Problems 2-7 and 2-8.

3   Use the periodic table to predict chemical and physical properties. See Problems 2-9, 2-10, 2-13, and 2-14.

4   Name chemical compounds using the periodic table and Tables 2-3 and 2-4. See Examples 2-10 and 2-12 and Problems 2-17, 2-18, 2-25 through 2-28, 2-33, and 2-34.

5   Write chemical formulas from the names of compounds using Figure 2-14 and Tables 2-3 and 2-4. See Examples 2-8, 2-9 and 2-13 and Problems 2-19 through 2-22, 2-29 through 2-32, 2-35, and 2-36.

6   Predict reaction products:

(a) For combination reactions, see Example 2-11 and Problems 2-41 and 2-42.

(b) For single-replacement reactions, see Examples 2-17, 2-18, and 2-19 and Problems 2-43 and 2-44.

(c) For double-replacement reactions, see Example 2-21 and Problems 2-55 and 2-56.

7   Write net ionic equations. See Example 2-20 and Problems 2-49 through 2-52.

D   SOLUTIONS TO THE ODD-NUMBERED PROBLEMS

2-1   The procedure for balancing equations of the type considered in this chapter is the balancing by inspection method outlined in Section 2-2.

(a) $2P(s) + 3Br_2(l) \rightarrow 2PBr_3(l)$

(b) $2H_2O_2(l) \rightarrow 2H_2O(l) + O_2(g)$

(c) $4CoO(s) + O_2(g) \rightarrow 2Co_2O_3(s)$

(d) $PCl_5(s) + 4H_2O(l) \rightarrow H_3PO_4(l) + 5HCl(g)$

2-3   (a) $CaH_2(s) + 2H_2O(l) \rightarrow Ca(OH)_2(aq) + 2H_2(g)$

(b) $CaCO_3(s) + 2HCl(aq) \rightarrow CaCl_2(aq) + CO_2(g) + H_2O(l)$

(c) $C_6H_{12}O_2(aq) + 8O_2(g) \rightarrow 6CO_2(g) + 6H_2O(l)$

(d) $2Li(s) + 2CO_2(g) + 2H_2O(g) \rightarrow 2LiHCO_3(s) + H_2(g)$

2-5 This problem differs from Problems 2-1 through 2-4 in that we also are asked to give the names of the reactant(s) and product(s). Recall that in naming a compound composed of a metal and a nonmetal, we first name the metal and then the nonmetal, using an *-ide* ending for the nonmetal. Compounds composed of two nonmetals are named in a similar manner, with the second listed element given the *-ide* ending and prefixes *(mono-, di-, tri-, tetra-, penta-, and hexa-)* used to distinguish cases where more than one compound is possible between the two elements.

(a) $NaH(s)$ + $H_2O(l) \rightarrow NaOH(aq)$ + $H_2(g)$
sodium hydride   water   sodium hydroxide   hydrogen

(b) $2SO_2(g)$ + $O_2(g) \rightarrow$ $2SO_3(g)$
sulfur dioxide   oxygen   sulfur trioxide

(c) $H_2S(g)$ + $2LiOH(aq)$ $\rightarrow$ $Li_2S(aq)$ + $2H_2O(l)$
hydrogen sulfide   lithium hydroxide   lithium sulfide   water

(d) $ZnO(s)$ + $CO(g)$ $\rightarrow Zn(s)$ + $CO_2(g)$
zinc oxide   carbon monoxide   zinc   carbon dioxide

2-7 The following reactions are all combination reactions. See Figure 2-14 in order to write the correct formula for each product.

(a) $2Na(s) + I_2(s) \rightarrow$ $2NaI(s)$
sodium iodide

(b) $Sr(s) + H_2(g) \rightarrow$ $SrH_2(s)$
strontium hydride

(c) $3Ca(s) + N_2(g) \rightarrow$ $Ca_3N_2(s)$
calcium nitride

(d) $2Mg(s) + O_2(g) \rightarrow$ $2MgO(s)$
magnesium oxide

2-9 By analogy with the properties of the other halogens, we predict the following:

(a) solid   (b) NaAt   (c) white   (d) At_2 (e) black

2-11 Tl, a main-group (5) metal; Eu, an inner transition metal; Xe, a main-group (8) nonmetal; Hf, a transition metal; Ru, a transition metal; Am, an inner transition metal; B, a main-group (3) semimetal

2-13 Radium is a Group 2 metal, and thus we predict the reactions of Ra by analogy with the other Group 2 metals.

(a) $2Ra(s) + O_2(g) \rightarrow 2RaO(s)$

(b) $Ra(s) + Cl_2(g) \rightarrow RaCl_2(s)$

(c) $Ra(s) + 2HCl(g) \rightarrow RaCl_2(s) + H_2(g)$

(d) $Ra(s) + H_2(g) \rightarrow RaH_2(s)$

(e) $Ra(s) + S(s) \rightarrow RaS(s)$

2-15 We first determine the number of electrons in the ion and then compare the result with the Z values for the noble gases.

(a) yes; Xe   (b) no   (c) yes; Ar   **(d) yes; Ar**   (e) yes; Ne   (f) no

2-17 We determine the charges on the atomic ions in ionic compounds using Figure 2-14.

(a) Mg^{2+} S^{2-} magnesium sulfide

(b) Al^{3+} P^{3-} aluminum phosphide

(c) Ba^{2+} F^- barium fluoride

(d) Ga^{3+} O^{2-} gallium oxide

2-19 To determine the chemical formula of an ionic compound, we use the procedure outlined in Example 2-9. The ionic charges are given in Figure 2-14.

(a) Ga_2S_3 (b) AlP   (c) KI   (d) SrF_2

2-21 (a) Li_3N (b) Ga_2Te_3 (c) Ba_3N_2 (d) $MgBr_2$

2-23 To determine the chemical formula of an ionic compound formed from a positive ion and a negative ion, we use the fact that the compound has no net charge.

(a) Fe_2O_3 (b) CdS

(c) RuF_3 (d) Tl_2S

2-25 In order to name the following compound, we need to know the names and formulas of the polyatomic ions given in Table 2-4.

(a) calcium cyanide   (b) silver perchlorate

(c) potassium permanganate   (d) strontium chromate

2-27 (a) ammonium sulfate   (b) ammonium phosphate

(c) calcium phosphate   (d) potassium phosphate

2-29 In order to write the chemical formula for each of the following compounds, we need to know the formula and ionic charge of the polyatomic ions given in Table 2-4. Recall that the net charge on the ionic compound must be zero.

(a) $Na_2S_2O_3$ (b) $KHCO_3$ (c) NaClO   (d) $CaSO_3$

2-31 See the solution to Problem 2-29.

(a) Na_2SO_3 (b) K_3PO_4 (c) Ag_2SO_4 (d) NH_4NO_3

2-33 The following compounds contain transition metal ions. The value of the metal charge is indicated by a Roman numeral. See Example 2-10.

(a) mercury(I) chloride   (b) chromium(III) nitrate

(c) cobalt(II) bromide   (d) copper(II) carbonate

2-35 The Roman numeral following the name of the transition metal ion indicates the ionic charge of the metal ion.

(a) Cr_2O_3 (b) $Sn(OH)_2$ (c) $Cu(C_2H_3O_2)_2$ (d) $Co_2(SO_4)_3$

2-37 (a) decomposition   (b) combination

(c) single-replacement   (d) double-replacement

2-39   (a) decomposition; already balanced

(b) combination
$$4Fe(s) + 3O_2(g) \rightarrow 2Fe_2O_3(s)$$

(c) single-replacement
$$2Al(s) + Mn_2O_3(s) \rightarrow 2Mn(s) + Al_2O_3(s)$$

(d) double-replacement
$$2AgNO_3(aq) + H_2SO_4(aq) \rightarrow Ag_2SO_4(s) + 2HNO_3(aq)$$

(e) double-replacement
$$Ca(OH)_2(aq) + 2HBr(aq) \rightarrow CaBr_2(aq) + 2H_2O(l)$$

(f) single-replacement
$$Cd(s) + 2HCl(aq) \rightarrow CdCl_2(aq) + H_2(g)$$

2-41   (a) $3Mg(s) + N_2(g) \rightarrow Mg_3N_2(s)$

(b) $H_2(g) + S(s) \rightarrow H_2S(g)$

(c) $2K(s) + Br_2(l) \rightarrow 2KBr(s)$

(d) $4Al(s) + 3O_2(g) \rightarrow 2Al_2O_3(s)$

(e) $MgO(s) + SO_2(g) \rightarrow MgSO_3(s)$

2-43   In order for a metal-metal replacement reaction to occur, the free metal must be a more reactive metal than the metal in the compound (see Table 2-7). Also, a more reactive free halogen will replace a less reactive halogen in compounds.

(a) $Zn(s) + 2HBr(aq) \rightarrow ZnBr_2(aq) + H_2(g)$

(b) $2Al(s) + Fe_2O_3(s) \rightarrow 2Fe(s) + Al_2O_3(s)$

(c) $Pb(s) + Cu(NO_3)_2(aq) \rightarrow Cu(s) + Pb(NO_3)_2(aq)$

(d) $Br_2(l) + 2NaI(aq) \rightarrow 2NaBr(aq) + I_2(s)$

2-45   (a) Calcium atoms are neutral and so have no charge. A chlorine molecule is neutral; each chlorine atom has zero charge. In $CaCl_2$ the ionic charge of calcium is $+2$ and the ionic charge of chlorine is -1. Thus calcium is oxidized and chlorine is reduced.

(b) Aluminum atoms have no charge, and oxygen atoms in O_2 have no charge. In Al_2O_3 the ionic charges of aluminum and oxygen are $+3$ and -2, respectively. Thus aluminum is oxidized and oxygen is reduced.

(c) Rubidium is oxidized and bromine is reduced.

(d) Sodium is oxidized and sulfur is reduced.

2-47   (a) Each calcium atom loses two electrons, and each of the two chlorine atoms gains one electron. Thus a total of two electrons is transferred.

(b) Each aluminum atom loses three electrons, and each oxygen atom gains two electrons. Because the formula unit of the product Al_2O_3 involves two aluminum atoms, a total of 2×3 or 6 electrons is transferred per formula unit of product. The overall balanced equation shows that two formula units ($2Al_2O_3$) are produced.

(c) One electron. However, two formula units are produced.

(d) Two electrons

2-49 To determine the net ionic equation that corresponds to the complete ionic equation, we determine the precipitate or molecular product formed. The ions that are used to form this species are the reactants in the net ionic equation.

(a) $2H^+(aq) + S^{2-}(aq) \rightarrow H_2S(g)$

(b) $Pb^{2+}(aq) + S^{2-}(aq) \rightarrow PbS(s)$

(c) $H^+(aq) + OH^-(aq) \rightarrow H_2O(l)$

(d) $OH^-(aq) + H^+(aq) \rightarrow H_2O(l)$ (Na_2O is a basic anhydride.)

(e) $NH_3(aq) + H^+(aq) \rightarrow NH_4^+(aq)$

2-51 (a) $Fe(NO_3)_3(aq) + 3NaOH(aq) \rightarrow Fe(OH)_3(s) + 3NaNO_3(aq)$

$Fe^{3+}(aq) + 3OH^-(aq) \rightarrow Fe(OH)_3(s)$

(b) $Zn(ClO_4)_2(aq) + K_2S(aq) \rightarrow ZnS(s) + 2KClO_4(aq)$

$Zn^{2+}(aq) + S^{2-}(aq) \rightarrow ZnS(s)$

(c) $Pb(NO_3)_2(aq) + 2KOH(aq) \rightarrow Pb(OH)_2(s) + 2KNO_3(aq)$

$Pb^{2+}(aq) + 2OH^-(aq) \rightarrow Pb(OH)_2(s)$

(d) $Zn(NO_3)_2(aq) + Na_2CO_3(aq) \rightarrow ZnCO_3(s) + 2NaNO_3(aq)$

$Zn^{2+}(aq) + CO_3^{2-}(aq) \rightarrow ZnCO_3(s)$

(e) $Cu(ClO_4)_2(aq) + Na_2CO_3(aq) \rightarrow CuCO_3(s) + 2NaClO_4(aq)$

$Cu^{2+}(aq) + CO_3^{2-}(aq) \rightarrow CuCO_3(s)$

2-53 (a) acidic   (b) acidic   (c) basic   (d) acidic   (e) basic

2-55 (a) $2HClO_3(aq) + Ba(OH)_2(aq) \rightarrow Ba(ClO_3)_2(aq) + 2H_2O(l)$
barium chlorate

(b) $HC_2H_3O_2(aq) + KOH(aq) \rightarrow KC_2H_3O_2(aq) + H_2O(l)$
potassium acetate

(c) $2HI(aq) + Mg(OH)_2(s) \rightarrow MgI_2(aq) + 2H_2O(l)$
magnesium iodide

(d) $H_2SO_4(aq) + 2RbOH(aq) \rightarrow Rb_2SO_4(aq) + 2H_2O(l)$
rubidium sulfate

2-57 (a) $HCl(aq) + KCN(aq) \rightarrow HCN(g) + KCl(aq)$

(b) $2K(s) + 2H_2O(l) \rightarrow H_2(g) + 2KOH(aq)$

(c) $2H_2O_2(aq) \rightarrow O_2(g) + 2H_2O(l)$

(d) $H_2(g) + Br_2(l) \rightarrow 2HBr(g)$

2-59 $2Pb(l) + O_2(g) \rightarrow 2PbO(s)$

$Ag(l) + O_2(g) \rightarrow$ N.R.

2-61   To work a problem like this you have to know how to write a chemical formula from the name. Once we have written the formulas for the reactants and the products, we then proceed to balance the equation.

(a) $2Na(s) + S(s) \rightarrow Na_2S(s)$

(b) $Ca(s) + Br_2(l) \rightarrow CaBr_2(s)$

(c) $2Ba(s) + O_2(g) \rightarrow 2BaO(s)$

(d) $2SO_2(g) + O_2(g) \rightarrow 2SO_3(g)$

(e) $3Mg(s) + N_2(g) \rightarrow Mg_3N_2(s)$

2-63 $HgS(s) + O_2(g) \xrightarrow{heat} Hg(g) + SO_2(g) \xrightarrow{cool} Hg(l) + SO_2(g)$

2-65   See Table 2-7. Na, Fe, Sn, Au

2-67   (a) $2Na(s) + H_2(g) \rightarrow 2NaH(s)$

(b) $2Al(s) + 3S(s) \rightarrow Al_2S_3(s)$

(c) $H_2O(g) + C(s) \rightarrow CO(g) + H_2(g)$

(d) $C(s) + 2H_2(g) \rightarrow CH_4(g)$

(e) $PCl_3(l) + Cl_2(g) \rightarrow PCl_5(s)$

2-69 $2CuO(s) + C(s) \xrightarrow{high\ T} 2Cu(s) + CO_2(g)$

$SnO_2(s) + C(s) \xrightarrow{high\ T} Sn(s) + CO_2(g)$

$2Fe_2O_3(s) + 3C(s) \xrightarrow{high\ T} 4Fe(s) + 3CO_2(g)$

E   ANSWERS TO THE SELF-TEST

1   false

2   false

3   false

4   in front

5   be the same as

6   false

7   sodium, potassium (or other Group 1 metals)

8   (a) $2Li(s) + Cl_2(g) \rightarrow 2LiCl(s)$

(b) $2Na(s) + 2H_2O(l) \rightarrow$
$\qquad\qquad 2NaOH(s) + H_2(g)$

9   calcium, strontium, barium

10   (a) $2Mg(s) + O_2(g) \rightarrow 2MgO(s)$

(b) $Ca(s) + 2H_2O(g) \rightarrow$
$\qquad\qquad Ca(OH)_2(s) + H_2(g)$

11   fluorine, chlorine, bromine, iodine, and astatine

12   (a) $2Na(s) + F_2(g) \rightarrow 2NaF(s)$

(b) $H_2(g) + Br_2(l) \rightarrow 2HBr(g)$

13   atomic mass

14   atomic number

15   false

16   true

17   alkali metals

18 alkaline earth metals

19 7

20 8

21 the inert gases

22 false (Si is a semimetal.)

23 semiconducting, brittle, dull surface, nonductile

24 false

25 in groups that are headed by numbers (first two columns on the left and last six columns on the right in the table)

26 false

27 true

28 Group 2 and Group 3

29 lanthanum, actinium

30 the rare earths

31 true

32 radioactive

33 The members of each series have such similar chemical properties that they can be placed in one position in the periodic table. Also, this version of the periodic table is more compact.

34 false

35 false (The properties of the first member are not as typical as those of the other members.)

36 true

37 false

38 loses

39 gains

40 positive ions and negative ions

41 zero

42 $+2$, -1, $MgBr_2$

43 false

44 $+4$

45 increases

46 a transfer of electrons

47 the number of electrons gained by the element that is reduced

48 combination (also oxidation-reduction)

49 ionic

50 a combination (or combustion) reaction

51 $Mg^{2+}(aq)$, $SO_4^{2-}(aq)$

52 polyatomic ion

53 false (For example, Al_2O_3 is insoluble in water.)

54 hydroxide ions, $OH^-(aq)$

55 yields hydroxide ions

56 basic

57 yields hydrogen ions, $H^+(aq)$, in water

58 an acid

59 acidic

60 false (The hydrogen ion in water is associated with one or more water molecules and is represented as $H^+(aq)$.)

61 sulfuric acid, H_2SO_4

62 true

63 one

64 $KClO_3$, potassium chlorate; HgO, mercury(II) oxide

65 the metal oxide and carbon dioxide, CO_2

66 hydrogen, H_2

67 false

68 true

69 reactivity series

70 below

71 carbon

72 true

73 fluorine

74 insoluble

75 the cations in two different compounds exchange anions

76 (a) $Na^+(aq)$ and $NO_3^-(aq)$

 (b) $AgCl(s)$

 (c) $Ag^+(aq) + Cl^-(aq) \rightarrow AgCl(s)$

77 the formation of the precipitate $AgCl(s)$

78 (a) $NO_3^-(aq)$ and $K^+(aq)$

 (b) $H^+(aq) + OH^-(aq) \rightarrow H_2O(l)$

79 the formation of water molecules

80 neutralization

81 salt

82 sour

83 bitter

84 red, blue

CHEMICAL CALCULATIONS

A OUTLINE OF CHAPTER 3

3-1 The quantity of a substance that is equal to its formula mass in grams is called a mole.

> One formula mass in grams of any substance contains the same number of formula units as the corresponding quantity of any other substance.

> The number of moles in a given mass of a substance is calculated using the unit conversion factor

$$1 = \frac{1 \text{ mol}}{\text{formula mass in grams}}$$

3-2 One mole of any substance contains Avogadro's number of formula units.

> Avogadro's number, 6.022×10^{23}, is the number of formula units in one mole of a substance.

> The formula unit is the group of atoms or ions represented by the chemical formula of a substance (see Table 3-1).

> The mass of a formula unit is calculated by dividing the formula mass in grams by Avogadro's number (Example 3-2).

> The number of atoms and molecules in a given mass of a substance is found using Avogadro's number and the formula mass of the substance (Example 3-3).

3-3 Simplest formulas can be determined by chemical analysis.

> Stoichiometry is the calculation of the quantities of elements or compounds involved in chemical equations.

> The simplest chemical formula of a substance is given as the number of atoms of

each type in the substance expressed as smallest whole numbers (Examples 3-4 and 3-5).

The empirical formula is the simplest chemical formula of a substance.

The mass percentage of an element in a compound can be calculated if the chemical formula of the compound is known (Example 3-6).

3-4   Empirical formulas can be used to determine an unknown atomic mass.

The atomic mass of an element can be determined from the empirical formula of one of its compounds (Example 3-7).

3-5   An empirical formula along with the molecular mass determines the molecular formula.

The molecular formula of a substance is found from the empirical formula and the molecular mass of the substance (Example 3-8).

3-6   The coefficients in chemical equations can be interpreted as numbers of moles.

The balancing coefficients in a chemical equation are the relative numbers of moles of each reactant and product in the balanced equation.

The various interpretations of chemical equations in terms of molecules, moles, and grams are summarized in Table 3-2.

Some calculations involving chemical reactions are discussed.

3-7   The percentage composition of many compounds can be determined by combustion analysis.

When compounds containing only C and H or C, H, and O are burned in excess O_2, all the C ends up as CO_2 and all the H ends up as H_2O.

The mass of C is related to the mass of CO_2 produced.

The mass of H is related to the mass of H_2O produced.

The procedure for the determination of the empirical formula from combustion data is outlined in Example 3-11.

3-8   Calculations involving chemical equations are carried out in terms of moles.

The procedure for calculations involving chemical equations is given in Figure 3-3.

3-9   When two or more substances react, the quantity of product is determined by the limiting reactant.

The limiting reactant is the reactant that is consumed completely in a chemical reaction.

An excess reactant is a reactant that is not consumed completely in a chemical reaction.

When the quantities of two or more reactants are given, it is necessary to determine which is the limiting reactant (Examples 3-12 and 3-13).

3-10   For many chemical reactions the amount of the desired product obtained is less than the theoretical amount.

The theoretical yield of a reaction is the mass of a particular product that is calculated from the limiting reactant.

The actual yield is the mass of the product that is actually obtained.

The percent yield is defined as

$$\text{percent yield} = \left(\frac{\text{actual yield}}{\text{theoretical yield}}\right) \times 100 \tag{3-5}$$

3-11   Many reactions take place in solution.

A solution is a mixture of two or more substances that is uniform at the molecular level.

The solute is the substance that is dissolved.

The solvent is the liquid in which the solute is dissolved.

The process of dissolving a substance in water can be represented by a chemical equation.

The concentration of a solution can be expressed in terms of molarity.

Molarity is defined as the number of moles of solute per liter of solution; the equation is

$$\text{molarity} = \frac{\text{moles of solute}}{\text{liters of solution}} \tag{3-6}$$

or in symbols,

$$M = \frac{n}{V} \tag{3-7}$$

The molarity of a solution can be calculated from the mass of solute in a given volume of solution.

The procedure for preparing a solution of known molarity is described.

Calculations involving reactions in solution are discussed.

A more dilute solution can be prepared from a more concentrated solution.

The number of moles of solute does not change upon dilution:

$$\text{moles of solute} = n = M_1 V_1 = M_2 V_2 \tag{3-8}$$

3-12   The concentration of an acid or a base can be determined by titration.

A titration is a process in which a given volume of a base or acid is neutralized by a measured volume of an acid or base of known concentration (Figure 3-7).

A buret is used to measure the volume of the solution added in a titration.

The end point of a titration is the point at which the base or acid has been completely neutralized by the added acid or base.

An acid-base indicator is used to signal the end point in a titration.

Titration calculations involve the equation $n = MV$ where M usually is expressed as $\text{mmol} \cdot \text{mL}^{-1}$ and V as mL.

B SELF-TEST

1 The atomic mass of an element is the mass of an atom of the element relative to

_____ .

2 The atomic mass of helium is 4.003 g. *True/False*

3 The formula mass of a substance is the _____ .

4 A sample of 4.0 g of helium contains the same number of atoms as 4.0 g of carbon. *True/False*

5 One mole of a substance is the quantity of the substance that is equal to _____

_____ .

6 Two moles of H_2 has a mass of _____ grams.

7 The number of moles in 36 g of carbon is _____ .

8 The number of moles in 36 g of water, H_2O, is _____ .

9 One mole of ammonia, NH_3, has the same mass as one mole of nitrogen dioxide, NO_2. *True/False*

10 The value of Avogadro's number is _____ .

11 _____ of any substance contains Avogadro's number of formula units.

12 Two moles of hydrogen chloride, HCl, contain _____ molecules.

13 One mole of carbon dioxide, CO_2, contains the same number of molecules as one mole of carbon monoxide, CO. *True/False*

14 One mole of CO_2 contains Avogadro's number of oxygen atoms. *True/False*

15 Two moles of NaCl contain _____ chloride ions.

16 Two moles of $CaCl_2$ contain _____ chloride ions.

17 The simplest chemical formula of a compound in which two atoms of Cu combine with one atom of O is _____ .

18 Chemical analysis of a compound provides us with the number of each kind of atom in the compound. *True/False*

19 The expression 88.82 g Cu $\approx$ 11.18 g O means that _____

_____ .

20 The number of moles of Cu and O that combine can be found from the data in Question 19 by _____.

21 The simplest chemical formula of the compound of Cu and O given in Question 19 is Cu_4O_2. *True/False*

22 The empirical formula of a compound is always the actual molecular formula of the compound. *True/False*

23 The molecular formula of a compound can be determined from the empirical formula and its _____.

24 A substance has the empirical formula CH_2 and its molecular mass is 42. The molecular formula is _____.

25 A hydrocarbon is a compound that consists of the elements _____ and

_____.

26 The balancing coefficients in a chemical equation can be interpreted as

_____.

Questions 27 through 30 refer to the balanced chemical equation

$$2C_2H_6(g) + 7O_2(g) \longrightarrow 4CO_2(g) + 6H_2O(l)$$

27 How many moles of C_2H_6 react with 14 mol of O_2?

28 In order to calculate the number of grams of CO_2 produced from 14 mol of O_2, we first must calculate the _____ of CO_2 produced.

29 We can calculate the mass of CO_2 produced from 14 mol of O_2 by _____

_____.

30 The procedure to calculate the mass of O_2 that is necessary for the complete combustion of a given mass of C_2H_6 is

(1) _____

(2) _____

(3) _____

31 When a compound containing only carbon, hydrogen, and oxygen is burned in an excess of O_2, all the carbon ends up as _____ and all the hydrogen ends up as _____.

32 The data in a combustion analysis of a compound can be used to calculate the mass percentage of carbon from the mass of _____.

33 The mass percentage of hydrogen in a compound can be calculated from combustion analysis using the relationship

34 In a reaction between 10 g of hydrogen, H_2, and 32 g of oxygen, O_2, 6 g of hydrogen remains after the consumption of all the oxygen. The limiting reactant is _____ and the excess reactant is _____.

35 The actual yield of a product in a reaction is always equal to the theoretical yield. *True/False*

36 A solution is prepared by dissolving 1.0 g of sodium chloride in 100 mL of water. The solute is _____ and the solvent is _____.

37 Molarity is defined as _____

_____.

38 The molarity of a solution in which 0.50 mol of sodium chloride is dissolved in 500 mL of solution is _____.

39 A 1.0 M solution of sodium chloride is prepared by dissolving 1.0 mol of sodium chloride in 1.0 L of water. *True/False*

40 The procedure to prepare 500 mL of a 0.50 M solution of sodium chloride is as follows: _____

_____.

41 There are _____ moles of sodium chloride in 10 mL of a 1.0 M solution of sodium chloride.

42 Zinc reacts with sulfuric acid according to

$$Zn(s) + H_2SO_4(aq) \longrightarrow ZnSO_4(aq) + H_2(g)$$

What volume of 1.0 M H_2SO_4 is required to react with 0.50 mol of zinc?

43   A more dilute solution can be prepared from a more concentrated solution. *True/False*

44   The number of moles of solute decreases upon dilution with solvent. *True/False*

45   In a titration experiment, an acid solution is added to a given volume of a base solution until _____.

46   The end point in an acid-base titration is the experimental estimate of the _____ for the titration.

47   The end point of a titration is signaled by _____.

48   The concentration of a solution of a base can be determined by a titration experiment using a solution of NaOH of known concentration. *True/False*

49   The formula mass of an acid can be determined in a titration experiment. *True/False*

50   There are _____ mmoles of sodium hydroxide in 50 mL of 1.0 M NaOH(*aq*).

C   CALCULATIONS YOU SHOULD KNOW HOW TO DO

Chapter 3 contains many different types of calculations. You should learn how all the calculations presented are unified by the concept of a mole. The procedure for any calculation involving chemical equations is summarized in Figure 3-3. You should be able to do the following types of calculations.

1   Calculate the number of moles in a given mass of a substance. You must know the formula of the substance to be able to do this. See Example 3-1 and Problems 3-1 through 3-4.

2   Calculate the mass of a given number of formula units of a substance. See Example 3-2 and Problems 3-7 through 3-10.

3   Calculate the number of molecules in a given mass of a substance. See Example 3-3 and Problems 3-11 through 3-14.

4   Determine the simplest formula from chemical analysis. See Examples 3-4 and 3-5 and Problems 3-15 through 3-24.

5   Determine the atomic mass from the empirical formula. See Example 3-7 and Problems 3-25 through 3-28.

6   Determine the molecular formula from the empirical formula and the molecular mass. See Example 3-8 and Problems 3-35 through 3-38.

7 Calculate the quantities of reactants and products that are involved in chemical reactions. See Examples 3-9 and 3-10 and Problems 3-39 through 3-50.

8 Determine the empirical formula of a compound from combustion data. See Example 3-11 and Problems 3-29 through 3-34.

9 Calculate quantities involving limiting reactants. See Examples 3-12 and 3-13 and Problems 3-51 through 3-54.

10 Calculate the percent yield of a product. See Example 3-14 and Problems 3-55 through 3-58.

11 Calculate the molarity of a solution. See Section 3-11 and Problems 3-59 through 3-62.

12 Calculate quantities in order to prepare solutions of a given molarity. See Example 3-15 and 3-17 and Problems 3-63, 3-64, and 3-67 through 3-70.

13 Calculate quantities of reactants and products of reactions that take place in solution. See Example 3-16 and Problems 3-71 through 3-74.

14 Calculate the concentration of an acid or a base in a titration experiment. See Example 3-18 and Problems 3-75 through 3-82.

15 Calculate the molecular mass of an acid or a base in a titration experiment. See Example 3-19 and Problems 3-83 and 3-84.

D   SOLUTIONS TO THE ODD-NUMBERED PROBLEMS

3-1   (a) Formula mass of $H_2O = 18.02$

$$\text{number of moles} = (28.0 \text{ g})\left(\frac{1 \text{ mol}}{18.02 \text{ g}}\right) = 1.55 \text{ mol}$$

(b) Formula mass of $C = 12.01$

$$\text{number of moles} = (200 \text{ mg})\left(\frac{1 \text{ g}}{10^3 \text{ mg}}\right)\left(\frac{1 \text{ mol}}{12.01 \text{ g}}\right) = 0.0167 \text{ mol}$$

(c) Formula mass of $NaCl = 58.44$

$$\text{number of moles} = (454 \text{ g})\left(\frac{1 \text{ mol}}{58.44 \text{ g}}\right) = 7.77 \text{ mol}$$

(d) Formula mass of $CaO = 56.08$

$$\text{number of moles} = (1000 \text{ kg})\left(\frac{1000 \text{ g}}{1 \text{ kg}}\right)\left(\frac{1 \text{ mol}}{56.08 \text{ g}}\right) = 1.78 \times 10^4 \text{ mol}$$

3-3   (a) formula mass of malathion $= 330.34$

$$\text{number of moles} = (1.00 \text{ kg})\left(\frac{10^3 \text{ g}}{1 \text{ kg}}\right)\left(\frac{1 \text{ mol}}{330.34 \text{ g}}\right) = 3.03 \text{ mol}$$

(b) formula mass of aluminum sulfate $= 342.14$

$$\text{number of moles} = (75.0 \text{ g})\left(\frac{1 \text{ mol}}{342.14 \text{ g}}\right) = 0.219 \text{ mol}$$

(c) formula mass of oil of peppermint $= 156.26$

$$\text{number of moles} = (50.0 \text{ mg})\left(\frac{1 \text{ g}}{10^3 \text{ mg}}\right)\left(\frac{1 \text{ mol}}{156.26 \text{ g}}\right) = 3.20 \times 10^{-4} \text{ mol}$$

(d) formula mass of potassium dichromate $= 294.20$

$$\text{number of moles} = (2.756 \text{ g})\left(\frac{1 \text{ mol}}{294.20 \text{ g}}\right) = 9.368 \times 10^{-3} \text{ mol}$$

3-5   mass of Avogadro's number of baseballs $= (142 \text{ g})(6.022 \times 10^{23})$
$$= 8.55 \times 10^{25} \text{ g}$$

The mass of the earth is $6.0 \times 10^{24} \text{ kg} = 6.0 \times 10^{27} \text{ g}$.

The ratio of the mass of one mol of baseballs to the mass of the earth is

$$\frac{8.55 \times 10^{25} \text{ g}}{6.0 \times 10^{27} \text{ g}} = 1.4 \times 10^{-2}$$

The mass of one mol of baseballs is 1.4×10^{-2} that of the mass of the earth.

3-7   (a) formula mass of $CO_2 = 44.01$

$$\text{mass of one } CO_2 \text{ molecule} = \left(\frac{44.01 \text{ g}}{1 \text{ mol}}\right)\left(\frac{1 \text{ mol}}{6.022 \times 10^{23} \text{ molecules}}\right)$$
$$= 7.308 \times 10^{-23} \text{ g}$$

(b) formula mass of $C_6H_{12}O_6 = 180.16$

$$\text{mass of one } C_6H_{12}O_6 \text{ molecule} = \left(\frac{180.16 \text{ g}}{1 \text{ mol}}\right)\left(\frac{1 \text{ mol}}{6.022 \times 10^{23} \text{ molecules}}\right)$$
$$= 2.992 \times 10^{-22} \text{ g}$$

(c) formula mass of $CaCl_2 = 110.98$

$$\left(\begin{matrix}\text{mass of one } CaCl_2 \\ \text{formula unit}\end{matrix}\right) = \left(\frac{110.98 \text{ g}}{1 \text{ mol}}\right)\left(\frac{1 \text{ mol}}{6.022 \times 10^{23} \text{ formula units}}\right)$$
$$= 1.843 \times 10^{-22} \text{ g}$$

3-9 (a) formula mass of Fe = 55.85

$$\text{mass of 200 Fe atoms} = \left(\frac{55.85\ g}{1\ mol}\right)\left(\frac{1\ mol}{6.022 \times 10^{23}\ atoms}\right)(200\ atoms)$$
$$= 1.855 \times 10^{-20}\ g$$

(b) formula mass of H_2O = 18.02

$$\left(\begin{array}{c}\text{mass of } 1.0 \times 10^{16}\ H_2O \\ \text{molecules}\end{array}\right) = \left(\frac{18.02\ g}{1\ mol}\right)\left(\frac{1\ mol}{6.022 \times 10^{23}\ molecules}\right)$$
$$\times (1.0 \times 10^{16}\ molecules)$$
$$= 3.0 \times 10^{-7}\ g$$

(c) formula mass of O = 16.00

$$\text{mass of } 1.0 \times 10^6\ O\ atoms = \left(\frac{16.00\ g}{1\ mol}\right)\left(\frac{1\ mol}{6.022 \times 10^{23}\ atoms}\right)$$
$$\times (1.0 \times 10^6\ atoms)$$
$$= 2.7 \times 10^{-17}\ g$$

(d) formula mass of O_2 = 32.00

$$\left(\begin{array}{c}\text{mass of } 1.0 \times 10^6\ O_2 \\ \text{molecules}\end{array}\right) = \left(\frac{32.00\ g}{1\ mol}\right)\left(\frac{1\ mol}{6.022 \times 10^{23}\ molecules}\right)$$
$$\times (1.0 \times 10^6\ molecules)$$
$$= 5.3 \times 10^{-17}\ g$$

3-11 The number of moles that corresponds to 50.0 g of H_2O is

$$\text{number of moles} = (50.0\ g)\left(\frac{1\ mol}{18.02\ g}\right) = 2.78\ mol$$

The number of H_2O molecules in 2.78 mol is

$$\text{number of molecules} = (2.78\ mol)\left(\frac{6.022 \times 10^{23}\ molecules}{1\ mol}\right)$$
$$= 1.67 \times 10^{24}\ molecules$$

There are three atoms in each H_2O molecule, and so the total number of atoms is

$$\text{number of atoms} = (1.67 \times 10^{24}\ molecules)\left(\frac{3\ atoms}{1\ H_2O\ molecule}\right)$$
$$= 5.01 \times 10^{24}\ atoms$$

3-13 (a) The number of moles in 100 g of NH_3 is

$$\text{number of moles} = (100\ g)\left(\frac{1\ mol}{17.03\ g}\right) = 5.871\ mol$$

The number of NH_3 molecules in 5.871 mol is

$$\text{number of molecules} = (5.871 \text{ mol})\left(\frac{6.022 \times 10^{23} \text{ molecules}}{1 \text{ mol}}\right)$$
$$= 3.54 \times 10^{24} \text{ molecules}$$

(b) The number of molecules in 200 g of $C_{12}H_{22}O_{11}$ is

$$\text{number of molecules} = (200 \text{ g})\left(\frac{1 \text{ mol}}{342.30 \text{ g}}\right)\left(\frac{6.022 \times 10^{23} \text{ molecules}}{1 \text{ mol}}\right)$$
$$= 3.52 \times 10^{23} \text{ molecules}$$

(c) The number of molecules in 400 g of H_2SO_4 is

$$\text{number of molecules} = (400 \text{ g})\left(\frac{1 \text{ mol}}{98.08 \text{ g}}\right)\left(\frac{6.022 \times 10^{23} \text{ molecules}}{1 \text{ mol}}\right)$$
$$= 2.46 \times 10^{24} \text{ molecules}$$

(d) The number of molecules in 100 mg of $C_{55}H_{72}MgN_4O_5$ is

$$\text{number of molecules} = (100 \text{ mg})\left(\frac{1 \text{ g}}{10^3 \text{ mg}}\right)\left(\frac{1 \text{ mol}}{893.48 \text{ g}}\right)$$
$$\times \left(\frac{6.022 \times 10^{23} \text{ molecules}}{1 \text{ mol}}\right)$$
$$= 6.74 \times 10^{19} \text{ molecules}$$

3-15 Take a 100-g sample and write

$$62.5 \text{ g Ca} \backsimeq 37.5 \text{ g C}$$

Divide each quantity by its corresponding atomic mass to get

$$(62.5 \text{ g})\left(\frac{1 \text{ mol}}{40.08 \text{ g}}\right) = 1.56 \text{ mol Ca} \backsimeq (37.5 \text{ g})\left(\frac{1 \text{ mol}}{12.01 \text{ g}}\right) = 3.12 \text{ mol C}$$

Divide by the smaller quantity (1.56) to obtain

$$1.00 \text{ mol Ca} \backsimeq 2.00 \text{ mol C}$$

The empirical formula is CaC_2.

3-17 The mass percentage of Cu in the compound is

$$\text{mass \% Cu} = \left(\frac{2.46 \text{ g}}{5.22 \text{ g}}\right) \times 100 = 47.1\%$$

Therefore, mass % Cl = 52.9%. Assume a 100-g sample and write

$$47.1 \text{ g Cu} \backsimeq 52.9 \text{ g Cl}$$

Divide each quantity by the corresponding atomic mass to get

$$(47.1 \text{ g})\left(\frac{1 \text{ mol}}{63.55 \text{ g}}\right) = 0.741 \text{ mol Cu} \backsimeq (52.9 \text{ g})\left(\frac{1 \text{ mol}}{35.45 \text{ g}}\right) = 1.49 \text{ mol Cl}$$

Divide both quantities by the smaller number (0.741) to get

$$1.00 \text{ mol Cu} \backsimeq 2.01 \text{ mol Cl}$$

Now recognize that 2.01 is essentially 2 and write the empirical formula as $CuCl_2$.

3-19 We are given that 28.1 g of cobalt react with chlorine to yield 61.9 g of the compound. Therefore, the mass of Cl_2 that reacted was $61.9 \text{ g} - 28.1 \text{ g} = 33.8 \text{ g}$. Thus the mass of Cl in the compound is 33.8 g, and so we have the stoichiometric correspondence

$$28.1 \text{ g Co} \backsimeq 33.8 \text{ g Cl}$$

Divide each quantity by its corresponding atomic mass to get

$$0.4768 \text{ mol Co} \backsimeq 0.9535 \text{ mol Cl}$$

or

$$1.00 \text{ mol Co} \backsimeq 2.00 \text{ mol Cl}$$

The empirical formula is $CoCl_2$.

3-21 Take a 100-g sample and write

$$9.9 \text{ g C} \backsimeq 58.7 \text{ g Cl} \backsimeq 31.4 \text{ g F}$$

Divide each quantity by its corresponding atomic mass to obtain

$$0.82 \text{ mol C} \backsimeq 1.66 \text{ mol Cl} \backsimeq 1.65 \text{ mol F}$$

Divide by the smallest quantity (0.82) to obtain

$$1.0 \text{ mol C} \backsimeq 2.0 \text{ mol Cl} \backsimeq 2.0 \text{ mol F}$$

The empirical formula is CCl_2F_2.

3-23 (a) Take a 100-g sample and write

$$46.45 \text{ g Li} \backsimeq 53.55 \text{ g O}$$

$$\frac{46.45 \text{ g}}{6.941 \text{ g} \cdot \text{mol}^{-1}} = 6.692 \text{ mol Li} \backsimeq \frac{53.55 \text{ g}}{16.00 \text{ g} \cdot \text{mol}^{-1}} = 3.347 \text{ mol O}$$

$$2.00 \text{ mol Li} \backsimeq 1.00 \text{ mol O}$$

The empirical formula is Li_2O.

(b) Take a 100-g sample and write

$$59.78 \text{ g Li} \Leftrightarrow 40.22 \text{ g N}$$

$$\frac{59.78 \text{ g}}{6.941 \text{ g} \cdot \text{mol}^{-1}} = 8.613 \text{ mol Li} \Leftrightarrow \frac{40.22 \text{ g}}{14.01 \text{ g} \cdot \text{mol}^{-1}} = 2.871 \text{ mol N}$$

$$3.00 \text{ mol Li} \Leftrightarrow 1.00 \text{ mol N}$$

The empirical formula is Li_3N.

(c) Take a 100-g sample and write

$$14.17 \text{ g Li} \Leftrightarrow 85.83 \text{ g N}$$

$$\frac{14.17 \text{ g}}{6.941 \text{ g} \cdot \text{mol}^{-1}} = 2.041 \text{ mol Li} \Leftrightarrow \frac{85.83 \text{ g}}{14.01 \text{ g} \cdot \text{mol}^{-1}} = 6.126 \text{ mol N}$$

$$1.00 \text{ mol Li} \Leftrightarrow 3.00 \text{ mol N}$$

The empirical formula is LiN_3.

(d) Take a 100-g sample and write

$$36.11 \text{ g Ca} \Leftrightarrow 63.89 \text{ g Cl}$$

$$\frac{36.11 \text{ g}}{40.08 \text{ g} \cdot \text{mol}^{-1}} = 0.9009 \text{ mol Ca} \Leftrightarrow \frac{63.89 \text{ g}}{35.45 \text{ g} \cdot \text{mol}^{-1}} = 1.802 \text{ mol Cl}$$

$$1.00 \text{ mol Ca} \Leftrightarrow 2.00 \text{ mol Cl}$$

The empirical formula is $CaCl_2$.

3-25   The mass percentage of the metal is

$$\text{mass \% M} = \left(\frac{1.443 \text{ g}}{1.683 \text{ g}} \right) \times 100 = 85.74\%$$

Assuming a 100-g sample, we have

$$85.74 \text{ g M} \Leftrightarrow 100.00 \text{ g} - 85.74 \text{ g} = 14.26 \text{ g O}$$

We do not know the atomic mass of M, but we can divide 14.26 g O by the atomic mass of O (16.00) to obtain

$$85.74 \text{ g M} \Leftrightarrow 0.8913 \text{ mol O}$$

We know from the given empirical formula that

$$2 \text{ mol M} \Leftrightarrow 3 \text{ mol O}$$

Thus we have

$$85.74 \text{ g M} \backsimeq 0.8913 \text{ mol O} \left(\frac{2 \text{ mol M}}{3 \text{ mol O}} \right)$$

or

$$85.74 \text{ g M} \backsimeq 0.5942 \text{ mol M}$$

Divide by 0.5942 to get

$$144.3 \text{ g M} \backsimeq 1.000 \text{ mol M}$$

The atomic mass of M is 144.3, which corresponds to neodymium (Nd).

3-27 $\text{mass \% of H}_2\text{O} = \left(\dfrac{0.0949 \text{ g}}{0.642 \text{ g}} \right) \times 100 = 14.8\%$

Therefore, mass % MCl_2 = 85.2%. Assuming a 100-g sample, we have

$$14.8 \text{ g H}_2\text{O} \backsimeq 85.2 \text{ g MCl}_2$$

Divide by the formula mass of H_2O (we do not know the formula mass of MCl_2 because we do not know the atomic mass of M) to obtain

$$0.821 \text{ mol H}_2\text{O} \backsimeq 85.2 \text{ g MCl}_2$$

We know from the chemical formula of the compound that

$$2 \text{ mol H}_2\text{O} \backsimeq 1 \text{ mol MCl}_2$$

Thus we have

$$0.821 \text{ mol H}_2\text{O} \left(\frac{1 \text{ mol MCl}_2}{2 \text{ mol H}_2\text{O}} \right) \backsimeq 85.2 \text{ g MCl}_2$$

or

$$0.4105 \text{ mol MCl}_2 \backsimeq 85.2 \text{ g MCl}_2$$

Divide both sides of the correspondence by 0.4105 to get

$$1.00 \text{ mol MCl}_2 \backsimeq 208 \text{ g MCl}_2$$

There are two chlorine atoms in MCl_2, and so the atomic mass of M is

$$\text{atomic mass of M} = 208 - (2 \times 35.45) = 137$$

The metal is barium.

3-29   The masses of carbon and hydrogen in the original sample are

$$\text{mass of C} = (1.500 \text{ g CO}_2)\left(\frac{12.01 \text{ g C}}{44.01 \text{ g CO}_2}\right) = 0.4093 \text{ g C}$$

$$\text{mass of H} = (0.409 \text{ g H}_2\text{O})\left(\frac{2 \times 1.000 \text{ g H}}{18.02 \text{ g H}_2\text{O}}\right) = 0.04576 \text{ g H}$$

The mass percentages of C and H are

$$\text{mass \% of C} = \frac{0.4093 \text{ g}}{1.000 \text{ g}} \times 100 = 40.93\%$$

$$\text{mass \% of H} = \frac{0.04576 \text{ g}}{1.000 \text{ g}} \times 100 = 4.576\%$$

The mass percentage of oxygen is obtained by difference

$$\text{mass \% of O} = 100.00 - 40.93 - 4.58 = 54.49$$

Take a 100-g sample and write

$$40.93 \text{ g C} \backsimeq 4.576 \text{ g H} \backsimeq 54.49 \text{ g O}$$
$$3.408 \text{ mol C} \backsimeq 4.540 \text{ mol H} \backsimeq 3.406 \text{ mol O}$$
$$1.00 \text{ mol C} \backsimeq 1.33 \text{ mol H} \backsimeq 1.00 \text{ mol O}$$

or

$$3.00 \text{ mol C} \backsimeq 3.99 \text{ mol H} \backsimeq 3.00 \text{ mol O}$$

The empirical formula is $C_3H_4O_3$.

3-31   The masses of carbon and hydrogen in the original sample are

$$\text{mass of C} = (2.92 \text{ g CO}_2)\left(\frac{12.01 \text{ g C}}{44.01 \text{ g CO}_2}\right) = 0.7968 \text{ g C}$$

$$\text{mass of H} = (1.49 \text{ g H}_2\text{O})\left(\frac{2 \times 1.008 \text{ g H}}{18.02 \text{ g H}_2\text{O}}\right) = 0.1667 \text{ g H}$$

The mass percentages of C and H are

$$\text{mass \% of C} = \frac{0.7968 \text{ g}}{1.23 \text{ g}} \times 100 = 64.78\%$$

$$\text{mass \% of H} = \frac{0.1667 \text{ g}}{1.23 \text{ g}} \times 100 = 13.55\%$$

The mass percentage of oxygen is obtained by difference.

$$\text{mass \% of O} = 100.00 - 64.78 - 13.55 = 21.67\%$$

Take a 100-g sample and write

$$64.78 \text{ g C} \leftrightharpoons 13.55 \text{ g H} \leftrightharpoons 21.67 \text{ g O}$$
$$5.394 \text{ mol C} \leftrightharpoons 13.44 \text{ mol H} \leftrightharpoons 1.354 \text{ mol O}$$
$$3.98 \text{ mol C} \leftrightharpoons 9.93 \text{ mol H} \leftrightharpoons 1.00 \text{ mol O}$$

The empirical formula is $C_4H_{10}O$.

3-33   The mass percentages of carbon, hydrogen, and nitrogen are

$$\text{mass \% of C} = \frac{(1.518 \text{ g CO}_2)\left(\dfrac{12.01 \text{ g C}}{44.01 \text{ g CO}_2}\right)}{0.546 \text{ g}} \times 100 = 75.87\%$$

$$\text{mass \% of H} = \frac{(0.311 \text{ g H}_2\text{O})\left(\dfrac{2 \times 1.008 \text{ g H}}{18.02 \text{ g H}_2\text{O}}\right)}{0.546 \text{ g}} \times 100 = 6.372\%$$

$$\text{mass \% of N} = 100.00 - 75.87 - 6.372 = 17.76\%$$

Take a 100-g sample and write

$$75.87 \text{ g C} \leftrightharpoons 6.372 \text{ g H} \leftrightharpoons 17.76 \text{ g N}$$
$$6.317 \text{ mol C} \leftrightharpoons 6.321 \text{ mol H} \leftrightharpoons 1.268 \text{ mol N}$$
$$4.98 \text{ mol C} \leftrightharpoons 4.99 \text{ mol H} \leftrightharpoons 1.00 \text{ mol N}$$

The empirical formula is C_5H_5N.

3-35   Take a 100-g sample and write

$$62.0 \text{ g C} \leftrightharpoons 10.4 \text{ g H} \leftrightharpoons 27.5 \text{ g O}$$

Divide by the corresponding atomic masses to get

$$5.16 \text{ mol C} \leftrightharpoons 10.3 \text{ mol H} \leftrightharpoons 1.72 \text{ mol O}$$

Now divide by the smallest quantity (1.72) to get

$$3.00 \text{ mol C} \leftrightharpoons 5.99 \text{ mol H} \leftrightharpoons 1.00 \text{ mol O}$$

The simplest formula is C_3H_6O, whose formula mass is 58.1. Given that the formula mass is 58.1, the molecular formula is C_3H_6O.

3-37   Assume a 100-g sample and write

$$22.5 \text{ g Na} \leftrightharpoons 30.4 \text{ g P} \leftrightharpoons 47.1 \text{ g O}$$

Divide by the corresponding atomic masses to get

$$0.979 \text{ mol Na} \backsim 0.982 \text{ mol P} \backsim 2.94 \text{ mol O}$$

Divide through by 0.979 to obtain

$$1.00 \text{ mol Na} \backsim 1.00 \text{ mol P} \backsim 3.00 \text{ mol O}$$

The empirical formula is $NaPO_3$. The formula mass corresponding to this empirical formula is 102, and this divides into the observed molecular mass (612) six times. Thus the molecular formula is $Na_6P_6O_{18}$.

3-39   The number of moles that corresponds to 10.0 g of propane, C_3H_8, is

$$\text{number of moles} = (10.0 \text{ g})\left(\frac{1 \text{ mol}}{44.09 \text{ g}}\right) = 0.2268 \text{ mol}$$

We see from the reaction that 5 mol of O_2 are required for each mol of C_3H_8 that reacts.

$$\text{mol of } O_2 = (0.2268 \text{ mol } C_3H_8)\left(\frac{5 \text{ mol } O_2}{1 \text{ mol } C_3H_8}\right)$$

$$= 1.134 \text{ mol}$$

The mass of O_2 required is

$$\text{mass of } O_2 = (1.134 \text{ mol})\left(\frac{32.00 \text{ g}}{1 \text{ mol}}\right) = 36.3 \text{ g}$$

3-41   The number of moles of MnO_2 reacted is

$$\text{mol of } MnO_2 = (100 \text{ g})\left(\frac{1 \text{ mol}}{86.94 \text{ g}}\right) = 1.150 \text{ mol}$$

According to the equation, one mole of Cl_2 is produced from one mole of MnO_2. Therefore,

$$\text{mol of } Cl_2 = (1.150 \text{ mol } MnO_2)\left(\frac{1 \text{ mol } Cl_2}{1 \text{ mol } MnO_2}\right)$$

$$= 1.150 \text{ mol}$$

The mass of Cl_2 prepared is

$$\text{mass of } Cl_2 = (1.150 \text{ mol})\left(\frac{70.90 \text{ g}}{1 \text{ mol}}\right) = 81.6 \text{ g}$$

3-43   The number of moles of ND_3 produced is

$$\text{mol of } ND_3 = (200 \text{ mg})\left(\frac{1 \text{ g}}{10^3 \text{ mg}}\right)\left(\frac{1 \text{ mol}}{20.05 \text{ g}}\right) = 0.009975 \text{ mol}$$

According to the equation, 3 mol of D_2O are required to produce one mole of ND_3. Therefore,

$$\text{mol of } D_2O = (0.009975 \text{ mol } ND_3)\left(\frac{3 \text{ mol } D_2O}{1 \text{ mol } ND_3}\right) = 0.02993 \text{ mol}$$

The mass of heavy water required is

$$\text{mass of } D_2O = (0.02993 \text{ mol})\left(\frac{20.03 \text{ g}}{1 \text{ mol}}\right) = 0.599 \text{ g} = 599 \text{ mg}$$

3-45 The number of moles of As produced is

$$\text{mol of As} = (10.0 \text{ g})\left(\frac{1 \text{ mol}}{74.92 \text{ g}}\right) = 0.133 \text{ mol}$$

There is a one-to-one correspondence between moles of As and moles of FeSAs, and we see that 0.133 mol of FeSAs are required to produce 10.0 g of As. The mass required is

$$\text{mass of FeSAs} = (0.133 \text{ mol})\left(\frac{162.83 \text{ g}}{1 \text{ mol}}\right) = 21.7 \text{ g}$$

3-47 Note that one mole of Zn results from each mole of ZnS. The number of moles of ZnS is

$$\text{mol of ZnS} = (2.00 \times 10^5 \text{ kg})\left(\frac{10^3 \text{ g}}{1 \text{ kg}}\right)\left(\frac{1 \text{ mol}}{97.44 \text{ g}}\right) = 2.05 \times 10^6 \text{ mol}$$

This is the number of moles of Zn produced. The mass of Zn produced is

$$\text{mass of Zn} = (2.05 \times 10^6 \text{ mol})\left(\frac{65.38 \text{ g}}{1 \text{ mol}}\right) = 1.34 \times 10^8 \text{ g Zn}$$
$$= 1.34 \times 10^5 \text{ kg Zn}$$

3-49 The number of moles of ammonia, NH_3, is

$$\text{mol of } NH_3 = (6.40 \times 10^4 \text{ kg})\left(\frac{10^3 \text{ g}}{1 \text{ kg}}\right)\left(\frac{1 \text{ mol}}{17.03 \text{ g}}\right) = 3.76 \times 10^6 \text{ mol}$$

From the set of three reactions, we see that

$$1 \text{ mol } NH_3 \longrightarrow 1 \text{ mol NO} \longrightarrow 1 \text{ mol } NO_2 \longrightarrow \frac{2}{3} \text{ mol } HNO_3$$

Thus, there are 2 mol of HNO_3 produced from 3 mol of NH_3. The number of moles of HNO_3 produced is

$$\text{mol of HNO}_3 = (3.76 \times 10^6 \text{ mol NH}_3)\left(\frac{2 \text{ mol HNO}_3}{3 \text{ mol NH}_3}\right)$$

$$= 2.51 \times 10^6 \text{ mol HNO}_3$$

The mass of HNO_3 produced is

$$\text{mass of HNO}_3 = (2.51 \times 10^6 \text{ mol})\left(\frac{63.02 \text{ g}}{1 \text{ mol}}\right)$$

$$= 1.58 \times 10^8 \text{ g HNO}_3 = 1.58 \times 10^5 \text{ kg HNO}_3$$

In practice, the $NO(g)$ produced in Step 3 is cycled back into Step 2, and so the theoretical yield is greater (see Solution to Problem I-15).

3-51 Because we are given the quantities of two reactants, we must check to see if one of them is a limiting reactant. The number of moles of KCl is

$$\text{mol of KCl} = (50.0 \text{ kg})\left(\frac{10^3 \text{ g}}{1 \text{ kg}}\right)\left(\frac{1 \text{ mol}}{74.55 \text{ g}}\right) = 670.7 \text{ mol}$$

and the number of moles of HNO_3 is

$$\text{mol of HNO}_3 = (50.0 \text{ kg})\left(\frac{10^3 \text{ g}}{1 \text{ kg}}\right)\left(\frac{1 \text{ mol}}{63.02 \text{ g}}\right) = 793.4 \text{ mol}$$

Because one mol of KCl reacts with one mol of HNO_3, we see that HNO_3 is in excess and KCl is the limiting reactant. The mass of KNO_3 produced is

$$\text{mass of KNO}_3 = (670.7 \text{ mol KCl})\left(\frac{4 \text{ mol KNO}_3}{4 \text{ mol KCl}}\right)\left(\frac{101.11 \text{ g KNO}_3}{1 \text{ mol KNO}_3}\right)$$

$$= 6.780 \times 10^4 \text{ g} = 67.80 \text{ kg}$$

The mass of Cl_2 produced is

$$\text{mass of Cl}_2 = (670.7 \text{ mol KCl})\left(\frac{2 \text{ mol Cl}_2}{4 \text{ mol KCl}}\right)\left(\frac{70.90 \text{ g Cl}_2}{1 \text{ mol Cl}_2}\right)$$

$$= 2.380 \times 10^4 = 23.80 \text{ kg}$$

3-53 The number of moles of NaOH is

$$\text{mol of NaOH} = (60.0 \text{ g})\left(\frac{1 \text{ mol}}{40.00 \text{ g}}\right) = 1.50 \text{ mol}$$

and the number of moles of H_2SO_4 is

$$\text{mol of H}_2\text{SO}_4 = (20.0 \text{ g})\left(\frac{1 \text{ mol}}{98.08 \text{ g}}\right) = 0.204 \text{ mol}$$

Each mole of H_2SO_4 requires two mol of NaOH, or 0.204 mol of H_2SO_4 requires 0.408 mol of NaOH. Thus the NaOH is in excess and H_2SO_4 is the limiting reactant. The mass of Na_2SO_4 that will be produced is

$$\text{mass of } Na_2SO_4 = (0.204 \text{ mol } H_2SO_4)\left(\frac{1 \text{ mol } Na_2SO_4}{1 \text{ mol } H_2SO_4}\right)\left(\frac{142.04 \text{ g } Na_2SO_4}{1 \text{ mol } Na_2SO_4}\right)$$

$$= 29.0 \text{ g}$$

3-55 The theoretical yield of $TiCl_4$ is

$$\binom{\text{theoretical}}{\text{yield}} = (50.0 \text{ g } TiO_2)\left(\frac{1 \text{ mol } TiO_2}{79.90 \text{ g } TiO_2}\right)\left(\frac{1 \text{ mol } TiCl_4}{1 \text{ mol } TiO_2}\right)\left(\frac{189.70 \text{ g } TiCl_4}{1 \text{ mol } TiCl_4}\right)$$

$$= 118.7 \text{ g}$$

The percent yield is

$$\% \text{ yield} = \left(\frac{\text{actual yield}}{\text{theoretical yield}}\right) \times 100$$

$$= \frac{55.0 \text{ g}}{118.7 \text{ g}} \times 100 = 46.3\%$$

3-57 The theoretical yield of $C_2H_5O_2CC_2H_5$ is

$$\binom{\text{theoretical}}{\text{yield}} = (250 \text{ g } C_2H_5OH)\left(\frac{1 \text{ mol } C_2H_5OH}{46.07 \text{ g } C_2H_5OH}\right)\left(\frac{1 \text{ mol } C_2H_5O_2CC_2H_5}{1 \text{ mol } C_2H_5OH}\right)$$

$$\times \left(\frac{102.13 \text{ g } C_2H_5O_2CC_2H_5}{1 \text{ mol } C_2H_5O_2CC_2H_5}\right)$$

$$= 554 \text{ g}$$

The percent yield is

$$\% \text{ yield} = \left(\frac{\text{actual yield}}{\text{theoretical yield}}\right) \times 100$$

$$= \frac{349 \text{ g}}{554 \text{ g}} \times 100 = 63.0\%$$

3-59 The number of moles of $Ca(OH)_2$ is

$$\text{mol of } Ca(OH)_2 = (0.185 \text{ g})\left(\frac{1 \text{ mol}}{74.10 \text{ g}}\right) = 2.50 \times 10^{-3} \text{ mol}$$

The molarity is calculated by using Equation (3-7):

$$\text{molarity} = \frac{n}{V} = \left(\frac{2.50 \times 10^{-3} \text{ mol}}{100 \text{ mL}}\right)\left(\frac{1000 \text{ mL}}{1 \text{ L}}\right) = 0.0250 \text{ M}$$

3-61   The number of moles of NaOH is

$$\text{mol of NaOH} = (572 \text{ g})\left(\frac{1 \text{ mol}}{40.00 \text{ g}}\right) = 14.3 \text{ mol}$$

Because the 14.3 mol are dissolved in one liter of solution, the molarity of the solution is 14.3 M.

3-63   The number of moles of $C_{12}H_{22}O_{11}$ in 500 mL of a 0.250 M solution is

$$\text{moles of } C_{12}H_{22}O_{11} = MV = (0.250 \text{ mol} \cdot L^{-1})(0.500 \text{ L})$$
$$= 0.125 \text{ mol}$$

The mass of $C_{12}H_{22}O_{11}$ required is

$$\text{mass of } C_{12}H_{22}O_{11} = (0.125 \text{ mol})\left(\frac{342.3 \text{ g}}{1 \text{ mol}}\right) = 42.8 \text{ g}$$

Dissolve 42.8 g of sucrose in about 250 mL of water in a 500-mL volumetric flask and then dilute the solution to the 500-mL mark, and shake to make the solution homogeneous.

3-65   (a) The number of moles of $K_2Cr_2O_7$ in the solution is

$$\text{mol } K_2Cr_2O_7 = MV$$
$$= (0.1255 \text{ mol} \cdot L^{-1})(25.46 \text{ mL})\left(\frac{1 \text{ L}}{10^3 \text{ mL}}\right)$$
$$= 3.195 \times 10^{-3} \text{ mol}$$

(b) The number of moles of $C_6H_{12}O_6$ in the solution is

$$\text{mol } C_6H_{12}O_6 = MV$$
$$= (0.020 \text{ mol} \cdot L^{-1})(50 \text{ } \mu L)\left(\frac{1 \text{ L}}{10^6 \text{ } \mu L}\right)$$
$$= 1.0 \times 10^{-6} \text{ mol}$$

3-67   From Equation (3-8) we have

$$M_1 V_1 = M_2 V_2$$
$$(1.0 \text{ mol} \cdot L^{-1})(V_1) = (0.050 \text{ mol} \cdot L^{-1})(0.500 \text{ L})$$

Thus

$$V_1 = \frac{(0.050)(0.500 \text{ L})}{1.0} = 0.025 \text{ L} = 25 \text{ mL}$$

Thus we add 25 mL of 1.0 M $NaH_2PO_4(aq)$ to a 500-mL volumetric flask that is about half filled with water, swirl the solution, and dilute with water to the 500-mL mark on the flask.

3-69 From Equation (3-8) we have

$$M_1V_1 = M_2V_2$$

Thus

$$(18.0 \text{ mmol} \cdot \text{mL}^{-1})V_1 = (0.30 \text{ mmol}^{-1} \cdot \text{mL}^{-1})(500 \text{ mL})$$

and

$$V_1 = \frac{(0.30)(500 \text{ mL})}{18.0} = 8.3 \text{ mL}$$

3-71 The number of moles of Zn that react is

$$\text{mol of Zn} = (2.55 \text{ g})\left(\frac{1 \text{ mol}}{65.38 \text{ g}}\right) = 3.90 \times 10^{-2} \text{ mol}$$

The number of moles of HCl required is

$$\text{mol of HCl} = (3.90 \times 10^{-2} \text{ mol Zn})\left(\frac{2 \text{ mol HCl}}{1 \text{ mol Zn}}\right) = 7.80 \times 10^{-2} \text{ mol}$$

The volume of a 2.00 M solution to use can be found by using Equation (3-7).

$$V = \frac{n}{M} = \frac{7.80 \times 10^{-2} \text{ mol}}{2.00 \text{ mol} \cdot \text{L}^{-1}} = 0.0390 \text{ L} = 39.0 \text{ mL}$$

3-73 We must first determine the number of moles of NaOH. Using Equation (3-7), we have

$$\text{mol of NaOH} = MV = (6.00 \text{ mol} \cdot \text{L}^{-1})(5.00 \text{ L}) = 30.0 \text{ mol}$$

The number of moles of Cl_2 required is

$$\text{mol of Cl}_2 = (30.0 \text{ mol NaOH})\left(\frac{1 \text{ mol Cl}_2}{2 \text{ mol NaOH}}\right) = 15.0 \text{ mol Cl}_2$$

and the mass of Cl_2 is

$$\text{mass of Cl}_2 = (15.0 \text{ mol})\left(\frac{70.90 \text{ g}}{1 \text{ mol}}\right) = 1060 \text{ g Cl}_2$$

3-75 The number of millimoles of NaOH required to neutralize the HCl solution is

$$\text{mmol NaOH} = MV = (0.155 \text{ mmol} \cdot \text{mL}^{-1})(27.5 \text{ mL})$$
$$= 4.263 \text{ mmol}$$

We see from the neutralization reaction

$$NaOH(aq) + HCl(aq) \longrightarrow NaCl(aq) + H_2O(l)$$

that it requires one mole of NaOH to neutralize one mole of HCl. Thus we have

$$\text{mmol HCl} = \text{mmol NaOH} = 4.263 \text{ mmol}$$

The concentration of the HCl solution is

$$\text{molarity} = \frac{n}{V} = \frac{4.263 \text{ mmol}}{25.0 \text{ mL}} = 0.171 \text{ M}$$

3-77 (a) The number of millimoles of $Ca(OH)_2$ that is neutralized is

$$\text{mmol Ca(OH)}_2 = MV = (0.010 \text{ mmol} \cdot \text{mL}^{-1})(15.0 \text{ } \mu L)\left(\frac{1 \text{ mL}}{10^3 \text{ } \mu L}\right)$$
$$= 1.5 \times 10^{-4} \text{ mmol}$$

We see from the neutralization equation

$$2HNO_3(aq) + Ca(OH)_2(aq) \longrightarrow Ca(NO_3)_2(aq) + 2H_2O(l)$$

that it requires two mol of HNO_3 to neutralize one mol of $Ca(OH)_2$. Thus we have

$$\text{mol of HNO}_3 = [1.5 \times 10^{-4} \text{ mmol Ca(OH)}_2]\left(\frac{2 \text{ mol HNO}_3}{1 \text{ mol Ca(OH)}_2}\right)$$
$$= 3.0 \times 10^{-4} \text{ mmol}$$

The volume of HNO_3 required is

$$V = \frac{n}{M} = \frac{3.0 \times 10^{-4} \text{ mmol}}{0.108 \text{ mmol} \cdot \text{mL}^{-1}} = 0.0028 \text{ mL} = 2.8 \text{ } \mu L$$

(b) The number of millimoles of NaOH that is neutralized is

$$\text{mmol NaOH} = MV = (0.200 \text{ mmol} \cdot \text{mL}^{-1})(25.0 \text{ mL})$$
$$= 5.00 \text{ mmol}$$

From the neutralization equation

$$2NaOH(aq) + H_2SO_4(aq) \longrightarrow Na_2SO_4(aq) + 2H_2O(l)$$

we have

$$\text{mmol H}_2SO_4 = (5.00 \text{ mmol NaOH})\left(\frac{1 \text{ mol H}_2SO_4}{2 \text{ mol NaOH}}\right)$$
$$= 2.50 \text{ mmol}$$

The volume of the H_2SO_4 solution required is

$$V = \frac{n}{M} = \frac{2.50 \text{ mmol}}{0.300 \text{ mmol} \cdot \text{mL}^{-1}} = 8.33 \text{ mL}$$

3-79 The number of moles of OH^- added to the $HCl(aq)$ solution is

$$\text{mol of } OH^- = \text{moles of } KOH(s) = (40.0 \text{ g})\left(\frac{1 \text{ mol}}{56.11 \text{ g}}\right) = 0.713 \text{ mol}$$

The number of moles of $HCl(aq)$ initially present is

$$\text{mol of } HCl = MV = (0.125 \text{ mol} \cdot \text{L}^{-1})(2.00 \text{ L}) = 0.250 \text{ mol}$$

Thus an amount of KOH *in excess* of that required to neutralize all of the HCl was added. The neutralization reaction is

$$HCl(aq) + KOH(aq) \longrightarrow H_2O(l) + KCl(aq)$$

The number of moles of KCl produced is equal to the number of moles of HCl initially present, which is 0.250 mol. The molarity of KCl is the number of moles of KCl per liter of solution. The volume of the final solution is

$$\text{final volume} = \text{initial volume} + \text{volume added}$$
$$= 2.00 \text{ L} + 0.20 \text{ L} = 2.20 \text{ L}$$

Thus,

$$\text{molarity of } KCl = \frac{n}{V} = \frac{0.250 \text{ mol}}{2.20 \text{ L}} = 0.114 \text{ M}$$

3-81 The number of moles of NaOH present in the sample is equal to the number of moles of HCl required for neutralization. Thus,

$$\text{mol of } NaOH = (0.0317 \text{ L})(0.150 \text{ mol} \cdot \text{L}^{-1} \text{ HCl})\left(\frac{1 \text{ mol NaOH}}{1 \text{ mol HCl}}\right)$$
$$= 0.00476 \text{ mol NaOH}$$
$$\text{mass of } NaOH = (0.00476 \text{ mol})\left(\frac{40.00 \text{ g}}{1 \text{ mol}}\right)$$
$$= 0.190 \text{ g}$$

The percent NaOH in the mixture equals the mass of NaOH divided by the total mass times 100:

$$\% \text{ NaOH} = \frac{0.190 \text{ g NaOH}}{0.365 \text{ g mixture}} \times 100$$
$$= 52.1\%$$

3-83   The number of moles of base required to neutralize the acid is

$$\text{mol of NaOH} = MV = (0.250 \text{ mol} \cdot \text{L}^{-1})(0.0666 \text{ L}) = 0.01665 \text{ mol}$$

Therefore, the number of moles of acid present in the original 100-mL solution was 0.01665 mol. Thus we have

$$1.00 \text{ g acid} \approx 0.01665 \text{ mol acid}$$

Dividing by 0.01665, we obtain

$$60.1 \text{ g} \approx 1.00 \text{ mol}$$

The formula mass of the acid is 60.1.

3-85   The numbers of moles of the reactants are

$$\text{mol of CS}_2 = (1000 \text{ g})\left(\frac{1 \text{ mol}}{76.13 \text{ g}}\right) = 13.1 \text{ mol}$$

$$\text{mol of NaOH} = (1000 \text{ g})\left(\frac{1 \text{ mol}}{40.00 \text{ g}}\right) = 25.0 \text{ mol}$$

Because 25.0 mol NaOH requires only 12.5 mol CS_2, the CS_2 is in excess and NaOH is the limiting reagent. The mass of each product that is produced is

$$\text{mass of Na}_2\text{CS}_3 = (25.0 \text{ mol NaOH})\left(\frac{2 \text{ mol Na}_2\text{CS}_3}{6 \text{ mol NaOH}}\right)\left(\frac{154.17 \text{ g Na}_2\text{CS}_3}{1 \text{ mol Na}_2\text{CS}_3}\right)$$
$$= 1280 \text{ g}$$

$$\text{mass of Na}_2\text{CO}_3 = (25.0 \text{ mol NaOH})\left(\frac{1 \text{ mol Na}_2\text{CO}_3}{6 \text{ mol NaOH}}\right)\left(\frac{105.99 \text{ g Na}_2\text{CO}_3}{1 \text{ mol Na}_2\text{CO}_3}\right)$$
$$= 442 \text{ g}$$

$$\text{mass of H}_2\text{O} = (25.0 \text{ mol NaOH})\left(\frac{3 \text{ mol H}_2\text{O}}{6 \text{ mol NaOH}}\right)\left(\frac{18.02 \text{ g H}_2\text{O}}{1 \text{ mol H}_2\text{O}}\right)$$
$$= 225 \text{ g}$$

3-87   The number of moles of KMO_4, H_2O_2, and HCl are

$$\text{mol of KMnO}_4 = (20.0 \text{ g})\left(\frac{1 \text{ mol}}{158.04 \text{ g}}\right) = 0.1266 \text{ mol}$$

$$\text{mol of H}_2\text{O}_2 = (10.0 \text{ g})\left(\frac{1 \text{ mol}}{34.02 \text{ g}}\right) = 0.2939 \text{ mol}$$

$$\text{mol of HCl} = (1.00 \times 10^2 \text{ g})\left(\frac{1 \text{ mol}}{36.46 \text{ g}}\right) = 2.743 \text{ mol}$$

We can find the limiting reactant by dividing the number of available moles of each reactant by the corresponding balancing coefficient in the chemical equation. Thus

$$\frac{0.1266 \text{ mol } KMnO_4}{2 \text{ mol } KMnO_4} = 0.06330$$

$$\frac{0.2939 \text{ mol } H_2O_2}{5 \text{ mol } H_2O_2} = 0.05878$$

$$\frac{2.743 \text{ mol } HCl}{6 \text{ mol } HCl} = 0.4572$$

The smallest (limiting) value is that for H_2O_2, and so we see that H_2O_2 is the limiting reactant. The number of grams of $MnCl_2$ that can be produced is

$$\text{mass of } MnCl_2 = (0.2939 \text{ mol } H_2O_2)\left(\frac{2 \text{ mol } MnCl_2}{5 \text{ mol } H_2O_2}\right)\left(\frac{125.84 \text{ g } MnCl_2}{1 \text{ mol } MnCl_2}\right)$$

$$= 14.8 \text{ g}$$

The percent yield is

$$\% \text{ yield} = \left(\frac{\text{actual yield}}{\text{theoretical yield}}\right) \times 100$$

$$= \frac{9.82 \text{ g}}{14.8 \text{ g}} \times 100 = 66.4\%$$

3-89 The mass of As in the ore is equal to the mass of As in Ag_3AsO_4.

$$\text{mass of As} = (3.09 \text{ g } Ag_3AsO_4)\left(\frac{1 \text{ mol } Ag_3AsO_4}{462.6 \text{ g } Ag_3AsO_4}\right)\left(\frac{1 \text{ mol As}}{1 \text{ mol } Ag_3AsO_4}\right)$$

$$\times \left(\frac{74.92 \text{ g As}}{1 \text{ mol As}}\right)$$

$$= 0.5004 \text{ g}$$

The percent arsenic in the ore sample is

$$\% \text{ As} = \frac{0.5004 \text{ g As}}{5.00 \text{ g ore}} \times 100 = 10.0\%$$

3-91 The equation for the combustion of sugar is

$$C_{12}H_{22}O_{11}(s) + 12O_2(g) \longrightarrow 12CO_2(g) + 11H_2O(g)$$

The mass of sugar that produces 2.20 g of CO_2 is

$$\text{mass of } C_{12}H_{22}O_{11} = (2.20 \text{ g } CO_2)\left(\frac{1 \text{ mol } CO_2}{44.01 \text{ g } CO_2}\right)\left(\frac{1 \text{ mol } C_{12}H_{22}O_{11}}{12 \text{ mol } CO_2}\right)$$
$$\times \left(\frac{342.30 \text{ g } C_{12}H_{22}O_{11}}{1 \text{ mol } C_{12}H_{22}O_{11}}\right)$$
$$= 1.43 \text{ g}$$

The mass of NaCl in the sample is

$$\text{mass of NaCl} = 5.00 \text{ g} - 1.43 \text{ g} = 3.57 \text{ g}$$

The percent NaCl in the sample is

$$\% \text{ NaCl} = \frac{3.57 \text{ g NaCl}}{5.00 \text{ g sample}} \times 100 = 71.4\%$$

3-93 Take 1000-mL of solution. The mass of HCl in 1.00 L of solution is

$$\text{mass of HCl} = (1.20 \text{ g}\cdot\text{mL}^{-1})(1000 \text{ mL})(0.40)$$
$$= 480 \text{ g}$$

The number of moles of HCl in 1000 mL of solution is

$$\text{mol of HCl} = (480 \text{ g})\left(\frac{1 \text{ g mol}}{36.46 \text{ g}}\right) = 13.2 \text{ mol}$$

The molarity of the solution is

$$M = \frac{n}{V} = \frac{13.2 \text{ mol}}{1.00 \text{ L}} = 13.2 \text{ M}$$

3-95 The number of moles of $Cr_2O_7^{2-}(aq)$ and C_2H_5OH are

$$\text{mol of } Cr_2O_7^{2-} = MV = (0.560 \text{ mol}\cdot\text{L}^{-1})(55.0 \text{ mL})\left(\frac{1 \text{ L}}{10^3 \text{ mL}}\right)$$
$$= 0.0308 \text{ mol}$$

$$\text{mol of } C_2H_5OH = MV = (0.963 \text{ mol}\cdot\text{L}^{-1})(100.0 \text{ mL})\left(\frac{1 \text{ L}}{10^3 \text{ mL}}\right)$$
$$= 0.0963 \text{ mol}$$

From the equation for the reaction, we see that two mol of $Cr_2O_7^{2-}$ reacts with three mol of C_2H_5OH or 0.0308 mol $Cr_2O_7^{2-}$ reacts with 0.0462 mol C_2H_5OH. The limiting reactant is $Cr_2O_7^{2-}(aq)$. Thus the number of grams of $HC_2H_3O_2$ produced is

$$\text{(mass of } HC_2H_3O_2) = (0.0308 \text{ mol } Cr_2O_7^{2-})\left(\frac{3 \text{ mol } HC_2H_3O_2}{2 \text{ mol } Cr_2O_7^{2-}}\right)\left(\frac{60.05 \text{ g } HC_2H_3O_2}{1 \text{ mol } HC_2H_3O_2}\right)$$

$$= 2.77 \text{ g}$$

E   ANSWERS TO THE SELF-TEST

1 carbon-12 being assigned a mass of exactly 12

2 false (Atomic masses have no units because they are relative quantities.)

3 mass of the formula unit of the substance on the atomic mass scale

4 false

5 its formula mass in grams or contains Avogadro's number of formula units

6 $2 \times 2.016 = 4.032$

7 3.0 mol

8 2.0 mol

9 false

10 6.022×10^{23}

11 one mole

12 $2 \times 6.022 \times 10^{23} = 1.204 \times 10^{24}$

13 true

14 false

15 $2 \times 6.022 \times 10^{23} = 1.204 \times 10^{24}$

16 $4 \times 6.022 \times 10^{23} = 2.408 \times 10^{24}$

17 Cu_2O

18 false (only relative numbers)

19 88.82 g of Cu combines with or is stoichiometrically equivalent to 11.18 g of O.

20 dividing the mass of each by its atomic mass

21 false (The simplest formula is Cu_2O.)

22 false

23 molecular mass

24 C_3H_6

25 carbon and hydrogen

26 See Table 3-2.

27 4 mol

28 number of moles

29 multiplying the number of moles of CO_2 by the unit conversion factor 44.01 g CO_2/1 mol CO_2

30 (1) Calculate the number of moles of C_2H_6.
(2) Calculate the number of moles of O_2 that is required to react with the number of moles of C_2H_6 in (1).
(3) Calculate the mass of the number of moles of O_2 in (2).

31 CO_2; H_2O

32 CO_2 produced

33 mass of H = (mass of H_2O)
$$\times \left(\frac{2 \times \text{atomic mass of H}}{\text{formula mass of } H_2O}\right)$$
mass % of H
$$= \left(\frac{\text{mass of H}}{\text{mass of sample}}\right) \times 100$$

34 O_2; H_2

35 false

36 NaCl; H_2O

37 the number of moles of solute per liter of solution

38 1.0 M

39 false

40 Dissolve 0.50 mol (29.22 g) of NaCl in about 400 mL of H_2O and then dilute to 500 mL.

41 0.010

42 0.50 L

43 true

44 false

45 the base just has been completely neutralized

46 equivalence point

47 the change in color of the added indicator (litmus)

48 false (You would use a solution of acid of known concentration.)

49 true

50 50

THE PROPERTIES OF GASES

A   OUTLINE OF CHAPTER 4

4-1   Most of the volume of a gas is empty space.

The physical states of matter are solid, liquid, and gas.

A solid has a fixed volume and shape.

A solid is a dense and ordered array of particles.

A liquid has a fixed volume but assumes the shape of its container.

A liquid is a dense and random array of particles.

A gas occupies the entire volume of its container.

The molecules of a gas are widely separated.

4-2   A manometer is used to measure the pressure of a gas.

Gas molecules are in constant motion.

The pressure exerted by a gas is due to the collisions of the gas molecules with the walls of the vessel that contains the gas.

Pressure is force per unit area.

The pressure of a gas can be expressed as the height of a column of mercury supported by the gas (Figure 4-3).

The pressure unit mmHg is called a torr.

The height of a column of liquid supported by a gas depends on the density of the liquid.

4-3   A standard atmosphere is 760 torr.

Barometric pressure is the pressure due to the atmosphere.

A barometer is used to measure the pressure due to the atmosphere (Figure 4-4).

Pressure is expressed in various units.

The pascal is the SI unit of pressure.

One standard atmosphere equals 1.013×10^5 Pa.

The various units of pressure are given in Table 4-1.

4-4   The volume of a gas is inversely proportional to its pressure and directly proportional to its Kelvin temperature.

Boyle's law can be expressed as $V \propto 1/P$ or as $V = c/P$ (constant temperature), where c is a proportionality constant (Equation 4-1).

The equation expressing Charles's law is $V = kT$ (constant pressure), where k is a proportionality constant. (Equation 4-2).

The absolute temperature scale is related to the Celsius scale by the expression T (in K) $= t$ (in °C) $+ 273.15$ (Equation 4-3).

The absolute (Kelvin) temperature scale has the units of kelvin, K.

A gas thermometer is based on Charles's law (Figure 4-8).

4-5   Equal volumes of gases at the same pressure and temperature contain equal numbers of molecules.

Gay-Lussac's law of combining volumes states that when all volumes are measured at the same pressure and temperature, the volumes in which gases combine in chemical reactions are related by simple, whole numbers (Figure 4-9).

4-6   The ideal-gas equation is a combination of Boyle's, Charles's, and Avogadro's laws.

The ideal-gas law is expressed by the ideal-gas equation

$$PV = nRT \qquad (4\text{-}5)$$

One value of the gas constant R is 0.0821 L·atm·K^{-1}·mol^{-1}.

An ideal gas is a gas that obeys the ideal-gas law.

The molar volume of an ideal gas is 22.4 L at 0°C and 1.00 atm.

Applications of the ideal-gas equation are discussed.

4-7   The ideal-gas equation can be used to calculate the molar masses of gases.

The density of an ideal gas in grams per liter, ρ, is given by

$$\rho = \frac{MP}{RT} \qquad (4\text{-}8)$$

Gas density increases as gas pressure increases and as gas temperature decreases.

Molar mass is the mass of one mole and has the units g·mol^{-1}.

The molar mass of a gas can be determined from the density of the gas (Example 4-9).

4-8   The total pressure of a mixture of ideal gases is the sum of the partial pressures of all the gases in the mixture.

Dalton's law of partial pressures states that for a mixture of two ideal gases

$$P_{total} = P_1 + P_2 \tag{4-9}$$

The total pressure of a mixture of gases is determined by the total number of moles of gas in the mixture, or

$$P_{total} = n_{total}\left(\frac{RT}{V}\right) \tag{4-11}$$

The mole fraction of species i in a mixture, denoted by X_i, is given by

$$X_i = \frac{n_i}{n_{total}} \tag{4-13}$$

The partial pressure of species i is given by

$$P_i = X_i P_{total} \tag{4-14}$$

When a gas is collected over water, Dalton's law of partial pressures

$$P_{total} = P_{gas} + P_{H_2O}$$

is used to find the pressure of the gas.

4-9   The molecules of a gas have a distribution of speeds.

Collisions of gas molecules with the container walls give rise to the gas pressure.
Kinetic energy is the energy associated with the motion of a body.
The kinetic energy of a particle of mass m and speed v is given by $E = \frac{1}{2}mv^2$ [Equation (4-15)].
The SI unit of energy is the joule, where 1 joule $= 1\,\text{J} = 1\,\text{kg} \cdot \text{m}^2 \cdot \text{s}^{-2}$.
There is a distribution of molecular speeds in a gas (Figures 4-13 and 4-14).
The average kinetic energy per mole of a gas, E_{av}, is directly proportional to the absolute temperature of the gas

$$E_{av} = \tfrac{3}{2}RT \tag{4-16}$$

where R is the gas constant, $8.314\,\text{J} \cdot \text{K}^{-1} \cdot \text{mol}^{-1}$.
The average speed, v_{av} in $\text{m} \cdot \text{s}^{-1}$, of a molecule in a gas is defined by

$$E_{av} = \tfrac{1}{2}M_{kg}v_{av}^2$$

where M_{kg} is the molar mass in kilograms [Equation (4-17)].
The average speed is given by

$$v_{av} = \left(\frac{3RT}{M_{kg}}\right)^{1/2} \tag{4-18}$$

The average molecular speed increases with increasing temperature and decreases with increasing molar mass at a fixed temperature (Table 4-2).

The kinetic theory of gases presents the properties of gases in terms of molecular quantities.

The rate of effusion, the process of leaking through a small hole, is directly proportional to the average speed of the gas molecules.

Graham's law of effusion is expressed by the relation

$$\frac{\text{rate}_A}{\text{rate}_B} = \left(\frac{M_B}{M_A}\right)^{1/2} \tag{4-19}$$

4-10 The average distance a molecule travels between collisions is the mean free path.

At $0°C$ and 1 atm a gas molecule undergoes about 10^{10} collisions per second, and travels about 10^5 picometers between collisions.

The mean free path is given by

$$l = (3.1 \times 10^7 \text{ pm}^3 \cdot \text{atm} \cdot \text{K}^{-1})\frac{T}{\sigma^2 P} \tag{4-20}$$

where σ is the molecular diameter of the gas molecule (see Table 4-3).

An estimate of the number of collisions a gas molecule undergoes per second is given by $z = v_{av}/l$ [Equation (4-21)].

4-11 The van der Waals equation accounts for deviations from gas ideality.

Deviations from ideal-gas behavior are due to the volume of the gas molecules and the attraction between gas molecules.

The ideal-gas equation is not valid at high pressure (Figure 4-17).

The ratio PV/RT for one mol of gas is less than 1 at low pressures because of the attraction between the gas molecules.

The ratio PV/RT for one mol of gas is greater than 1 at higher pressures because of the volume of the gas molecules.

One equation for non-ideal-gas behavior is the van der Waals equation

$$\left(P + \frac{n^2 a}{V^2}\right)(V - nb) = nRT \tag{4-22}$$

where a and b are van der Waals constants, whose values depend upon the particular gas (Table 4-4).

B   SELF-TEST

1   The particles in a solid move throughout the solid. *True/False*

2   The particles in a liquid move throughout the liquid. *True/False*

3   When a solid melts, the liquid has a much lower density. *True/False*

4   When a liquid is vaporized, there is a large increase in *(volume/density)*.

5   Most of the volume of a gas is _____ .

6   A gas has a large compressibility because _____
_____ .

7   A manometer is a device used to measure _____ .

8   The height of mercury in a manometer depends on _____
_____ .

9   The pressure of a gas is given as mm of Hg, which is also called _____ .

10   A barometer is a device used to measure _____ .

11   The pressure due to the atmosphere is a constant. *True/False*

12   At sea level atmospheric pressure is always 760 torr. *True/False*

13   The pressure of a gas may be expressed as the height of a column of mercury.
True/False

14   One standard atmosphere is defined as _____ .

15   The SI unit of pressure is _____ .

16   Boyle's law states that the volume of a gas is _____ proportional
to the _____ at constant _____ .

17   A volume of 2.4 L of gas whose pressure is 1.5 atm is compressed to 1.2 L with no
change in temperature. The pressure of the gas is now _____ atm.

18   Charles's law states that the volume of a gas is _____ proportional
to the _____ at constant _____ .

19   A volume of 3.4 L of gas at 100°C is heated to 200°C with no change in pressure.
The volume of the gas is now 6.8 L. *True/False*

20   The absolute temperature scale is also called the _____ scale and has
the unit _____ .

21   A temperature of 20°C is equivalent to _____ K.

22   The lowest possible temperature on the absolute temperature scale is
_____ ; on the Celsius scale it is _____ .

23 A constant-pressure gas thermometer measures _____ through its proportionality to the _____ of a gas at _____ .

24 At the same temperature and pressure, 3 volumes of hydrogen, H_2, and 1 volume of nitrogen, N_2, produce _____ volumes of ammonia, NH_3.

25 The ideal-gas law can be expressed as _____ = _____ .

26 An ideal gas is a gas that _____ .

27 The value of the gas constant depends on the units used. *True/False*

28 One value of the gas constant is _____ .

29 When $R = 0.821$ L·atm·mol^{-1}·K^{-1} is used in the ideal-gas equation, P must be expressed in _____ , V in _____ , n in _____ , and T in _____ .

30 One mole of an ideal gas at $0°C$ and 1 atm occupies a volume of _____ .

31 The volume of a gas *(increases, decreases)* when the temperature of the gas decreases and the pressure of the gas remains constant.

32 The pressure of a gas *(increases, decreases)* when the temperature of the gas increases and the volume of the gas remains constant.

33 A reaction between a gas and a solid to produce a solid product takes place at constant temperature and volume. After the consumption of part of the gas, the pressure due to the gas *(increases, decreases)*.

34 The partial pressure of one gas in a mixture of gases depends on the pressure of the other gases. *True/False*

35 The mole fraction of oxygen in a mixture of O_2 and CO_2 is given by $X_{O_2} =$ _____ .

36 The partial pressure of O_2 in a mixture of O_2 and CO_2 is related to the mole fraction of O_2 by $P_{O_2} =$ _____ .

37 When a gas such as nitrogen is collected over water, the pressure of the nitrogen gas is the total pressure *(plus, minus)* the pressure due to water vapor.

38 The pressure exerted by a gas is caused by _____ .

39 All the molecules of a **gas travel at the same** speed. *True/False*

40 The average kinetic energy of a gas depends only on its _____.

41 The average speed of the molecules in a gas *(increases, decreases)* as the temperature increases.

42 Heavier gas molecules have a *(higher, lower)* average speed than lighter molecules at the same temperature.

43 The average distance traveled between collisions by a molecule in a gas whose pressure is 1 atm is quite small when compared to the distance between the walls of the container. *True/False*

44 The mean free path is the average distance _____.

45 The number of collisions that one gas molecule undergoes in one second is approximately _____ collisions per second at 0°C and 1 atm.

46 The average speed of nitrogen molecules at 20°C is approximately *(50, 500, 5000)* $m \cdot s^{-1}$.

47 The mean free path of a molecule depends on the _____, _____, and _____.

48 The number of collisions that a gas molecule undergoes in one second can be estimated from the _____ and the _____ of the molecule.

49 All gases effuse at the same rate. *True/False*

50 Propane (C_3H_8) will effuse at a slower rate than methane (CH_4). *True/False*

51 The ideal-gas equation is valid at high pressures and low temperatures. *True/False*

52 The van der Waals equation describes *(ideal, nonideal)* gas behavior.

53 The value of the ratio PV/RT for one mole of gas is less than 1 when _____.

C CALCULATIONS YOU SHOULD KNOW HOW TO DO

1 Convert from one unit of pressure to another (torr $\rightleftharpoons$ pascals $\rightleftharpoons$ atm). See Examples 4-2 and 4-3, Table 4-1, and Problems 4-1 and 4-2.

2 Convert between Kelvin and Celsius temperature scales, using the relation T (in K) $= t$ (in °C) $+ 273.15$. See Problems 4-7 and 4-8.

3   Use Boyle's law in the form $P_i V_i = P_f V_f$. See Problems 4-3 through 4-6.

4   Use Charles's law in the form $V_i/T_i = V_f/T_f$. See Example 4-4 and Problems 4-9 and 4-10.

5   Use Gay-Lussac's law of combining volumes. See Problems 4-11 and 4-12.

6   Use the ideal-gas law, $PV = nRT$. See Examples 4-5 through 4-7, Problems 4-13 through 4-22, and Problems 4-61 through 4-66, in which P is expressed in pascals.

7   Use the ideal-gas law in stoichiometric calculations. See Problems 4-23 through 4-28.

8   Use the ideal-gas law in the form $\rho = MP/RT$ to calculate gas density, ρ, and to determine molar mass. See Examples 4-8 through 4-10 and Problems 4-29 through 4-36.

9   Use Dalton's law of partial pressures

$$P_{total} = P_1 + P_2$$

See Examples 4-11 and 4-12 and Problems 4-37 through 4-42.

10   Calculate the average speed of a gas molecule using $v_{av} = (3\ RT/M_{kg})^{1/2}$. See Example 4-13 and Problems 4-43 through 4-48.

11   Calculate the mean free path of a gas molecule by using the equation

$$l = (3.1 \times 10^7 \text{ pm}^3 \cdot \text{atm} \cdot \text{K}^{-1}) \frac{T}{\sigma^2 P}$$

See Table 4-3 and Problems 4-49 through 4-52.

12   Estimate the number of collisions (collision frequency) that a gas molecule undergoes per second using $z = v_{av}/l$. See Problems 4-53 and 4-54.

13   Use Graham's law of effusion

$$\frac{\text{rate}_A}{\text{rate}_B} = \frac{t_B}{t_A} = \left(\frac{M_B}{M_A}\right)^{1/2}$$

See Problems 4-55 through 4-58.

14   Calculate the pressure of a gas by using the van der Waals equation [Equation (4-26)]. See Table 4-4 and Problems 4-59 and 4-60.

Plotting Data

It is usually desirable to plot equations or experimental data such that a straight line is obtained. The mathematical equation of a straight line is of the form

$$y = mx + b \tag{1}$$

In this equation, m and b are constants: m is the *slope* of the line and b is its *intercept* with the y axis. The slope of a straight line is a measure of its steepness; it is defined as the ratio of its vertical rise to the corresponding horizontal distance.

Let's plot the two straight lines

$$\text{(I)} \quad y = x + 1$$

and

$$\text{(II)} \quad y = 2x - 2$$

We first make a table of values of x and y

Equation I		Equation II	
x	y	x	y
-3	-2	-3	-8
-2	-1	-2	-6
-1	0	-1	-4
0	1	0	-2
1	2	1	0
2	3	2	2
3	4	3	4
4	5	4	6
5	6	5	8

These results are plotted in Figure 1. Note that curve I intersects the y axis at $y = 1$ ($b = 1$) and has a slope of 1 ($m = 1$). Curve II intersects the y axis at $y = -2$ ($b = -2$) and has a slope of 2 ($m = 2$).

Usually the equation to be plotted will not appear to be of the form of Equation 1 at first. For example, consider Boyle's law

$$V = \frac{c}{P} \quad \text{(constant temperature)} \tag{2}$$

where c is a proportionality constant. The value of the proportionality constant

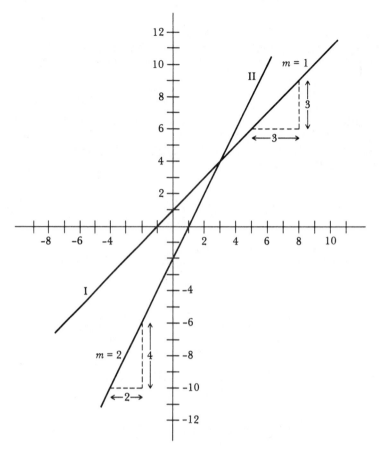

Figure 1. Plot of Equation I: $y = x + 1$ Plot of Equation II: $y = 2x - 2$

depends on the temperature for a given sample. For example, for a 0.29-g sample of air at 25°C, $c = 0.244$ L·atm. Some results for such a sample are presented in Table 1. The data in Table 1 are plotted as volume versus pressure in Figure 2.

Table 1   Pressure-volume data for a sample of 0.29 g of air at 25°C

P/atm	V/L	$\dfrac{1}{P}$/atm^{-1}	P/atm	V/L	$\dfrac{1}{P}$/atm^{-1}
0.26	0.938	3.85	2.10	0.116	0.48
0.41	0.595	2.44	2.63	0.093	0.38
0.83	0.294	1.20	3.14	0.078	0.32
1.20	0.203	0.83			

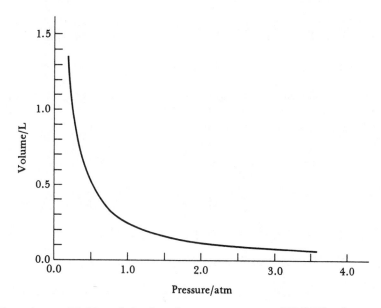

Figure 2. The volume of 0.29 g of air plotted versus pressure at 25°C. The data are given in Table 1. The curve in this figure obeys the equation $V = 0.244 \text{ L·atm}/P$, which is an expression of Boyle's law.

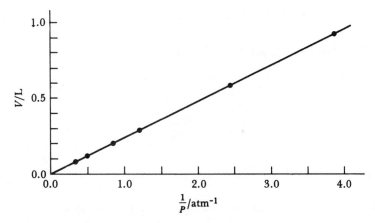

Figure 3. The volume of 0.29 g of air plotted versus the reciprocal of the pressure $(1/P)$ at 25°C. If we compare this curve to that of **Figure 2**, we see that a straight line results by plotting V versus $1/P$ instead of versus P.

It may appear at first sight that Equation 2 is not of the form $y = mx + b$. However, if we let $V = y$ and $1/P = x$, then Equation 2 becomes

$$y = cx$$

which is the equation of a straight line with $m = c$ and $b = 0$. Thus, if we plot V versus $1/P$ instead of P, a straight line will result. The data in Table 1 are plotted as V versus $1/P$ in Figure 3. Note that a straight line is obtained.

D   SOLUTIONS TO THE ODD-NUMBERED PROBLEMS

4-1   The conversion factors for the units of pressure are given in Table 4-1.

(a) The atmospheric pressure at the surface of Venus is

$$(75 \text{ atm})\left(\frac{760 \text{ torr}}{1 \text{ atm}}\right) = 5.7 \times 10^4 \text{ torr}$$

and

$$(75 \text{ atm})\left(\frac{1.013 \text{ bar}}{1 \text{ atm}}\right) = 76 \text{ bar}$$

(b) The atmospheric pressure in Mexico City is

$$(580 \text{ torr})\left(\frac{1 \text{ atm}}{760 \text{ torr}}\right) = 0.763 \text{ atm}$$

$$(580 \text{ torr})\left(\frac{1 \text{ atm}}{760 \text{ torr}}\right)\left(\frac{1013 \text{ mbar}}{1 \text{ atm}}\right) = 773 \text{ mbar}$$

(c) The pressure of CO_2 in the gas cylinder is

$$(5.2 \text{ atm})\left(\frac{1.013 \times 10^5 \text{ Pa}}{1 \text{ atm}}\right) = 5.3 \times 10^5 \text{ Pa}$$

$$(5.2 \text{ atm})\left(\frac{101.3 \text{ kPa}}{1 \text{ atm}}\right) = 530 \text{ kPa}$$

(d) The pressure of the N_2 gas is

$$(920 \text{ torr})\left(\frac{1.013 \times 10^5 \text{ Pa}}{760 \text{ torr}}\right) = 1.23 \times 10^5 \text{ Pa}$$

$$(920 \text{ torr})\left(\frac{1 \text{ atm}}{760 \text{ torr}}\right) = 1.21 \text{ atm}$$

4-3   Boyle's law problems are worked by using Boyle's law in the form

$$P_i V_i = P_f V_f \quad \text{(constant } T\text{)}$$

where i stands for initial and f for final. Thus we have for the volume V_f

$$V_f = \frac{P_i V_i}{P_f} = \frac{(3.46 \text{ atm})(0.650 \text{ mL})}{(1.00 \text{ atm})} = 2.25 \text{ mL}$$

The relation between the volume and the radius of a sphere is

$$V = \tfrac{4}{3}\pi r^3$$

where r is the radius. The diameter is twice the radius; thus

$$V = \tfrac{4}{3}\pi \left(\frac{d}{2}\right)^3 = \tfrac{1}{6}\pi d^3$$

and

$$d = \left(\frac{6V}{\pi}\right)^{1/3}$$

For the 0.650-cm³ (1 mL = 1 cm³) bubble we have

$$d = \left(\frac{6 \times 0.650 \text{ cm}^3}{3.14}\right)^{1/3} = 1.07 \text{ cm}$$

At the surface the volume of the bubble is 2.25 cm³, thus

$$d = \left(\frac{6 \times 2.25 \text{ cm}^3}{3.14}\right)^{1/3} = 1.63 \text{ cm}$$

4-5   We use Boyle's law, $P_i V_i = P_f V_f$.

Solving for P_f, we have

$$P_f = \frac{P_i V_i}{V_f} = \frac{(0.44 \text{ L})(1.0 \text{ atm})}{(0.073 \text{ L})} = 6.0 \text{ atm}$$

4-7   The relationship between the Celsius scale and the Kelvin scale is T (in K) = t (in °C) + 273.15 [Equation (4-3)].

(a) $T = 37 + 273.15 = 310$ K   (b) $T = 20 + 273.15 = 293$ K

(c) $T = -259 + 273.15 = 14$ K   (d) $T = 199 + 273.15 = 472$ K

4-9   Charles's law problems are worked using Charles's law in the form

$$\frac{V_i}{T_i} = \frac{V_f}{T_f} \quad \text{(constant pressure)} \tag{4-4}$$

where T_i and T_f are Kelvin temperatures. Celsius temperatures must be converted to Kelvin temperatures before substituting into Charles's law.

$$T_i = 0 + 273 = 273 \text{ K}$$
$$T_f = 100 + 273 = 373 \text{ K}$$

Solving Charles's law for V_f, we have

$$V_f = \frac{T_f V_i}{T_i} = \frac{(373 \text{ K})(14.7 \text{ mL})}{273 \text{ K}} = 20.1 \text{ mL at } 100°C$$

4-11   We see from Gay-Lussac's law and the reaction stoichiometry that one volume of CH_4 reacts with two volumes of O_2, or 5.0 L of CH_4 reacts with 10.0 L of O_2. Because air is 20% O_2, the volume of air needed is

$$(0.20)V = 10.0 \text{ L}$$
$$V = \frac{10.0 \text{ L}}{0.20} = 50 \text{ L}$$

4-13   The first step in the solution of an ideal-gas problem is to write the ideal-gas law

$$PV = nRT$$

Next we note which quantities are given. In this problem we are given that the gas pressure is 600 torr, the temperature is $37°C$, and the number of moles of gas is 0.65 mol. We want to calculate the volume, V, of the gas. We solve the ideal-gas equation for V (divide both sides by P) to obtain

$$V = \frac{nRT}{P}$$

Recall that using the gas constant, R, in the units $0.0821 \text{ L·atm·mol}^{-1}\text{·K}^{-1}$ requires P in atm and T in kelvin. We must convert P and T to the proper units:

$$P = (600 \text{ torr})\left(\frac{1 \text{ atm}}{760 \text{ torr}}\right) = 0.789 \text{ atm}$$
$$T = 37 + 273 = 310 \text{ K}$$

Substituting these values into the ideal-gas equation yields

$$V = \frac{(0.65 \text{ mol})(0.0821 \text{ L·atm·mol}^{-1}\text{·K}^{-1})(310 \text{ K})}{(0.789 \text{ atm})}$$
$$= 21 \text{ L}$$

It is a good idea to check the cancellation of units to make sure that the answer is obtained in the desired units and that the right units were used for the various quantities involved in the calculation.

4-15 In order to use the idea-gas law we must first convert the mass of water to moles of water.

$$n = (18 \text{ g})\left(\frac{1 \text{ mol}}{18.02 \text{ g}}\right) = 1.0 \text{ mol}$$

The ideal-gas equation is then used to calculate the gas pressure. Solving for P, we have

$$P = \frac{nRT}{V}$$

Converting the temperature to kelvin, we obtain

$$T = 100 + 273 = 373 \text{ K}$$

and substituting the values for n, R, T, and V into the expression for P, we have

$$P = \frac{(1.0 \text{ mol})(0.0821 \text{ L} \cdot \text{atm} \cdot \text{mol}^{-1} \cdot \text{K}^{-1})(373 \text{ K})}{(18 \text{ L})} = 1.7 \text{ atm}$$

The volume of water is calculated from the density of water, $d = m/V$, or

$$\text{volume of water} = \frac{m}{d} = \frac{18 \text{ g}}{1.00 \text{ g} \cdot \text{mL}^{-1}} = 18 \text{ mL}$$

4-17 In this problem we first use the ideal-gas equation to compute the number of moles, n, of helium. Then we compute the number of molecules by multiplying n by Avogadro's number. The expression for n is

$$n = \frac{PV}{RT}$$

The temperature in kelvin is

$$T = -200 + 273 = 73 \text{ K}$$

Substituting the values for P, V, R, and T into the expression for n, we have

$$n = \frac{(0.0010 \text{ atm})(1.0 \text{ L})}{(0.0821 \text{ L} \cdot \text{atm} \cdot \text{mol}^{-1} \cdot \text{K}^{-1})(73 \text{ K})} = 1.67 \times 10^{-4} \text{ mol}$$

The number of molecules of helium is given by

$$\text{number of molecules} = (1.67 \times 10^{-4} \text{ mol})(6.022 \times 10^{23} \text{ molecules} \cdot \text{mol}^{-1})$$
$$= 1.0 \times 10^{20} \text{ molecules}$$

Recall that at 1.0 atm and 0°C one mole of an ideal gas occupies 22.4 L. Thus the number of moles in 1.0 L at 1.0 atm and 0°C is

$$n = \frac{1.0 \text{ L}}{22.4 \text{ L} \cdot \text{mol}^{-1}} = 4.46 \times 10^{-2} \text{ mol}$$

and the number of molecules is

$$\text{number of molecules} = (4.46 \times 10^{-2} \text{ mol})(6.022 \times 10^{23} \text{ molecules} \cdot \text{mol}^{-1})$$
$$= 2.7 \times 10^{22} \text{ molecules}$$

We could also have calculated n at 0°C, 1.0 atm, and 1.0 mL from the ideal-gas equation.

4-19 We use the ideal-gas equation to calculate the number of moles of ozone in 1.0 mL and then multiply n by Avogadro's number to obtain the number of molecules.

$$n = \frac{PV}{RT}$$

The temperature in kelvin is

$$T = -23 + 273 = 250 \text{ K}$$

Substituting the values for P, V, R, and T into the expression for n, we have

$$n = \frac{(1.4 \times 10^{-7} \text{ atm})(1.0 \times 10^{-3} \text{ L})}{(0.0821 \text{ L} \cdot \text{atm} \cdot \text{mol}^{-1} \cdot \text{K}^{-1})(250 \text{ K})} = 6.8 \times 10^{-12} \text{ mol}$$

$$\text{number of molecules} = (6.8 \times 10^{-12} \text{ mol})(6.022 \times 10^{23} \text{ molecules} \cdot \text{mol}^{-1})$$
$$= 4.1 \times 10^{12} \text{ molecules}$$

4-21 The number of moles of gas, n, and the volume, V, of the gas remain constant while the pressure P and temperature T change. Application of the ideal-gas equation to the initial and final conditions yields

$$P_i V = nRT_i \qquad P_f V = nRT_f$$

If we divide the first equation into the second, we obtain

$$\frac{P_f \cancel{V}}{P_i \cancel{V}} = \frac{\cancel{n}RT_f}{\cancel{n}RT_i}$$

Solving for T_f, the unknown temperature, we have

$$T_f = \frac{T_i P_f}{P_i}$$

Both pressures must be in the same units. Let's convert 800 torr to atm.

$$P_i = (800 \text{ torr})\left(\frac{1 \text{ atm}}{760 \text{ torr}}\right) = 1.05 \text{ atm}$$

Thus

$$T_f = \frac{(273 \text{ K})(3.0 \text{ atm})}{1.05 \text{ atm}} = 780 \text{ K}$$

or

$$t_f = 780 - 273 = 510°C$$

4-23 The solution to a problem involving the application of the ideal-gas equation to a chemical reaction proceeds in two stages. One stage involves the use of the reaction stoichiometry to compute the numbers of moles of a reactant consumed and product produced. The other stage involves the use of the ideal-gas equation and is similar to the calculation carried out in Problems 4-13 through 4-22. The number of moles of CaC_2 in 100 g is

$$n = (100 \text{ g})\left(\frac{1 \text{ mol}}{64.10 \text{ g}}\right) = 1.56 \text{ mol}$$

and the number of moles of water is

$$n = (100 \text{ g})\left(\frac{1 \text{ mol } H_2O}{18.02 \text{ g } H_2O}\right) = 5.55 \text{ mol}$$

Thus we see that CaC_2 is the limiting reactant. From the reaction stoichiometry we note that 1 mol of CaC_2 yields 1 mol of C_2H_2; thus the number of the moles of C_2H_2 produced is

$$n = (1.56 \text{ mol } CaC_2)\left(\frac{1 \text{ mol } C_2H_2}{1 \text{ mol } CaC_2}\right) = 1.56 \text{ mol } C_2H_2$$

We now use the ideal-gas equation to compute the volume, V, from the known values of n, T, and P:

$$V = \frac{nRT}{P}$$

At 0°C and 1.00 atm, we have

$$V = \frac{(1.56 \text{ mol})(0.0821 \text{ L} \cdot \text{atm} \cdot \text{mol}^{-1} \cdot \text{K}^{-1})(273 \text{ K})}{(1.00 \text{ atm})} = 35.0 \text{ L}$$

At 120°C and 1.00 atm, we have

$$V = \frac{(1.56 \text{ mol})(0.0821 \text{ L} \cdot \text{atm} \cdot \text{mol}^{-1} \cdot \text{K}^{-1})(393 \text{ K})}{(1.00 \text{ atm})} = 50.3 \text{ L}$$

4-25 The number of moles of glucose in 1.00 g is

$$n = (1.00 \text{ g})\left(\frac{1 \text{ mol}}{180.2 \text{ g}}\right) = 0.00555 \text{ mol}$$

From the reaction stoichiometry, the number of moles of CO_2 produced is

$$n = (0.00555 \text{ mol } C_6H_{12}O_6)\left(\frac{6 \text{ mol } CO_2}{1 \text{ mol } C_6H_{12}O_6}\right) = 0.0333 \text{ mol } CO_2$$

We now compute the volume by using the ideal-gas equation.

$$V = \frac{nRT}{P} = \frac{(0.0333 \text{ mol})(0.0821 \text{ L·atm·mol}^{-1}\text{·K}^{-1})(310 \text{ K})}{(1.00 \text{ atm})}$$
$$= 0.848 \text{ L} = 848 \text{ mL}$$

4-27 The equation for the reaction is

$$MnO_2(s) + 4HCl(aq) \longrightarrow MnCl_2(aq) + 2H_2O(l) + Cl_2(g)$$

The number of moles of chlorine desired is

$$n = \frac{PV}{RT} = \frac{(750 \text{ torr})\left(\dfrac{1 \text{ atm}}{760 \text{ torr}}\right)(0.500 \text{ L})}{(0.0821 \text{ L·atm·mol}^{-1}\text{·K}^{-1})(298 \text{ K})}$$
$$= 0.0202 \text{ mol}$$

The mass of MnO_2 required is

$$\text{mass of } MnO_2 = (0.0202 \text{ mol } Cl_2)\left(\frac{1 \text{ mol } MnO_2}{1 \text{ mol } Cl_2}\right)\left(\frac{86.94 \text{ g } MnO_2}{1 \text{ mol } MnO_2}\right)$$
$$= 1.75 \text{ g}$$

4-29 Problems involving gas density usually involve the ideal-gas equation in the form

$$\rho = \frac{MP}{RT}$$

where ρ is the density and M is the molar mass. Thus for $H_2O(g)$ at $100°C$ and 1.00 atm we compute

$$\rho = \frac{(18.02 \text{ g·mol}^{-1})(1.00 \text{ atm})}{(0.0821 \text{ L·atm·mol}^{-1}\text{·K}^{-1})(373 \text{ K})} = 0.588 \text{ g·L}^{-1}$$

The density of liquid water at $100°C$ is 0.958 g·mL^{-1}, or

$$d = (0.958 \text{ g·mL}^{-1})\left(\frac{1000 \text{ mL}}{1 \text{ L}}\right) = 958 \text{ g·L}^{-1}$$

The ratio of the densities of $H_2O(l)$ and $H_2O(g)$ at $100°C$ is

$$\frac{958 \text{ g} \cdot \text{L}^{-1}}{0.588 \text{ g} \cdot \text{L}^{-1}} = 1630$$

Notice that we use ρ to represent gas density and d to represent solid or liquid density.

4-31 We can use the ideal-gas equation, Equation (4-5), to calculate n

$$n = \frac{PV}{RT} = \frac{(1473 \text{ torr})\left(\dfrac{1 \text{ atm}}{760 \text{ torr}}\right)(0.250 \text{ L})}{(0.0821 \text{ L} \cdot \text{atm} \cdot \text{mol}^{-1} \cdot \text{K}^{-1})(295 \text{ K})}$$
$$= 0.0200 \text{ mol}$$

Thus 2.42 g of Freon corresponds to 0.0200 mol.

$$2.42 \text{ g} \approx 0.0200 \text{ mol}$$

Dividing both sides by 0.0200, we obtain

$$121 \text{ g} \approx 1.00 \text{ mol}$$

Thus the molar mass of the Freon gas is $121 \text{ g} \cdot \text{mol}^{-1}$.

An alternative solution is to use the relation

$$n = \frac{m}{M}$$

Solving for M, we have

$$M = \frac{m}{n} = \frac{2.42 \text{ g}}{0.0200 \text{ mol}} = 121 \text{ g} \cdot \text{mol}^{-1}$$

4-33 We must calculate the molar mass of the gas. We can use Equation (4-5) to calculate n

$$n = \frac{PV}{RT} = \frac{(765 \text{ torr})\left(\dfrac{1 \text{ atm}}{760 \text{ torr}}\right)(0.294 \text{ L})}{(0.0821 \text{ L} \cdot \text{atm} \cdot \text{mol}^{-1} \cdot \text{K}^{-1})(373 \text{ K})}$$
$$= 0.00966 \text{ mol}$$

The molar mass of the vapor is

$$M = \frac{m}{n} = \frac{0.271 \text{ g}}{0.00966 \text{ mol}} = 28.1 \text{ g} \cdot \text{mol}^{-1}$$

The molar mass of CH_2 is $14.03 \text{ g} \cdot \text{mol}^{-1}$. Thus the molecular formula of the compound is C_2H_4.

4-35 We first determine the empirical formula of the compound. Taking a 100-g sample, we have

$$85.60 \text{ g C} \cong 14.40 \text{ g H}$$

Dividing the mass of each by its atomic mass, we have

$$7.127 \text{ mol C} \cong 14.29 \text{ mol H}$$

Dividing by 7.127, we have

$$1.00 \text{ mol C} \cong 2.00 \text{ mol H}$$

Thus the empirical formula is CH_2. The molar mass is computed from the gas density at a known temperature and pressure.

$$M = \frac{\rho RT}{P}$$

$$= \frac{(0.9588 \text{ g} \cdot L^{-1})(0.0821 \text{ L} \cdot \text{atm} \cdot \text{mol}^{-1} \cdot K^{-1})(298 \text{ K})}{(635 \text{ torr})\left(\dfrac{1 \text{ atm}}{760 \text{ torr}}\right)}$$

$$= 28.1 \text{ g} \cdot \text{mol}^{-1}$$

The formula mass of CH_2 is 14.03. Two CH_2 units, that is, C_2H_4, has a formula mass of $14.03 \times 2 = 28.06$. Thus the molecular formula of ethylene is C_2H_4.

4-37 The number of moles of H_2 is

$$\text{mol of } H_2 = (0.513 \text{ g})\left(\frac{1 \text{ mol}}{2.016 \text{ g}}\right) = 0.254 \text{ mol}$$

and the number of moles of N_2 is

$$\text{mol of } N_2 = (16.1 \text{ g})\left(\frac{1 \text{ mol}}{28.02 \text{ g}}\right) = 0.575 \text{ mol}$$

The total number of moles is 0.829 mol. We can calculate the total pressure by using the ideal-gas equation, Equation (4-5).

$$P = \frac{nRT}{V} = \frac{(0.829 \text{ mol})(0.0821 \text{ L} \cdot \text{mol}^{-1} \cdot K^{-1})(293 \text{ K})}{10.0 \text{ L}}$$

$$= 1.99 \text{ atm}$$

The partial pressure of each gas is

$$P_{H_2} = X_{H_2} P_{total} = \left(\frac{0.254 \text{ mol}}{0.829 \text{ mol}}\right)(1.99 \text{ atm}) = 0.610 \text{ atm}$$

$$P_{N_2} = X_{N_2} P_{total} = \left(\frac{0.575 \text{ mol}}{0.829 \text{ mol}}\right)(1.99 \text{ atm}) = 1.38 \text{ atm}$$

4-39   The pressure of nitrogen when the volume is 35.0 mL is

$$P_{N_2} = 740 \text{ torr}$$

If we now increase the volume available to the N_2 from 35.0 mL to 50.0 mL, then the partial pressure of nitrogen decreases. Because T and n_{N_2} are constant we have

$$P_i V_i = P_f V_f$$

and thus

$$P_f(\text{of } N_2) = \frac{P_i V_i}{V_f} = \frac{(740 \text{ torr})(35.0 \text{ mL})}{(50.0 \text{ mL})}$$
$$= 518 \text{ torr}$$

The mixture of N_2 and O_2 in the 50.0-mL volume has a total pressure of 740 torr:

$$P_{total} = 740 \text{ torr} = P_{O_2} + P_{N_2}$$

thus

$$P_{O_2} = 740 \text{ torr} - 518 \text{ torr} = 222 \text{ torr}$$

4-41   The reaction stoichiometry is

$$4C_3H_5(NO_3)_3(s) \longrightarrow 12CO_2(g) + 10H_2O(l) + 6N_2(g) + O_2(g)$$

Because the gases are collected at 25°C, $H_2O(g)$ will condense to $H_2O(l)$ and so 4 moles of nitroglycerin yield $12 + 6 + 1 = 19$ moles of gas. Thus 10 g of nitroglycerin yields the following number of moles of gas at 25°C:

$$n = (10 \text{ g nitro})\left(\frac{1 \text{ mol nitro}}{227.1 \text{ g nitro}}\right)\left(\frac{19 \text{ mol gas}}{4 \text{ mol nitro}}\right) = 0.209 \text{ mol gas}$$

The volume is calculated from the ideal-gas equation:

$$V = \frac{nRT}{P} = \frac{(0.209 \text{ mol})(0.0821 \text{ L·atm·mol}^{-1}\text{·K}^{-1})(298 \text{ K})}{(1.0 \text{ atm})} = 5.1 \text{ L}$$

The pressure produced when the reaction is confined to 0.50 L is given by

$$P = \frac{nRT}{V} = \frac{(0.209 \text{ mol})(0.0821 \text{ L·atm·mol}^{-1}\text{·K}^{-1})(298 \text{ K})}{0.50 \text{ L}}$$
$$= 10 \text{ atm}$$

4-43   Recall that in working kinetic theory problems we use the value of $R = 8.314$ $J \cdot mol^{-1} \cdot K^{-1}$. The average speed in $m \cdot s^{-1}$ of a gas molecule is calculated from the equation

$$v_{av} = \left(\frac{3RT}{M_{kg}}\right)^{1/2}$$

where M_{kg} is the molar mass in kilogram-per-mole units. For F_2 we have

$$M_{kg} = \frac{38.00 \text{ g} \cdot \text{mol}^{-1}}{1000 \text{ g} \cdot \text{kg}^{-1}} = 0.03800 \text{ kg} \cdot \text{mol}^{-1}$$

Thus at 298 K we have for the average speed of a Cl_2 molecule

$$v_{av} = \left[\frac{(3)(8.314 \text{ J} \cdot \text{mol}^{-1} \cdot \text{K}^{-1})(298 \text{ K})}{(0.03800 \text{ kg} \cdot \text{mol}^{-1})} \right]^{1/2} = 442 \text{ m} \cdot \text{s}^{-1}$$

4-45 Application of the equation for the average speed

$$v_{av} = \left(\frac{3RT}{M_{kg}} \right)^{1/2}$$

to the temperatures T_f and T_i yields

$$\frac{v_{av_f}}{v_{av_i}} = \frac{\left(\dfrac{3RT_f}{M_{kg}} \right)^{1/2}}{\left(\dfrac{3RT_i}{M_{kg}} \right)^{1/2}} = \left(\frac{\cancel{3R}T_f}{\cancel{M_{kg}}} \cdot \frac{\cancel{M_{kg}}}{\cancel{3R}T_i} \right)^{1/2} = \left(\frac{T_f}{T_i} \right)^{1/2}$$

But $T_f = 2T_i$. Thus,

$$\frac{v_{av_f}}{v_{av_i}} = \left(\frac{2T_i}{T_i} \right)^{1/2} = 2^{1/2} = \sqrt{2}$$

Solving for v_{av_f}, we have

$$v_{av_f} = \sqrt{2} \, v_{av_i}$$

The average speed of a molecule is increased by a factor of $\sqrt{2}$ when the temperature, T, is doubled.

4-47 The average speed of a gas molecule decreases as the molar mass increases at the same temperature. Thus we have

$$^{238}UF_6 < {}^{235}UF_6 < NO_2 < CO_2 < O_2 < N_2 < H_2O$$

4-49 The mean free path is given by

$$l = (3.1 \times 10^7 \text{ pm}^3 \cdot \text{atm} \cdot \text{K}^{-1}) \frac{T}{\sigma^2 P}$$

From Table 4-3 we find that the molecular diameter of O_2 is 370 pm. Thus,

$$l = \frac{(3.1 \times 10^7 \text{ pm}^3 \cdot \text{atm} \cdot \text{K}^{-1})(310 \text{ K})}{(370 \text{ pm})^2(0.20 \text{ atm})} = 3.51 \times 10^5 \text{ pm}$$

$$= (3.51 \times 10^5 \text{ pm})\left(\frac{1 \text{ m}}{10^{12} \text{ pm}}\right) = 3.5 \times 10^{-7} \text{ m}$$

The collision frequency per molecule, z, is given by

$$z = \frac{v_{av}}{l}$$

Thus,

$$z = \frac{\left(\dfrac{3RT}{M_{kg}}\right)^{1/2}}{l}$$

For O_2 at 293 K we compute for z,

$$z = \frac{[(3)(8.314 \text{ J} \cdot \text{mol}^{-1} \cdot \text{K}^{-1})(310 \text{ K})/0.0320 \text{ kg} \cdot \text{mol}^{-1}]^{1/2}}{3.51 \times 10^{-7} \text{ m}}$$

$$= 1.4 \times 10^9 \text{ collisions} \cdot \text{s}^{-1}$$

4-51 In order to calculate the mean free path by using the equation

$$l = (3.1 \times 10^7 \text{ pm}^3 \cdot \text{atm} \cdot \text{K}^{-1})\frac{T}{\sigma^2 P}$$

we need the pressure expressed in atmospheres. We have to compute the pressure corresponding to a density of one atom/m^3 at 10 K. From the ideal-gas equation we have

$$P = \left(\frac{n}{V}\right)RT$$

If we convert n/V in atoms/m^3 to mol/L, then we can compute P in atm using the above equation

$$\frac{n}{V} = \left(\frac{1 \text{ atom}}{1 \text{ m}^3}\right)\left(\frac{1 \text{ mol}}{6.022 \times 10^{23} \text{ atom}}\right)\left(\frac{1 \text{ m}}{100 \text{ cm}}\right)^3\left(\frac{1000 \text{ cm}^3}{1 \text{ L}}\right)$$

$$= 1.7 \times 10^{-27} \text{ mol} \cdot \text{L}^{-1}$$

Thus,

$$P = (1.7 \times 10^{-27} \text{ mol} \cdot \text{L}^{-1})(0.0821 \text{ L} \cdot \text{atm} \cdot \text{mol}^{-1} \cdot \text{K}^{-1})(10 \text{ K})$$

$$= 1.4 \times 10^{-27} \text{ atm}$$

We can now compute the mean free path:

$$l = \frac{(3.1 \times 10^7 \text{ pm}^3 \cdot \text{atm} \cdot \text{K}^{-1})(10 \text{ K})}{(100 \text{ pm})^2(1.4 \times 10^{-27} \text{ atm})} = 2.2 \times 10^{31} \text{ pm}$$

$$= (2.2 \times 10^{31} \text{ pm})\left(\frac{1 \text{ m}}{10^{12} \text{ pm}}\right) = 2.2 \times 10^{19} \text{ m}$$

4-53 The number of collisions per second (collision frequency) is given by

$$z = \frac{v_{av}}{l}$$

The average speed of H_2 molecules at 20°C is

$$v_{av} = \left(\frac{3RT}{M_{kg}}\right)^{1/2} = \left[\frac{3(8.314 \text{ J} \cdot \text{mol}^{-1} \cdot \text{K}^{-1})(293 \text{ K})}{(2.016 \times 10^{-3} \text{ kg} \cdot \text{mol}^{-1})}\right]^{1/2}$$

$$= 1903 \text{ m} \cdot \text{s}^{-1}$$

The mean free path of H_2 at 20°C and 1.00 atm is ($\sigma_{H_2} = 280$ pm from Table 4-3).

$$l = (3.1 \times 10^7 \text{ pm}^3 \cdot \text{atm} \cdot \text{K}^{-1})\frac{T}{\sigma^2 P}$$

$$= \frac{(3.1 \times 10^7 \text{ pm}^3 \cdot \text{atm} \cdot \text{K}^{-1})(293 \text{ K})}{(280 \text{ pm})^2(1.00 \text{ atm})} = 1.16 \times 10^5 \text{ pm}$$

$$= (1.16 \times 10^5 \text{ pm})\left(\frac{1 \text{ m}}{10^{12} \text{ pm}}\right) = 1.16 \times 10^{-7} \text{ m}$$

Thus,

$$z = \frac{1904 \text{ m} \cdot \text{s}^{-1}}{1.16 \times 10^{-7} \text{ m}} = 1.6 \times 10^{10} \text{ collisions} \cdot \text{s}^{-1}$$

4-55 The ratio of the rates of effusion of the two gases is given by Graham's law:

$$\frac{\text{rate}_A}{\text{rate}_B} = \left(\frac{M_B}{M_A}\right)^{1/2}$$

If we take A = helium and B = nitrogen, then we have

$$\text{rate}_{He} = (\text{rate}_{N_2})\left(\frac{M_{N_2}}{M_{He}}\right)^{1/2}$$

Substituting in the values for rate_{N_2}, M_{N_2}, and M_{He}, we have

$$\text{rate}_{He} = (75 \text{ mL} \cdot \text{h}^{-1})\left(\frac{28.02}{4.003}\right)^{1/2} = 200 \text{ mL} \cdot \text{h}^{-1}$$

4-57 Graham's law gives

$$\frac{\text{rate}_A}{\text{rate}_B} = \left(\frac{M_B}{M_A}\right)^{1/2}$$

or

$$\frac{M_B}{M_A} = \left(\frac{\text{rate}_A}{\text{rate}_B}\right)^2$$

If we let B = unknown gas and A = nitrogen, then we have

$$M_{unknown} = (M_{N_2})\left(\frac{\text{rate}_{N_2}}{\text{rate}_{unknown}}\right)^2$$

The rate of effusion of N_2 is

$$\text{rate}_{N_2} = \frac{1.00 \text{ mL}}{145 \text{ s}} = 6.90 \times 10^{-3} \text{ mL} \cdot \text{s}^{-1}$$

The rate of effusion of the unknown gas is

$$\text{rate}_{unknown} = \frac{1.00 \text{ mL}}{230 \text{ s}} = 4.35 \times 10^{-3} \text{ mL} \cdot \text{s}^{-1}$$

Thus,

$$M_{unknown} = (28.02 \text{ g} \cdot \text{mol}^{-1})\left(\frac{6.90 \times 10^{-3} \text{ mL} \cdot \text{s}^{-1}}{4.35 \times 10^{-3} \text{ mL} \cdot \text{s}^{-1}}\right)^2 = 70.5 \text{ g} \cdot \text{mol}^{-1}$$

4-59 We shall use Equation (4-26) to calculate the pressure

$$P = \frac{nRT}{V - nb} - \frac{n^2a}{V^2}$$

The number of moles of NH_3 is

$$n = (24.5 \text{ g})\left(\frac{1 \text{ mol}}{17.03 \text{ g}}\right) = 1.439 \text{ mol}$$

We obtain the values of a and b for NH_3 from Table 4-4. Thus we have

$$P = \frac{(1.439 \text{ mol})(0.0821 \text{ L} \cdot \text{atm} \cdot \text{mol}^{-1} \cdot \text{K}^{-1})(300 \text{ K})}{2.15 \text{ L} - (1.439 \text{ mol})(0.0371 \text{ L} \cdot \text{mol}^{-1})}$$
$$- \frac{(1.439 \text{ mol})^2(4.170 \text{ L}^2 \cdot \text{atm} \cdot \text{mol}^{-2})}{(2.15 \text{ L})^2}$$

$$= 16.90 \text{ atm} - 1.87 \text{ atm} = 15.0 \text{ atm}$$

The pressure calculated by using the ideal-gas equation is

$$P = \frac{nRT}{V} = \frac{(1.439 \text{ mol})(0.0821 \text{ L} \cdot \text{atm} \cdot \text{mol}^{-1} \cdot \text{K}^{-1})(300 \text{ K})}{2.15 \text{ L}}$$
$$= 16.5 \text{ atm}$$

4-61 From the ideal-gas equation we have for the number of moles of Cl_2,

$$n = \frac{PV}{RT}$$

Note that $1 \text{ Pa} = 1 \text{ N} \cdot \text{m}^{-2}$ and $1 \text{ J} = 1 \text{ N} \cdot \text{m}$. When we use R in the units $J \cdot K^{-1} \cdot \text{mol}^{-1}$, we must express the volume in the units m^3. Thus

$$V = (5.00 \text{ mL})\left(\frac{1 \text{ cm}^3}{1 \text{ mL}}\right)\left(\frac{1 \text{ m}}{100 \text{ cm}}\right)^3 = 5.00 \times 10^{-6} \text{ m}^3$$

$$n = \frac{(2.15 \times 10^4 \text{ N} \cdot \text{m}^{-2})(5.00 \times 10^{-6} \text{ m}^3)}{(8.314 \text{ N} \cdot \text{m} \cdot \text{mol}^{-1} \cdot \text{K}^{-1})(313 \text{ K})} = 4.13 \times 10^{-5} \text{ mol}$$

The number of molecules is obtained by multiplying n by Avogadro's number:

number of molecules $= (4.13 \times 10^{-5} \text{ mol})(6.022 \times 10^{23} \text{ molecules} \cdot \text{mol}^{-1})$
$$= 2.49 \times 10^{19} \text{ molecules}$$

4-63 Using the ideal-gas law, we have

$$\frac{P_i V_i}{T_i} = \frac{P_f V_f}{T_f}$$

Solving for the final volume, we have

$$V_f = V_i \left(\frac{T_f}{T_i}\right)\left(\frac{P_i}{P_f}\right)$$

Thus,

$$V_f = (7.12 \text{ } \mu L)\left(\frac{273 \text{ K}}{295 \text{ K}}\right)\left(\frac{8.72 \times 10^4 \text{ Pa}}{1.013 \times 10^5 \text{ Pa}}\right)$$
$$= 5.67 \text{ } \mu L$$

The number of moles of radon is

$$n = \frac{PV}{RT}$$

We must first convert the volume to cubic meters, m^3:

$$V = (7.12\ \mu\text{L})\left(\frac{1\ \text{mL}}{10^3\ \mu\text{L}}\right)\left(\frac{1\ \text{cm}^3}{1\ \text{mL}}\right)\left(\frac{1\ \text{m}}{100\ \text{cm}}\right)^3 = 7.12 \times 10^{-9}\ \text{m}^3$$

Thus,

$$n = \frac{(8.72 \times 10^4\ \text{N} \cdot \text{m}^{-2})(7.12 \times 10^{-9}\ \text{m}^3)}{(8.314\ \text{N} \cdot \text{m} \cdot \text{K}^{-1} \cdot \text{mol}^{-1})(295\ \text{K})} = 2.53 \times 10^{-7}\ \text{mol}$$

The mass of radon is

$$m = (2.53 \times 10^{-7}\ \text{mol})\left(\frac{222\ \text{g}}{1\ \text{mol}}\right) = 5.62 \times 10^{-5}\ \text{g}$$

$$= 56.2\ \mu\text{g}$$

Note that either set of conditions can be used in the ideal-gas equation to calculate n.

4-65 From the ideal-gas equation we have

$$\rho = \frac{MP}{RT}$$

$$= \frac{(20.06\ \text{g} \cdot \text{mol}^{-1})(2.00 \times 10^3\ \text{N} \cdot \text{m}^{-2})}{(8.314\ \text{N} \cdot \text{m} \cdot \text{K}^{-1} \cdot \text{mol}^{-1})(273\ \text{K})}$$

$$= 17.7\ \text{g} \cdot \text{m}^{-3}$$

4-67 We must calculate the force exerted by a column of mercury 760.0 mm high and 1 m² in cross-sectional area. The volume of the column of mercury in cm³ is

$$V = (760.0\ \text{mm})\left(\frac{1\ \text{cm}}{10\ \text{mm}}\right)(1\ \text{m}^2)\left(\frac{10^2\ \text{cm}}{1\ \text{m}}\right)^2$$

$$= 7.600 \times 10^5\ \text{cm}^3$$

The mass of the mercury column is

$$\text{mass of Hg} = (13.59\ \text{g} \cdot \text{cm}^{-3})(7.600 \times 10^5\ \text{cm}^3)$$

$$= 1.033 \times 10^7\ \text{g}$$

The force exerted by the column of mercury is

$$F = mg$$

$$= (1.033 \times 10^7\ \text{g})\left(\frac{1\ \text{kg}}{10^3\ \text{g}}\right)(9.806\ \text{m} \cdot \text{s}^{-2})$$

$$= 1.013 \times 10^5\ \text{kg} \cdot \text{m} \cdot \text{s}^{-2}$$

$$= 1.013 \times 10^5\ \text{N}$$

and so the pressure is $1.013 \times 10^5\ \text{N} \cdot \text{m}^{-2}$.

4-69	*V*/L	$\dfrac{1}{P}$ / atm^{-1}	*PV*/L·atm
	0.938	3.8	0.244
	0.595	2.4	0.244
	0.294	1.2	0.244
	0.203	0.83	0.244
	0.116	0.48	0.244
	0.093	0.38	0.244
	0.078	0.32	0.245

Boyle's law in an equation states that

$$V = \frac{c}{P}$$

Thus

$$PV = \text{constant}$$

as the data show. A plot of *V* versus $1/P$ should be a straight line of the form $y = ax$, where $y = V$ and $x = 1/P$.

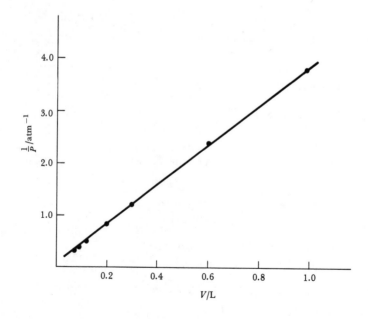

4-71   We use the ideal-gas equation to calculate the volume.

$$V = \frac{nRT}{P} = \frac{(1.00 \text{ mol})(0.0821 \text{ L·atm·mol}^{-1} \cdot \text{K}^{-1})(1073 \text{ K})}{75 \text{ atm}}$$
$$= 1.2 \text{ L}$$

4-73   The balanced equation for the combustion of octane is

$$2C_8H_{18}(g) + 25O_2(g) \longrightarrow 16CO_2(g) + 18H_2O(l)$$

The mass of 1 gallon of gasoline is

$$\text{mass} = (1.00 \text{ gal})\left(\frac{4 \text{ qt}}{1 \text{ gal}}\right)\left(\frac{0.946 \text{ L}}{1 \text{ qt}}\right)\left(\frac{10^3 \text{ mL}}{1 \text{ L}}\right)\left(\frac{0.70 \text{ g}}{1 \text{ mL}}\right) = 2.65 \times 10^3 \text{ g}$$

The number of moles of oxygen required to react with 2.65×10^3 g of C_8H_{18} is

$$\text{moles of O}_2 = (2.65 \times 10^3 \text{ g C}_3H_8)\left(\frac{1 \text{ mol C}_8H_{18}}{114.22 \text{ g C}_8H_{18}}\right)\left(\frac{25 \text{ mol O}_2}{2 \text{ mol C}_8H_{18}}\right)$$
$$= 2.90 \times 10^2 \text{ mol}$$

The volume of O_2 required at 0°C and 1 atm is

$$V = \frac{nRT}{P} = \frac{(2.90 \times 10^2 \text{ mol})(0.0821 \text{ L·atm·mol}^{-1} \cdot \text{K}^{-1})(273 \text{ K})}{1.00 \text{ atm}}$$
$$= 6.50 \times 10^3 \text{ L}$$

The volume of air required is

$$V(\text{of air}) = \frac{6.50 \times 10^3 \text{ L}}{0.20} = 3.25 \times 10^4 \text{ L}$$
$$= 8600 \text{ gallons}$$

4-75   We shall start with the van der Waals equation in the form

$$P = \frac{nRT}{V - nb} - \frac{n^2 a}{V^2}$$

At low densities, n/V and thus n^2/V^2 are very small and can be neglected in comparison with the first term. We now have

$$P = \frac{nRT}{V - nb}$$

If we divide the numerator and denominator by V, then we have

$$P = \frac{\dfrac{nRT}{V}}{1 - \dfrac{nb}{V}}$$

When V is large (low gas density),

$$\frac{nb}{V} \ll 1 \quad \text{and} \quad P \approx \frac{nRT}{V}$$

4-77 The equation for the reaction that takes place when the mixture is heated is

$$2KClO_3(s) \longrightarrow 2KCl(s) + 3O_2(g)$$

The pressure of O_2 is

$$P = 756 \text{ torr} - 15.5 \text{ torr} = 740 \text{ torr}$$

The number of moles of O_2 produced is

$$n = \frac{PV}{RT} = \frac{(740 \text{ torr})\left(\dfrac{1 \text{ atm}}{760 \text{ torr}}\right)(0.0807 \text{ L})}{(0.0821 \text{ L·atm·mol}^{-1}\text{·K}^{-1})(291 \text{ K})}$$
$$= 3.289 \times 10^{-3} \text{ mol}$$

The mass of $KClO_3$ that produced 3.289×10^{-3} mol of O_2 is

$$\text{mass of } KClO_3 = (3.289 \times 10^{-3} \text{ mol } O_2)\left(\frac{2 \text{ mol } KClO_3}{3 \text{ mol } O_2}\right)\left(\frac{122.55 \text{ g } KClO_3}{1 \text{ mol } KClO_3}\right)$$
$$= 0.2687 \text{ g}$$

The mass percentage of $KClO_3$ in the mixture is

$$\text{mass \% of } KClO_3 = \frac{0.2687 \text{ g}}{0.428 \text{ g}} \times 100 = 62.8\%$$

4-79 We use Equation (4-8) for the expression for the density

$$\rho = \frac{MP}{RT}$$

The partial pressure of O_2 is $(0.20)(1.00 \text{ atm}) = 0.200$ atm. The density due to O_2 is

$$\rho = \frac{(32.00 \text{ g} \cdot \text{mol}^{-1})(0.200 \text{ atm})}{(0.0821 \text{ L} \cdot \text{atm} \cdot \text{mol}^{-1} \cdot \text{K}^{-1})(293 \text{ K})}$$
$$= 0.266 \text{ g} \cdot \text{L}^{-1}$$

The partial pressure of N_2 is $(0.80)(1.00 \text{ atm}) = 0.800 \text{ atm}$. The density due to N_2 is

$$\rho = \frac{(28.02 \text{ g} \cdot \text{mol}^{-1})(0.800 \text{ atm})}{(0.0821 \text{ L} \cdot \text{atm} \cdot \text{mol}^{-1} \cdot \text{K}^{-1})(293 \text{ K})}$$
$$= 0.932 \text{ g} \cdot \text{L}^{-1}$$

The total density is

$$\rho = \rho_{O_2} + \rho_{N_2} = 0.266 \text{ g} \cdot \text{L}^{-1} + 0.932 \text{ g} \cdot \text{L}^{-1}$$
$$= 1.198 \text{ g} \cdot \text{L}^{-1}$$

The effective molar mass of air is

$$M = \frac{\rho RT}{P} = \frac{(1.198 \text{ g} \cdot \text{L}^{-1})(0.0821 \text{ L} \cdot \text{atm} \cdot \text{mol}^{-1} \cdot \text{K}^{-1})(293 \text{ K})}{1.00 \text{ atm}}$$
$$= 28.9 \text{ g} \cdot \text{mol}^{-1}$$

4-81 The number of moles of H_2 produced is

$$n = \frac{PV}{RT} = \frac{(750 \text{ torr})\left(\dfrac{1 \text{ atm}}{760 \text{ torr}}\right)(0.150 \text{ L})}{(0.0821 \text{ L} \cdot \text{atm} \cdot \text{mol}^{-1} \cdot \text{K}^{-1})(283 \text{ K})}$$
$$= 6.371 \times 10^{-3} \text{ mol}$$

The number of moles of NaOH required is

$$n = (6.371 \times 10^{-3} \text{ mol H}_2)\left(\frac{2 \text{ mol NaOH}}{3 \text{ mol H}_2}\right)$$
$$= 4.247 \times 10^{-3} \text{ mol}$$

The volume of NaOH(aq) required is

$$V = \frac{n}{M} = \frac{4.247 \times 10^{-3} \text{ mol}}{0.200 \text{ mol} \cdot \text{L}^{-1}}$$
$$= 0.0212 \text{ L} = 21.2 \text{ mL}$$

4-83 The number of moles of NH_3 added is

$$\text{mol of NH}_3 = (5.0 \text{ g})\left(\frac{1 \text{ mol}}{17.03 \text{ g}}\right) = 0.2936 \text{ mol}$$

and the number of moles of HCl added is

$$\text{mol HCl} = (10.0 \text{ g})\left(\frac{1 \text{ mol}}{36.46 \text{ g}}\right) = 0.2743 \text{ mol}$$

We see that HCl is the limiting reactant. The number of moles of NH_3 remaining is

$$\text{mol } NH_3 = 0.2936 \text{ mol} - 0.2743 \text{ mol} = 0.0193 \text{ mol}$$

The pressure of NH_3 is

$$P = \frac{nRT}{V} = \frac{(0.0193 \text{ mol})(0.0821 \text{ L·atm·mol}^{-1}\text{·K}^{-1})(348 \text{ K})}{1.00 \text{ L}}$$
$$= 0.55 \text{ atm}$$

4-85 The volume of air breathed in per day is

$$V \text{ of air} = (0.5 \text{ L})\left(\frac{14 \text{ breaths}}{1 \text{ min}}\right)\left(\frac{60 \text{ min}}{1 \text{ hr}}\right)\left(\frac{24 \text{ hr}}{1 \text{ day}}\right)$$
$$= 1.008 \times 10^4 \text{ L}$$

The number of moles of O_2 in 1.008×10^4 L of air is [(recall that the partial pressure of O_2 in air is $(0.20)(1.00 \text{ atm})$]

$$n = \frac{PV}{RT} = \frac{(0.20 \text{ atm})(1.008 \times 10^4 \text{ L})}{(0.0821 \text{ L·atm·mol}^{-1}\text{·K}^{-1})(310 \text{ K})}$$
$$= 79.2 \text{ mol}$$

The number of moles of O_2 utilized per day is

$$n = (0.25)(79.2 \text{ mol}) = 19.8 \text{ mol}$$

The mass of O_2 utilized per day is

$$\text{mass of } O_2 = (19.8 \text{ mol})\left(\frac{32.00 \text{ g}}{1 \text{ mol}}\right) = 634 \text{ g}$$
$$= (634 \text{ g})\left(\frac{1 \text{ lb}}{453.5 \text{ g}}\right) = 1.4 \text{ lb}$$

4-87 The relationship between the average speed and the temperature is

$$v_{av} = \left(\frac{3RT}{M_{kg}}\right)^{1/2}$$

Squaring both sides of this equation and solving for T yields

$$T = \frac{M_{kg} v_{aq}^2}{3R}$$

Thus we have

$$T = \frac{(0.04401 \text{ kg} \cdot \text{mol}^{-1})(1000 \text{ m} \cdot \text{s}^{-1})^2}{(3)(8.314 \text{ J} \cdot \text{K}^{-1} \cdot \text{mol}^{-1})}$$
$$= 1764 \text{ K}$$

4-89 Using the equation given we have

$$v_{sound} = \left(\frac{7RT}{5M_{kg}}\right)^{1/2} = \left[\frac{(7)(8.314 \text{ J} \cdot \text{mol}^{-1} \cdot \text{K}^{-1})(273 \text{ K})}{(5)(0.02802 \text{ kg} \cdot \text{mol}^{-1})}\right]^{1/2}$$
$$= 337 \text{ m} \cdot \text{s}^{-1}$$

The value of v_{av} is calculated by using Equation (4-18).

$$v_{av} = \left(\frac{3RT}{M_{kg}}\right)^{1/2} = \left[\frac{(3)(8.314 \text{ J} \cdot \text{mol}^{-1} \cdot \text{K}^{-1})(273 \text{ K})}{(0.02802 \text{ kg} \cdot \text{mol}^{-1})}\right]^{1/2}$$
$$= 493 \text{ m} \cdot \text{s}^{-1}$$

Sound is transmitted in a gas by molecular collisions. The sound cannot be transmitted faster than, but is comparable to, the speed of the molecules of the gas.

E   ANSWERS TO THE SELF-TEST

1   false

2   true

3   false (The density usually does not change much.)

4   volume

5   empty space

6   the gas molecules occupy only a small fraction of the available space

7   gas pressure

8   the difference in pressures on the two mercury surfaces

9   torr

10   the pressure due to the atmosphere

11   false (It depends on weather conditions and altitude.)

12   false

13   true

14   760 torr or 1.013×10^5 Pa

15   the pascal

16   inversely . . . pressure . . . temperature

17   3.0 atm $(P_iV_i = P_fV_f)$

18   directly . . . absolute temperature . . . pressure

19   false [Volume is proportional to the absolute temperature, not the Celsius temperature. $V_f = (T_f/T_i)V_i = (473 \text{ K}/373 \text{ K})(3.4 \text{ L}).$]

20   Kelvin temperature . . . kelvin, K

21   293

22 0K . . . $-273.15°C$

23 temperature . . . volume . . . constant pressure

24 2

25 $PV = nRT$

26 obeys the ideal-gas equation $PV = nRT$

27 true

28 0.0821 $L \cdot atm \cdot mol^{-1} \cdot K^{-1}$ or 8.314 $J \cdot mol^{-1} \cdot K^{-1}$

29 atmospheres . . . liters . . . moles . . . kelvin

30 22.4 L

31 decreases

32 increases

33 decreases

34 false

35 $\dfrac{n_{O_2}}{n_{O_2} + n_{CO_2}}$

36 $X_{O_2} P_{total}$

37 minus

38 collisions of the gas molecules with the walls of the container

39 false (There is a distribution of molecular speeds.)

40 absolute temperature

41 increases

42 lower

43 true

44 traveled by a molecule between collisions

45 10^{10}

46 500

47 temperature . . . pressure . . . molecular diameter

48 average speed . . . mean free path

49 false

50 true

51 false

52 nonideal

53 the effect of the attraction between the molecules of the gas becomes important

THERMOCHEMISTRY

A   OUTLINE OF CHAPTER 5

5-1   Energy is conserved.

Chemical reactions almost always involve a change in energy.

The first law of thermodynamics states that energy is neither created nor destroyed but is converted from one form to another.

Energy can be transferred as work or as heat.

The amount of energy transferred as heat is denoted by q.

The amount of energy transferred as work is denoted by w.

The work done on a system that is compressed or expanded at a constant pressure is given by $w = -P\,\Delta V = -P(V_f - V_i)$ [Equation (5-3)].

The work done on a system due to compression is a positive quantity.

Energy as heat flows spontaneously from higher to lower temperature regions.

The energy change of a chemical reaction is denoted by ΔU_{rxn}.

For a chemical reaction, $\Delta U_{rxn} = q + w$ [Equation (5-4)].

When a reaction takes place at constant volume, the energy change is equal to the heat evolved or absorbed.

$\Delta U_{rxn} = q_V$ at constant volume [Equation (5-6)].

The enthalpy, H, is defined as $H = U + PV$ [Equation (5-7)].

When a reaction takes place at constant pressure, the enthalpy change is equal to the heat evolved or absorbed.

$\Delta H_{rxn} = q_P$ at constant pressure [Equation (5-10)].

5-2   Chemical reactions evolve or absorb energy as heat.

An exothermic reaction is a reaction that evolves energy as heat.

An endothermic reaction is a reaction that absorbs energy as heat.

The enthalpy change for a chemical reaction is

$$\Delta H_{rxn} = H_{prod} - H_{react} \qquad (5\text{-}11)$$

For an exothermic reaction, $\Delta H_{rxn} < 0$.

For an endothermic reaction, $\Delta H_{rxn} > 0$ (Figure 5-3).

The standard enthalpy change for a reaction, for which the reactants and products are at 1 atm pressure, is denoted by ΔH_{rxn}°.

5-3 Enthalpy changes for chemical equations are additive.

Hess's law states that if two or more chemical equations are added together, then the value of ΔH_{rxn}° for the resulting equation is equal to the sum of the ΔH_{rxn}° values for the separate equations.

ΔH_{rxn}° (reverse reaction) $= -\Delta H_{rxn}^{\circ}$ (forward reaction) [Equation (5-13)].

5-4 Heats of reaction can be calculated from tabulated heats of formation.

The standard molar enthalpy of formation, ΔH_f°, is the value of ΔH_{rxn}° of the reaction in which one mole of a substance is formed from its constituent elements in their most stable form at 25°C and 1 atm.

The value of ΔH_f° is zero for an element in its normal state at 25°C and 1 atm.

For the general chemical equation aA + bB → yY + zZ, the value of ΔH_{rxn}° is given by

$$\Delta H_{rxn}^{\circ} = y\,\Delta H_f^{\circ}[Y] + z\,\Delta H_f^{\circ}[Z] - a\,\Delta H_f^{\circ}[A] - b\,\Delta H_f^{\circ}[B] \qquad (5\text{-}14)$$

Values of ΔH_f° of some substances are given in Table 5-1.

5-5 The value of ΔH_{rxn}° is determined primarily by the difference in the bond enthalpies of the reactant and product molecules.

The molar bond enthalpy is the energy required to break Avogadro's number of bonds.

The total enthalpy change for a reaction is approximately given by

$$\Delta H_{rxn}^{\circ} \approx H(\text{bond})_R - H(\text{bond})_P \qquad (5\text{-}15)$$

where $H(\text{bond})_R$ represents the sum of the molar bond enthalpies for all the reactant bonds and $H(\text{bond})_P$ represents the sum of the molar bond enthalpies for all the product bonds.

The values of average molar bond enthalpies of some bonds are given in Table 5-2.

5-6 Heat capacity measures the ability of a substance to take up energy as heat.

At constant pressure, the heat capacity is given by

$$c_P = \frac{q_P}{\Delta T} \qquad (5\text{-}16)$$

where q_P is the heat input and ΔT is the change in temperature.

The molar heat capacity, C_P, is the heat capacity per mole of a substance at constant pressure.

The molar heat capacities at constant pressure of some substances are given in Table 5-3.

5-7 A calorimeter is a device used to measure the amount of heat evolved or absorbed in a reaction.

For a reaction that takes place in a calorimeter (Figure 5-7)

$$\Delta H_{rxn} = -\Delta H_{calorimeter} \tag{5-17}$$

which is equivalent to

$$\Delta H_{rxn} = -c_{P,calorimeter} \Delta T \tag{5-19}$$

where ΔT is the measured temperature change and $c_{P,calorimeter}$ is the heat capacity of the calorimeter.

For reactions that take place in solution, $\Delta H_{rxn} \approx \Delta H_{rxn}^\circ$.

5-8 Combustion reactions are used as energy sources.

The heat of combustion of a substance can be measured in a bomb calorimeter (Figure 5-8).

In a bomb calorimeter, $\Delta U_{rxn} = q_V$.

In most cases, $\Delta U_{rxn} \approx \Delta H_{rxn}$.

5-9 Food is fuel.

The popular term calorie is actually a kilocalorie.

One calorie is equal to 4.184 J.

The approximate energy values of some common foods are given in Table 5-4.

B SELF TEST

1 The first law of thermodynamics states that _____

_____.

2 Chemical reactions involve energy transfers in the form of _____ and

_____.

3 The transfer of energy as work involves the action of a _____

_____.

4 The work done on a system is a (*positive, negative*) quantity.

5 The work done on a system that expands is a (*positive, negative*) quantity.

6 The transfer of energy as heat requires a _____

_____.

7 For a chemical reaction, the energy change, ΔU_{rxn}, is equal to _____.

8 For a chemical reaction that takes place at constant volume, the energy change is equal to _____.

9 The thermodynamic function, enthalpy, H, is defined as _____.

10 For a chemical reaction that takes place at constant pressure, the enthalpy change, ΔH_{rxn}, is equal to _____.

11 When a chemical reaction is run in a reaction vessel open to the atmosphere, the reaction takes place at constant _____.

12 The enthalpy change for a chemical reaction is given by $\Delta H_{rxn} = H_{prod} + H_{react}$. *True/False*

13 Reactions that give off energy as heat are called _____.

14 Reactions that take up energy as heat are called _____.

15 If the value of ΔH_{rxn} is negative, then the reaction is _____ thermic.

16 If the value of ΔH_{rxn} is positive, then heat is absorbed by a reaction. *True/False*

17 The value of ΔH_{rxn} is equal to the heat absorbed or evolved by a reaction when the reaction takes place at constant _____.

18 If a reaction takes place at constant volume, then the heat absorbed or evolved by the reaction is equal to _____.

19 If two chemical equations are added together, then the value of ΔH°_{rxn} for the resulting equation equals _____.

20 State Hess's law in your own words.

21 The standard molar enthalpy of formation, ΔH°_f, of a substance is defined as

_____

_____.

22 The value of ΔH_f° of N_2 at 25 °C and 1 atm is _____.

23 For the equation

$$CH_4(g) + 2O_2(g) \longrightarrow CO_2(g) + 2H_2O(g)$$

the values of ΔH_f° of the reactants and products are known. The value of ΔH_{rxn}° can be found by the relation $\Delta H_{rxn}^\circ =$ _____.

24 Energy is required to break a bond between two atoms. *True/False*

25 The reaction between hydrogen and oxygen to form water is exothermic. The dissociation of water to form hydrogen and oxygen is an *(exothermic, endothermic)* reaction.

26 The values of the bond enthalpies of the bonds in the products and reactants of a reaction can be used to predict the value of ΔH_{rxn}°. *True/False*

27 The amount of heat required to raise the temperature of one mole of a substance by one kelvin is the _____ of the substance.

28 The heat capacity per gram of water is $4.18 \text{ J} \cdot \text{K}^{-1} \cdot \text{g}^{-1}$ and the heat capacity per gram of sodium is $1.34 \text{ J} \cdot \text{K}^{-1} \cdot \text{g}^{-1}$. It will require *(more, less)* heat to raise the temperature of one gram of water by one degree than one gram of sodium.

29 An input of 100 J of heat will heat 10 g of water to a *(higher, lower)* temperature than 10 g of sodium when both are initially at the same temperature.

30 Suggest a reason why the heat capacity of a substance is given as the molar heat capacity instead of simply as the heat capacity _____

_____.

31 A calorimeter is a device used to measure _____.

32 Only heats of combustion can be measured in a calorimeter. *True/False*

33 Why is the heat absorbed or given off by a calorimeter equal to the heat of the reaction taking place in the calorimeter? _____

_____.

34 In a calorimeter, the change in _____ is the physical change measured.

35 The value of ΔH_{rxn}° is determined from the _____ of the calorimeter and the change in _____.

36 Combustion is an example of an ――――――― thermic reaction.

37 An apparatus in which ΔU_{rxn} can be measured is called a ――――――――
calorimeter.

38 The enthalpy change for a reaction often is almost equal to the energy change for the
reaction. *True/False*

39 Why is the heat of combustion of a substance important in deciding whether a
substance can be used as a fuel? ―――――――――――――――――――――.

40 The value of ΔH_{rxn}° for the reaction between glucose and oxygen depends on
whether the reaction takes place in a calorimeter or in the body. *True/False*

C CALCULATIONS YOU SHOULD KNOW HOW TO DO

1 Use Hess's law to calculate ΔH_{rxn}° for an equation by adding or subtracting ΔH_{rxn}°'s for
two or more equations. See Example 5-1 and Problems 5-5 through 5-14.

2 Calculate ΔH_{rxn}° by using values of ΔH_f° given in Table 5-1 and Equation (5-14),
$\Delta H_{rxn}^{\circ} = y \, \Delta H_f^{\circ}[Y] + z \, \Delta H_f^{\circ}[Z] - a \, \Delta H_f^{\circ}[A] - b \, \Delta H_f^{\circ}[B]$. See Example 5-2 and Problems 5-15 through 5-26.

3 Use the bond enthalpies in Table 5-2 to calculate ΔH_{rxn}°. See Example 5-3 and Problems 5-29 and 5-30.

4 Calculate bond enthalpies from ΔH_{rxn}° for certain reactions. See Problems 5-27, 5-28,
and 5-31 through 5-34.

5 Use heat capacity to calculate the heat absorbed or evolved by a temperature change.
See Example 5-5 and Problems 5-35 through 5-38.

6 Calculate the final temperature when two substances at different temperatures are
brought into contact. See Problems 5-39 through 5-42.

7 Calculate ΔH_{rxn}° by using data that are obtained from running the reaction in a
calorimeter. See Examples 5-6 and 5-7 and Problems 5-43 through 5-52.

D SOLUTIONS TO THE ODD-NUMBERED PROBLEMS

5-1 We are given the amount of heat evolved (1503 kJ) when 30.0 g of methane is
burned. The amount of heat that is evolved when one mole (16.04 g) of methane is
burned is

$$q = \left(\frac{1503 \text{ kJ}}{30.0 \text{ g}}\right)\left(\frac{16.04 \text{ g}}{1 \text{ mol}}\right) = 804 \text{ kJ} \cdot \text{mol}^{-1}$$

5-3   The reaction is

$$C(s) + 2S(s) \longrightarrow CS_2(l)$$

One mole of CS_2 is formed when one mole of carbon reacts. Therefore,

$$\text{heat evolved per mole of } CS_2 = \left(\frac{9.52 \text{ kJ}}{1.280 \text{ g}}\right)\left(\frac{12.01 \text{ g}}{1 \text{ mol}}\right) = 89.3 \text{ kJ} \cdot \text{mol}^{-1}$$

5-5   We can obtain the second equation from the first by reversing the first equation and dividing the balancing coefficients by 2. Thus

$$\Delta H^\circ_{rxn}(2) = \frac{[-\Delta H^\circ_{rxn}(1)]}{2} = \frac{290.8 \text{ kJ}}{2} = 145.4 \text{ kJ}$$

5-7   To obtain the third equation, reverse the second equation, add it to the first equation,

$$C_2H_5OH(l) + 3O_2(g) \longrightarrow 2CO_2(g) + 3H_2O(g)$$
$$\Delta H^\circ_{rxn} = -1239.7 \text{ kJ}$$
$$2CO_2(g) + 3H_2O(g) \longrightarrow CH_3OCH_3(l) + 3O_2(g)$$
$$\Delta H^\circ_{rxn} = -(-1328.3 \text{ kJ})$$

$$\overline{C_2H_5OH(l) \longrightarrow CH_3OCH_3(l)}$$
$$\Delta H^\circ_{rxn} = 1328.3 \text{ kJ} - 1239.7 \text{ kJ}$$
$$= 88.6 \text{ kJ}$$

5-9   The equation that we want can be obtained from the two given equations by reversing the first equation, multiplying it by 3, and then adding it to 2 times the second equation

$$3Fe_2O_3(s) \longrightarrow 6Fe(s) + \tfrac{9}{2}O_2(g) \qquad \Delta H^\circ_{rxn} = -(3)(-823.41 \text{ kJ})$$
$$= 2470.23 \text{ kJ}$$

$$6Fe(s) + 4O_2(g) \longrightarrow 2Fe_3O_4(s) \qquad \Delta H^\circ_{rxn} = (2)(-1120.48 \text{ kJ})$$
$$= -2240.96 \text{ kJ}$$

$$\overline{3Fe_2O_3(s) \longrightarrow 2Fe_3O_4(s) + \tfrac{1}{2}O_2(g)} \qquad \Delta H^\circ_{rxn} = 2470.23 \text{ kJ} - 2240.96 \text{ kJ}$$
$$= +229.27 \text{ kJ}$$

5-11   The equations that correspond to the combustion reactions are

(1) $C_{12}H_{22}O_{11}(s) + 12O_2(g) \longrightarrow 12CO_2(g) + 11H_2O(l)$ $\Delta H^\circ_{rxn}(1) = -5646.7 \text{ kJ}$
    sucrose

(2) $C_6H_{12}O_6(s) + 6O_2(g) \longrightarrow 6CO_2(g) + 6H_2O(l)$ $\Delta H^\circ_{rxn}(2) = -2815.8 \text{ kJ}$
    glucose

(3) $C_6H_{12}O_6(s) + 6O_2(g) \longrightarrow 6CO_2(g) + 6H_2O(l)$ $\Delta H^\circ_{rxn}(3) = -2826.7 \text{ kJ}$
    fructose

To obtain the desired equation, reverse Equations (2) and (3) and add them to Equation (1):

$$C_{12}H_{22}O_{11}(s) + 12O_2(g) \longrightarrow 12CO_2(g) + 11H_2O(l) \qquad \Delta H^\circ_{rxn} = -5646.7 \text{ kJ}$$
sucrose

$$6CO_2(g) + 6H_2O(l) \longrightarrow C_6H_{12}O_6(s) + 6O_2(g) \qquad \Delta H^\circ_{rxn} = +2815.8 \text{ kJ}$$
glucose

$$6CO_2(g) + 6H_2O(l) \longrightarrow C_6H_{12}O_6(s) + 6O_2(g) \qquad \Delta H^\circ_{rxn} = +2826.7 \text{ kJ}$$
fructose

$$(4) \ C_{12}H_{22}O_{11}(s) + H_2O(l) \longrightarrow C_6H_{12}O_6(s) + C_6H_{12}O_6(s)$$
sucrose   glucose   fructose

$$\Delta H^\circ_{rxn}(4) = -5646.7 \text{ kJ} + 2815.8 \text{ kJ} + 2826.7 \text{ kJ} = -4.2 \text{ kJ}$$

5-13 If we let the first two equations be 1 and 2, then the equation

$$N_2(g) + O_2(g) \rightarrow 2NO(g)$$

(equation 3) can be obtained from the first two equations by

$$\text{equation (3)} = \frac{\text{equation (1)}}{2} - \frac{\text{equation (2)}}{2}$$

According to Hess's law then, we write

$$\Delta H^\circ_{rxn}(3) = \frac{\Delta H^\circ_{rxn}(1)}{2} - \frac{\Delta H^\circ_{rxn}(2)}{2}$$

$$= \frac{-1170 \text{ kJ}}{2} + \frac{1530 \text{ kJ}}{2} = 180 \text{ kJ}$$

5-15 Using Equation (5-14) and the data given, we have

$$\Delta H^\circ_{rxn} = \Delta H^\circ_f[O_3(g)] - \Delta H^\circ_f[O_2(g)] - \Delta H^\circ_f[O(g)]$$
$$= (1 \text{ mol})(142 \text{ kJ} \cdot \text{mol}^{-1}) - (0) - (1 \text{ mol})(247.5 \text{ kJ} \cdot \text{mol}^{-1})$$
$$= -106 \text{ kJ}$$

5-17 (a) $\Delta H^\circ_{rxn} = \Delta H^\circ_f[N_2(g)] + 2\,\Delta H^\circ_f[H_2O(g)] - \Delta H^\circ_f[N_2H_4(l)] - \Delta H^\circ_f[O_2(g)]$

Using the data in Table 5-1, we have

$$\Delta H^\circ_{rxn} = (1 \text{ mol})(0 \text{ kJ} \cdot \text{mol}^{-1}) + (2 \text{ mol})(-241.8 \text{ kJ} \cdot \text{mol}^{-1})$$
$$- (1 \text{ mol})(50.6 \text{ kJ} \cdot \text{mol}^{-1}) - (1 \text{ mol})(0 \text{ kJ} \cdot \text{mol}^{-1})$$
$$= -534.2 \text{ kJ} \qquad \text{exothermic}$$

(b) $\Delta H^\circ_{rxn} = \Delta H^\circ_f[C_2H_5OH(l)] - \Delta H^\circ_f[C_2H_4(g)] - \Delta H^\circ_f[H_2O(l)]$
$$= (1 \text{ mol})(-277.7 \text{ kJ} \cdot \text{mol}^{-1}) - (1 \text{ mol})(52.28 \text{ kJ} \cdot \text{mol}^{-1})$$
$$- (1 \text{ mol})(-285.8 \text{ kJ} \cdot \text{mol}^{-1})$$
$$= -44.2 \text{ kJ} \qquad \text{exothermic}$$

(c) $\Delta H^{\circ}_{rxn} = \Delta H^{\circ}_f [CCl_4(l)] + 4 \Delta H^{\circ}_f [HCl(g)] - \Delta H^{\circ}_f [CH_4(g)] - 4 \Delta H^{\circ}_f [Cl_2(g)]$

$= (1 \text{ mol})(-135.4 \text{ kJ} \cdot \text{mol}^{-1}) + (4 \text{ mol})(-92.31 \text{ kJ} \cdot \text{mol}^{-1})$

$- (1 \text{ mol})(-74.86 \text{ kJ} \cdot \text{mol}^{-1}) - (4 \text{ mol})(0 \text{ kJ} \cdot \text{mol}^{-1})$

$= -429.8 \text{ kJ}$ exothermic

5-19 (a) $\Delta H^{\circ}_{rxn} = 2 \Delta H^{\circ}_f [CO_2(g)] + 3 \Delta H^{\circ}_f [H_2O(l)] - \Delta H^{\circ}_f [C_2H_5OH(l)]$

$- 3 \Delta H^{\circ}_f [O_2(g)]$

$= (2 \text{ mol})(-393.5 \text{ kJ} \cdot \text{mol}^{-1}) + (3 \text{ mol})(-285.8 \text{ kJ} \cdot \text{mol}^{-1})$

$- (1 \text{ mol})(-277.7 \text{ kJ} \cdot \text{mol}^{-1}) - (0)$

$= -1366.7 \text{ kJ}$

The heat of combustion of $C_2H_5OH(l)$ per gram is

$$\left(\frac{-1366.7 \text{ kJ}}{1 \text{ mol}} \right) \left(\frac{1 \text{ mol}}{46.07 \text{ g}} \right) = -29.67 \text{ kJ} \cdot \text{g}^{-1}$$

(b) $\Delta H^{\circ}_{rxn} = 2 \Delta H^{\circ}_f [CO_2(g)] + 3 \Delta H^{\circ}_f [H_2O(l)] - \Delta H^{\circ}_f [C_2H_6(g)]$

$- \tfrac{7}{2} \Delta H^{\circ}_f [O_2(g)]$

$= (2 \text{ mol})(-393.5 \text{ kJ} \cdot \text{mol}^{-1}) + (3 \text{ mol})(-285.8 \text{ kJ} \cdot \text{mol}^{-1})$

$- (1 \text{ mol})(-84.68 \text{ kJ} \cdot \text{mol}^{-1}) - (0)$

$= -1559.7 \text{ kJ}$

The heat of combustion of $C_2H_6(g)$ per gram is

$$\left(\frac{-1559.7 \text{ kJ}}{1 \text{ mol}} \right) \left(\frac{1 \text{ mol}}{30.07 \text{ g}} \right) = -51.87 \text{ kJ} \cdot \text{g}^{-1}$$

The combustion of $C_2H_6(g)$ produces almost twice as much heat per gram as does the combustion of $C_2H_5OH(l)$.

5-21 $\Delta H^{\circ}_{rxn} = 6 \Delta H^{\circ}_f [CO_2(g)] + 6 \Delta H^{\circ}_f [H_2O(l)] - \Delta H^{\circ}_f [C_6H_{12}O_6(s)] - 6 \Delta H^{\circ}_f [O_2(g)]$

In this case we are given ΔH°_{rxn} and must determine $\Delta H^{\circ}_f [C_6H_{12}O_6(s)]$. Using the data in Table 5-1, we have

$-2826.7 \text{ kJ} = (6 \text{ mol})(-393.5 \text{ kJ} \cdot \text{mol}^{-1}) + (6 \text{ mol})(-285.8 \text{ kJ} \cdot \text{mol}^{-1})$
$- (1 \text{ mol}) \Delta H^{\circ}_f [C_6H_{12}O_6(s)] - (0)$

Solving for $\Delta H^{\circ}_f [C_6H_{12}O_6(s)]$, we have

$(1 \text{ mol}) \Delta H^{\circ}_f [C_6H_{12}O_6(s)] = (6 \text{ mol})(-393.5 \text{ kJ} \cdot \text{mol}^{-1})$
$+ (6 \text{ mol})(-285.8 \text{ kJ} \cdot \text{mol}^{-1}) + 2826.7 \text{ kJ}$

$\Delta H^{\circ}_f [C_6H_{12}O_6(s)] = -1249.1 \text{ kJ} \cdot \text{mol}^{-1}$

5-23 (a) $\Delta H^{\circ}_{rxn} = 2 \Delta H^{\circ}_f [N(g)] - \Delta H^{\circ}_f [N_2(g)]$

$945.2 \text{ kJ} = (2 \text{ mol}) \Delta H^{\circ}_f [N(g)] - (0)$

or

$$\Delta H_f^\circ [N(g)] = \frac{945.2 \text{ kJ}}{2 \text{ mol}} = 472.6 \text{ kJ} \cdot \text{mol}^{-1}$$

Similarly,

(b) $\Delta H_f^\circ [F(g)] = \dfrac{158.0 \text{ kJ}}{2 \text{ mol}} = 79.0 \text{ kJ} \cdot \text{mol}^{-1}$

(c) $\Delta H_f^\circ [H(g)] = \dfrac{436.0 \text{ kJ}}{2 \text{ mol}} = 218.0 \text{ kJ} \cdot \text{mol}^{-1}$

(d) $\Delta H_f^\circ [Cl(g)] = \dfrac{243.4 \text{ kJ}}{2 \text{ mol}} = 121.7 \text{ kJ} \cdot \text{mol}^{-1}$

The bond strength of each diatomic molecule given is equal to the value of the corresponding ΔH_{rxn}°. Therefore, $N_2(g)$ has the greatest bond strength.

5-25 The reaction is

$$CCl_4(l) \longrightarrow CCl_4(g)$$

The heat required to vaporize one mole of CCl_4 at 25°C is equal to ΔH_{rxn}°. Thus

$$\text{heat} = \Delta H_{rxn}^\circ = \Delta H_f^\circ [CCl_4(g)] - \Delta H_f^\circ [CCl_4(l)]$$

From Table 5-1 we have

$$\Delta H_{rxn}^\circ = (1 \text{ mol})(-103.0 \text{ kJ} \cdot \text{mol}^{-1}) - (1 \text{ mol})(-135.4 \text{ kJ} \cdot \text{mol}^{-1})$$
$$= 32.4 \text{ kJ}$$

5-27 The reaction involves breaking three Cl—F bonds; thus

$$\Delta H_{rxn}^\circ \approx 3H(Cl—F)$$

Given the value of ΔH_{rxn}°, we can calculate $H(Cl—F)$.

$$514 \text{ kJ} \approx (3 \text{ mol})H(Cl—F)$$

$$H(Cl—F) \approx \frac{514 \text{ kJ}}{3 \text{ mol}} = 171 \text{ kJ} \cdot \text{mol}^{-1}$$

5-29 In the reaction

$$CCl_4(g) + 2F_2(g) \longrightarrow CF_4(g) + 2Cl_2(g)$$

we break four Cl—Cl bonds and two F—F bonds, and we make four C—F bonds and two Cl—Cl bonds. The enthalpy required to break the bonds of the reactant molecules is given by

$$H_{input} = 4H(C—Cl) + 2H(F—F)$$
$$= (4\ mol)(331\ kJ \cdot mol^{-1}) + (2\ mol)(155\ kJ \cdot mol^{-1})$$
$$= 1634\ kJ$$

The enthalpy released upon the formation of the bonds in the product molecules is

$$H_{released} = 4H(C—F) + 2H(Cl—Cl)$$
$$= (4\ mol)(439\ kJ \cdot mol^{-1}) + (2\ mol)(243\ kJ \cdot mol^{-1})$$
$$= 2242\ kJ$$

The enthalpy change of the reaction is given by

$$\Delta H^{\circ}_{rxn} = H_{input} - H_{released} = 1634\ kJ - 2242\ kJ = -608\ kJ$$

5-31 $\Delta H^{\circ}_{rxn} \approx 2H(H—H) + H(O—O) - 4H(O—H)$

The value of ΔH°_{rxn} is

$$\Delta H^{\circ}_{rxn} = 2\ \Delta H^{\circ}_f\ [H_2O(g)] = (2\ mol)(-241.8\ kJ \cdot mol^{-1}) = -483.6\ kJ.$$

Thus we can write

$$-483.6\ kJ \approx 2H(H—H) + H(O—O) - 4H(O—H)$$
$$= (2\ mol)(435\ kJ \cdot mol^{-1}) + (1\ mol)H(O—O)$$
$$- (4\ mol)(464\ kJ \cdot mol^{-1})$$
$$= 870\ kJ + (1\ mol)H(O—O) - 1856\ kJ$$
$$H(O—O) \approx +\frac{502\ kJ}{1\ mol} = +502\ kJ \cdot mol^{-1}$$

5-33 The relevant equation is

$$CH_4(g) \longrightarrow C(g) + 4H(g)$$

We have that $\Delta H^{\circ}_{rxn} \approx 4H(C—H)$ and

$$\Delta H^{\circ}_{rxn} = \Delta H^{\circ}_f\ [C(g)] + 4\Delta H^{\circ}_f\ [H(g)] - \Delta H^{\circ}_f\ [CH_4(g)]$$
$$= (1\ mol)(709\ kJ \cdot mol^{-1}) + (4\ mol)(218\ kJ \cdot mol^{-1})$$
$$- (1\ mol)(-74.86\ kJ \cdot mol^{-1})$$
$$= 1656\ kJ$$

Therefore, we have that $4H(C—H) = 1656\ kJ$, or

$$H(C—H) = \frac{1656\ kJ}{4\ mol} = 414\ kJ \cdot mol^{-1}$$

5-35 Use Equation (5-16),

$$c_P = \frac{q_P}{\Delta T}$$

In this case, $q_P = 1105$ J and $\Delta T = 12.3°C = 12.3$ K. Therefore, the total heat capacity is

$$c_P = \frac{1105 \text{ J}}{12.3 \text{ K}} = 89.84 \text{ J} \cdot \text{K}^{-1}$$

for the 36.5-g sample of C_2H_5OH. The molar heat capacity is

$$C_P = \left(\frac{89.84 \text{ J} \cdot \text{K}^{-1}}{36.5 \text{ g}}\right)\left(\frac{46.07 \text{ g}}{1 \text{ mol}}\right) = 113 \text{ J} \cdot \text{K}^{-1} \cdot \text{mol}^{-1}$$

5-37 For this problem, $\Delta T = (100.0 - 20.0)°C = 80.0°C = 80.0$ K. The heat capacity of 10.0 kg of water is

$$c_P = (75.2 \text{ J} \cdot \text{K}^{-1} \cdot \text{mol}^{-1})\left(\frac{1 \text{ mol}}{18.02 \text{ g}}\right)(10.0 \times 10^3 \text{ g})$$

$$= 4.17 \times 10^4 \text{ J} \cdot \text{K}^{-1}$$

Using Equation (5-16), we have

$$q_P = c_P \Delta T = (4.17 \times 10^4 \text{ J} \cdot \text{K}^{-1})(80.0 \text{ K}) = 3.34 \times 10^6 \text{ J}$$

5-39 The sample of copper, being at a higher temperature than the water, will give up heat to the water and so decrease in temperature. As heat is absorbed by the water, it will heat up. This process will continue until the copper and the water are at the same temperature. The key fact here is that the heat given up by the copper must be equal to the heat absorbed by the water. In an equation, we have

$$q_{P,\text{Cu}} = -q_{P,\text{H}_2\text{O}}$$

Using Equation (5-16), this equation becomes

$$c_{P,\text{Cu}} \Delta T_{\text{Cu}} = -c_{P,\text{H}_2\text{O}} \Delta T_{\text{H}_2\text{O}}$$

For the sample of copper

$$\Delta T_{\text{Cu}} = t_f - 90.0°C$$

and for the sample of water

$$\Delta T_{\text{H}_2\text{O}} = t_f - 20.0°C$$

where t_f is the final Celsius temperature. The value of $c_{P,\text{Cu}}$ is

$$c_{P,Cu} = (24.5 \text{ J} \cdot \text{K}^{-1} \cdot \text{mol}^{-1})\left(\frac{1 \text{ mol}}{63.55 \text{ g}}\right)(25.0 \text{ g})$$
$$= 9.638 \text{ J} \cdot \text{K}^{-1}$$

The value of c_{P,H_2O} is

$$c_{P,H_2O} = (75.2 \text{ J} \cdot \text{K}^{-1} \cdot \text{mol}^{-1})\left(\frac{1 \text{ mol}}{18.02 \text{ g}}\right)(100.0 \text{ g})$$
$$= 417.3 \text{ J} \cdot \text{K}^{-1}$$

Therefore

$$(9.638 \text{ J} \cdot \text{K}^{-1})(t_f - 90.0°C) = -(417.3 \text{ J} \cdot \text{K}^{-1})(t_f - 20.0°C)$$
$$9.638 \text{ J} \cdot \text{K}^{-1} t_f - 867.4 \text{ J} \cdot \text{K}^{-1} \cdot °C = -417.3 \text{ J} \cdot \text{K}^{-1} t_f + 8346.3 \text{ J} \cdot \text{K}^{-1} \cdot °C$$
$$9213.7 \text{ J} \cdot \text{K}^{-1} \cdot °C = 426.9 \text{ J} \cdot \text{K}^{-1} t_f$$

Solving for t_f

$$t_f = \frac{9213.7 \text{ J} \cdot \text{K}^{-1} \cdot °C}{426.9 \text{ J} \cdot \text{K}^{-1}} = 21.6°C$$

5-41 As in Problem 5-39, the heat balance equation is

$$c_{P,Al} \Delta T_{Al} = -c_{P,Cu} \Delta T_{Cu}$$

For the aluminum

$$c_{P,Al} = (24.2 \text{ J} \cdot \text{K}^{-1} \cdot \text{mol}^{-1})(1.00 \text{ kg})\left(\frac{10^3 \text{ g}}{1 \text{ kg}}\right)\left(\frac{1 \text{ mol}}{26.98 \text{ g}}\right)$$
$$= 897 \text{ J} \cdot \text{K}^{-1} = 897 \text{ J} \cdot °C^{-1}$$
$$\Delta T_{Al} = t_f - 500°C$$

For the copper

$$c_{P,Cu} = (24.5 \text{ J} \cdot \text{K}^{-1} \cdot \text{mol}^{-1})(1.00 \text{ kg})\left(\frac{10^3 \text{ g}}{1 \text{ kg}}\right)\left(\frac{1 \text{ mol}}{63.55 \text{ g}}\right)$$
$$= 386 \text{ J} \cdot \text{K}^{-1} = 386 \text{ J} \cdot °C^{-1}$$
$$\Delta T_{Cu} = t_f - 10°C$$

Putting all this into the heat balance equation gives

$$(897 \text{ J} \cdot °C^{-1})(t_f - 500°C) = -(386 \text{ J} \cdot °C^{-1})(t_f - 10°C)$$

or

$$1283 \, t_f = 4.524 \times 10^5 °C$$

or

$$t_f = 353\,^\circ\text{C}$$

5-43   The heat evolved by the reaction is given by Equation (5-19):

$$\Delta H_{rxn} = -c_{P,calorimeter}\,\Delta T$$
$$= -(480\ \text{J}\cdot\text{K}^{-1})(2.34\ \text{K}) = -1123\ \text{J}$$

This amount of heat is evolved when 0.100 L of 0.200 M solutions react. The number of moles that react is given by

$$n = MV = (0.200\ \text{mol}\cdot\text{L}^{-1})(0.100\ \text{L}) = 0.0200\ \text{moles}$$

The heat of reaction for one mole of reactants is

$$\Delta H^\circ_{rxn} = \frac{-1123\ \text{J}}{0.0200\ \text{mol}} = -56.2\ \text{kJ}\cdot\text{mol}^{-1}$$

5-45   The value of ΔH_{rxn} is

$$\Delta H_{rxn} = -(4.92\ \text{kJ}\cdot\text{K}^{-1})(0.300\ \text{K}) = -1.48\ \text{kJ}$$

This is the heat evolved when 1.00 g of NH_4NO_3 reacts. The heat of reaction for 1.00 kg of NH_4NO_3 reacting is

$$\Delta H_{rxn} = \left(\frac{-1.48\ \text{kJ}}{1.00\ \text{g}}\right)(1.00\times10^3\ \text{g}) = -1.48\times10^3\ \text{kJ}$$

5-47   The temperature of the calorimeter *decreases,* and so heat is absorbed in the process of dissolving KCl in water. The heat absorbed is

$$\Delta H_{rxn} = -(4.51\ \text{kJ}\cdot\text{K}^{-1})(-0.256\ \text{K}) = +1.155\ \text{kJ}$$

A 5.00-g sample of KCl corresponds to

$$(5.00\ \text{g})\left(\frac{1\ \text{mol}}{74.55\ \text{g}}\right) = 0.06707\ \text{mol KCl}$$

The molar heat of solution of KCl in H_2O is

$$\Delta H^\circ_{soln} = \frac{1.155\ \text{kJ}}{0.06707\ \text{mol}} = 17.2\ \text{kJ}\cdot\text{mol}^{-1}$$

5-49 $\Delta H_{rxn} = -(32.7\ \text{kJ}\cdot\text{K}^{-1})(42.5\ \text{K}) = -1390\ \text{kJ}$

$$\Delta H^\circ_{comb} = \frac{-1390\ \text{kJ}}{30.0\ \text{g}} = -46.3\ \text{kJ}\cdot\text{g}^{-1}$$
$$= (-46.3\ \text{kJ}\cdot\text{g}^{-1})\left(\frac{44.09\ \text{g}}{1\ \text{mol}}\right) = -2040\ \text{kJ}\cdot\text{mol}^{-1}$$

5-51 $\Delta H_{rxn}^{\circ} = -(8.75 \text{ kJ} \cdot \text{K}^{-1})(0.780 \text{ K}) = -6.825 \text{ kJ}$

$$\Delta H_{comb}^{\circ} = \left(\frac{-6.825 \text{ kJ}}{2.50 \text{ g}}\right)\left(\frac{90.04 \text{ g}}{1 \text{ mol}}\right) = -246 \text{ kJ} \cdot \text{mol}^{-1}$$

The equation for the combustion of oxalic acid is

$$H_2C_2O_4(s) + \frac{1}{2}O_2(g) \longrightarrow 2CO_2(g) + H_2O(l)$$

The value of ΔH_{rxn}° for the combustion of oxalic acid is given by

$$\Delta H_{rxn}^{\circ} = 2 \, \Delta H_f^{\circ} [CO_2(g)] + \Delta H_f^{\circ} [H_2O(l)] - \Delta H_f^{\circ} [H_2C_2O_4(s)] - \frac{1}{2}\Delta H_f^{\circ} [O_2(g)]$$

Using the above value for ΔH_{rxn}° and the data in Table 5-1, we have

$$
\begin{aligned}
-246 \text{ kJ} &= (2 \text{ mol})(-393.5 \text{ kJ} \cdot \text{mol}^{-1}) + (1 \text{ mol})(-285.8 \text{ kJ} \cdot \text{mol}^{-1}) \\
&\quad - (1 \text{ mol}) \, \Delta H_f^{\circ} [H_2C_2O_4(s)] - (\tfrac{1}{2} \text{ mol})(0) \\
&= -1072.8 \text{ kJ} - (1 \text{ mol}) \, \Delta H_f^{\circ} [H_2C_2O_4(s)]
\end{aligned}
$$

Solving for $\Delta H_f^{\circ} [H_2C_2O_4(s)]$, we get

$$\Delta H_f^{\circ} [H_2C_2O_4(s)] = -827 \text{ kJ} \cdot \text{mol}^{-1}$$

5-53 The heat required to raise the temperature of 1.0 L of water by 37°C is

$$\Delta H = (75.2 \text{ J} \cdot \text{K}^{-1} \cdot \text{mol}^{-1})\left(\frac{1 \text{ mol}}{18.02 \text{ g}}\right)(1.00 \text{ g} \cdot \text{mL}^{-1})(1000 \text{ mL})(37 \text{ K})$$

$$= 150 \text{ kJ}$$

Given that one gram of body fat yields 39 kJ, we see that

$$\frac{150 \text{ kJ}}{39 \text{ kJ} \cdot \text{g}^{-1}} = 3.8 \text{ g}$$

of body fat must be burned. The number of moles of ice required to produce the same effect is

$$150 \text{ kJ} = (6.0 \text{ kJ} \cdot \text{mol}^{-1})n + (75.2 \text{ J} \cdot \text{K}^{-1} \cdot \text{mol}^{-1})(37 \text{ K})n$$

$$= (8.8 \text{ kJ} \cdot \text{mol}^{-1})n$$

$$n = \frac{150 \text{ kJ}}{8.8 \text{ kJ} \cdot \text{mol}^{-1}} = 17 \text{ mol}$$

The mass of ice required is

$$\text{mass of ice} = (17 \text{ mol})\left(\frac{18.02 \text{ g}}{1 \text{ mol}}\right) = 310 \text{ g}$$

5-55 Let's set up the following table for the proposed formula of the compound of thallium and chlorine.

Proposed formula	Value of N in Dulong and Petit's rule	Predicted value of $C_P/\text{J} \cdot \text{K}^{-1} \cdot \text{mol}^{-1}$	Observed value of C_P from specific heat and proposed formula
TlCl	2	50	$(0.208 \, \text{J} \cdot \text{K}^{-1} \cdot \text{g}^{-1})\left(\dfrac{239.9 \, \text{g}}{1 \, \text{mol}}\right)$ $= 49.9 \, \text{J} \cdot \text{K}^{-1} \cdot \text{mol}^{-1}$
TlCl$_2$	3	75	$(0.208 \, \text{J} \cdot \text{K}^{-1} \cdot \text{g}^{-1})\left(\dfrac{275.3 \, \text{g}}{1 \, \text{mol}}\right)$ $= 57.3 \, \text{J} \cdot \text{K}^{-1} \cdot \text{mol}^{-1}$
TlCl$_3$	4	100	$(0.208 \, \text{J} \cdot \text{K}^{-1} \cdot \text{g}^{-1})\left(\dfrac{310.8 \, \text{g}}{1 \, \text{mol}}\right)$ $= 64.6 \, \text{J} \cdot \text{K}^{-1} \cdot \text{mol}^{-1}$

Because of the agreement between the predicted and observed values of C_P, we conclude that the formula of the compound is TlCl.

5-57 The molar heat capacity of stilleite, using Dulong and Petit's Rule, is

$$C_P = (2)(25 \, \text{J} \cdot \text{K}^{-1} \cdot \text{mol}^{-1}) = 50 \, \text{J} \cdot \text{K}^{-1} \cdot \text{mol}^{-1}$$

if stilleite is ZnSe. The observed molar heat capacity of stilleite is

$$C_P = (0.348 \, \text{J} \cdot \text{K}^{-1} \cdot \text{g}^{-1})\left(\frac{144.34 \, \text{g}}{1 \, \text{mol}}\right) = 50.2 \, \text{J} \cdot \text{K}^{-1} \cdot \text{mol}^{-1}$$

if stilleite is ZnSe. Thus we determine the formula of stilleite to be ZnSe.

5-59 We assume that the energy consumed in riding is due to the combustion of body fat. Given that one gram of body fat yields 39 kJ, we have

$$1 \, \text{lb} = 454 \, \text{g}$$

$$(39 \, \text{kJ} \cdot \text{g}^{-1})(454 \, \text{g}) = 18{,}000 \, \text{kJ} = (2000 \, \text{kJ} \cdot \text{hr}^{-1})(\text{number of hours})$$

$$\text{number of hours of riding} = \frac{18000 \, \text{kJ}}{2000 \, \text{kJ} \cdot \text{hr}^{-1}} = 9.0 \, \text{hr}$$

The distance traveled in 9.0 hr is

$$\text{distance} = (13 \, \text{mi} \cdot \text{hr}^{-1})(9.0 \, \text{hr}) = 120 \, \text{mi}$$

5-61 The relation between ΔH°_{rxn} and ΔU°_{rxn} is given by Equation (5-9):

$$\Delta H^\circ_{rxn} = \Delta U^\circ_{rxn} + P\,\Delta V$$

The term $P\,\Delta V$ will have units of L·atm. An easy way to convert L·atm to joules is to use the fact that the values of the molar gas constant are $8.314\,J\cdot mol^{-1}\cdot K^{-1}$ and $0.0821\,L\cdot atm\cdot mol^{-1}\cdot K^{-1}$. Thus we have the unit conversion factor

$$1 = \frac{8.314\,J\cdot mol^{-1}\cdot K^{-1}}{0.0821\,L\cdot atm\cdot mol^{-1}\cdot K^{-1}} = \frac{101.3\,J}{1.00\,L\cdot atm}$$

(a) $\Delta U^\circ_{rxn} = \Delta H^\circ_{rxn} - P\,\Delta V$

$$= (-572\,kJ) - (1.00\,atm)(-67.2\,L)\left(\frac{101.3\,J}{1.00\,L\cdot atm}\right)$$

$$= -565\,kJ$$

(b) $\Delta U^\circ_{rxn} = \Delta H^\circ_{rxn} - P\,\Delta V$

$$= (-545\,kJ) - (1.00\,atm)(-44.8\,L)\left(\frac{101.3\,J}{1.00\,L\cdot atm}\right)$$

$$= -540\,kJ$$

(c) $\Delta U^\circ_{rxn} = \Delta H^\circ_{rxn} - P\,\Delta V$
$$= (-180\,kJ) - (1.00\,atm)(0\,L)$$
$$= -180\,kJ$$

Notice that $\Delta U^\circ_{rxn} \approx \Delta H^\circ_{rxn}$ in each case.

5-63 $\Delta H^\circ_{rxn} = 3\,\Delta H^\circ_f\,[N_2(g)] + 4\,\Delta H^\circ_f\,[H_2O(g)] - 2\,\Delta H^\circ_f\,[N_2H_4(l)] - \Delta H^\circ_f\,[N_2O_4(l)]$
$$= (3\,mol)(0\,kJ\cdot mol^{-1}) + (4\,mol)(-241.8\,kJ\cdot mol^{-1})$$
$$- (2\,mol)(50.6\,kJ\cdot mol^{-1}) - (1\,mol)(-19.5\,kJ\cdot mol^{-1})$$
$$= -1049\,kJ$$

5-65 In the reaction

We are breaking one C—N bond, one C—H bond, and one C—C bond, and we are forming one N—H bond and one C=C bond. The enthalpy change of the reaction is given by

$$\Delta H^\circ_{rxn} = H(C—N) + H(C—H) + H(C—C) - H(N—H) - H(C=C)$$

Using the data given in Table 5-2, we write

$$\Delta H^\circ_{rxn} = 293\,kJ + 414\,kJ + 347\,kJ - 390\,kJ - 615\,kJ$$
$$= 49\,kJ$$

E   ANSWERS TO THE SELF-TEST

1   energy is neither created nor destroyed but is transformed from one form to another; energy is conserved

2   heat . . . work

3   force through a distance

4   positive

5   negative

6   difference in temperature

7   the energy transferred as heat plus the energy transferred as work, $\Delta U_{rxn} = q + w$

8   heat evolved or absorbed, q_V

9 $U + PV$

10   heat evolved or absorbed, q_P

11   pressure

12   false

13   exothermic

14   endothermic

15   exo-

16   true

17   pressure

18 ΔU_{rxn}

19   the sum of the ΔH_{rxn}° values for the two equations

20   See Section 5-3.

21   the energy that is evolved or absorbed as heat when one mole of the substance is formed directly from its elements in their standard forms at one atm and 25°C

22   0 kJ·mol^{-1}

23 $\Delta H_f^{\circ}\,[CO_2(g)] + 2\Delta H_f^{\circ}\,[H_2O(g)] - \Delta H_f^{\circ}\,[CH_4(g)] - 2\,\Delta H_f^{\circ}\,[O_2(g)]$

24   true

25   endothermic

26   true (See Example 5-3.)

27   molar heat capacity

28   more

29   lower

30   The value of the heat capacity of a substance depends on its mass.

31   heat evolved or absorbed in a process by measuring ΔT

32   false

33   All the heat that is evolved or absorbed by the reaction is absorbed or supplied by the calorimeter.

34   temperature

35   heat capacity . . . temperature

36   exo-

37   bomb

38   true

39   The heat of combustion is the quantity of heat that is evolved when the substance burns

40   false (assuming that the temperatures are equal)

THE QUANTUM THEORY AND ATOMIC STRUCTURE

A   OUTLINE OF CHAPTER 6

6-1   First ionization energy is one of many periodic properties of the elements.

The ionization energy is the minimum energy required to remove an electron from an atom or ion.

A plot of the first ionization energy I_1 against atomic number (Figure 6-1) displays the periodic nature of I_1.

I_1 increases across each row of the periodic table (Figure 6-2).

The electronic structure of the noble gases is relatively stable.

6-2   The values of successive ionization energies suggest a shell structure.

Table 6-1 lists successive ionization energies of the elements hydrogen through argon.

The inner-core electronic structure of an atom is that of the preceding noble gas.

A plot of the ionization energies versus number of electrons removed suggests a shell structure.

A Lewis electron-dot formula (Table 6-2) is a representation of an atom with the noble-gas-like inner electrons represented by the symbol of the element and the outer electrons represented by dots around the symbol.

The outer electrons are also called valence electrons.

6-3   The regions of the electromagnetic spectrum are characterized by radiation of different wavelengths.

The wavelength, λ, and frequency, v, of electromagnetic radiation are related by $\lambda v = c$ [Equation (6-1)], where c is the speed of light, 3.00×10^8 m·s^{-1}.

The complete range of wavelengths or frequencies of electromagnetic radiation is called the electromagnetic spectrum.

6-4   The spectra emitted by atoms are line spectra.

Electromagnetic radiation can be separated into its components.

The visible region consists of electromagnetic radiation in the range 400 nm to 700 nm.

A continuous spectrum consists of all wavelengths.

A line spectrum consists of only certain wavelengths.

An atomic spectrum is a line spectrum. Each type of atom has a characteristic atomic spectrum (Figure 6-5).

Atomic spectra can be used to determine the atomic composition of a substance.

6-5   Electromagnetic radiation can be viewed as a beam of photons.

Blackbody radiation is continuous radiation emitted by solid bodies when they are heated to high temperatures.

Planck assumed that radiation could be emitted only in energy packets called quanta. The energy associated with these quanta is related to the frequency by $E = h\nu$ [Equation (6-2)].

Planck's constant, h, is equal to 6.626×10^{-34} J·s.

The photoelectric effect is the ejection of electrons from the surface of a metal when it is irradiated with ultraviolet radiation.

The threshold frequency, ν_0, of a metal is the minimum frequency required to eject electrons from the metal.

Each metal has a characteristic value of ν_0. The graph of the kinetic energy of the ejected electrons versus the frequency of the radiation is a straight line when $\nu > \nu_0$ (Figure 6-7).

Einstein postulated that the radiation consists of little packets of energy, $E = h\nu$.

The packets of energy of electromagnetic radiation are called photons.

6-6   Einstein applied conservation of energy to the photoelectric effect.

The work function of a metal is the minimum energy required to remove an electron from the surface of the metal.

The work function is denoted by Φ.

The work function is related to ν_0 by $\Phi = h\nu_0$ [Equation (6-3)].

The kinetic energy of the ejected electrons is given by $h\nu - \Phi$ [Equation (6-4)].

In the quantum theory, only certain discrete values of the energy are allowed.

6-7   De Broglie was the first to propose that matter has wavelike properties.

The wave-particle duality of light suggested to de Broglie that matter may appear wavelike.

De Broglie proposed that a moving mass has a wavelength associated with it.

The wavelength of a particle of mass m and speed v is given by $\lambda = h/mv$ [Equation (6-5)].

6-8   The electron microscope utilizes the wavelike properties of electrons.

A beam of electrons can behave similarly to a beam of X-rays (Figure 6-10).

6-9   The energy of the electron in a hydrogen atom is quantized.

Bohr postulated that the electron in a hydrogen atom is restricted to only certain circular orbits about the nucleus.

The radius, r, is subject to the quantum condition $2\pi r = n\lambda$, where $n = 1, 2, 3 \ldots$ [Equation (6-6)].

Bohr showed that the energies of the electron in a hydrogen atom are given by

$$E_n = \frac{-2.18 \times 10^{-18}\,J}{n^2} \qquad n = 1, 2, 3, \ldots \qquad (6\text{-}7)$$

The energy of the electron is quantized or restricted to only certain values.

A stationary state is an allowed energy state.

The ground state is the stationary state of lowest energy, $n = 1$.

An excited state is a stationary state of higher energy than the ground state, $n = 2, 3, \ldots$.

The energy states of the electron in a hydrogen atom are shown in Figure 6-13.

6-10   Atoms emit or absorb electromagnetic radiation when they undergo transitions from one stationary state to another.

When the electron in a hydrogen atom goes from a higher energy state to the ground state, the frequency of the emitted radiation is given by $\Delta E = E_n - E_1 = h\nu_{n\to 1}$ or

$$\nu_{n\to 1} = (3.29 \times 10^{15}\,s^{-1})\left(\frac{1}{1^2} - \frac{1}{n^2}\right) \qquad n = 2, 3, 4, \ldots \qquad (6\text{-}11)$$

These frequencies correspond to the series of lines in the hydrogen atom emission spectrum called the Lyman series (Table 6-4).

When the electron goes from a higher energy state to the $n = 2$ state, the frequency of the emitted radiation is given by $\Delta E = E_n - E_2 = h\nu_{n\to 2}$ or

$$\nu_{n\to 2} = (3.29 \times 10^{15}\,s^{-1})\left(\frac{1}{2^2} - \frac{1}{n^2}\right) \qquad n = 3, 4, 5, \ldots \qquad (6\text{-}12)$$

These frequencies correspond to the Balmer series in the hydrogen atom emission spectrum (Figure 6-14).

An emission spectrum occurs when excited atoms return to the ground state.

An absorption spectrum occurs when atoms in the ground state absorb energy and are excited to higher energy states (Figure 6-15).

6-11   The Bohr theory is not consistent with the Heisenberg uncertainty principle.

The Bohr theory cannot be extended to other atoms.

The Heisenberg uncertainty principle states that it is not possible to measure accurately both the position and the momentum of a particle simultaneously.

The uncertainty in the position, Δx, and the momentum, Δp, are related by $(\Delta x)(\Delta p) \approx h$ [Equation (6-15)].

The central equation of the quantum theory is the Schrödinger equation.

The Schrödinger equation is consistent with the wave nature of particles and the Heisenberg uncertainty principle.

Solution of the Schrödinger equation for a hydrogen atom gives the same set of energy levels as that predicted by the Bohr theory.

The electron in the hydrogen atom is not restricted to certain sharp orbits.

The Schrödinger equation also provides an associated set of functions called wave functions (orbitals), ψ.

The value of the square of the wave function is a probability density, $\psi^2(x, y, z)$.

The electron cannot be located precisely, but can be assigned only a probability of being located in a certain region.

The principal quantum number n specifies the energy of the electron in a hydrogen atom.

The quantum numbers n, l, and m_l are needed to specify the wave functions.

The ground state of a hydrogen atom is described by ψ_{1s}, where $n = 1$ (Figure 6-19).

The ψ_{1s}, or $1s$, orbital is spherically symmetric.

The $1s$ orbital can be represented by a stippled diagram or a 99% probability sphere as shown in Figure 6-20.

6-12   The shape of an orbital depends on the value of the azimuthal quantum number.

The azimuthal quantum number l is restricted to the values $l = 0, 1, \ldots, n - 1$.

s, p, d, and f orbitals are those for which $l = 0, 1, 2,$ and 3, respectively.

Orbitals are usually designated by the values of n and l (Table 6-5).

All s orbitals are spherically symmetric (Figure 6-23).

The $2p$ orbitals are cylindrically symmetric.

The $2p$ orbitals can be represented by a stippled diagram or a 99% probability surface as shown in Figure 6-24.

A surface on which the probability density is zero is a nodal surface.

6-13   The spatial orientation of an orbital depends on the value of the magnetic quantum number.

The magnetic quantum number m_l is restricted to the values $m_l = -l, -l + 1, \ldots, -1, 0, 1, 2, \ldots, l$.

The allowed values of the quantum numbers l and m_l for $n = 1$ to $n = 4$ are given in Table 6-6.

The three $2p$ orbitals are designated p_x, p_y, and p_z; the subscript indicates the axis along which the orbital is directed (Figure 6-25).

6-14   An electron has an intrinsic spin.

The spin quantum number m_s is restricted to the values $m_s = +\frac{1}{2}$ or $-\frac{1}{2}$.

The allowed combinations of the four quantum numbers for $n = 1$ to $n = 3$ are given in Table 6-7.

6-15 The energy states of atoms with two or more electrons depend on the values of both n and l.

Multielectron atoms involve electron-electron interactions.

The relative energies of the orbitals of atoms with two or more electrons are given in Figures 6-27 and 6-28.

6-16 The Pauli exclusion principle states that no two electrons in the same atom can have the same set of four quantum numbers.

The Pauli exclusion principle is used to assign electrons to orbitals.

The sets of allowed quantum numbers are given in Table 6-8.

Shells are the levels designated by n.

Subshells are the groups of orbitals designated by l within the shells.

6-17 Electron configurations designate the occupancy of electrons in atomic orbitals.

The assignment of electrons to orbitals of lowest energies give the ground-state electron configuration of an atom or an ion.

The value of the first ionization energy of an atom depends on the electron configuration of the atom.

6-18 Hund's rule is used to predict ground-state electron configurations.

Hund's rule states that for any set of orbitals of the same energy, the ground-state electron configuration is obtained by placing the electrons into different orbitals of this set with parallel spins until each of the orbitals has one electron before any electrons are paired.

Hund's rule is used to predict the ground-state electron configuration of an atom with a partially filled subshell.

6-19 Elements in the same column of the periodic table have similar outer electron configurations.

The electron configurations of atoms are correlated to their positions in the periodic table (Figure 6-30).

The outer electrons are often called valence electrons.

The number at the top of each column in the periodic table is equal to the number of valence electrons.

The number of the row in the periodic table is equal to the principal quantum number of the outer s electrons.

The alkali metals have the electron configuration [noble gas]ns^1.

The alkaline earth metals have the electron configuration [noble gas]ns^2.

6-20 The occupied orbitals of highest energy are d orbitals for transition metals and f orbitals for lanthanides and actinides.

In the first set of transition metals the five $3d$ orbitals are filled sequentially.

The $3d$ transition metal series consists of the elements Sc through Zn (Figure 6-31).

The 4d transition metal series consists of the elements Y through Cd (Figure 6-31).

Half-filled and completely filled d subshells are relatively stable.

The inner transition metals involve the filling of f orbitals.

The lanthanides La through Yb involve the filling of the 4f orbitals (Figure 6-31).

The lanthanides have similar chemical properties.

The 4f electrons tend to lie in the interior of the atom and have little effect on chemical activity.

The 5d transition metals follow the lanthanides and involve the filling of the 5d orbitals (Figure 6-31).

The actinide series, Ac through No, involves the filling of the 5f orbitals (Figure 6-31).

The transuranium elements are all radioactive.

6-21   Atomic radius is another periodic property.

Atomic radii determined by X-ray analysis of crystal structures are called crystallographic radii (Figure 6-34).

Atomic radii usually decrease from left to right across the periodic table.

Atomic radii increase going down a column of the periodic table (Figure 6-35).

First ionization energies decrease going down a column of the periodic table.

___

SELF-TEST

1   The first-ionization energy of an atom is always greater than the second ionization energy of that atom. *True/False*

2   The atoms of which group in the periodic table have the largest first ionization energies for a given row? _____

3   A small first ionization energy indicates a stable electronic structure. *True/False*

4   The alkali metals have relatively *(small, large)* values of the first ionization energy.

5   The chemically active electrons that are most responsible for the chemical activity of an atom are located _____.

6   A plot of successive ionization energies versus number of electrons removed suggests that the electrons in atoms are arranged in shells. *True/False*

7   A lithium atom consists of a _____-like inner shell and _____.

8   The Lewis dot formula of a lithium atom is _____.

9 The wavelength and frequency of electromagnetic radiation are related by the equation _____ .

10 The speed of light is denoted by the symbol _____ and has the value _____ $m \cdot s^{-1}$.

11 The spectrum of white light is an example of a *(continuous, line)* spectrum.

12 A line spectrum consists of _____ .

13 An atomic spectrum is a *(continuous, line)* spectrum.

14 The atomic spectrum of an element is unique to that element. *True/False*

15 Blackbody radiation is radiation that _____ .

16 Planck assumed that radiation from a blackbody could be emitted _____ _____ .

17 The energy associated with quanta of electromagnetic radiation is given by the equation $E =$ _____ where _____ _____ .

18 Planck's constant is denoted by _____ and is equal to _____ .

19 The photoelectric effect is the _____ _____ .

20 The threshold frequency, v_0, of a metal is the _____ _____ .

21 Electrons are ejected from the surface of a metal when irradiated with radiation of any frequency. *True/False*

22 In order to explain the photoelectric effect, Einstein proposed that the incident radiation _____ .

23 The work function of a metal is _____ _____ .

24 The plot of the kinetic energy of the ejected electrons versus the frequency of the incident radiation is a straight line when $v > v_0$. *True/False*

25 A photon is a quantum of _____ .

26 A moving particle may behave like a wave. *True/False*

27 The de Broglie wavelength of a moving particle is given by the expression $\lambda =$ _____ where _____.

28 The de Broglie wavelength of a particle is significant when the mass of the particle is _____.

29 The _____ property of electrons is exploited in electron microscopes.

30 The Bohr theory for an electron in a hydrogen atom predicts that energies the electron may have are restricted to discrete values. *True/False*

31 The energies of the electron in a hydrogen atom are given by $E_n =$ _____ where _____.

32 The interaction energy between an electron and a proton is zero when _____.

33 A negative energy state is *(more, less)* stable relative to a zero energy state.

34 The ground state in the quantum theory is _____.

35 Excited states in the quantum theory are _____.

36 When an atom undergoes a transition from a higher energy state to a lower energy state, the atom *(emits, absorbs)* electromagnetic radiation.

37 When the electron in a hydrogen atom goes from the $n = 3$ state to the $n = 1$ state, energy is *(emitted, absorbed)* and the value of the energy is given by $\Delta E =$ _____.

38 The atomic absorption spectrum of an element is due to _____.

39 The Bohr theory cannot be extended to other atoms. *True/False*

40 The Heisenberg uncertainty principle states that _____.

41 The Heisenberg uncertainty principle is important mainly for small particles. *True/False*

42 The Bohr theory for the hydrogen atom is not consistent with the Heisenberg uncertainty principle. *True/False*

43 The central equation of the quantum theory is the _____ _____.

44 Solutions of the Schrödinger equation for a hydrogen atom give the same set of values of the energy as does the Bohr theory. *True/False*

45 The Schrödinger equation can be applied to atoms other than hydrogen. *True/False*

46 The Schrödinger equation restricts the electron in a hydrogen atom to certain sharp orbits. *True/False*

47 Wave functions are a set of functions that are solutions of _____ _____.

48 The value of the square of a wave function is _____.

49 The electron can be assigned a precise location by ψ^2. *True/False*

50 The principal quantum number n determines the _____ of the electron in a hydrogen atom.

51 The orbital that the electron occupies in the ground state of the hydrogen atom is designated _____.

52 The wave function that describes the ground state of a hydrogen atom depends only on the _____.

53 The value of ψ^2_{1s} *(increases, decreases)* with the distance of the electron from the nucleus.

54 The orbital ψ^2_{1s} is _____ symmetric.

55 A stippled diagram of an orbital represents _____ _____.

56 The azimuthal quantum number _____ determines _____ _____ of an orbital.

57 The azimuthal quantum number, l, may have the values _____ when $n = 2$.

58 The $2s$ orbital is _____ symmetric.

59 A $2p$ orbital is _____ symmetric.

60 For a $2p$ orbital, n equals _____ and l equals _____.

61 When $n = 3$ and $l = 2$, the orbital is designated _____.

62 The magnetic quantum number _____ determines _____ _____ of an orbital.

63 The magnetic quantum number may have the values _____ when $n = 2$ and $l = 1$.

64 A $2p$ hydrogen atomic orbital for which $m_l = 0$ and one for which $m_l = 1$ differ in energy. *True/False*

65 The three $2p$ orbitals are directed along _____.

66 The spin quantum number m_s designates _____.

67 The values of m_s are _____.

68 The electronic energy of the hydrogen atom depends on the quantum numbers n and l. *True/False*

69 The electronic energy of multielectron atoms depends on the three quantum numbers, n, l, and m_l. *True/False*

70 The $3p$ orbitals and the $3d$ orbitals of an iron atom have the same energy. *True/False*

71 The Pauli exclusion principle states that _____ _____.

72 The term "spin up" refers to electrons with _____.

73 The set of $2p$ orbitals may hold a maximum of _____ electrons.

74 The $1s$ orbital may hold two electrons with parallel spins. *True/False*

75 The L shell is the level for which n equals _____.

76 The L shell can contain a maximum of _____ electrons.

77 The L shell contains _____ subshells.

78 The symbol $2p^5$ signifies that _____.

79 The symbol _____ signifies that there are six electrons in the $3d$ orbitals.

80 In neutral atoms the $4s$ orbital is of higher energy than the $3d$ orbital. *True/False*

81 The $5d$ orbital is of higher energy than the $4f$ orbital in neutral atoms. *True/False*

82 Hund's rule states that _____

_____ .

83 The outer electron configuration of the ground state of the Group 2 metals is

_____ .

84 The outer electron configuration of the ground state of the halogens is

_____ .

85 The first member of each row of the periodic table is an _____ metal.

86 The last member of each row of the periodic table is a _____ .

87 The transition metals occur because of the sequential filling of the _____ orbitals.

88 A half-filled subshell has an extra stability compared to other partially filled subshells. *True/False*

89 The outer electron configurations of the $3d$ transition metals are

_____ .

90 The lanthanides occur because of the sequential filling of the _____ orbitals.

91 The rare earths are difficult to separate because _____

_____ .

92 The actinide series occurs because of the sequential filling of the _____ _____ orbitals.

93 The actinides are all radioactive. *True/False*

94 Atomic radii can be determined from _____

_____ .

95 Atomic radii *(increase, decrease)* in going from left to right across a row in the periodic table.

96 Atomic radii *(increase, decrease)* in going down a column in the periodic table.

97   The Group _____ elements have the largest atomic radius in a row of the periodic table.

98   The first ionization energy decreases as the radius increases because

_____ .

99   Sodium has a *(larger, smaller)* first ionization energy than potassium.

CALCULATIONS YOU SHOULD KNOW HOW TO DO

1   Convert between the frequency and wavelength of electromagnetic radiation by using Equation (6-1), $\lambda v = c$. See Example 6-1 and Problems 6-9 and 6-10.

2   Calculate the energy associated with electromagnetic radiation by using Equation (6-2), $E = hv$. See Example 6-2.
     The energy can be calculated directly in terms of the wavelength λ by solving Equation (6-1) for v and then substituting the result into Equation (6-2). The result is

$$E = \frac{hc}{\lambda}$$

See Problems 6-11 through 6-14.

3   Calculate the number of photons in a given amount of electromagnetic radiation of a specified frequency or wavelength. To do this type of problem, first calculate the energy of one photon by using Equation (6-1) and then divide this result into the energy of the electromagnetic radiation. See Problems 6-13 and 6-14.

4   Calculate the work function or the threshold frequency of a metal by using Equation (6-3), $\Phi = hv_0$. See Example 6-3 and Problems 6-15 and 6-16.

5   Calculate the kinetic energy of electrons ejected from a metal by using Equation (6-4), K.E. $= hv - \Phi$. See Example 6-4 and Problems 6-17 and 6-18.

6   Calculate the de Broglie wavelengths of moving bodies by using Equation (6-5),

$$\lambda = \frac{h}{mv}$$

See Example 6-5 and Problems 6-19 through 6-22.

7   Calculate the frequencies and wavelengths in the hydrogen atomic spectrum. The starting point for calculations like these is Equation (6-7), which gives the energy states of the electron in a hydrogen atom.

$$E_n = -\frac{2.18 \times 10^{-18}\,\text{J}}{n^2} \qquad n = 1, 2, 3, \ldots \qquad (6\text{-}7)$$

Using Equation (6-7), the energy and the frequency associated with a transition from state n to state m are obtained by using conservation of energy. For a transition from state n to state m, we write

$$\nu_{n \rightarrow m} = \frac{E_m - E_n}{h} \qquad m > n \qquad \text{(absorption)}$$

$$\nu_{m \rightarrow n} = \frac{E_m - E_n}{h} \qquad m > n \qquad \text{(emission)}$$

See Examples 6-6 and 6-7 and Problems 6-23 through 6-28.

8   Know the mnemonic for the order of the orbital energies in neutral gas atoms

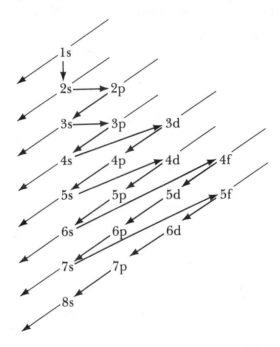

9   Determine the allowed sets of quantum numbers (n, l, m_l, m_s). See Example 6-11 and Problems 6-29 through 6-40.

10   Assign electrons to orbitals in atoms and write out ground-state electron configurations. See Problems 6-41 through 6-46.

11   Correlate ground-state electron configurations and the periodic table. See Problems 6-47 through 6-50.

12   Use Hund's rule to write ground-state electron configurations. See Example 6-13 and Problems 6-51 and 6-52.

13   Write the ground-state electron configurations of ions. See Example 6-12 and Problems 6-55 through 6-60.

14   Write excited-state electron configurations. See Example 6-14 and Problems 6-61 and 6-62.

15 Use the periodic table to predict relative values of atomic and ionic radii. See Problems 6-63 through 6-66.

16 Use the periodic table to predict relative values of first ionization energies. See Problems 6-67 and 6-68.

D SOLUTIONS TO THE ODD-NUMBERED PROBLEMS

6-1 Of the four species listed, Be^+ has the largest ionization energy because it is positively charged. The ionization energies of the remaining three species decrease in the order He, Ne, and Kr because ionization energies decrease with increasing atomic size within a family. The farther away an electron is from the nucleus, the easier it is to remove the electron from the atom. Thus we write Kr, Ne, He, and Be^+.

6-3 Using the data in Table 6-1, we have for a boron atom

n	$I_n/\text{MJ} \cdot \text{mol}^{-1}$	$\log[I_n/\text{MJ} \cdot \text{mol}^{-1}]$
1	0.80	-0.097
2	2.42	0.384
3	3.66	0.563
4	25.02	1.400
5	32.82	1.516

The plot on page 135 suggests that the five electrons are arranged in two shells, with two electrons in an inner, tightly held shell and three in an outer shell.

6-5 The alkali metals are in Group 1 and have one outer electron. The Lewis electron-dot formulas of the alkali metals are

$$\text{Li} \cdot \quad \text{Na} \cdot \quad \text{K} \cdot \quad \text{Rb} \cdot \quad \text{Cs} \cdot \quad \text{Fr} \cdot$$

The halogens are in Group 7 and have seven outer electrons. The electron-dot formulas of the halogen atoms are

$$:\!\overset{..}{\underset{..}{F}}\!\cdot \quad :\!\overset{..}{\underset{..}{Cl}}\!\cdot \quad :\!\overset{..}{\underset{..}{Br}}\!\cdot \quad :\!\overset{..}{\underset{..}{I}}\!\cdot \quad :\!\overset{..}{\underset{..}{At}}\!\cdot$$

6-7 Argon (Group 8) has eight outer electrons and so we write $:\!\overset{..}{\underset{..}{Ar}}\!:$, or simply Ar.

Sulfur (Group 6) has six outer electrons and so we write $\cdot\overset{..}{\underset{..}{S}}\!\cdot$.

S^{2-} has eight outer electrons and so we write $:\!\overset{..}{\underset{..}{S}}\!:^{2-}$.

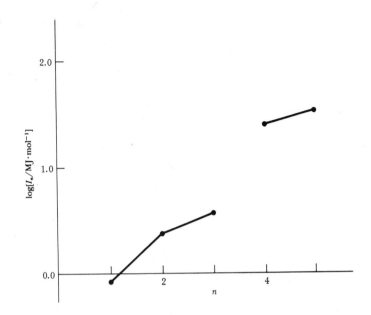

Aluminum (Group 3) has three outer electrons, Al^{3+} has zero outer electrons, and so we write Al^{3+}.

Chlorine (Group 7) has seven outer electrons, Cl^- has eight outer electrons, and so we write $:\ddot{\underset{..}{Cl}}:^-$.

6-9 Solve Equation (6-1) for ν.

$$\nu = \frac{c}{\lambda} = \frac{3.00 \times 10^8 \text{ m} \cdot \text{s}^{-1}}{633 \times 10^{-9} \text{ m}} = 4.74 \times 10^{14} \text{ s}^{-1}$$

6-11 We first convert the value of the first ionization energy of potassium from units of $kJ \cdot mol^{-1}$ to units of $J \cdot atom^{-1}$:

$$E = (419 \text{ kJ} \cdot \text{mol}^{-1})\left(\frac{10^3 \text{ J}}{1 \text{ kJ}}\right)\left(\frac{1 \text{ mol}}{6.022 \times 10^{23} \text{ atom}}\right) = 6.96 \times 10^{-19} \text{ J} \cdot \text{atom}^{-1}$$

We then use Equations (6-1) and (6-2) to calculate the wavelength of the radiation that corresponds to this energy:

$$E = h\nu = \frac{hc}{\lambda}$$

or

$$\lambda = \frac{hc}{E} = \frac{(6.626 \times 10^{-34} \text{ J} \cdot \text{s})(3.00 \times 10^8 \text{ m} \cdot \text{s}^{-1})}{6.96 \times 10^{-19} \text{ J}}$$

$$= 2.86 \times 10^{-7} \text{ m} = 286 \text{ nm}$$

6-13 The energy per photon of green light is given by Equations (6-1) and (6-2).

$$E = h\nu = \frac{hc}{\lambda} = \frac{(6.626 \times 10^{-34}\,\text{J·s})(3.00 \times 10^8\,\text{m·s}^{-1})}{510 \times 10^{-9}\,\text{m}}$$
$$= 3.90 \times 10^{-19}\,\text{J·photon}^{-1}$$

The number of photons in 2.35×10^{-18} J of light is

$$\frac{2.35 \times 10^{-18}\,\text{J}}{3.90 \times 10^{-19}\,\text{J·photon}^{-1}} = 6 \text{ photons}$$

6-15 The energy of 200-nm radiation is given by Equations (6-1) and (6-2).

$$E = h\nu = \frac{hc}{\lambda} = \frac{(6.626 \times 10^{-34}\,\text{J·s})(3.00 \times 10^8\,\text{m·s}^{-1})}{200 \times 10^{-9}\,\text{m}}$$
$$= 9.94 \times 10^{-19}\,\text{J}$$

This is larger than the work function of gold, and so electrons will be ejected from the surface of the gold.

6-17 The energy of 400-nm radiation is given by Equations (6-1) and (6-2).

$$E = h\nu = \frac{hc}{\lambda} = \frac{(6.626 \times 10^{-34}\,\text{J·s})(3.00 \times 10^8\,\text{m·s}^{-1})}{400 \times 10^{-9}\,\text{m}}$$
$$= 4.97 \times 10^{-19}\,\text{J}$$

We calculate the kinetic energy of an ejected electron by using Equation (6-4).

$$\text{K.E.} = h\nu - \Phi$$
$$= 4.97 \times 10^{-19}\,\text{J} - 2.90 \times 10^{-19}\,\text{J}$$
$$= 2.07 \times 10^{-19}\,\text{J}$$

6-19 We use Equation (6-5),

$$\lambda = \frac{h}{m\upsilon}$$

The mass and the speed of the proton are given, and so

$$\lambda = \frac{6.626 \times 10^{-34}\,\text{J·s}}{(1.67 \times 10^{-27}\,\text{kg})(1.00 \times 10^5\,\text{m·s}^{-1})}$$
$$= 3.97 \times 10^{-12}\,\text{m} = 3.97 \text{ pm}$$

Don't forget that a joule is equal to a $\text{kg·m}^2\text{·s}^{-2}$.

6-21 The mass of a hydrogen molecule is

$$m = \frac{2.016 \text{ g} \cdot \text{mol}^{-1}}{6.022 \times 10^{23} \text{ molecule} \cdot \text{mol}^{-1}} = 3.348 \times 10^{-24} \text{ g}$$
$$= 3.348 \times 10^{-27} \text{ kg}$$

Therefore,

$$\lambda = \frac{h}{mv} = \frac{6.626 \times 10^{-34} \text{ J} \cdot \text{s}}{(3.348 \times 10^{-27} \text{ kg})(2000 \text{ m} \cdot \text{s}^{-1})} = 9.90 \times 10^{-11} \text{ m}$$
$$= 99.0 \text{ pm}$$

We have used the fact that a joule is equal to a $\text{kg} \cdot \text{m}^2 \cdot \text{s}^{-2}$.

6-23 The energy required for the electron in a hydrogen atom to make a transition from the $n = 2$ state to the $n = 3$ state is given by

$$\Delta E = E_3 - E_2 = -\frac{2.18 \times 10^{-18} \text{ J}}{3^2} - \left(-\frac{2.18 \times 10^{-18} \text{ J}}{2^2}\right)$$
$$= 3.03 \times 10^{-19} \text{ J}$$

The wavelength of a photon with this energy is obtained from Equations (6-1) and (6-2).

$$\lambda = \frac{hc}{\Delta E} = \frac{(6.626 \times 10^{-34} \text{ J} \cdot \text{s})(3.00 \times 10^8 \text{ m} \cdot \text{s}^{-1})}{3.03 \times 10^{-19} \text{ J}} = 6.56 \times 10^{-7} \text{ m}$$
$$= 656 \text{ nm}$$

6-25 We use Equations (6-14) and (6-7) to determine the state that results when a 97.2-nm photon is absorbed by a ground-state hydrogen atom.

$$h v_{1 \to n} = E_n - E_1 = 2.18 \times 10^{-18} \text{ J}\left(1 - \frac{1}{n^2}\right)$$

or

$$\left(1 - \frac{1}{n^2}\right) = \frac{(6.626 \times 10^{-34} \text{ J} \cdot \text{s})\left(\dfrac{3.00 \times 10^8 \text{ m} \cdot \text{s}^{-1}}{97.2 \times 10^{-9} \text{ m}}\right)}{2.18 \times 10^{-18} \text{ J}}$$
$$= 0.938$$

Thus

$$\frac{1}{n^2} = 1 - 0.938 = 0.0679$$

or

$$n^2 = 16.1$$

Therefore

$$n = 4$$

The electron then makes a transition from the $n = 4$ state to some lower state and emits a 486-nm photon. The final state can be determined from

$$h\nu_{4 \to n} = (2.18 \times 10^{-18} \text{ J}) \left(\frac{1}{n^2} - \frac{1}{4^2} \right)$$

or

$$\frac{1}{n^2} - \frac{1}{16} = \frac{(6.626 \times 10^{-34} \text{ J} \cdot \text{s}) \left(\dfrac{3.00 \times 10^8 \text{ m} \cdot \text{s}^{-1}}{486 \times 10^{-9} \text{ m}} \right)}{2.18 \times 10^{-18} \text{ J}} = 0.188$$

or

$$\frac{1}{n^2} = 0.188 + \frac{1}{16} = 0.250$$

Thus

$$n^2 = 4$$

and

$$n = 2$$

6-27 To calculate the ionization energies, we let $Z = 2$ for He^+, $Z = 3$ for Li^{2+}, and $Z = 4$ for Be^{3+}. The results are

$$IE(He^+) = E_\infty - E_1 = \frac{(2.18 \times 10^{-18} \text{ J})2^2}{1^2} = 8.72 \times 10^{-18} \text{ J}$$

$$IE(Li^{2+}) = \frac{(2.18 \times 10^{-18} \text{ J})3^2}{1^2} = 1.96 \times 10^{-17} \text{ J}$$

$$IE(Be^{3+}) = \frac{(2.18 \times 10^{-18} \text{ J})4^2}{1^2} = 3.49 \times 10^{-17} \text{ J}$$

The values given in Table 6-1 are per mole, and so we must multiply each of these results by Avogadro's number in order to compare with Table 6-1. The results are

$$IE(He^+) = 5.25 \text{ MJ} \cdot \text{mol}^{-1} = I_2$$
$$IE(Li^{2+}) = 11.8 \text{ MJ} \cdot \text{mol}^{-1} = I_3$$
$$IE(Be^{3+}) = 21.0 \text{ MJ} \cdot \text{mol}^{-1} = I_4$$

in excellent agreement with the values in Table 6-1.

6-29   (a) $n = 7, l = 0$ (possible)

      (b) $n = 1, l = 1$ (not possible, because $l = n$)

      (c) $n = 5, l = 2$ (possible)

      (d) $n = 2, l = 2$ (not possible, because $l = n$)

      (e) $n = 4, l = 3$ (possible)

6-31   (a) If $n = 4$ and $l = 1$, then the orbital is a $4p$ orbital.

      (b) If $n = 3$ and $l = 2$, then the orbital is a $3d$ orbital.

      (c) If $n = 4$ and $l = 2$, then the orbital is a $4d$ orbital.

      (d) If $n = 2$ and $l = 0$, then the orbital is a $2s$ orbital.

6-33   If $l = 2$, then n must be at least 3 because $l = 0, 1, 2, \ldots, n - 1$.
If $m_l = 3$, then l must be at least 3 because $m_l = -l, -l + 1, \ldots, -1, 0, +1, \ldots, l$.

6-35   For a $3d$ orbital $n = 3$ and $l = 2$; thus m_l can be $-2, -1, 0, 1$ or 2. For each value of m_l, m_s can be $+\frac{1}{2}$ or $-\frac{1}{2}$. Therefore, the 10 possible sets of four quantum numbers are

n	l	m_l	m_s
3	2	-2	$+\frac{1}{2}$
			$-\frac{1}{2}$
		-1	$+\frac{1}{2}$
			$-\frac{1}{2}$
		0	$+\frac{1}{2}$
			$-\frac{1}{2}$
		$+1$	$+\frac{1}{2}$
			$-\frac{1}{2}$
		$+2$	$+\frac{1}{2}$
			$-\frac{1}{2}$

6-37   Note that for each value of m_l, m_s can have the values $+\frac{1}{2}$ or $-\frac{1}{2}$. Thus the maximum number of electrons in a subshell is equal to two times the number of possible values of m_l.

				Maximum number of electrons
s orbital	$l = 0$	$m_l = 0$	$m_s = +\frac{1}{2}, -\frac{1}{2}$	$2 \times 1 = 2$ electrons
p orbital	$l = 1$	$m_l = -1, 0, 1$	$m_s = +\frac{1}{2}, -\frac{1}{2}$	$2 \times 3 = 6$ electrons
d orbital	$l = 2$	$m_l = -2, -1, 0, 1, 2$	$m_s = +\frac{1}{2}, -\frac{1}{2}$	$2 \times 5 = 10$ electrons
f orbital	$l = 3$	$m_l = -3, -2, -1, 0,$ $1, 2, 3$	$m_s = +\frac{1}{2}, -\frac{1}{2}$	$2 \times 7 = 14$ electrons

6-39   In a d transition series the five d orbitals are being filled. A set of five d orbitals can hold up to 10 electrons.

6-41   (a) Ruled out; the $2p$ orbitals cannot hold seven electrons.

(b) Ruled out; a $3s$ orbital cannot hold three electrons.

(c) Ruled out; the $3d$ orbitals hold only 10 electrons.

(d) Allowed

6-43   (a) $1s^2 2s^2 2p^6 3s^2 3p^2$ 14 electrons, silicon

(b) $1s^2 2s^2 2p^6 3s^2 3p^6 4s^1 3d^5$ 24 electrons, chromium

(c) $1s^2 2s^2 2p^6 3s^2 3p^6 4s^2 3d^{10} 4p^2$ 32 electrons, germanium

(d) $1s^2 2s^2 2p^6 3s^2 3p^6 4s^2 3d^{10} 4p^5$ 35 electrons, bromine

(e) $1s^2 2s^2 2p^1$ 5 electrons, boron

6-45   (a) Ti: $[Ar]4s^2 3d^2$ (b) K: $[Ar]4s^1$

(c) Fe: $[Ar]4s^2 3d^6$ (d) As: $[Ar]4s^2 3d^{10} 4p^3$

6-47   (a) Ca: $[Ar]4s^2$ (b) Br: $[Ar]4s^2 3d^{10} 4p^5$

(c) Ag: $[Kr]5s^1 4d^{10}$ (d) Zn: $[Ar]4s^2 3d^{10}$

6-49   (a) Groups 1 and 2   (b) Groups 3, 4, 5, 6, 7, 8

(c) the transition metals   (d) the lanthanides and the actinides

6-51   We write the ground-state electron configuration and apply Hund's rule to each case.

(a) Ge: $[Ar]4s^2 3d^{10} 4p_x^1 4p_y^1$; two unpaired electrons

(b) Se: $[Ar]4s^2 3d^{10} 4p^4$; two unpaired electrons

(c) V: $[Ar]4s^2 3d^3$; three unpaired electrons

(d) Fe: $[Ar]4s^2 3d^6$; four unpaired electrons

6-53   The number of electrons gained is equal to the number of electrons that must be added to attain the noble-gas configuration at the end of the row in which the element is located in the periodic table.

(a) 1 electron $\cdot H \cdot^-$ helium

(b) 2 electrons $:\overset{\cdot\cdot}{O}:^{2-}$ neon

(c) 4 electrons $: \overset{\cdot\cdot}{\underset{\cdot\cdot}{C}} :^{4-}$ neon

(d) 2 electrons $: \overset{\cdot\cdot}{\underset{\cdot\cdot}{S}} :^{2-}$ argon

6-55 First we determine the number of electrons in the ion, and then we write the ground-state electron configuration.

(a) $15 + 3 = 18$ electrons: $1s^22s^22p^63s^23p^6$; [Ar]

(b) $35 + 1 = 36$ electrons: $1s^22s^22p^63s^23p^64s^23d^{10}4p^6$; [Kr]

(c) $34 + 2 = 36$ electrons: $1s^22s^22p^63s^23p^64s^23d^{10}4p^6$; [Kr]

(d) $56 - 2 = 54$ electrons: $1s^22s^22p^63s^23p^64s^23d^{10}4p^65s^24d^{10}5p^6$; [Xe]

6-57 We first determine the total number of electrons in the ion, then we figure out the ground-state electron configuration, and finally we count the number of unpaired electrons.

Species	Ground-state configuration	Number of unpaired electrons
(a) F^+	$[He]2s^22p^4$	2
(b) Sn^{2+}	$[Kr]5s^24d^{10}$	0
(c) Bi^{3+}	$[Xe]6s^24f^{14}5d^{10}$	0
(d) Ar^+	$[Ne]3s^23p^5$	1

6-59 In this problem we work out the electronic configurations of the reactants and the products.

(a) $O(g) + 2e^- \rightarrow O^{2-}(g)$
$[He]2s^22p^4 + 2e^- \rightarrow [He]2s^22p^6$ or   [Ne]

(b) $Ca(g) + Sr^{2+}(g) \rightarrow Sr(g) + Ca^{2+}(g)$
$[Ar]4s^2 + [Kr] \rightarrow [Kr]5s^2 + [Ar]$

6-61 First we figure out the electron configuration of the ground state; then we promote one electron from the highest energy subshell that is occupied to the lowest energy subshell that is unoccupied.

(a) The ground state of Be^{2+} ($4 - 2 = 2$ electrons) is $1s^2$. The highest energy occupied subshell is the $1s$, and the lowest energy unoccupied subshell is the $2s$; thus the first excited state is obtained by promoting an electron from the $1s$ subshell to the $2s$ subshell to yield $1s^12s^1$.

(b) The ground state of He^+ (1 electron) is $1s^1$. The first excited state is $2s^1$.

(c) The ground state of F^- (10 electrons) is $1s^22s^22p^6$. The first excited state is $1s^22s^22p^53s^1$.

(d) The ground state of O^{2-} is $1s^22s^22p^6$. The first excited state is $1s^22s^22p^53s^1$.

6-63 Recall that atomic radii increase as we move down a column of the periodic table, whereas atomic radii decrease as we move from left to right across a row of the periodic table.

(a) $P > N$ (b) $P > S$

(c) $S > Ar$ (d) $Kr > Ar$

6-65 (a) $Li < Na < Rb < Cs$

(b) $P < Al < Mg < Na$

(c) $Ca < Sr < Ba$

6-67 The electron configurations of the alkaline earth metals are classified as the [noble gas]ns^2 type. The energy of attraction between the nucleus and the outer electrons is greater the higher the value of the nuclear charge Z and is less the higher the value of n, the principal quantum number. These two effects oppose one another as we move down a group. However, the underlying electrons in the noble-gas-like core partially screen the nuclear charge, and the farther an electron is from the nucleus (larger n) the lower is the ionization energy.

6-69 The energy of a 900-nm photon is given by Equations (6-1) and (6-2):

$$E = h\nu = \frac{hc}{\lambda} = \frac{(6.626 \times 10^{-34}\,J \cdot s)(3.00 \times 10^8\,m \cdot s^{-1})}{900 \times 10^{-9}\,m}$$
$$= 2.21 \times 10^{-19}\,J \cdot photon^{-1}$$

The amount of energy required to raise the temperature of 1.00 L of water by 1.00°C is

$$q = (4.18\,J \cdot K^{-1} \cdot g^{-1})(1.00\,L)\left(\frac{1000\,mL}{1\,L}\right)(1.00\,g \cdot mL^{-1})(1.00\,K)$$
$$= 4180\,J$$

The number of 900-nm photons required to supply this energy is given by

$$\text{number of photons} = \frac{4180\,J}{2.21 \times 10^{-19}\,J \cdot photon^{-1}} = 1.89 \times 10^{22}\,\text{photons}$$

6-71 The data are plotted on page 143. Equation (6-4), K.E. $= h\nu - \Phi = h\nu - h\nu_0$ tells us that a plot of K.E. versus ν is a straight line whose slope is Planck's constant. The intercept of the straight line with the horizontal axis (where K.E. $= 0$) gives the threshold frequency. From the graph we find that $\nu_0 = 1.1 \times 10^{15}\,s^{-1}$ and that the slope is given by (for example, if we take the second and fourth sets of data)

$$\text{slope} = h = \frac{(15.84 - 9.21) \times 10^{-19}\,J}{(3.50 - 2.50) \times 10^{15}\,s^{-1}} = 6.63 \times 10^{-34}\,J \cdot s$$

6-73 The energy of one photon is given by

$$E = \frac{hc}{\lambda} = \frac{(6.626 \times 10^{-34}\,J \cdot s)(3.00 \times 10^8\,m \cdot s^{-1})}{10.6 \times 10^{-6}\,m} = 1.88 \times 10^{-20}\,J$$

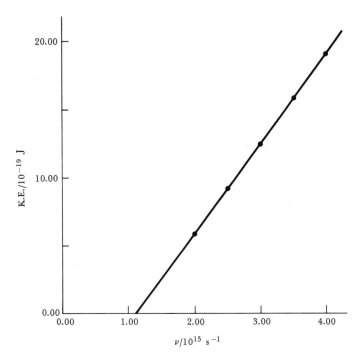

The number of photons in a pulse of 1 J is

$$\frac{1\text{ J}}{1.88 \times 10^{-20}\text{ J} \cdot \text{photon}^{-1}} = 5 \times 10^{19} \text{ photons}$$

6-75 The speed of the electrons is given by Equation (6-5):

$$v = \frac{h}{m\lambda} = \frac{(6.626 \times 10^{-34}\text{ J} \cdot \text{s})}{(9.11 \times 10^{-31}\text{ kg})(2.00 \times 10^{-9}\text{ m})} = 3.637 \times 10^{5}\text{ m} \cdot \text{s}^{-1}$$

The kinetic energy of an electron with this speed is given by

$$E = \tfrac{1}{2}mv^2 = \frac{(9.11 \times 10^{-31}\text{ kg})(3.637 \times 10^{5}\text{ m} \cdot \text{s}^{-1})^2}{2}$$

$$= 6.02 \times 10^{-20}\text{ J}$$

6-77 The frequencies of the lines in the Lyman series of the hydrogen atom are given by Equation (6-11):

$$\nu_{n \to 1} = (3.29 \times 10^{15}\text{ s}^{-1})\left(\frac{1}{1^2} - \frac{1}{n^2}\right)$$

The values of v and $1/n^2$ are given by

Transition	$v_{n\to 1}/10^{15}$ s^{-1}	$1/n^2$
$2 \to 1$	2.47	0.250
$3 \to 1$	2.92	0.111
$4 \to 1$	3.08	0.0625
$5 \to 1$	3.16	0.040

These data are plotted below. Note that a plot of $v_{n\to 1}$ versus $1/n^2$ is a straight line.

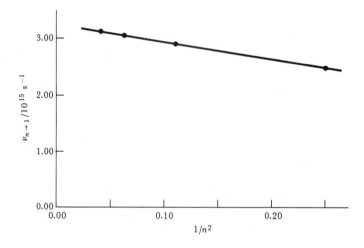

6-79 We must use Hess's law to do this problem. From Table 6-1, we find that

(a)
$$\text{Li}(g) \to \text{Li}^+(g) + e^-(g) \qquad \Delta H^\circ_{rxn} = I_1 = 0.52 \text{ MJ}$$
$$\underline{\text{Na}^+(g) + e^-(g) \to \text{Na}(g) \qquad \Delta H^\circ_{rxn} = -I_1 = -0.50 \text{ MJ}}$$
$$\text{Li}(g) + \text{Na}^+(g) \to \text{Li}^+(g) + \text{Na}(g) \qquad \Delta H^\circ_{rxn} = 0.020 \text{ MJ}$$
$$= 20 \text{ kJ}$$

(b)
$$\text{Mg}^{2+}(g) + e^-(g) \to \text{Mg}^+(g) \qquad \Delta H^\circ_{rxn} = -I_2 = -1.45 \text{ MJ}$$
$$\underline{\text{Mg}(g) \to \text{Mg}^+(g) + e^-(g) \qquad \Delta H^\circ_{rxn} = I_1 = 0.74 \text{ MJ}}$$
$$\text{Mg}^{2+}(g) + \text{Mg}(g) \to 2\text{Mg}^+(g) \qquad \Delta H^\circ_{rxn} = -0.71 \text{ MJ}$$
$$= -710 \text{ kJ}$$

(c)
$$\text{Al}^{3+}(g) + e^-(g) \to \text{Al}^{2+}(g) \qquad \Delta H^\circ_{rxn} = -I_3 = -2.74 \text{ MJ}$$
$$\text{Al}^{2+}(g) + e^-(g) \to \text{Al}^+(g) \qquad \Delta H^\circ_{rxn} = -I_2 = -1.82 \text{ MJ}$$
$$\underline{\text{Al}^+(g) + e^-(g) \to \text{Al}(g) \qquad \Delta H^\circ_{rxn} = -I_1 = -0.58 \text{ MJ}}$$
$$\text{Al}^{3+}(g) + 3e^-(g) \to \text{Al}(g) \qquad \Delta H^\circ_{rxn} = -5.14 \text{ MJ}$$

6-81 Once we determine the outer electron configuration of the element with $Z = 16$, then we proceed to find the next element with the same outer electron configuration.

(a) The electron configuration corresponding to $Z = 16$ electrons is $1s^2 2s^2 2p^6 3s^2 3p^4$. The outer electron configuration is $3p^4$. The next element with an np^4 configuration is $[Ar]4s^2 3d^{10} 4p^4$ and $Z = 34$. The next element with np^4 is $[Kr]5s^2 4d^{10} 5p^4$ and $Z = 52$. The next element with np^4 is $[Xe]6s^2 4f^{14} 5d^{10} 6p^4$ and $Z = 84$. The first element with np^4 is $[He]2s^2 2p^4$ and $Z = 8$.

(b) Eleven electrons corresponds to the electron configuration $1s^2 2s^2 2p^6 3s^1$. The succeeding elements with ns^1 outer electron configurations are $[Ar]4s^1$, $Z = 19$; $[Kr]5s^1$, $Z = 37$; $[Xe]6s^1$, $Z = 55$; and $[Rn]7s^1$, $Z = 87$. The first elements are $[He]2s^1$, $Z = 3$, and $1s^1$, $Z = 1$.

6-83 The order of the orbital energies goes as

$$1s < 2s < 2p < 3s < 3p < 4s < 3d < 4p < \cdots$$

(a) 15 electrons: $1s^2 2s^2 2p^6 3s^2 3p^3$
no d electrons
nine electrons with $l = 1$ (p electrons)
three unpaired electrons (Hund's rule)

(b) 26 electrons: $1s^2 2s^2 2p^6 3s^2 3p^6 4s^2 3d^6$
six d electrons
12 electrons with $l = 1$ (p electrons)
four unpaired electrons (Hund's rule)

(c) 32 electrons: $1s^2 2s^2 2p^6 3s^2 3p^6 4s^2 3d^{10} 4p^2$
10 d electrons
14 electrons with $l = 1$ (p electrons)
two unpaired electrons (Hund's rule)

6-85 If the $2s$ and $2p$ orbitals had the same energy, the ground-state outer electron configurations of the second-row elements would be

$$2s^1, \ 2s^1 2p_x^1, \ 2s^1 2p_x^1 2p_y^1, \ 2s^1 2p_x^1 2p_y^1 2p_z^1, \ 2s^2 2p_x^1 2p_y^1 2p_z^1,$$
$$2s^2 2p_x^2 2p_y^1 2p_z^1, \ 2s^2 2p_x^2 2p_y^2 2p_z^1, \ 2s^2 2p_x^2 2p_y^2 2p_z^2$$

E   ANSWERS TO THE SELF-TEST

1 false

2 the noble gases

3 false

4 small

5 in the outer shell

6 true

7 helium . . . a lone outer electron

8 Li·

9 $\lambda v = c$

10 c . . . 3.00×10^8 m·s^{-1}

11   continuous

12   a set of lines

13   line

14   true

15   is emitted by a solid body when heated to high temperatures

16   only in quantized packets

17 $E = hv$ . . . h is Planck's constant (6.626×10^{-34} J·s) and v is the frequency

18 h . . . 6.626×10^{-34} J·s

19   ejection of electrons from the surface of a metal when it is irradiated with ultraviolet radiation

20   minimum frequency required to eject electrons from the metal

21   false

22   consists of little packets of energy

23   the minimum energy required to remove an electron from the surface of the metal

24   true

25   electromagnetic radiation

26   true

27 $\lambda = h/mv$ . . . h is Planck's constant, m is the mass of the particle, and v is its speed

28   small

29   wavelike

30   true

31 $E_n = -(2.18 \times 10^{-18}$ J$)/n^2$ . . . $n = 1, 2, 3, . . .$

32   they are infinitely far apart

33   more

34   the state of lowest **possible energy**

35   states with energies greater than the ground state

36   emits

37   emitted . . . $\Delta E = E_3 - E_1$

38   electrons making transitions from states of lower energies to states of higher energies

39   true

40   it is not possible to measure accurately both the position and the momentum of a particle simultaneously

41   true

42   true

43   Schrödinger equation

44   true

45   true

46   false

47   the Schrödinger equation

48   a probability density

49   false

50   energy

51 $1s$

52   distance of the electron from the nucleus

53   decreases

54   spherically

55   the probability density of finding an electron

56 l . . . the shape

57   0 and 1

58   spherically

59   cylindrically

60 $n = 2$ and $l = 1$

61 $3d$

62 m_l . . . the spatial orientation

63 $+1, 0, -1$

64 false (Energy levels of a hydrogen atom depend upon only n.)

65 x, y, z axes

66 the spin of an electron

67 $+\frac{1}{2}$ and $-\frac{1}{2}$

68 false

69 false (It depends only on n and l.)

70 false

71 no two electrons in the same atom can have the same four quantum numbers

72 positive spin, or $m_s = +\frac{1}{2}$

73 six

74 false (the spins must be opposed.)

75 2

76 eight

77 two (s and p)

78 there are five electrons in the $2p$ orbitals

79 $3d^6$

80 false

81 true

82 for any set of orbitals of the same energy, the ground-state electron configuration is obtained by placing the electrons into different orbitals of this set with parallel spins until each of the orbitals has one electron before any electrons are paired.

83 ns^2

84 ns^2np^5

85 alkali

86 noble gas

87 d

88 true

89 $4s^23d^1$ through $4s^23d^{10}$

90 $4f$

91 they have similar chemical properties

92 $5f$

93 true

94 crystallographic data (X-ray analysis of crystal structure)

95 decrease

96 increase

97 1

98 the outer electron is farther from the nucleus

99 larger

IONIC BONDS AND COMPOUNDS

A   OUTLINE OF CHAPTER 7

7-1   Solutions that contain ions conduct an electric current.

Ionic compounds yield ions when they dissolve in water.

Moving charges (ions) constitute an electric current.

Electrolytes in aqueous solution conduct an electric current.

Nonelectrolytes in aqueous solution do not conduct an electric current.

Some guidelines for predicting whether a substance is a strong, weak, or nonelectrolyte are given on pages 248 and 249 (Example 7-1).

7-2   The electrostatic attraction that binds oppositely charged ions together is called an ionic bond.

Electrostatic attraction binds ions together in an ionic bond.

Certain metals lose electrons and nonmetals gain electrons to attain noble-gas electron configurations (Figure 7-2).

A cation is a positively charged ion.

An anion is a negatively charged ion.

An ionic compound is composed of cations and anions.

Reactive metals combine with reactive nonmetals to produce ionic compounds.

Lewis electron-dot formulas can be used to predict the products of reactions between certain metals and nonmetals.

7-3   The orbitals of transition metal ions are filled in a regular order.

Some metals lose electrons to form ions with an 18-electron outer configuration, $ns^2np^6nd^{10}$ (Figure 7-3).

Some transition metals form ions with the outer electron configuration [noble gas] $(n + 1)s^2nd^{10}$ (Figure 7-4).

In the d transition metal ions, the nd orbital is of lower energy than the $(n + 1)s$ orbital.

7-4 Cations are smaller and anions are larger than their corresponding neutral atoms.

The relative sizes of atoms and ions are shown in the frontispiece to Chapter 7.

For positive ions in the same row of the periodic table, the higher the positive charge, the smaller the ion.

Isoelectronic species contain the same number of electrons.

The values of some ionic radii are given in Table 7-1.

7-5 Coulomb's law is used to calculate the energy of an ion pair.

The ionization energy is the energy required to remove an electron from an atom or ion.

The first electron affinity, EA_1, of an atom is the energy change per mole for the process

$$A(g) + e^- \longrightarrow A^-(g)$$

The second electron affinity, EA_2, is the energy change per mole for the process

$$A^-(g) + e^- \longrightarrow A^{2-}(g)$$

The values of the electron affinities of some nonmetals are given in Table 7-2.

The distance between the centers of the ions in an ion pair is the sum of the radii of the ions.

Coulomb's law is given by

$$E = (2.31 \times 10^{-16}\,\text{J}\cdot\text{pm})\frac{Z_1 Z_2}{d} \tag{7-1}$$

where E is the Coulombic ion pairing energy, d is the sum of the ionic radii, and Z_1 and Z_2 are the charges on the ions.

The energy change for the reaction

$$M(g) + X(g) \longrightarrow M^+X^-(g)$$

equals the sum of the ionization energy of $M(g)$, the electron affinity of $X(g)$, and the Coulombic energy of the ion pair (Figure 7-7).

7-6 The formation of ionic solids from their elements is an exothermic process.

The energy change for the reaction

$$M(s) + \tfrac{1}{2}X_2(s,\, l,\, \text{or}\ g) \longrightarrow M^+X^-(s)$$

equals the sum of the vaporization energy of $M(s)$, one half of the vaporization energy and dissociation energy of X_2, the ionization energy of $M(g)$, the electron affinity of $X(g)$, and the lattice energy of $M^+X^-(s)$ (see Figure 7-9).

The set of steps used to calculate the energy of formation of an ionic solid from its elements is called a Born-Haber cycle.

B   SELF-TEST

1   An aqueous solution of sodium chloride contains _____ and _____ .

2   A substance that exists as ions when dissolved in water will conduct an electric current. *True/False*

3   All substances that dissolve in water produce solutions that conduct electricity. *True/False*

4   All electrolytes are good conductors of electricity. *True/False*

5   Weak electrolytes are substances that dissociate completely in water. *True/False*

6   Hydrochloric acid, HCl(*aq*), is a _____ electrolyte.

7   Acetic acid, $HC_2H_3O_2$(*aq*), is a _____ electrolyte.

8   The soluble hydroxides are _____ electrolytes.

9   Most organic compounds are _____ electrolytes.

10 A Group 1 metal loses an electron to obtain a _____ electron configuration.

11 A halogen atom gains an electron to obtain a _____ electron configuration.

12 An ionic compound consists of _____ and _____ .

13 The bond in an ionic compound is called _____ bond.

14 Using Lewis electron-dot formulas, the reaction between barium atoms and chlorine atoms is _____

_____ .

15 The Group 2 metals lose _____ electron(s) to attain a

_____ configuration.

16 The Group 6 nonmetals gain _____ electron(s) to attain a

_____ configuration.

17   The group of transition metals headed by Cu lose _____ electron(s) to attain a
_____ configuration.

18   The Group 5 metals lose _____ electron(s) to attain
_____ configuration.

19   The most stable ionic charge of scandium is $+3$. *True/False*

20   The energy of the $3d$ orbitals is lower than the $4s$ orbital in a transition metal ion.
True/False

21   The radius of an ion is the same as the radius of the atom. *True/False*

22   The radius of a chloride ion is *(larger, smaller)* than the radius of a chlorine atom
because _____.

23   The radius of a potassium ion is *(larger, smaller)* than the radius of a potassium atom
because _____.

24   Isoelectronic species always have the same size. *True/False*

25   Energy is required to remove an electron from a metal atom. *True/False*

26   Energy is required to add an electron to a fluorine atom. *True/False*

27   Electron affinity is the energy _____
_____.

28   The electron affinity of a chlorine atom has a *(positive, negative)* value.

29   The energy required to bring two ions together in the gas phase is found from
_____ law.

30   The energy required to bring a positive ion and a negative ion together is negative.
The ion pair is *(more, less)* stable than the separated ions.

31   Coulomb's law states that $E = $ _____ where _____
_____.

32   The Coulombic energy for the process

$$M^+(g) + X^-(g) \longrightarrow MX(g)$$

is greater the *(greater, less)* the separation between the ions.

33   The energies used to calculate the energy evolved in the process

$$Na(g) + Cl(g) \longrightarrow Na^+Cl^-(g)$$

are

(a) _____

(b) _____

(c) _____

34 Energy is *(absorbed, released)* when isolated fluoride ions and isolated lithium ions are brought together to form crystalline lithium fluoride.

35 The lattice energy of an ionic crystal has a *(positive, negative)* value relative to the energy of the gaseous ions.

36 The reaction between a metal and a nonmetal to form an ionic crystal is an *(exothermic, endothermic)* reaction.

37 Write out the five steps used to analyze the energetics of the formation of LiF*(s)* from Li*(s)* and F$_2$*(g)*.

(a) _____

(b) _____

(c) _____

(d) _____

(e) _____

38 The sum of the energy terms in the five steps involved in Question 37 is equal to the energy change for the reaction _____ .

39 The lattice energy of NaCl*(s)* is equal to the energy released in the process

_____ .

40 The Born-Haber cycle for NaCl*(s)* is the process in which

_____

_____ .

C   CALCULATIONS YOU SHOULD KNOW HOW TO DO

1 Use the electron configurations and the Lewis electron-dot formulas to predict reaction products and chemical formulas. See Example 7-2 and Problems 7-1 through 7-4 (reaction products) and Problems 7-13 and 7-14 (chemical formulas).

2 Determine the electron configurations for transition metal ions. See Examples 7-3 through 7-5, and Problems 7-5 through 7-10.

3 Use electron configurations and the charges on the ions to predict the relative sizes of ions. See Example 7-6 and Problems 7-15 and 7-16.

4 Calculate the energy released in the formation of ion pairs from their gaseous ions. See Example 7-7 and Problems 7-23 through 7-30.

5 Calculate the energy released in the formation of ionic crystals from the elements. See Section 7-6, Figure 7-9, and Problems 7-31 through 7-36.

D SOLUTIONS TO THE ODD-NUMBERED PROBLEMS

7-1 In order to emphasize the attainment of noble-gas configurations for ions, we write the electron configurations in terms of noble-gas configurations. Thus [Ar] denotes the configuration $1s^2 2s^2 2p^6 3s^2 3p^6$.

(a) $Ca([Ar]4s^2) + 2F([He]2s^2 2p^5) \rightarrow Ca^{2+}([Ar]) + 2F^-([Ne]) \rightarrow CaF_2(g)$

(b) $Sr([Kr]5s^2) + 2Br([Ar]4s^2 3d^{10} 4p^5) \rightarrow Sr^{2+}([Kr]) + 2Br^-([Kr]) \rightarrow SrBr_2(g)$

(c) $2Al([Ne]3s^2 3p^1) + 3O([He]2s^2 2p^4) \rightarrow 2Al^{3+}([Ne]) + 3O^{2-}([Ne]) \rightarrow Al_2O_3(g)$

7-3 (a) $3Li\cdot + \cdot\ddot{\underset{\cdot}{N}}\cdot \longrightarrow \underbrace{3Li^+ + \;:\!\ddot{\underset{\cdot\cdot}{N}}\!:^{3-}}_{Li_3N}$

(b) $Na\cdot + H\cdot \longrightarrow \underbrace{Na^+ + H\!:^-}_{NaH}$

(c) $\cdot\dot{Al}\cdot + 3:\!\ddot{I}\cdot \longrightarrow \underbrace{Al^{3+} + 3:\!\ddot{\underset{\cdot\cdot}{I}}\!:^-}_{AlI_3}$

7-5 Recall that for neutral atoms the $(n + 1)s$ orbitals are of lower energy than the nd orbitals, for example, $4s < 3d$. For ions, however, the reverse is true, that is, $3d < 4s$. Thus we first determine the number of electrons in the ion, and then we write the electron configuration filling the orbitals in the order $1s$, $2s$, $2p$, $3s$, $3p$, $3d$, $4s$, and so forth. For Cr^{2+} we have $Z - 2 = 24 - 2 = 22$ electrons; thus we have

(a) $Cr^{2+}([Ar]3d^4)$ (b) $Cu^{2+}([Ar]3d^9)$

(c) $Co^{3+}([Ar]3d^6)$ (d) $Mn^{2+}([Ar]3d^5)$

7-7 For $+2$ ions the nth member of a d transition series has nd electrons, because the two $(n + 1)s$ electrons have been removed. Thus the sixth member has six d electrons, and so forth.

(a) Fe, Ru, Os   (b) Zn, Cd, Hg

(c) Sc, Y, Lu   (d) Mn, Tc, Re

7-9 (a) For $n = 3$ or 4, an 18-electron outer configuration is one of the type $ns^2 np^6 nd^{10}$. For $n = 4$ the corresponding noble gas is Kr (the fourth noble gas); thus for Cd^{2+} we have $Cd^{2+}([Kr]4d^{10})$.

(b) $In^{3+}([Kr]4d^{10})$

(c) In this case, $n = 5$ and the corresponding 18-electron outer configuration is of the type $ns^2np^6(n-1)f^{14}nd^{10}$ or $5s^25p^64f^{14}5d^{10}$; thus we have $Tl^{3+}([Xe]4f^{14}5d^{10})$.

(d) $Zn^{2+}([Ar]3d^{10})$

7-11 In this problem we simply determine the number of electrons in the positive ion and in the negative ion. If the numbers are the same, then the ions are isoelectronic.

(a) $Li^+(2)$, $F^-(10)$, not isoelectronic

(b) $Na^+(10)$, $F^-(10)$, isoelectronic

(c) $K^+(18)$, $Br^-(36)$, not isoelectronic

(d) KCl, isoelectronic ions, each has 18 electrons

(e) BaI_2, isoelectronic ions, each has 54 electrons

(f) AlF_3, isoelectronic ions, each has 10 electrons

7-13 Figure 7-1 gives the ionic charges of various ions that correspond to noble-gas electron configurations. We use these charges, together with the requirement that the ionic compound must be electrically neutral, to work out the formula.

(a) Y_2S_3 (b) $LaBr_3$ (c) MgTe   (d) Rb_3N (e) Al_2Se_3 (f) CaO

7-15 (a) Cl^- A negative ion is larger than a positive ion with the same number of electrons.

(b) Ag^+ The higher charged ion is smaller because of the larger nuclear attraction for the same number of electrons.

(c) Cu^+ Same reason as (b).

(d) O^{2-} The higher the negative charge for the same number of electrons, the larger the ion is, because the electrons repel each other.

7-17 See Table 7-2 for electron affinities. The larger the magnitude of the electron affinity of an atom, the easier it is to add an electron. Thus we have

$$Cl > Br > I > H$$

7-19 In going from Cl to Br and from Br to I, the electron affinity decreases in magnitude by about 25 $kJ \cdot mol^{-1}$ at each step. Thus we estimate the electron affinity of At to be about -270 $kJ \cdot mol^{-1}$.

7-21 In each case we add the electron affinity of the second reactant to the ionization energy of the first reactant.

(a) $Li(g) + Br(g) \rightarrow Li^+(g) + Br^-(g)$

$$\Delta H^{\circ}_{rxn} = 520 \text{ kJ} \cdot mol^{-1} + (-324 \text{ kJ} \cdot mol^{-1}) = 196 \text{ kJ} \cdot mol^{-1}$$

(b) $I^-(g) + Cl(g) \rightarrow I(g) + Cl^-(g)$
The ionization energy of $I^-(g)$ is the negative of the electron affinity of $I(g)$.

Thus

$$\Delta H^\circ_{rxn} = +295 \text{ kJ} \cdot \text{mol}^{-1} + (-348 \text{ kJ} \cdot \text{mol}^{-1}) = -53 \text{ kJ} \cdot \text{mol}^{-1}$$

(c) $Na(g) + H(g) \rightarrow Na^+(g) + H^-(g)$

$$\Delta H^\circ_{rxn} = 500 \text{ kJ} \cdot \text{mol}^{-1} + (-72 \text{ kJ} \cdot \text{mol}^{-1}) = 428 \text{ kJ} \cdot \text{mol}^{-1}$$

7-23 The equation for Coulomb's law is

$$E = \frac{(2.31 \times 10^{-16} \text{ J} \cdot \text{pm})(Z_1 Z_2)}{d}$$

The input data are the radius of $Zn^{2+} = 74$ pm, the radius of $O^{2-} = 140$ pm (Table 7-1), $Z_1 = +2$, and $Z_2 = -2$. Thus we have

$$E = \frac{(2.31 \times 10^{-16} \text{ J} \cdot \text{pm})(2)(-2)}{(74 \text{ pm} + 140 \text{ pm})} = -4.32 \times 10^{-18} \text{ J}$$

7-25 (a) For the ionization of K

$$K(g) \longrightarrow K^+(g) + e^- \qquad I_1 = 419 \text{ kJ} \cdot \text{mol}^{-1}$$

(b) For the addition of an electron to Br (Table 7-2)

$$Br(g) + e^- \longrightarrow Br^-(g) \qquad EA_1 = -324 \text{ kJ} \cdot \text{mol}^{-1}$$

If we add steps (a) and (b), then we have

$$K(g) + Br(g) \longrightarrow K^+(g) + Br^-(g) \qquad \Delta H^\circ_{rxn} = 95 \text{ kJ} \cdot \text{mol}^{-1}$$

(c) We now bring together K^+ and Br^- to their ion-pair separation. According to Table 7-1, the radius of K^+ is 133 pm and the radius of Br^- is 195 pm. Their separation as an ion pair is 328 pm. We now use Coulomb's law to calculate the energy released by the formation of one ion pair from the separated ions:

$$K^+(g) + Br^-(g) \longrightarrow K^+Br^-(g)$$

$$E = (2.31 \times 10^{-16} \text{ J} \cdot \text{pm}) \frac{Z_1 Z_2}{d}$$

$$= \frac{(2.31 \times 10^{-16} \text{ J} \cdot \text{pm})(+1)(-1)}{328 \text{ pm}}$$

$$= -7.04 \times 10^{-19} \text{ J}$$

For the energy released on the formation of one mole of ion pairs, we multiply this result by Avogadro's number:

$$E = \left(-7.04 \times 10^{-19} \frac{\text{J}}{\text{ion pair}}\right)\left(6.02 \times 10^{23} \frac{\text{ion pair}}{\text{mol}}\right) = -424 \text{ kJ} \cdot \text{mol}^{-1}$$

Thus, we have

$$K^+(g) + Br^-(g) \longrightarrow K^+Br^-(g) \qquad \Delta H^\circ_{rxn} = -424 \text{ kJ} \cdot \text{mol}^{-1}$$
$$d = 328 \text{ pm}$$

We combine this result with the result

$$K(g) + Br(g) \longrightarrow K^+(g) + Br^-(g) \qquad \Delta H^\circ_{rxn} = 95 \text{ kJ} \cdot \text{mol}^{-1}$$

to obtain the final result

$$K(g) + Br(g) \longrightarrow K^+Br^-(g) \qquad \Delta H^\circ_{rxn} = -329 \text{ kJ} \cdot \text{mol}^{-1}$$
$$d = 328 \text{ pm}$$

7-27 (a) For the ionization of Na (Table 6-1)

$$Na(g) \longrightarrow Na^+(g) + e^- \qquad I_1 = 500 \text{ kJ} \cdot \text{mol}^{-1}$$

(b) For the addition of an electron to H (Table 7-2),

$$H(g) + e^- \longrightarrow H^-(g) \qquad EA_1 = -72 \text{ kJ} \cdot \text{mol}^{-1}$$

Adding steps (a) and (b), we have

$$Na(g) + H(g) \longrightarrow Na^+(g) + H^-(g) \qquad \Delta H^\circ_{rxn} = 428 \text{ kJ} \cdot \text{mol}^{-1}$$

(c) We now bring together the Na^+ and H^- to their ion-pair separation. We use Coulomb's law to calculate the energy released by the formation of one ion pair:

$$E = (2.31 \times 10^{-16} \text{ J} \cdot \text{pm}) \frac{Z_1 Z_2}{d}$$
$$= \frac{(2.31 \times 10^{-16} \text{ J} \cdot \text{pm})(+1)(-1)}{(95 \text{ pm} + 154 \text{ pm})}$$
$$= -9.28 \times 10^{-19} \text{ J}$$

The energy released on formation of one mole of ion pairs is

$$E = \left(-9.28 \times 10^{-19} \frac{\text{J}}{\text{ion pair}}\right)\left(6.02 \times 10^{23} \frac{\text{ion pair}}{\text{mol}}\right)$$
$$= -558 \text{ kJ} \cdot \text{mol}^{-1}$$

Thus we have for the reaction

$$Na^+(g) + H^-(g) \longrightarrow NaH(g) \qquad \Delta H^\circ_{rxn} = -558 \text{ kJ} \cdot \text{mol}^{-1}$$
$$d = 249 \text{ pm}$$

Combining the above result with

$$Na(g) + H(g) \longrightarrow Na^+(g) + H^-(g) \qquad \Delta H^\circ_{rxn} = 428 \text{ kJ·mol}^{-1}$$

we obtain

$$Na(g) + H(g) \longrightarrow NaH(g) \qquad \Delta H^\circ_{rxn} = -130 \text{ kJ·mol}^{-1}$$
$$d = 249 \text{ pm}$$

7-29

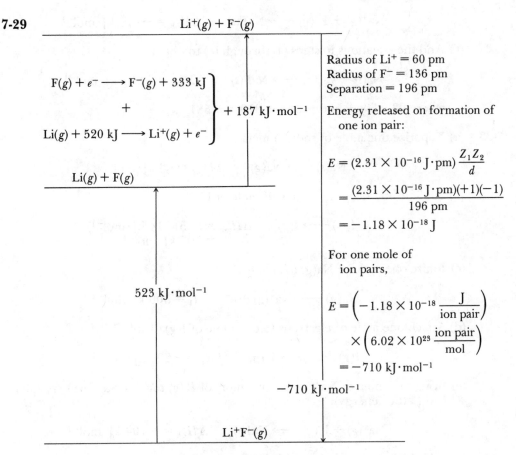

Radius of $Li^+ = 60$ pm
Radius of $F^- = 136$ pm
Separation $= 196$ pm

Energy released on formation of one ion pair:

$$E = (2.31 \times 10^{-16} \text{ J·pm}) \frac{Z_1 Z_2}{d}$$

$$= \frac{(2.31 \times 10^{-16} \text{ J·pm})(+1)(-1)}{196 \text{ pm}}$$

$$= -1.18 \times 10^{-18} \text{ J}$$

For one mole of ion pairs,

$$E = \left(-1.18 \times 10^{-18} \frac{\text{J}}{\text{ion pair}}\right)$$
$$\times \left(6.02 \times 10^{23} \frac{\text{ion pair}}{\text{mol}}\right)$$
$$= -710 \text{ kJ·mol}^{-1}$$

7-31 Following the steps outlined in Section 7-6, we have

(a) Vaporize one mole of sodium metal:

$$Na(s) \longrightarrow Na(g) \qquad \Delta H^\circ_{vap} = 93 \text{ kJ·mol}^{-1}$$

(b) Dissociate one-half mole of $F_2(g)$:

$$\tfrac{1}{2}F_2(g) \longrightarrow F(g) \qquad \Delta H^\circ_{rxn} = (0.5)(155 \text{ kJ·mol}^{-1}) = 78 \text{ kJ·mol}^{-1}$$

(c) Ionize one mole of $Na(g)$ (Table 6-1):

$$Na(g) \longrightarrow Na^+(g) + e^- \qquad I_1 = 500 \text{ kJ·mol}^{-1}$$

(d) Attach one mole of electrons to one mole of fluorine atoms (Table 7-2):

$$F(g) + e^- \longrightarrow F^-(g) \qquad EA_1 = -333 \text{ kJ} \cdot \text{mol}^{-1}$$

(e) Bring one mole of $Na^+(g)$ and one mole of $F^-(g)$ together to form crystalline $NaF(s)$ (lattice energy):

$$Na^+(g) + F^-(g) \longrightarrow NaF(s) \qquad \Delta H_{LE}^\circ = -919 \text{ kJ} \cdot \text{mol}^{-1}$$

(f) Add the equations in steps (a) through (e) to obtain

$$Na(s) + \tfrac{1}{2}F_2(g) \longrightarrow NaF(s) \qquad \Delta H_{rxn}^\circ = -581 \text{ kJ} \cdot \text{mol}^{-1}$$

where $93 + 78 + 500 - 333 - 919 = -581$

7-33 (a) Vaporize one mole of sodium metal:

$$Na(s) \longrightarrow Na(g) \qquad \Delta H_{vap}^\circ = 93 \text{ kJ} \cdot \text{mol}^{-1}$$

(b) Sublime and dissociate one-half mole of I_2

$$\tfrac{1}{2}I_2(s) \longrightarrow I(g) \qquad \begin{aligned} \Delta H_{rxn}^\circ &= (0.5)(214 \text{ kJ} \cdot \text{mol}^{-1}) \\ &= 107 \text{ kJ} \cdot \text{mol}^{-1} \end{aligned}$$

(c) Ionize one mole of $Na(g)$ (Table 6-1):

$$Na(g) \longrightarrow Na^+(g) + e^- \qquad I_1 = 500 \text{ kJ} \cdot \text{mol}^{-1}$$

(d) Attach one mole of electrons to one mole of $I(g)$ (Table 7-2):

$$I(g) + e^- \longrightarrow I^-(g) \qquad EA_1 = -295 \text{ kJ} \cdot \text{mol}^{-1}$$

(e) Bring one mole of $Na^+(g)$ and one mole of $I^-(g)$ together to form crystalline NaI (lattice energy):

$$Na^+(g) + I^-(g) \longrightarrow NaI(s) \qquad \Delta H_{LE}^\circ = -704 \text{ kJ} \cdot \text{mol}^{-1}$$

(f) Add the equations in steps (a) through (e) to obtain

$$Na(s) + \tfrac{1}{2}I_2(s) \longrightarrow NaI(s) \qquad \Delta H_{rxn}^\circ = -299 \text{ kJ} \cdot \text{mol}^{-1}$$

where $93 + 107 + 500 - 295 - 704 = -299$

7-35 (a) Vaporize one mole of calcium metal:

$$Ca(s) \longrightarrow Ca(g) \qquad \Delta H_{vap}^\circ = 193 \text{ kJ} \cdot \text{mol}^{-1}$$

(b) Dissociate one mole of $Cl_2(g)$:

$$Cl_2(g) \longrightarrow 2Cl(g) \qquad \Delta H_{diss}^\circ = 244 \text{ kJ} \cdot \text{mol}^{-1}$$

(c) Ionize one mole of $Ca(g)$ to $Ca^+(g)$:

$$Ca(g) \longrightarrow Ca^+(g) + e^- \qquad I_1 = 590 \text{ kJ} \cdot \text{mol}^{-1}$$

Ionize one mole of $Ca^+(g)$ to $Ca^{2+}(g)$:

$$Ca^+(g) \longrightarrow Ca^{2+}(g) + e^- \qquad I_2 = 1140 \text{ kJ} \cdot \text{mol}^{-1}$$

Thus for the production of $Ca^{2+}(g)$ from $Ca(g)$, we have

$$Ca(g) \longrightarrow Ca^{2+}(g) + 2e^- \qquad I = 1730 \text{ kJ} \cdot \text{mol}^{-1}$$

(d) Attach two moles of electrons to two moles of $Cl(g)$:

$$2Cl(g) + 2e^- \longrightarrow 2Cl^-(g) \qquad \Delta H^\circ_{rxn} = 2EA_1 = (2 \text{ mol})(-348 \text{ kJ} \cdot \text{mol}^{-1})$$
$$= -696 \text{ kJ}$$

(e) Bring one mole of $Ca^{2+}(g)$ and two moles of Cl^- together to form crystalline $CaCl_2$ (lattice energy):

$$Ca^{2+}(g) + 2Cl^-(g) \longrightarrow CaCl_2(s) \qquad \Delta H^\circ_{LE} = -2266 \text{ kJ} \cdot \text{mol}^{-1}$$

(f) Add the equations in steps (a) through (e) to obtain

$$Ca(s) + Cl_2(g) \longrightarrow CaCl_2(s) \qquad \Delta H^\circ_{rxn} = -795 \text{ kJ} \cdot \text{mol}^{-1}$$

where $193 + 244 + 1730 - 696 - 2266 = -795$

7-37 The ions N^{3-}, O^{2-}, Na^+, Mg^{2+}, and Al^{3+} are isoelectronic with F^-.

7-39 The ground-state electron configuration of K^+ is $1s^2 2s^2 2p^6 3s^2 3p^6$ and that of Cu^+ is $1s^2 2s^2 2p^6 3s^2 3p^6 3d^{10}$. The outer electrons are in the same shell, but the nuclear charge of Cu is greater than that of K and so the electrons are attracted more strongly to the nucleus.

7-41 We use a Born-Haber cycle (Figure 7-9) and write

$$\begin{aligned} \Delta H^\circ_f[CaCl_2(s)] = {} & \text{enthalpy of vaporization of } Ca(s) \\ & + (Cl\text{—}Cl \text{ bond energy}) \\ & + (\text{the sum of the first two ionization} \\ & \quad \text{energies of Ca}) \\ & + 2[\text{electron affinity of } Cl(g)] \\ & + \text{lattice energy of } CaCl_2(s) \end{aligned}$$

If we substitute the given numerical data into this equation, then we obtain

$$\begin{aligned} -795.0 \text{ kJ} \cdot \text{mol}^{-1} = {} & (193 \text{ kJ} \cdot \text{mol}^{-1}) + (244 \text{ kJ} \cdot \text{mol}^{-1}) \\ & + (590 \text{ kJ} \cdot \text{mol}^{-1} + 1140 \text{ kJ} \cdot \text{mol}^{-1}) \\ & + 2[\text{electron affinity of } Cl(g)] \\ & + (-2266 \text{ kJ} \cdot \text{mol}^{-1}) \end{aligned}$$

Solving for the electron affinity of Cl(g) gives

$$\text{electron affinity} = -348 \text{ kJ} \cdot \text{mol}^{-1}$$

7-43 The ground-state electron configuration of Fe^{2+} is $[Ar]3d^6$. According to Hund's rule, we fill all five $3d$ orbitals with one electron before we pair them up. Thus there are four unpaired electrons in Fe^{2+}.

The ground-state electron configuration of Zn^{2+} is $[Ar]3d^{10}$. Thus there are no unpaired electrons in Zn^{2+}.

7-45 There are two reasons: the magnitude of the electron affinity decreases and the ionic size of X^- increases, thus decreasing the Coulombic energy of the ion pair.

7-47 The $+1$ charged d^3 transition metal ions are Ti^+, Zr^+, and Hf^+.

7-49 (a) strong electrolyte, $K^+(aq) + NO_3^-(aq)$

(b) weak electrolyte

(c) nonelectrolyte (organic compound)

(d) nonelectrolyte (organic compound)

E   ANSWERS TO THE SELF-TEST

1   $Na^+(aq)$ and $Cl^-(aq)$

2   true

3   false

4   false (Weak electrolytes are only poor conductors.)

5   false (Weak electrolytes are only partially dissociated.)

6   strong

7   weak

8   strong

9   non-

10   noble-gas

11   noble-gas

12   cations . . . anions

13   an ionic

14   $\cdot Ba \cdot + 2 : \overset{\cdot\cdot}{Cl} \cdot \rightarrow$
  $: \overset{\cdot\cdot}{\underset{\cdot\cdot}{Cl}} :^- + Ba^{2+} + : \overset{\cdot\cdot}{\underset{\cdot\cdot}{Cl}} :^- \rightarrow BaCl_2$

15   two . . . noble-gas electron

16   two . . . noble-gas electron

17   one . . . 18-electron outer

18   three . . . the outer electron configuration $ns^2np^6(n+1)s^2nd^{10}$

19   true

20   true

21   false (Cations are smaller and anions are larger than the parent atoms.)

22   larger . . . inter-electronic repulsion due to the additional electron

23   smaller . . . the net positive charge draws the electrons in toward the nucleus.

24   false

25   true

26 false [Energy is released in the process $F(g) + e^- \rightarrow F^-(g)$.]

27 associated with the process of adding an electron to an atom or an ion

28 negative

29 Coulomb's

30 more

31 $E = (2.31 \times 10^{-16} \text{ J} \cdot \text{pm}) Z_1 Z_2 / d$; . . . Z_1 and Z_2 are the ionic charges and d is the distance between the ion centers in picometers

32 less

33 (a) the ionization energy of $Na(g)$

(b) the electron affinity of $Cl(g)$

(c) the coulombic energy of the Na^+Cl^- ion pair

34 released

35 negative (The lattice is more stable than the gaseous ions.)

36 exothermic

37 (a) the sublimation of $Li(s)$:
$Li(s) \rightarrow Li(g)$

(b) the ionization of $Li(g)$:
$Li(g) \rightarrow Li^+(g) + e^-$

(c) the dissociation of $F_2(g)$:
$\frac{1}{2}F_2(g) \rightarrow F(g)$

(d) the formation of $F^-(g)$ from $F(g)$:
$F(g) + e^- \rightarrow F^-(g)$

(e) the formation of $LiF(s)$ from $Li^+(g)$ and $F^-(g)$:
$Li^+(g) + F^-(g) \rightarrow LiF(s)$

38 $Li(s) + \frac{1}{2}F_2(g) \rightarrow LiF(s)$

39 $Na^+(g) + Cl^-(g) \rightarrow NaCl(s)$

40 the ionic crystal lattice of NaCl is formed from the elements sodium metal and chlorine (Cl_2) gas.

LEWIS FORMULAS

A   OUTLINE OF CHAPTER 8

8-1   A covalent bond can be described as a pair of electrons shared by two atoms.

The Lewis formula of a molecule indicates the covalent bond between two atoms as a line joining the atoms.

The Lewis formula of a molecule indicates lone electron pairs on an atom as pairs of dots surrounding the atom.

Molecular compounds form molecular crystals in the solid state (Figure 8-1).

Bond length is the average distance between the centers of the two atoms joined by a covalent bond.

8-2   We always try to satisfy the octet rule when writing Lewis formulas.

The octet rule states that when writing Lewis formulas, arrange the valence electrons about the atoms so that there are eight valence electrons about each atom other than hydrogen (most useful for carbon, nitrogen, oxygen, and fluorine).

The unique atom in a molecule is often the central atom.

A systematic method for writing Lewis formulas is given on page 265.

8-3   Hydrogen atoms are always terminal atoms in Lewis formulas.

A hydrogen atom achieves a noble-gas-like electron configuration by having two electrons around it.

A hydrogen atom forms only one bond.

8-4   Formal charges can be assigned to atoms in Lewis formulas.

Formal charge is a positive or negative number that is assigned to each atom in a Lewis formula.

Formal charges are determined by a set of rules and do not necessarily represent the actual charges on the atoms.

The formal charge on an atom is defined by Equation (8-1):

$$\begin{pmatrix} \text{formal charge} \\ \text{on an atom in a} \\ \text{Lewis formula} \end{pmatrix} = \begin{pmatrix} \text{total number of} \\ \text{valence electrons} \\ \text{in the free atom} \end{pmatrix} - \begin{pmatrix} \text{total number} \\ \text{of lone-pair} \\ \text{electrons} \end{pmatrix} - \frac{1}{2}\begin{pmatrix} \text{total number} \\ \text{of shared} \\ \text{electrons} \end{pmatrix}$$

Formal charge can be used to choose a preferred Lewis formula.

The preferred Lewis formula generally has the lowest formal charges.

8-5   It is not always possible to satisfy the octet rule by using only single bonds.

A covalent double bond consists of two pairs of electrons.

A double bond is shorter and stronger than a single bond.

A covalent triple bond consists of three pairs of electrons.

Many molecules contain double or triple covalent bonds.

8-6   A resonance hybrid is a superposition of Lewis formulas.

When it is possible to write two or more satisfactory Lewis formulas *without altering the positions of the nuclei,* the actual formula is viewed as an average or a superposition of the individual formulas.

Each of the individual Lewis formulas is said to be a resonance form and the use of resonance forms to describe the electron distribution is called resonance.

Benzene has two major resonance forms.

An abbreviated formula for benzene is ⬡ .

All the carbon-carbon bonds in benzene are equivalent.

The stability of benzene is called resonance stability.

8-7   A species with one or more unpaired electrons is called a free radical.

An electron-deficient compound does not have enough valence electrons to satisfy the octet rule for each atom.

A coordinate-covalent bond is a covalent bond that is formed when one atom contributes both electrons to the covalent bond.

A donor-acceptor complex results from a coordinate-covalent bond.

8-8   Atoms of elements below carbon through neon in the periodic table can expand their valence shells.

Some atoms expand their valence shell by using their *d* orbitals to accommodate more than eight electrons.

Some atoms can bond to more than four other atoms.

8-9   Most chemical bonds are intermediate between purely ionic and purely covalent.

Electronegativity is a measure of the force with which an atom attracts the electrons in its covalent bonds.

The electronegativities of the elements are given in Figure 8-4.

Electronegativities tend to decrease going down a column and to increase going across from left to right in a row in the periodic table (Figure 8-5).

If the electronegativities of the two atoms joined by a covalent bond differ, then the electrons in the bond are not shared equally.

A polar bond occurs when the electrons in the covalent bond are attracted to the more electronegative atom.

The electrons in a nonpolar bond are shared equally by the two atoms.

8-10 Polyatomic molecules with polar bonds may be nonpolar.

The dipole moment of a bond is a measure of the polarity of a bond.

A dipole moment has both magnitude and direction.

CO_2 is a linear molecule and has no net dipole moment (Figure 8-6).

H_2O is a bent molecule and has a net dipole moment (Figure 8-7).

B SELF-TEST

1 A covalent bond results when electrons are _____ between two atoms.

2 The covalent bond in a Lewis formula of a molecule is represented as

_____ .

3 A pair of electrons that is not shared between two atoms is called

_____ .

4 The constituent units of a molecular crystal are _____ .

5 A molecular crystal has a higher melting point than an ionic crystal. *True/False*

6 The attraction between the molecules of a molecular crystal is stronger than the attraction between the ions in an ionic crystal. *True/False*

7 Bond length is _____

_____ .

8 A nitrogen atom usually forms _____ covalent bonds.

9 The octet rule states that _____

_____ .

10 The octet rule works best for carbon, oxygen, nitrogen, and fluorine. *True/False*

11 The hydrogen atom does not obey the octet rule because _____

_____

_____.

12 A hydrogen atom may form *(one, two, three)* covalent bond(s).

13 A double bond occurs when two atoms share _____ electrons.

14 The Lewis formula for CO_2 is _____.

15 A double bond can occur only when the two atoms are the same. *True/False*

16 A triple bond occurs when two atoms share _____ electrons.

17 A triple bond can occur only when the two atoms are the same. *True/False*

18 The Lewis formula for N_2 is _____.

19 The atoms in a polyatomic ion are joined by ionic bonds. *True/False*

20 The formal charge of an atom is a charge that is assigned by using the equation

_____.

21 The formal charge of an atom in a polyatomic species represents the actual charge on the atom. *True/False*

22 When it is possible to write two or more Lewis formulas for a molecule or ion without altering the positions of the nuclei, the actual structure is _____

_____.

23 Each of the individual Lewis formulas referred to in Question 22 is said to be a

_____.

24 Because of resonance in the nitrite ion, NO_2^-, the bond lengths of the two N—O bonds are _____.

25 The N—O bonds in the nitrite ion, NO_2^-, are both single bonds. *True/False*

26 A free radical is a species in which _____

_____.

27 A free radical must contain an odd number of electrons. *True/False*

28 An electron-deficient compound is a compound that _____

_____.

29 An atom in a compound may have more than eight electrons in its valence shell. *True/False*

30 An atom may expand its valence shell by using its _____ orbitals.

31 The electrons in all covalent bonds are shared equally by the two atoms. *True/False*

32 Electronegativity is a measure of _____

_____ .

33 Electronegativities increase from _____ to _____ across the second and third rows of the periodic table.

34 The most electronegative atom is _____ .

35 The oxygen atom is *(more, less)* electronegative than the carbon atom.

36 The electrons in a covalent bond are shared equally by the two atoms when the

_____ .

37 A polar bond occurs when _____

_____ .

38 When the bond between two atoms is a polar bond, one of the atoms has a

_____ charge and the other has a _____

_____ charge.

39 The symbol $\delta+$ in the Lewis formula $\overset{\delta+ \quad \delta-}{H\!-\!\overset{..}{\underset{..}{Cl}}}\!:$ represents _____

_____ .

40 The dipole moment of a bond is a measure of _____ .

41 A dipole moment has both _____ and _____ .

42 A nonpolar molecule has no net dipole moment. *True/False*

C   CALCULATIONS YOU SHOULD KNOW HOW TO DO

There are not many calculations in this chapter. The determination of formal charge by means of Equation (8-1) is the only type of numerical problem in the chapter. See Example 8-6.

D SOLUTIONS TO THE ODD-NUMBERED PROBLEMS

8-1 (a) Because sulfur is the unique atom in this molecule, we shall assume that it is central and that the two chlorine atoms are attached to it.

$$Cl \quad S \quad Cl$$

The total number of valence electrons is $(1 \times 6) + (2 \times 7) = 20$. We use four of the valence electrons to form sulfur-chlorine bonds. We now place valence electrons as lone pairs on the two chlorine atoms (accounting for 12 of the 16 valence electrons) and the remaining four on the sulfur atom. The completed Lewis formula is

$$:\overset{..}{\underset{..}{Cl}}-\overset{..}{S}-\overset{..}{\underset{..}{Cl}}:$$

Notice that all three atoms satisfy the octet rule.

(b) Because germanium is the unique atom in this molecule, we shall assume that it is central and that each chlorine atom is attached to it. The total number of valence electrons is $(1 \times 4) + (4 \times 7) = 32$. We use eight of the valence electrons to form Ge—Cl bonds, which satisfies the octet rule about the Ge atom. We place the remaining 24 as lone pairs on the Cl atoms. The completed Lewis formula is

$$\begin{array}{c} :\overset{..}{Cl}: \\ | \\ :\overset{..}{\underset{..}{Cl}}-Ge-\overset{..}{\underset{..}{Cl}}: \\ | \\ :\underset{..}{Cl}: \end{array}$$

(c) We shall assume that the arsenic atom is central and that each bromine atom is attached to it. The total number of valence electrons is $(1 \times 5) + (3 \times 7) = 26$. We use six of the valence electrons to form the As—Br bonds. We place 18 of the valence electrons as lone pairs on the three bromine atoms and the remaining two as a lone pair on the As atom. The Lewis formula is

$$\begin{array}{c} :\overset{..}{Br}-\overset{..}{As}-\overset{..}{Br}: \\ | \\ :\underset{..}{Br}: \end{array}$$

(d) The total number of valence electrons is $(1 \times 5) + (3 \times 1) = 8$. We use six of the valence electrons to form the P—H bonds. We place the remaining two valence electrons as a lone pair on the P atom. The Lewis formula is

$$\begin{array}{c} H-\overset{..}{P}-H \\ | \\ H \end{array}$$

8-3 Since there is no unique atom in the molecule, we shall assume that the two oxygen atoms are bonded together and that the hydrogen atoms are attached to the two oxygen atoms.

$$\text{H—O—O—H}$$

The total number of valence electrons is $(2 \times 1) + (2 \times 6) = 14$. We use two valence electrons to form the O—O bond and four valence electrons to form the H—O bonds. We place the eight remaining valence electrons as lone pairs on the O atoms. The Lewis formula is

$$\text{H—}\overset{..}{\underset{..}{\text{O}}}\text{—}\overset{..}{\underset{..}{\text{O}}}\text{—H}$$

8-5   (a) The eight valence electrons are used to form the four C—H bonds.

$$\begin{array}{c} \text{H} \\ | \\ \text{H—C—H} \\ | \\ \text{H} \end{array}$$

(b) Six of the 14 valence electrons are used to form the C—H bonds, two to form the C—F bond and the six remaining valence electrons are placed as lone pairs on the F atom.

$$\begin{array}{c} \text{H} \\ | \\ \text{H—C—}\overset{..}{\underset{..}{\text{F}}}\text{:} \\ | \\ \text{H} \end{array}$$

(c) The hydrogen atoms must be terminal atoms, and so we write

$$\begin{array}{c} \text{H} \\ | \\ \text{H—C—}\overset{..}{\text{N}}\text{—H} \\ | \quad | \\ \text{H} \quad \text{H} \end{array}$$

8-7   The hydrogen atoms must be terminal atoms, and so we have

$$\begin{array}{c} \text{H} \quad \text{H} \quad \text{H} \\ | \quad | \quad | \\ \text{H—C—C—C—H} \\ | \quad | \quad | \\ \text{H} \quad \text{H} \quad \text{H} \end{array} \qquad \text{(home heating gas)}$$

propane

For C_4H_{10} we have

$$\begin{array}{c} \text{H} \quad \text{H} \quad \text{H} \quad \text{H} \\ | \quad | \quad | \quad | \\ \text{H—C—C—C—C—H} \\ | \quad | \quad | \quad | \\ \text{H} \quad \text{H} \quad \text{H} \quad \text{H} \end{array} \qquad \text{(fuel in cigarette lighters)}$$

butane

and for C_8H_{18} we have

$$
\begin{array}{ccccccccccccccc}
 & H & & H & & H & & H & & H & & H & & H & & H & \\
 & | & & | & & | & & | & & | & & | & & | & & | & \\
H-\!\!\!& C &\!\!\!-\!\!\!& C &\!\!\!-\!\!\!& C &\!\!\!-\!\!\!& C &\!\!\!-\!\!\!& C &\!\!\!-\!\!\!& C &\!\!\!-\!\!\!& C &\!\!\!-\!\!\!& C &\!\!\!-H \\
 & | & & | & & | & & | & & | & & | & & | & & | & \\
 & H & & H & & H & & H & & H & & H & & H & & H &
\end{array}
$$

octane   (a component of gasoline)

8-9   Line up the carbon and oxygen atoms as they appear in the chemical formula and place the hydrogen atoms on them in terminal positions to get

(a)
$$
\begin{array}{ccc}
 & H & H \\
 & | & | \\
H-\!\!\! & C \!\!-\!\! & C \!\!-\!\! \overset{..}{\underset{..}{O}}\!\!-H \\
 & | & | \\
 & H & H
\end{array}
$$

ethyl alcohol

Similarly, we have

(b)
$$
\begin{array}{cccc}
 & H & H & H \\
 & | & | & | \\
H-\!\! & C \!\!-\!\! & C \!\!-\!\! & C \!\!-\!\! \overset{..}{\underset{..}{O}}\!\!-H \\
 & | & | & | \\
 & H & H & H
\end{array}
$$

n-propyl alcohol

and

(c)
$$
\begin{array}{cccc}
 & H & H & H \\
 & | & | & | \\
H-\!\! & C \!\!-\!\! & C \!\!-\!\! & C \!\!-H \\
 & | & | & | \\
 & H & :\!\ddot{O}\!: & H \\
 & & | & \\
 & & H &
\end{array}
$$

isopropyl alcohol

8-11   The Lewis formula for NH_3 is

$$
\begin{array}{c}
\overset{..}{} \\
H-N-H \\
|\\
H
\end{array}
$$

When a proton is removed, the electron remains with the nitrogen atom; thus the Lewis formula for the amide ion is

$$
\begin{array}{c}
\overset{\ominus}{} \\
\overset{..}{\underset{..}{H-N-H}}
\end{array}
$$

The names are:

$$NaNH_2 \qquad \text{sodium amide}$$

$$Ba(NH_2)_2 \qquad \text{barium amide}$$

8-13 (a) The hydrogen atoms must be in terminal positions, and so we write

$$H \qquad C \qquad C \qquad H$$

There is a total of $(2 \times 1) + (2 \times 4) = 10$ valence electrons. If we add one bond between each atom and then try to satisfy the octet rule about the carbon atoms, we find that we are four electrons short. Thus we add two more bonds between the carbon atoms and obtain

$$H—C{\equiv}C—H$$

(b) Arrange the atoms as

$$H \qquad N \qquad N \qquad H$$

There is a total of $(2 \times 1) + (2 \times 5) = 12$ valence electrons. If we add one bond between each H atom and each N atom and one bond between the two N atoms, we cannot satisfy the octet rule around each N atom. Thus we add one more bond between the two N atoms. We place the four remaining valence electrons as a lone pair on each N atom. The Lewis formula is

$$H—\overset{..}{N}{=}\overset{..}{N}—H$$

(c) Arrange the atoms as

$$Cl$$
$$Cl \qquad C \qquad O$$

There is a total of 24 valence electrons. If we add one bond between each Cl atom and the C atom and one between the O atom and the C atom, we cannot satisfy the octet rule around each atom. Thus we add one more bond between the C atom and the O atom. We place the remaining 16 valence electrons as lone pairs to satisfy the octet rule about each atom. The Lewis formula is

$$:\overset{..}{C}l:$$
$$|$$
$$:\overset{..}{\underset{..}{C}}l—C{=}\overset{..}{\underset{.}{O}}$$

8-15 There are 18 valence electrons, or nine electron pairs, in HCOOH. The only way to satisfy the octet rule for the carbon and oxygen atoms by using nine electron pairs is to write

$$
\begin{array}{c}
\overset{\cdot\cdot}{\underset{}{O}}\overset{\cdot}{} \\
\parallel \\
H-C-\overset{\cdot\cdot}{\underset{\cdot\cdot}{O}}-H
\end{array}
$$

8-17   The hydrogen atoms are terminal atoms. There are 18 valence electrons, or nine electrons pairs. In order to satisfy the octet rule about the carbon and chlorine atoms, we write

$$
\begin{array}{cc}
H & H \\
| & | \\
H-C=C-\overset{\cdot\cdot}{\underset{\cdot\cdot}{Cl}}:
\end{array}
$$

8-19   The Lewis formula of NF_3 in which the nitrogen atom and the fluorine atoms are connected in a row is

$$:\overset{\cdot\cdot}{\underset{\cdot\cdot}{F}}-\overset{\cdot\cdot}{\underset{\cdot\cdot}{N}}-\overset{\cdot\cdot}{\underset{\cdot\cdot}{F}}-\overset{\cdot\cdot}{\underset{\cdot\cdot}{F}}:$$

We now assign a formal charge to each atom according to Equation (8-1).

$$\text{formal charge on the left } F = 7 - 6 - \tfrac{1}{2}(2) = 0$$
$$\text{formal charge on } N = 5 - 4 - \tfrac{1}{2}(4) = -1$$
$$\text{formal charge on the middle } F = 7 - 4 - \tfrac{1}{2}(4) = +1$$
$$\text{formal charge on the right } F = 7 - 6 - \tfrac{1}{2}(2) = 0$$

Thus we write

$$:\overset{\cdot\cdot}{\underset{\cdot\cdot}{F}}-\overset{\ominus}{\overset{\cdot\cdot}{\underset{\cdot\cdot}{N}}}-\overset{\oplus}{\overset{\cdot\cdot}{\underset{\cdot\cdot}{F}}}-\overset{\cdot\cdot}{\underset{\cdot\cdot}{F}}:$$

A Lewis formula for NF_3 with lower formal charges (all zeros) is

$$
\begin{array}{c}
:\overset{\cdot\cdot}{\underset{\cdot\cdot}{F}}-\overset{\cdot\cdot}{\underset{}{N}}-\overset{\cdot\cdot}{\underset{\cdot\cdot}{F}}: \\
| \\
:\overset{}{\underset{\cdot\cdot}{F}}:
\end{array}
$$

which represents the preferred Lewis formula.

8-21   The Lewis formula for the arrangement NNO is

$$\overset{\ominus}{\underset{\cdot\cdot}{:}}\overset{}{N}=\overset{\oplus}{N}=\overset{\cdot\cdot}{\underset{\cdot\cdot}{O}}$$

where we have assigned formal charges according to Equation (8-1).

$$\text{formal charge on N} = 5 - 4 - \tfrac{1}{2}(4) = -1$$
$$\text{formal charge on N} = 5 - 0 - \tfrac{1}{2}(8) = +1$$
$$\text{formal charge on O} = 6 - 4 - \tfrac{1}{2}(4) = 0$$

The Lewis formula for the arrangement NON is

$$\overset{\ominus}{\cdot\ddot{N}}=\overset{2+}{O}=\overset{\ominus}{\ddot{N}\cdot}$$

where we have assigned formal charges according to Equation (8-1).

$$\text{formal charge on each N} = 5 - 4 - \tfrac{1}{2}(4) = -1$$
$$\text{formal charge on O} = 6 - 0 - \tfrac{1}{2}(8) = +2$$

Thus we predict that the arrangement NNO is the more likely.

8-23 There are 18 valence electrons, or nine electron pairs, in $HCOO^-$. Two resonance forms are

$$H-\overset{\overset{\textstyle \cdot\ddot{O}\cdot}{\|}}{C}-\ddot{\ddot{O}}{:}^{\ominus} \longleftrightarrow H-\overset{\overset{\textstyle \ominus{:}\ddot{O}{:}}{|}}{C}=\ddot{O}{\cdot}$$

The superposition of these two resonance forms gives the resonance hybrid

$$\left[H-\overset{\overset{\textstyle O}{\|}}{C}\cdots O \right]^{-}$$

The two carbon-oxygen bonds in $HCOO^-$ are equivalent; they have the same bond length and the same bond energy.

8-25 The three resonance forms are

$$\overset{\ominus}{{:}\ddot{O}}-\overset{\overset{\textstyle \cdot\ddot{O}\cdot}{\|}}{C}-\ddot{\ddot{O}}{:}^{\ominus} \longleftrightarrow {\cdot}\ddot{O}=\overset{\overset{\textstyle {:}\ddot{O}{:}^{\ominus}}{|}}{C}-\ddot{O}{:}^{\ominus} \longleftrightarrow \overset{\ominus}{{:}\ddot{O}}-\overset{\overset{\textstyle {:}\ddot{O}{:}^{\ominus}}{|}}{C}=\ddot{O}{\cdot}$$

The superposition of these three resonance forms is

$$\left[O\cdots\overset{\overset{\textstyle O}{\|}}{C}\cdots O \right]^{2-}$$

The three bonds in CO_3^{2-} are equivalent; they have the same bond length and the same bond energy.

8-27 (a) The thiocarbonate ion CS_3^{2-} is similar to the carbonate ion (Problem 8-25). Three Lewis formulas are

$$\overset{\ominus}{{:}\ddot{S}}-\overset{\overset{\textstyle}{|}}{\underset{\underset{\textstyle \overset{\ominus}{{:}\ddot{S}{:}}}{}}{C}}=\ddot{S}{\cdot} \longleftrightarrow {\cdot}\ddot{S}=\overset{\overset{\textstyle}{|}}{\underset{\underset{\textstyle {:}\ddot{S}{:}^{\ominus}}{}}{C}}-\ddot{S}{:}^{\ominus} \longleftrightarrow \overset{\ominus}{{:}\ddot{S}}-\overset{\overset{\textstyle}{\|}}{\underset{\underset{\textstyle {\cdot}\ddot{S}{\cdot}}{}}{C}}-\ddot{S}{:}^{\ominus}$$

and their superposition is

$$\left[\begin{matrix} S \\ \| \\ S \text{---} C \text{---} S \end{matrix} \right]^{2-}$$

(b) $:\overset{\ominus}{\underset{..}{O}}=\overset{..}{C}-\overset{..}{C}=\overset{..}{O}: \longleftrightarrow \overset{\ominus}{:}\overset{..}{\underset{..}{O}}-\overset{\overset{\displaystyle :\ddot{O}:^{\ominus}}{\|}}{C}-C=\overset{..}{O}: \longleftrightarrow \overset{\overset{\displaystyle \overset{\ominus}{:}\ddot{O}: \cdot\overset{..}{O}\cdot}{|}}{\underset{}{}}\;:O=C-\overset{..}{O}:^{\ominus} \longleftrightarrow$

$$\overset{\ominus}{:}\overset{..}{\underset{..}{O}}-\overset{\overset{\displaystyle \cdot\overset{..}{O}\cdot \; \cdot\overset{..}{O}\cdot}{\| \qquad \|}}{C}-C-\overset{..}{\underset{..}{O}}:^{\ominus}$$

Their superposition is

$$\left[\begin{matrix} O \quad\; O \\ \| \quad\; \| \\ O \text{---} C \text{---} C \text{---} O \end{matrix} \right]^{2-}$$

(c) $:N\equiv C-\overset{..}{\underset{..}{S}}:^{\ominus} \longleftrightarrow \overset{\ominus}{:}N=C=\overset{..}{\underset{..}{S}}: \longleftrightarrow \overset{2\ominus}{:}\overset{..}{\underset{..}{N}}-C\equiv S:^{\oplus}$

Their superposition is

$$[N\text{---}C\text{---}S]^-$$

(d) $\overset{\ominus}{:}\overset{..}{\underset{..}{O}}-\overset{..}{\underset{..}{O}}\cdot \longleftrightarrow \cdot\overset{..}{\underset{..}{O}}-\overset{..}{\underset{..}{O}}:^{\ominus}$

8-29 We shall use the abbreviation for the superimposed formula of benzene in writing the Lewis formula for the following benzene derivatives.

(a) $:\overset{..}{\underset{}{Cl}}:$

(b) $H-\overset{..}{N}-H$

(c) $:\overset{..}{\underset{..}{O}}=C-\overset{..}{\underset{..}{O}}-H$

(d) $:\overset{..}{\underset{..}{O}}-H$

8-31 (a) NO_2 contains a total of 23 electrons of which 17 are valence electrons. Lewis formulas for NO_2 are

$$\cdot\ddot{O}-N{=}\overset{..}{O}{:} \longleftrightarrow {:}\overset{..}{O}{=}N-\ddot{O}\cdot \qquad \text{odd electron}$$

(b) CO contains 14 electrons and ten valence electrons. The Lewis formula for CO is

$$:C{\equiv}O: \quad \overset{\ominus\quad\oplus}{}$$

(c) O_3^- contains 25 electrons and 19 valence electrons. Lewis formulas for O_3^- are

$$\cdot\ddot{O}-\ddot{O}-\overset{\ominus}{\ddot{O}}{:} \longleftrightarrow {:}\ddot{O}-\ddot{O}-\ddot{O}\cdot \qquad \text{odd electron}$$

(d) O_2^- contains 17 electrons and 13 valence electrons. Lewis formulas for O_2^- are

$$\overset{\ominus}{}{:}\ddot{O}-\ddot{O}\cdot \longleftrightarrow \cdot\ddot{O}-\ddot{O}{:}^{\ominus} \qquad \text{odd electron}$$

8-33 Write the C, N, N, O atoms in a row as suggested by the chemical formula and add the hydrogen atoms to the carbon atom. There is an odd number of valence electrons (23), and a Lewis formula is

$$\begin{array}{c} H \\ | \\ H\cdot{-}C{-}\ddot{N}{-}N{=}\overset{..}{O}{\cdot} \\ | \\ H \end{array}$$

Methylnitrosamine is a free radical.

8-35 (a) There are 48 valence electrons, or 24 electron pairs, in PCl_6^-. Putting the phosphorus atom as the central atom, we have

Notice that phosphorus does not obey the octet rule in this case.

(b) There are 22 valence electrons, or 11 electron pairs, in I_3^-.

$$:\ddot{I}-\overset{\ominus}{\underset{..}{I}}-\ddot{I}:$$

(c) There are 24 electron pairs in SiF_6^{2-}. Placing the silicon atom as the central atom, we have

$$\text{Si}F_6^{2-}$$ structure with six F atoms around Si, charge 2−

8-37   The Lewis formula of $BrCl$ is

$$: \overset{..}{\underset{..}{Br}} - \overset{..}{\underset{..}{Cl}} :$$

The electronegativity of chlorine is greater than that of bromine, and so we have

$$\overset{\delta+}{: \overset{..}{\underset{..}{Br}}} - \overset{\delta-}{\overset{..}{\underset{..}{Cl}}} :$$

or

$$\xrightarrow{\quad+\quad}$$
$$: \overset{..}{\underset{..}{Br}} - \overset{..}{\underset{..}{Cl}} :$$

8-39   (a) Fluorine is more electronegative than nitrogen, and so we have

$$\overset{\delta-}{:} \overset{..}{\underset{..}{F}} - \overset{3\delta+}{\overset{..}{N}} - \overset{..}{\underset{..}{F}} :^{\delta-}$$
$$\underset{\delta-}{\underset{|}{: \overset{..}{\underset{..}{F}} :}}$$

(b) Fluorine is more electronegative than oxygen, and so we have

$$\overset{\delta-}{:} \overset{..}{\underset{..}{F}} - \overset{2\delta+}{\overset{..}{O}} - \overset{..}{\underset{..}{F}} :^{\delta-}$$

(c) Oxygen is more electronegative than bromine, and so we have

$$\overset{\delta+}{: \overset{..}{\underset{..}{Br}}} - \overset{2\delta-}{\overset{..}{\underset{..}{O}}} - \overset{\delta+}{\overset{..}{\underset{..}{Br}}} :$$

8-41   (a) Some resonance forms are

The superposition of these resonance forms gives

$$\left[\begin{array}{c} O \diagdown\diagup O \\ S \\ O \diagup\diagdown O \end{array}\right]^{2-}$$

All four bonds are equivalent; they have the same bond lengths and the same bond energy.

(b) Some resonance forms are

The superposition of these resonance forms is

$$\left[\begin{array}{c} O \diagdown\diagup O \\ P \\ O \diagup\diagdown O \end{array}\right]^{3-}$$

All four bonds are equivalent; they have the same bond lengths and the same bond energy.

(c) Two resonance forms are

The superposition of these resonance forms is

$$\left[\begin{array}{c} H \quad O \\ | \quad || \\ H-C-C\!=\!\!=\!O \\ | \\ H \end{array}\right]^{-}$$

The two C—O bonds are equivalent; they have the same bond lengths and the same bond energy.

8-43 (a) 32 valence electrons, 16 electron pairs, nitrogen atom central

$$\begin{array}{c} :\ddot{F}: \\ | \\ :\ddot{F}-\overset{\oplus}{N}-\ddot{F}: \\ | \\ :\ddot{F}: \end{array}$$

(b) 34 valence electrons, 17 electron pairs, chlorine atom central

$$:\ddot{F}-\underset{\oplus}{\overset{..}{Cl}}-\ddot{F}: \quad \text{with } F \text{ atoms above}$$

(c) 8 valence electrons, 4 electron pairs, phosphorus atom central

$$\begin{array}{c} H \\ | \\ H-\overset{\oplus}{P}-H \\ | \\ H \end{array}$$

(d) 48 valence electrons, 24 electron pairs, arsenic atom central

$$:\ddot{F}-\overset{\ominus}{As}-\ddot{F}:$$

(e) 36 valence electrons, 18 electron pairs, bromine atom central

$$:\ddot{F}-\underset{\ominus}{\overset{..}{Br}}-\ddot{F}:$$

8-45 (a) 26 valence electrons, 13 electron pairs, chlorine atom central

$$\overset{\ominus}{:}\ddot{O}:-\overset{2+}{Cl}-\ddot{O}-H \longleftrightarrow \overset{.}{\cdot}\ddot{O}\cdot=\overset{.}{Cl}-\ddot{O}-H + \text{other resonance forms with an expanded valence shell}$$

(b) 18 valence electrons, 9 electron pairs, nitrogen atom central

$$\overset{.}{:}O=\ddot{N}-\ddot{O}-H$$

(c) 32 valence electrons, 16 electrons pairs, iodine atom central

$$\overset{\displaystyle :\ddot{O}: \ominus}{\underset{\displaystyle :\overset{..}{O}:\,\ominus}{\ominus:\overset{..}{\underset{..}{O}}-\overset{\scriptscriptstyle 3\oplus}{I}\overset{..}{\underset{..}{-}}\overset{..}{\underset{..}{O}}-H}} \longleftrightarrow \overset{\displaystyle \cdot\overset{\cdot}{O}\cdot}{\underset{\displaystyle \cdot\overset{..}{O}\cdot}{\cdot O=I-\overset{..}{\underset{..}{O}}-H}} + \text{ other resonance forms with an expanded valence shell}$$

(d) 20 valence electrons, ten electron pairs, bromine atom central

$$\ominus:\overset{..}{\underset{..}{O}}-\overset{\oplus}{Br}-\overset{..}{\underset{..}{O}}-H \longleftrightarrow \overset{\cdot}{}\overset{..}{O}=\overset{..}{Br}-\overset{..}{\underset{..}{O}}-H$$

8-47   (a) 20 valence electrons, ten electron pairs, sulfur atom central

$$:\overset{..}{\underset{..}{Cl}}-\overset{..}{\underset{..}{S}}-\overset{..}{\underset{..}{Cl}}:$$

(b) 34 valence electrons, 17 electron pairs, sulfur atom central

(c) 48 valence electrons, 24 electron pairs, selenium atom central

(d) 40 valence electrons, 20 electron pairs, sulfur atoms central

$$\overset{\displaystyle :\overset{..}{F}::\overset{..}{F}:}{:\overset{..}{\underset{..}{F}}-\overset{..}{\underset{..}{S}}=\overset{..}{\underset{..}{S}}-\overset{..}{\underset{..}{F}}:}$$

8-49   There are 56 valence electrons, or 28 electron pairs, in $Cr_2O_7^{2-}$. The Lewis formulas are

+ other resonance forms with expanded valence shells

8-51   The Lewis formulas of each species are

(a) H—C=C—C≡N: (b) H—O—C—C—O—H

(c) :C≡C: (d) H—C—C=C—H

The species with a triple bond are (a) and (c).

8-53   Each sulfur atom is covalently bonded to two other sulfur atoms to form an eight-membered ring. The Lewis formula for solid sulfur is

8-55   (a) 32 valence electrons, Mn atom central

:O—Mn—O: ⟷ O=Mn=O + other resonance forms with
                         expanded valence shells

(b) 24 valence electrons, Cr atom central

:O—Cr—O: ⟷ O=Cr=O + other resonance forms with
                         expanded valence shells

(c) 32 valence electrons, Ti atom central

:Cl—Ti—Cl:

(d) 16 valence electrons, V atom central

O=V=O

8-57 The Lewis formula of N_2F_2 with the arrangement FNNF is

$$:\ddot{F}-\ddot{N}=\ddot{N}-\ddot{F}:$$

The Lewis formula of N_2F_2 with the arrangement FFNN is

$$:\ddot{F}-\overset{\oplus}{\ddot{F}}-\ddot{N}=\overset{\ominus}{N}:$$

where the formal charges were assigned according to Equation (8-1). The arrangement FNNF has the lower formal charges, and so we predict that the structure of N_2F_2 is FNNF.

8-59 The Lewis formula of H_2CO is

$$H-\underset{\underset{H}{|}}{C}=\ddot{O}:$$

The Lewis formula of HCOH is

$$H-\overset{\ominus}{\ddot{C}}=\overset{\oplus}{\ddot{O}}-H$$

The Lewis formula of COH_2 is

$$\overset{2-}{:C}=\overset{\overset{\textstyle H}{|}}{\underset{}{O}}\overset{2+}{-}H$$

The arrangement H_2CO has the lowest formal charges, and so we predict that the structure of formaldehyde is H_2CO.

E ANSWERS TO SELF-TEST

1 shared

2 a line joining the two atoms

3 a lone pair

4 molecules

5 false

6 false

7 the distance between the nuclei of two atoms that are joined by a bond

8 three

9 many elements form covalent bonds so as to end up with eight electrons in their valence shells

10 true

11 a hydrogen atom can achieve a noble-gas-like electron configuration by having two electrons in its outer shell

12 one

13 two pairs of, or four

14 $\overset{\cdot\cdot}{}O{=}C{=}O\overset{\cdot\cdot}{}$

15 false

16 three pairs of, or six

17 false

18 $:N{\equiv}N:$

19 false

20 see Equation (8-1)

21 false

22 a superposition of the various Lewis formulas

23 resonance form

24 equivalent (They have the same bond length and the same energy.)

25 false

26 there is one or more unpaired electrons

27 false

28 does not contain enough electrons to satisfy the octet rule for each atom in the compound

29 true

30 d

31 false

32 the force with which an atom attracts the electrons in its covalent bonds

33 left (to) right

34 fluorine

35 more

36 electronegativities of the atoms are equal

37 the electronegativities of the atoms that are joined by the bond are not equal

38 small positive . . . small negative

39 a small positive charge (The magnitude of the charge is unspecified, but it is less than that of a proton.)

40 the polarity of the bond

41 magnitude . . . direction

42 true

VSEPR THEORY

A   OUTLINE OF CHAPTER 9

9-1   Lewis formulas do not represent the shapes of molecules.

Geometrical isomers are molecules that have the same chemical formula but different spatial arrangements of their atoms.

A regular tetrahedron has four equivalent vertices and four identical faces, each of which is an equilateral triangle (Figure 9-2).

9-2   All four vertices of a regular tetrahedron are equivalent.

When four atoms are bonded to a carbon atom, they are arranged in a tetrahedral array around the carbon atom, which is in the center of the tetrahedron (Figure 9-1).

The regular tetrahedron bond angle is 109.5° (for example, the H—C—H bond angle in CH_4 is 109.5°).

A space-filling model of a molecule represents the angles between bonds and the relative sizes of the atoms (Figure 9-3).

A ball-and-stick model of a molecule represents the angles between bonds (Figure 9-1).

Structural chemistry is the study of the shapes and sizes of molecules.

9-3   Valence-shell electron-pair repulsion theory is used to predict the shapes of molecules.

VSEPR theory postulates that the shape of a molecule is determined by the mutual repulsion of the electron pairs in the valence shell of the central atom (Figure 9-4).

The electron-deficient molecule $BeCl_2$ is linear.

The electron-deficient molecule BF_3 is trigonal planar.

9-4   The number of valence-shell electron pairs determines the shape of a molecule.

The arrangements of sets of electron pairs on the surface of spheres that minimize mutual repulsion between electron pairs are shown in Figure 9-4.

The five vertices of a trigonal bipyramid are not equivalent; the three lying on the equator are called equatorial vertices, and the two lying at the poles are called axial vertices (Figure 9-4d).

Molecules with six covalent bonds about a central atom are octahedral.

All six vertices of an octahedron are equivalent (Figure 9-6).

The bond angles for various molecular shapes are (Table 9-1):

linear	180°
trigonal planar	120°
tetrahedral	109.5°
trigonal bipyramidal	120° equatorial angles
	90°, 180° axial angles
octahedral	90°, 180°

9-5   Lone electron pairs in the valence shell affect the shapes of molecules.

Lone pairs are more spread out than bond pairs.

The repulsion between a lone pair and the electron pair in a covalent bond is greater than the repulsion between the electron pairs in two covalent bonds.

Many molecules can be classified by using the formula AX_mE_n, where A represents a central atom, X represents an attached ligand, and E is a lone pair of electrons on the central atom.

The total number of electron pairs in the valence shell of the central atom determines the shape of a molecule.

Lone-pair – lone-pair repulsion > lone-pair – bond-pair repulsion > bond-pair – bond-pair repulsion (Equation 9-1).

The numbers of bonds and lone pairs of electrons around the central atom result in the molecular shapes (Figure 9-9).

AX_2	linear
AX_3	trigonal planar
AX_2E	bent
AX_4	tetrahedral
AX_3E	trigonal pyramidal
AX_2E_2	bent
AX_5	trigonal bipyramidal
AX_4E	seesaw
AX_3E_2	T-shaped
AX_2E_3	linear
AX_6	octahedral
AX_5E	square pyramidal
AX_4E_2	square planar

9-6   VSEPR theory is applicable to molecules that contain multiple bonds.

A double or triple bond is counted simply as one bond connecting the ligand X to the central atom A.

Multiple bonds repel single bonds more strongly than single bonds repel other single bonds.

VSEPR theory can be applied to molecules that are described by resonance.

9-7   Lone-pair electrons occupy the equatorial vertices of a trigonal bipyramid.

An equatorial lone pair has only two neighbors at 90° (Figure 9-11).

AX_4E molecules are seesaw-shaped (Figure 9-12a).

AX_3E_2 molecules are T-shaped (Figure 9-12b).

AX_2E_3 molecules are linear (Figure 9-12c).

9-8   Two lone electron pairs occupy opposite vertices of an octahedron.

The lone-pair–lone-pair repulsion is minimized when the two lone pairs occupy opposite vertices of an octahedron.

AX_5E molecules are square pyramidal (Figure 9-16b).

AX_4E_2 molecules are square planar (Figure 9-16c).

A summary of the results of VSEPR theory is given in Table 9-3.

9-9   Symmetry determines whether or not a molecule has a net dipole moment.

A symmetric molecule with polar bonds may have no net dipole moment.

A nonsymmetric molecule with polar bonds has a net dipole moment.

B   SELF-TEST

1   The four single bonds about a central carbon atom are directed toward

———————————————————— .

2   All four vertices of a regular tetrahedron are equivalent. *True / False*

3   Dichloromethane, CH_2Cl_2, has ———————————— geometrical isomers.

4   The shape of a molecule can be determined experimentally. *True / False*

5   The basis of the VSEPR theory is the postulate that the shape of a molecule is determined by ————————————————————————

———————————————————————————————— .

6   The shape of a molecule in which the central atom forms two bonds and has no lone electron pairs is ———————————— .

7   The VSEPR theory predicts that two valence-shell electron pairs about a central atom lie _____.

8   The VSEPR theory predicts that three valence-shell electron pairs about a central atom lie _____.

9   The VSEPR theory predicts that four valence-shell electron pairs about a central atom lie _____.

10 The VSEPR theory predicts that five valence-shell electron pairs about a central atom lie _____.

11 The VSEPR theory predicts that six valence-shell electron pairs about a central atom lie _____.

12 The five vertices of a trigonal bipyramid are equivalent. *True / False*

13 The six vertices of an octahedron are equivalent. *True / False*

14 Axial vertices are the vertices of a _____ that lie _____.

15 Lone-electron pairs on the central atom in a molecule or ion do not affect the shape of the molecule or ion. *True / False*

16 The shape of ammonia, NH_3, is _____.

17 The H—N—H bond angle in ammonia is less than 109.5° because _____ _____.

18 The shape of the water molecule, H_2O, is _____.

19 The H—O—H bond angle in water is 109.5°. *True / False*

20 The symbol AX_3E indicates a molecule or ion that has _____ _____ around a central atom.

21 The shape of a molecule of class AX_3E is _____.

22 The symbol AX_4E indicates a molecule or ion that has _____ _____

around a central atom.

23 The lone electron pair in an AX_4E class of molecule is located at an *(axial, equatorial)* position on a trigonal bipyramid.

24 The shape of an AX$_4$E molecule is _____.

25 The shape of a molecule is described by the positions of the nuclei of the central atom and the ligands. *True/False*

26 The shape of an AX$_3$E$_2$ molecule is _____.

27 The shape of an AX$_2$E$_3$ molecule is _____.

28 In the molecule PCl$_5$, _____ is the central atom and _____ is a ligand.

29 The double bond in the formaldehyde molecule, H$_2$CO, is considered as two bonds in applying VSEPR theory. *True/False*

30 The formaldehyde molecule is an _____ class molecule.

31 The shape of the formaldehyde molecule is _____.

32 The F—Cl—F bond angle in the molecule ClF$_3$ is less than 90° because ___ _____.

33 The symbol AX$_5$E indicates a molecule or ion that has _____ _____ around the central atom.

34 The shape of an AX$_5$E molecule is _____.

35 It makes no difference at which vertex the lone electron pair in an AX$_5$E molecule is located. *True/False*

36 The shape of an AX$_4$E$_2$ molecule is _____.

37 The VSEPR theory cannot be applied to molecules that are described by resonance. *True/False*

38 The bond angles in a trigonal planar molecule are close to _____.

39 The bond angles in a trigonal bipyramidal molecule are close to _____, _____, and _____.

40 The bond angles in a square pyramidal molecule are all exactly 90°. *True/False*

41 A symmetric molecule with polar bonds may have no net dipole moment. *True/False*

C   CALCULATIONS YOU SHOULD KNOW HOW TO DO

There are no numerical calculations in this chapter. In Problems 9-1 through 9-34 you are asked to use VSEPR theory to predict molecular shapes.

D   SOLUTIONS TO THE ODD-NUMBERED PROBLEMS

9-1   In this problem we first use VSEPR theory to predict the molecular shape and from the shape we determine if there are any 90° bond angles. (See Table 9-1.)

(a) TeF_6 is an AX_6 octahedral molecule and thus has 90° bond angles.

(b) $AsBr_5$ is an AX_5 trigonal bipyramidal molecule and thus has some 90° bond angles.

(c) GaI_3 is an AX_3 trigonal molecule and thus has no 90° bond angles.

(d) XeF_4 is an AX_4E_2 square planar molecule and thus has 90° bond angles.

9-3   (a) ClF_3 is an AX_3E_2 T-shaped molecule and thus has no 120° bond angles.

(b) $SbBr_6^-$ is an AX_6 octahedral ion and thus has no 120° bond angles.

(c) $SbCl_5$ is an AX_5 trigonal bipyramidal molecule and thus has some 120° bond angles.

(d) $InCl_3$ is an AX_3 trigonal planar molecule and thus has 120° bond angles.

9-5   See Figure 9-9 or Table 9-3.

(a) :F̈—T̈e—F̈: AX_2E_2 bent

(b) :B̈r—S̈n—B̈r: AX_2E bent

(c) :F̈—K̈r—F̈: AX_2E_3 linear

(d) :F̈—Ö—F̈: AX_2E_2 bent

9-7   (a) 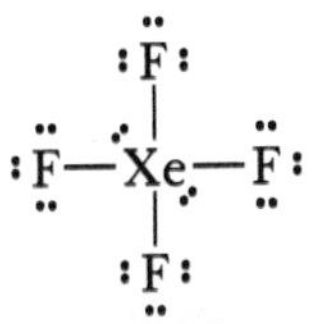
:F̈:
|
:F̈—Ẍe—F̈: AX_4E_2 square planar
|
:F̈:

(b) 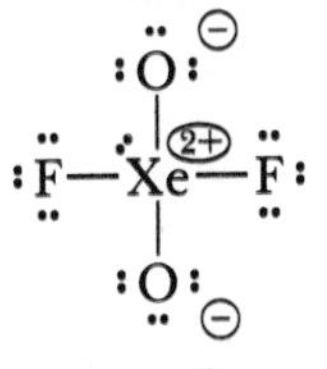
:Ö:⊖
|
:F̈—Xe⊕—F̈: AX_4E seesaw
|
:Ö:⊖

(c) 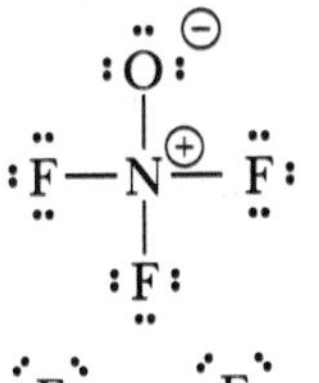
:Ö:⊖
|
:F̈—N⊕—F̈: AX_4 tetrahedral
|
:F̈:

(d) 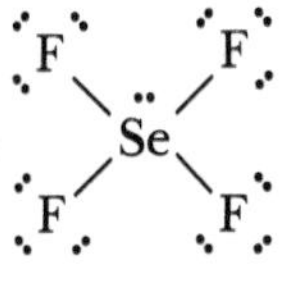
F   F
\ :: /
Se
/   \
F   F AX_4E seesaw

9-9   (a)   AX$_5$E   square pyramidal

(b)   AX$_5$ trigonal bipyramidal

(c)   AX$_5$ trigonal bipyramidal

(d)   AX$_5$E   square pyramidal

9-11   (a)   AX$_6$ octahedral   90°
                                                                                                       (1)

(b)   AX$_5$ trigonal
                                                       bipyramidal   90°, 120°
                                                                                                       (1, 3)

(c)   AX$_4$E$_2$ square planar   90°
                                                                                                       (1)

(d)   AX$_3$ trigonal
                                                       planar   120°
                                                                                                       (3)

9-13   (a)   AX$_4$ tetrahedral   109.5°
                                                                                                       (2)

(b)   AX$_6$ octahedral   90°
                                                                                                       (1)

(c) 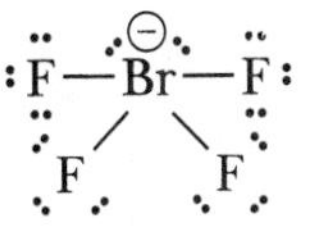 $:\!F\!\!-\!\!Br\!\!-\!\!F:$ AX_4E_2 square planar   90°

$$\overset{\displaystyle F}{\diagup}\overset{\displaystyle }{}\overset{\displaystyle F}{\diagdown}$$

(1)

(d) 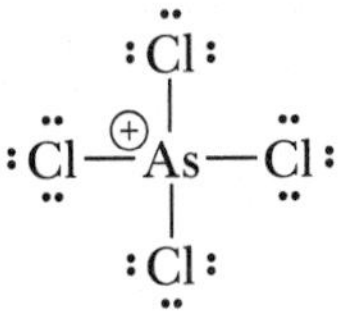 $:\!Cl\!\!-\!\!\overset{\oplus}{As}\!\!-\!\!Cl:$ AX_4 tetrahedral   109.5°

with Cl above and Cl below

(2)

9-15 AB compounds; for example

$$IF \qquad :\!I\!\!-\!\!F: \qquad \text{linear}$$

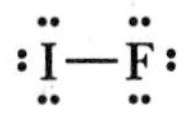

All AB compounds are linear.

AB_3 compounds; for example

$$IF_3 \qquad :\!F\!\!-\!\!I\!\!-\!\!F: \qquad AX_3E_2 \qquad \text{T-shaped}$$

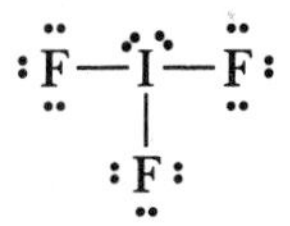

Thus BrF_3 and ClF_3 are T-shaped.

AB_5 compounds; for example

$$IF_5 \qquad \qquad AX_5E \qquad \text{square pyramidal}$$

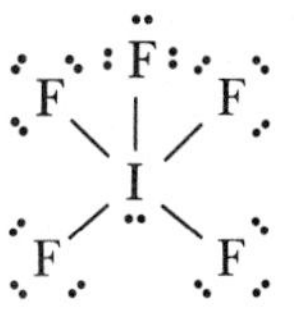

Thus BrF_5 and ClF_5 are square pyramidal.

9-17 (a) 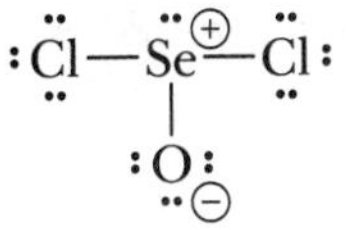 $:\!Cl\!\!-\!\!\overset{\oplus}{Se}\!\!-\!\!Cl:$ AX_3E trigonal pyramidal

(b) 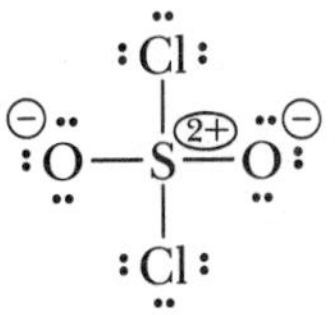 $\overset{\ominus}{O}\!\!-\!\!\overset{2+}{S}\!\!=\!\!\overset{\ominus}{O}:$ AX_4 tetrahedral

(c) 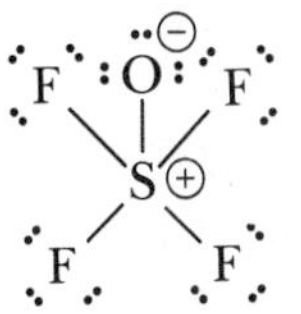 AX_5 trigonal bipyramidal

(d) $:\overset{..}{\underset{..}{O}}=\overset{..}{\underset{..}{Cl}}-\overset{..}{\underset{..}{O}}:$ with $:\overset{..}{F}:$ above and $:\overset{..}{O}:$ below AX_4 tetrahedral

9-19 (a) $\overset{Cl}{\underset{Cl}{>}}C=\overset{..}{\underset{..}{O}}:$ AX_3 trigonal planar

(b) $:\overset{..}{F}-\overset{\oplus}{N}-\overset{..}{F}:$ with $:\overset{\ominus}{\underset{}{S}}:$ above and $:\overset{..}{F}:$ below AX_4 tetrahedral

(c) $\overset{\ominus}{N}=\overset{\oplus}{N}=\overset{\ominus}{N}$ AX_2 linear

(d) $:\overset{..}{Cl}-\overset{..}{Sb}=\overset{..}{O}:$ AX_2E bent

9-21 (a) $\overset{\cdot\overset{\oplus}{Br}}{\underset{\ominus:O\quad O:\ominus}{}}$ AX_2E_2 bent

(b) $\underset{F\quad :F:\quad F}{\overset{F\quad \ominus\quad F}{Te}}$ AX_5E square pyramidal

(c) $:\overset{\ominus}{O}-\overset{2\oplus}{\underset{:O:^\ominus}{S}}=\overset{..}{O}:$ with $:Cl:$ above   or $:O=\overset{:Cl:}{\underset{:Cl:}{S}}=O:$ AX_4 tetrahedral

(d) $:\overset{..}{F}-\overset{\oplus}{\underset{:F:}{S}}-\overset{..}{F}:$ AX_3E trigonal pyramidal

9-23 (a) $\underset{F\quad :O:\quad F}{\overset{F\quad :O:^\ominus\quad F}{Xe}}$ or $\underset{F\quad O\quad F}{\overset{F\quad O\quad F}{Xe}}$ AX_6 octahedral

(b)   [diagram of IO_2F_3 structures]   or   [diagram] AX_5 trigonal bipyramidal

(c)   [diagram of IO_2F structures]   or   [diagram] AX_3E trigonal pyramidal

(d)   [diagram of IO_3F structures]   or   [diagram] AX_4 tetrahedral

9-25   The Lewis formula of the species NO_2^+ is

$$\overset{\oplus}{:O{=}N{=}O:}$$

Thus NO_2^+ is a linear molecule with an O—N—O bond angle of 180°. The Lewis formula of NO_2^- is

$$[O{\cdots}\overset{..}{N}{\cdots}O]^-$$

Thus NO_2^- is a bent molecule with a predicted O—N—O bond angle of slightly less than 120°.

9-27   (a)   :F—Xe—F: AX_2E_3 linear
(no dipole moment)

(b)   [diagram of AsF_5] AX_5 trigonal bipyramidal
(no dipole moment)

(c)   [diagram of $TeCl_4$] AX_4E seesaw
(dipole moment

(d)   :Cl—O—Cl: AX_2E_2 bent
(dipole moment)

9-29   (a)   [diagram of $GaCl_3$] AX_3 trigonal planar
(no dipole moment)

(b) $:\overset{..}{\underset{..}{Cl}}—\overset{..}{Te}—\overset{..}{\underset{..}{Cl}}:$ AX_2E_2 bent
(dipole moment)

(c) AX_4E seesaw
(dipole moment)

(d) AX_5 trigonal bipyramidal
(no dipole moment)

9-31 (a) CF_4, AX_4, tetrahedral, nonpolar

(b) AsF_3, AX_3E, trigonal pyramidal, polar

(c) XeF_4, AX_4E_2, square planar, nonpolar

(d) SeF_4, AX_4E, seesaw, polar

9-33 (a) Fluorine is more electronegative than nitrogen, and so we have

$$\overset{3\delta+}{\delta-:\overset{..}{\underset{..}{F}}—N—\overset{..}{\underset{..}{F}}:\delta-}$$
$$\underset{\delta-}{|}$$
$$:\overset{}{\underset{..}{F}}:$$

(b) Fluorine is more electronegative than oxygen, and so we have

$$\overset{2\delta+}{\delta-:\overset{..}{\underset{..}{F}}—\overset{..}{\underset{..}{O}}—\overset{..}{\underset{..}{F}}:\delta-}$$

(c) Oxygen is more electronegative than bromine, and so we have

$$\overset{\delta+}{:Br}—\overset{2\delta-}{\underset{..}{O}}—\overset{\delta+}{Br}:$$

9-35 (a) All the vertices of a tetrahedron are equivalent, and thus it makes no difference where the ligand Y is placed. Therefore, there is only one possible arrangement of the ligands for tetrahedral AX_3Y molecules.

(b) There is only one possible arrangement of the ligands in tetrahedral AX_2YZ molecules.

(c) All the vertices of a square are equivalent, and thus it makes no difference where ligand Y is placed. Therefore, there is only one possible arrangement of the ligands in a square planar AX_3Y molecule.

(d) Two isomers with identical ligands either **adjacent** or **opposite** to one another:

X's adjacent   X's opposite

9-37 (a) All octahedral vertices are equivalent. Thus there is only one possible arrangement for an octahedral AX_5Y molecule.

(b) Two isomers, one with the two Y's opposite and one with the two Y's adjacent:

Y's adjacent   Y's opposite

(c) Two isomers, one with the three Y's on an octahedral face and one with the three Y's along three of the four vertices of a square:

three Y's on the   three Y's
vertices of a square   on a face

9-39 (a) One isomer

(b) $Pt(NH_3)_5Cl^{3+}$ is an AX_5Y octahedral molecule; thus it has one isomer (Problem 9-37a).

(c) $Pt(NH_3)_4Cl_2^{2+}$ is an AX_4Y_2 octahedral molecule; thus it has two isomers. The two Cl atoms are adjacent in one isomer and the two Cl atoms are opposite one another in the other isomer (Problem 9-37b).

(d) $Pt(NH_3)_3Cl_3^+$ is an AX_3Y_3 octahedral molecule; thus it has two isomers. The three chlorine atoms lie on the vertices of a square in one isomer and the three chlorine atoms lie on a face in the other isomer (Problem 9-37c).

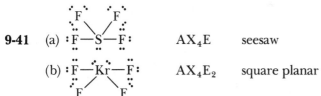

9-41 (a) AX_4E seesaw

(b) AX_4E_2 square planar

(c) 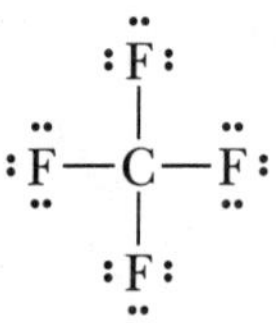 :F—C—F: (with :F: above and :F: below) AX_4 tetrahedral

(d) 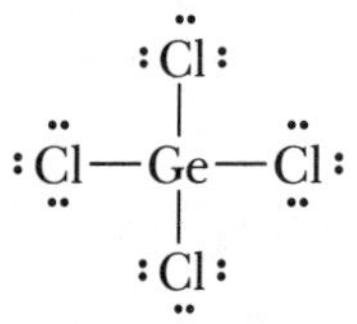 :Cl—Ge—Cl: (with :Cl: above and :Cl: below) AX_4 tetrahedral

9-43   (a) H_2O (AX_2E_2)

(b) NH_2^- (AX_2E_2)

(c) AlH_4^- (AX_4)

(d) SF_6 (AX_6)

See Table 9-3 for other examples of each case.

9-45   (a) 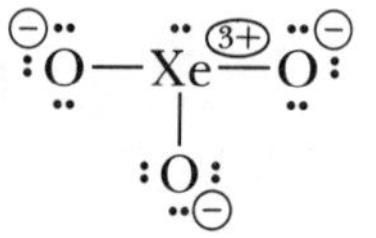   :O—Xe=O: or :O=Xe=O: AX_3E trigonal pyramidal
(with :O: below)

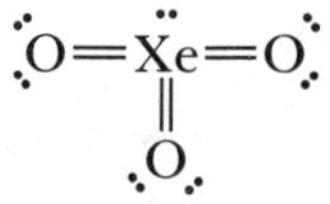

(b) 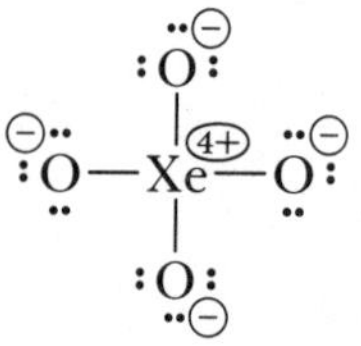   :O—Xe—O: or O=Xe=O AX_4 tetrahedral
(with :O: above and :O: below)

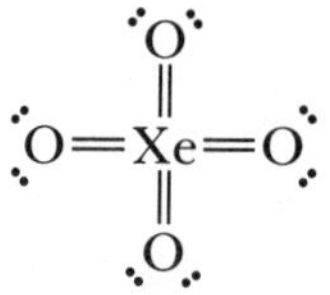

(c) 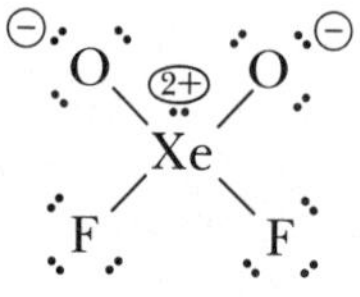   O—Xe—O with F, F   or   O=Xe=O with F, F AX_4E seesaw

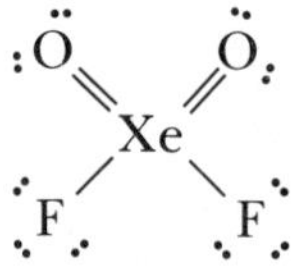

(d) 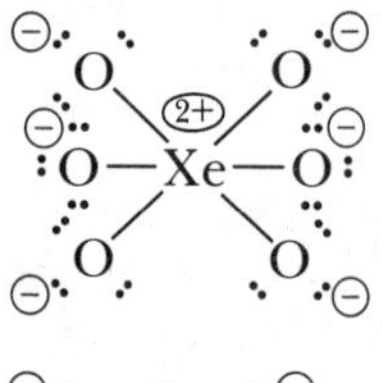   O—Xe—O with O, O, O, O AX_6 octahedral

9-47   (a) 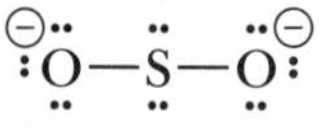   :O—S—O: AX_2E_2 bent

(b) 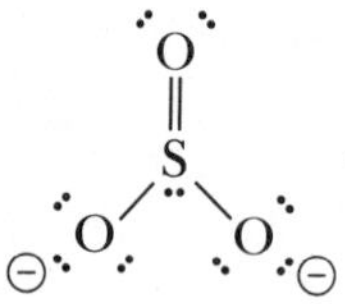   S with O (double bond) and O, O   + resonance forms AX_3E trigonal pyramidal

(c) $\overset{\ominus \cdots}{:\!O} - \overset{\underset{\displaystyle :\!\overset{\cdots\ominus}{O}:}{|}}{\underset{\displaystyle :\!\overset{\cdots}{O}:}{\overset{2+}{S}}} \overset{\cdots\ominus}{=\!\!O:}$ + resonance forms AX_4 tetrahedral

9-49 (a) The order of the electronegativities of the halogens increases as $F > Cl > Br > I$, and so the dipole moments of HX go as

$$HF > HCl > HBr > HI$$

(b) Electronegativity (Figure 8-4) goes as $N > P > As$, and so the XH_3 dipole moments go as

$$NH_3 > PH_3 > AsH_3$$

There is a small difference in the shapes of these molecules, but the electronegativity difference is more important.

(c) Referring to part (a), we write

$$IF_3 > BrF_3 > ClF_3$$

(d) Electronegativity increases as $O > S > Se > Te$, and so the dipole moments go as

$$H_2O > H_2S > H_2Se > H_2Te$$

There are small differences in the shapes of these molecules, but the electronegativity difference is more important.

9-51 Using the AX_mE_n notation, we find that (a) XeF_4 is AX_4E_2, (b) CF_4 is AX_4, (c) SF_2 is AX_2E_2, and (d) XeF_2 is AX_2E_3. The corresponding shapes are (a) square planar, (b) tetrahedral, (c) bent, and (d) linear. Thus only XeF_4 has $90°$ bond angles.

9-53 (a) $\begin{array}{c} :\!F \qquad F: \\ \diagdown \overset{2-}{\diagup} \\ :\!F - Ti - F: \\ \diagup \qquad \diagdown \\ :\!F \qquad F: \end{array}$ AX_6 octahedral

(b) $:\!O = \overset{\oplus}{V} = O:$ AX_2 linear

(c) $\begin{array}{c} :\!\overset{\cdots}{Cl}: \\ | \\ :\!\overset{\cdots}{Cl} - \overset{\oplus}{V} - \overset{\cdots}{Cl}: \\ | \\ :\!\overset{\cdots}{O}: \\ \ominus \end{array}$ or $\begin{array}{c} :\!\overset{\cdots}{Cl}: \\ | \\ :\!\overset{\cdots}{Cl} - V - \overset{\cdots}{Cl}: \\ \| \\ \overset{\cdots}{O} \end{array}$ AX_4 tetrahedral

(d) AX_4 tetrahedral

9-55 (a) AX_5 trigonal bipyramidal

(b) AX_6 octahedral

(c) AX_6 octahedral

(d) or AX_4 tetrahedral

9-57 (a) AX_5 trigonal bipyramidal

(b) AX_3E trigonal pyramidal

(c) AX_4 tetrahedral

E   ANSWERS TO SELF-TEST

1   the vertices of a tetrahedron

2   true

3   no

4   true

5   mutual repulsion of the electron pairs in the valence shell of the central atom

6   linear

7   on opposite sides of the central atom, at 180° from each other

8   at the vertices of an equilateral triangle

9   at the vertices of a tetrahedron

10   at the vertices of a trigonal bipyramid

11   at the vertices of an octahedron

12   false

13   true

14   trigonal bipyramid that lie at the poles (there are two axial vertices)

15   false

16   trigonal pyramidal (tripod)

17   lone-pair – bond-pair repulsions are greater than bond-pair – bond-pair repulsions

18   bent

19   true

20   three ligands (X) and a lone pair (E)

21   trigonal pyramidal

22   four ligands (X) and a lone pair (E)

23   equatorial

24   seesaw-shaped

25   true

26   T-shaped

27   linear

28   P . . . Cl

29   false

30   AX_3

31   trigonal planar

32   of lone-pair – bond-pair repulsions

33   five ligands (X) and one lone pair (E)

34   square pyramidal

35   true

36   square planar

37   false

38   120°

39   120°, 90°, and 180°

40   false (Angles are somewhat less than 90° because of lone-pair – bond-pair repulsions.)

41   true

COVALENT BONDING IN MOLECULES

A OUTLINE OF CHAPTER 10

10-1 A molecular orbital is a combination of atomic orbitals on different atoms.

The solution of the Schrödinger equation for H_2 gives the energies and wave functions that describe the two electrons.

A molecular orbital that encompasses both nuclei is shown in Figure 10-1.

The buildup of electron density between nuclei is responsible for attracting the nuclei together.

10-2 The bonding in polyatomic molecules can be described in terms of bond orbitals.

Localized bond orbitals describe the bonding electrons that are localized in covalent bonds.

10-3 Hybrid orbitals are combinations of atomic orbitals on the same atom.

The principle of maximum overlap of orbitals is used to describe localized bond orbitals.

Hybrid atomic orbitals are formed by combining atomic orbitals on the same atom.

The sp hybrid orbitals are the two equivalent hybrid orbitals that result from combining a $2s$ orbital and a $2p$ orbital (Figure 10-3).

The sp orbitals are directed $180°$ from each other.

The bonding in BeH_2 can be described by two localized bond orbitals, each of which is a combination of an sp hybrid orbital on the Be atom and a $1s$ atomic orbital on the H atom (Figure 10-4).

Bond orbitals that have circular cross sections when viewed along an internuclear axis are called σ orbitals.

A σ bond is a σ orbital occupied by two valence electrons of opposite spin.

There are two σ bonds in BeH_2.

10-4 sp^2 hybrid orbitals have trigonal planar symmetry.

The sp^2 hybrid orbitals are the three equivalent hybrid orbitals that are formed by combining a $2s$ orbital and two $2p$ orbitals on the same atom.

The sp^2 hybrid orbitals lie in a plane and are directed toward the vertices of an equilateral triangle (Figure 10-6).

The bonding in BF_3 can be described by three localized bond orbitals, each of which is a combination of an sp^2 hybrid orbital on the central B atom and a $2p$ atomic orbital on the F atom (Figure 10-7).

There are three σ bonds in BF_3.

10-5 sp^3 hybrid orbitals point toward the vertices of a tetrahedron.

The sp^3 hybrid orbitals are the four equivalent hybrid orbitals that result from combining the $2s$ orbital and the three $2p$ orbitals on the same atom.

The sp^3 hybrid orbitals are directed toward the vertices of a tetrahedron. (Figure 10-8).

The bonding in CH_4 can be described by four localized bond orbitals, each of which is a combination of an sp^3 hybrid orbital on the central carbon atom and a $1s$ atomic orbital on the hydrogen atom (Figure 10-9).

10-6   Hybrid atomic orbitals can involve d orbitals.

The dsp^3 hybrid orbitals are the five hybrid orbitals that result from combining the $3s$ orbital, the $3p$ orbitals, and one $3d$ orbital on the same atom.

The dsp^3 orbitals are directed toward the vertices of a trigonal bipyramid.

The five dsp^3 orbitals are not equivalent.

The d^2sp^3 hybrid orbitals are the six equivalent hybrid orbitals that result from combining the $3s$ orbital, the $3p$ orbitals, and two $3d$ orbitals on the same atom.

The d^2sp^3 orbitals are directed toward the vertices of a regular octahedron.

The conservation of orbitals states that the total number of hybrid orbitals is equal to the total number of atomic orbitals used to make them.

10-7   We use sp^3 orbitals to describe the bonding in molecules that have four electron pairs about the central atom.

The bonding in H_2O can be described in terms of sp^3 hybrid orbitals on the oxygen atom. Two of the sp^3 orbitals are used to form bonds with the hydrogen atoms, and the other two are occupied by the lone electron pairs on the oxygen atom (Figure 10-10).

The bonding in NH_3 can be described in terms of sp^3 orbitals on the nitrogen atom (Figure 10-11).

We can use sp^3 orbitals to describe the bonding in molecules that have no unique central atom (Figures 10-13, 10-14, and 10-15).

10-8   A double bond can be represented by a σ bond and a π bond.

The σ bonding in ethylene, C_2H_4, is described in terms of sp^2 orbitals on the carbon atoms (Figure 10-16).

The σ-bond framework of a molecule indicates all the σ bonds in the molecule (Figure 10-17).

A π orbital is formed by the combination of two p orbitals (Figure 10-18).

A π orbital in cross section is similar to an atomic p orbital.

A π bond is formed when two electrons of opposite spins occupy a π orbital.

The double bond in ethylene consists of a σ bond (overlap of an sp^2 orbital from each carbon atom) and a π bond (overlap of a p orbital from each carbon atom).

There is no free rotation about carbon-carbon double bonds.

Cis and trans isomers are stereoisomers.

10-9   A triple bond can be represented by one σ bond and two π bonds.

The σ bonding in acetylene, C_2H_2, is described in terms of sp orbitals on the carbon atoms (Figure 10-20).

The carbon-carbon triple bond consists of one σ bond (overlap of an sp orbital from each carbon atom) and two π bonds (overlap of two $2p$ orbitals from each carbon atom) (Figure 10-21).

10-10   The π electrons in benzene are delocalized.

There are two principal resonance forms of benzene.

The σ bonding in benzene is described in terms of sp^2 orbitals on the carbon atoms (Figure 10-22).

The three π orbitals in benzene are spread uniformly over the entire ring (Figure 10-23).

The delocalization of the π electrons in benzene is an example of charge delocalization.

10-11   The hydrogen molecular ion is the simplest diatomic species.

Molecular orbitals can be ordered according to their energies.

Molecular orbital theory is a theory of chemical bonding.

Molecular orbitals are solutions to the Schrödinger equation for H_2^+.

The shapes of some of the molecular orbitals are shown in Figure 10-24.

10-12   Molecular orbitals are bonding or antibonding.

A molecular orbital that is concentrated in a region between two nuclei is a bonding orbital.

The molecular orbital of lowest energy is a bonding orbital and is designated 1σ.

A molecular orbital that is zero in a region between two nuclei is an antibonding orbital.

An antibonding orbital is designated by the superscript *.

Electrons are placed into molecular orbitals according to the Pauli exclusion principle.

An antibonding electron annuls the effect of a bonding electron.

Bond order is given by Equation (10-1):

$$\text{bond order} = \frac{\left(\begin{array}{c}\text{number of electrons} \\ \text{in bonding orbitals}\end{array}\right) - \left(\begin{array}{c}\text{number of electrons} \\ \text{in antibonding orbitals}\end{array}\right)}{2}$$

10-13 Molecular orbital theory predicts molecular electron configurations.

The order of the molecular orbitals in terms of energy is given in Figure 10-27.

The ground-state electron configurations for the homonuclear diatomic molecules Li_2 through Ne_2 are given in Table 10-3.

Electrons are placed in 1π and $1\pi^*$ orbitals according to Hund's rule.

O_2 contains two unpaired electrons, one in each of the $1\pi^*$ orbitals.

Oxygen molecules are paramagnetic.

Molecular orbital theory can be applied to heteronuclear diatomic molecules.

10-14 Photoelectron spectra are consistent with molecular orbital theory.

The binding energy of an electron is the energy with which an electron is bound in a molecule.

A photoelectron spectrum of N_2 is shown in Figure 10-29.

B   SELF-TEST

1   The covalent bond joining the two hydrogen atoms in H_2 is due to the overlapping

of _____.

2   The localized bond orbitals that describe the electrons in a covalent bond are formed

from _____.

3   Hybrid atomic orbitals are obtained by _____

_____.

4   The *sp* orbitals are obtained by combining _____

_____.

5   There are (*one, two, three, four*) *sp* orbitals.

6   The *sp* orbitals are directed _____.

7   A σ orbital is _____ in cross section when viewed along an

internuclear axis.

8   A σ orbital may be occupied by a maximum of _____ electrons.

9   The two electrons in a σ bond are of opposite spin. *True / False*

10 The berylium-hydrogen bonds in BeH_2 are σ bonds. *True / False*

11 There are *(one, two, three, four)* σ bonds in BeH_2.

12 There are *(one, two, three, four)* sp^2 orbitals.

13 The sp^2 orbitals are obtained by combining _____

_____ .

14 The sp^2 orbitals point to _____

_____ .

15 The boron-fluorine bond in BF_3 is a σ bond. *True / False*

16 There are *(one, two, three, four)* σ bonds in BF_3.

17 The sp^3 orbitals are obtained by combining _____

_____ .

18 The sp^3 orbitals are directed toward _____ .

19 Each carbon-hydrogen bond orbital in methane, CH_4, is formed by _____

_____

_____ .

20 A carbon-hydrogen bond in CH_4 is a σ bond. *True / False*

21 The dsp^3 orbitals are obtained by combining _____

_____

_____ .

22 There are _____ dsp^3 orbitals.

23 The dsp^3 orbitals are directed toward _____

_____ .

24 The d^2sp^3 orbitals are obtained by combining _____

_____

_____ .

25 There are _____ d^2sp^3 orbitals.

26 The d^2sp^3 orbitals are directed toward _____

_____ .

27 The carbon-carbon bond in ethane is formed by _____

_____ .

28 The bond orbital that describes an H—O bond in H_2O is a combination of

_____ .

29 A π orbital results when _____

_____ .

30 A π orbital is circular in cross section when viewed along the internuclear axis.
True / False

31 The double bond in ethylene, C_2H_4, consists of a _____ bond and

a _____ bond.

32 How many valence electrons are there in ethylene? How many σ bonds and π

bonds are there? _____

_____ .

33 The C—H bond in ethylene, C_2H_4, is a combination of a(n) _____

orbital on the carbon atom and the _____ orbital of the hydrogen atom.

34 Ethylene is a planar molecule. *True / False*

35 A double bond results from the formation of two σ bonds between two atoms.
True / False

36 Rotation cannot occur about carbon-carbon double bonds. *True / False*

37 In *trans*-1,2-dichloroethene, $ClCH_2CH_2Cl$, the chlorine atoms lie _____

_____ .

38 Cis-trans isomers are examples of _____ isomers.

39 The physical properties of cis-trans isomers are identical. *True / False*

40 The triple bond in acetylene, C_2H_2, is described by a _____ bond and

_____ bonds.

41 The number of valence electrons in H—C≡C—CH_3 is _____ . There

are _____ σ bonds and _____ π bonds.

42   A C—H bond in acetylene, C_2H_2, is a combination of a(n) _____
_____ orbital on the carbon atom and a _____
orbital on the hydrogen atom.

43   Acetylene is a linear molecule. *True / False*

44   All the carbon-carbon bond lengths in benzene are the same. *True / False*

45   The shape of the benzene molecule is _____ and
_____ .

46   The C—C bond in benzene is formed by overlapping a(n) _____
orbital from each carbon atom.

47   There are _____ σ bonds and _____ π bonds in benzene.

48   The π electrons in benzene are said to be _____ .

49   Each π orbital in benzene is located between two adjacent carbon atoms. *True / False*

50   The simplest diatomic species is _____ .

51   All molecular orbitals have the same general shape. *True / False*

52   All molecular orbitals have the same energy. *True / False*

53   A bonding orbital is a molecular orbital that _____
_____ .

54   An antibonding orbital is a molecular orbital that _____
_____ .

55   The orbital designated by $1\sigma^*$ is the _____
_____ .

56   The ground-state electron configuration of homonuclear diatomic molecules is
constructed by placing all the electrons into the bonding orbital of lowest energy.
True / False

57   A 2σ orbital may contain a maximum of _____ electrons.

58   The set of 1π orbitals may contain a total of _____ electrons.

59   The bond order of a molecule must always be a whole number. *True / False*

60   A bond order of zero for a molecule indicates that the molecule does not exist.
True / False

61 The ground-state electron configuration of B_2 is $(1\sigma)^2(1\sigma*)^2(2\sigma)^2(2\sigma*)^2(1\pi)^2$; its bond order is ———— .

62 The 1π electrons in B_2 occupy the same 1π orbital. *True/False*

63 The experimental study of the energies of electrons that are ejected from molecules by electromagnetic radiation is called ———————————— .

64 The oxygen molecule is paramagnetic because ————————————

————————————— .

C   CALCULATIONS YOU SHOULD KNOW HOW TO DO

The only numerical calculations in Chapter 10 involve the equation

$$\text{bond order} = \frac{\left(\begin{array}{c}\text{number of electrons} \\ \text{in bonding orbitals}\end{array}\right) - \left(\begin{array}{c}\text{number of electrons} \\ \text{in antibonding orbitals}\end{array}\right)}{2}$$

D   SOLUTIONS TO THE ODD-NUMBERED PROBLEMS

10-1   The Lewis formula for propane is

$$
\begin{array}{ccc}
H & H & H \\
| & | & | \\
H-C-C-C-H \\
| & | & | \\
H & H & H
\end{array}
$$

There are ten localized bonds in propane. There are $3 \times 4 = 12$ valence electrons from the three carbon atoms and $8 \times 1 = 8$ valence electrons from the eight hydrogen atoms, giving a total of 20 valence electrons. The 20 valence electrons occupy the ten localized bond orbitals.

10-3   (a)
$$
\begin{array}{cc}
H & H \\
| & | \\
H-C-C-H \\
| & | \\
H & H
\end{array}
$$
14 valence electrons
7 localized bonds
0 lone pairs

(b)
$$
H-\overset{\cdot\cdot}{P}-H
$$
$$
\begin{array}{c}
| \\
H
\end{array}
$$
8 valence electrons
3 localized bonds
1 lone pair

(c) $H - \overset{\cdot\cdot}{N} - \overset{\cdot\cdot}{N} - H$ 14 valence electrons
     $\quad\; | \quad\; |$ 5 localized bonds
     $\quad\; H \;\; H$ 2 lone pairs

(d) $:\overset{\cdot\cdot}{\underset{\cdot\cdot}{C}l} - \overset{\cdot\cdot}{\underset{\cdot\cdot}{S}} - \overset{\cdot\cdot}{\underset{\cdot\cdot}{C}l}:$ 20 valence electrons
                2 localized bonds
                8 lone pairs

10-5   Boron has three valence electrons and each hydrogen has one, for a total of six valence electrons. The Lewis formula of BH_3 is

$$
\begin{array}{c}
H \\
| \\
B \\
\diagdown \\
H \qquad H
\end{array}
\qquad AX_3 \qquad \text{(trigonal planar)}
$$

We use sp^2 orbitals of the boron atom and form three localized bond orbitals by combining each boron sp^2 orbital with a hydrogen $1s$ orbital. The six valence electrons occupy the three localized bond orbitals pairwise to form three localized bonds.

10-7   There are four valence electrons from the carbon atom and seven from each fluorine atom, for a total of 32 valence electrons in CF_4. The Lewis formula of CF_4 is

$$
\begin{array}{c}
:\overset{\cdot\cdot}{F}: \\
| \\
:\overset{\cdot\cdot}{\underset{\cdot\cdot}{F}} - C - \overset{\cdot\cdot}{\underset{\cdot\cdot}{F}}: \\
| \\
:\underset{\cdot\cdot}{F}:
\end{array}
\qquad AX_4 \qquad \text{(tetrahedral)}
$$

We use sp^3 orbitals on the carbon atom and combine each carbon sp^3 orbital with a fluorine $2p$ orbital to form four localized bond orbitals that point toward the vertices of a regular tetrahedron. Eight of the valence electrons occupy these four localized bond orbitals pairwise to form four localized bonds. The remaining 24 valence electrons occupy the L shells on the fluorine atoms as three lone pairs on each fluorine atom.

10-9   The Lewis formula of $AlCl_3$ is

$$
\begin{array}{c}
\overset{\cdot\cdot}{\underset{\cdot}{C}l} \diagdown \qquad \diagup \overset{\cdot\cdot}{\underset{\cdot}{C}l} \\
Al \\
| \\
:\underset{\cdot\cdot}{C}l:
\end{array}
\qquad AX_3 \qquad \text{(trigonal planar)}
$$

The three $Al-Cl$ bonds in $AlCl_3$ are σ bonds. Each σ-bond orbital is formed by combining an sp^2 hybrid orbital on the aluminum atom with a $3p$ chlorine orbital. Six of the 24 valence electrons occupy these three bond orbitals pairwise to form three σ bonds, and the remaining 18 valence electrons are lone-pair electrons on the chlorine atoms.

10-11   The structure of H_3O^+ can be represented by

$$\begin{array}{c} \overset{\cdot\cdot\;\oplus}{O} \\ H \overset{|}{\diagup} \overset{}{\diagdown} H \\ \underset{H\,110°}{} \end{array}$$

Each of the three σ-bond orbitals is formed by combining an sp^3 orbital on the oxygen atom with a $1s$ hydrogen orbital. Six of the eight valence electrons occupy these σ-bond orbitals pairwise. The lone electron pair occupies the remaining sp^3 orbital on the oxygen atom.

10-13   The Lewis formula for NF_3 is

$$\overset{\cdot\cdot}{:}\overset{\cdot\cdot}{F}-\overset{\cdot\cdot}{\underset{\underset{\overset{\cdot\cdot}{:}\overset{\cdot\cdot}{F}:}{|}}{N}}-\overset{\cdot\cdot}{F}: \qquad AX_3E \qquad \text{(trigonal pyramidal)}$$

The three bond orbitals are formed by combining an sp^3 orbital on the nitrogen atom with a $2p$ orbital on a fluorine atom. The three σ-bond orbitals are occupied pairwise by six of the 26 valence electrons. The lone electron pair on the nitrogen atom occupies the remaining sp^3 orbital and the remaining 18 valence electrons are lone pairs on the fluorine atoms.

10-15   There are five valence electrons from the phosphorus atom and seven from each of the chlorine atoms for a total of 26 valence electrons in PCl_3. The Lewis formula of PCl_3 is

$$\overset{\cdot\cdot}{:}\overset{\cdot\cdot}{Cl}-\overset{\cdot\cdot}{\underset{\underset{\overset{\cdot\cdot}{:}\overset{\cdot\cdot}{Cl}:}{|}}{P}}-\overset{\cdot\cdot}{Cl}: \qquad AX_3E \qquad \text{(trigonal pyramidal)}$$

We use sp^3 orbitals on the phosphorus atom and combine each of the three of them with a chlorine $3p$ orbital to form the three localized bond orbitals. Six of the valence electrons occupy these localized bond orbitals to form three localized bonds. Two of the remaining valence electrons occupy the fourth sp^3 orbital on the phosphorus atom as a lone pair, and 18 occupy the M shells of the chlorine atoms to form three lone pairs on each chlorine atom.

10-17   The Lewis formula for hydrazine is

$$H-\overset{\cdot\cdot}{\underset{\underset{H}{|}}{N}}-\overset{\cdot\cdot}{\underset{\underset{H}{|}}{N}}-H$$

We shall use sp^3 orbitals on each nitrogen atom. The three σ-bond orbitals on each nitrogen atom are formed by combining two of the sp^3 orbitals on the nitrogen atom with two $1s$ hydrogen orbitals and one of the sp^3 nitrogen orbitals with an sp^3 orbital on the other nitrogen atom. Ten of the 14 valence electrons occupy the five σ-bond orbitals pairwise to form the five σ bonds. A lone electron pair occupies the remaining sp^3 orbital on each nitrogen atom.

10-19   We use sp^3 orbitals on both the carbon atom and the nitrogen atom. The formation of the localized bond orbitals can be illustrated by

$$
\begin{array}{c}
\overset{\displaystyle H}{|} \quad \overset{\displaystyle H}{|} \\
H-C-N \\
| \quad\; | \leftarrow sp^3(N) + 1s(H) \\
H \quad H
\end{array}
$$

$sp^3(C) + 1s(H)$ $sp^3(C) + sp^3(N)$

Twelve of the 14 valence electrons occupy the six σ-bond orbitals and the remaining two occupy an sp^3 orbital on the nitrogen atom as a lone pair. The shape around the carbon atom is tetrahedral and the shape around the nitrogen atom is trigonal pyramidal.

10-21   We use sp^3 orbitals on the oxygen atom and the two carbon atoms. The formation of the localized bond orbitals can be illustrated by

$$
\begin{array}{c}
\overset{\displaystyle H}{|} \qquad\; \overset{\displaystyle H}{|} \\
H-C-O-C-H \\
| \qquad\; | \\
H \qquad\; H
\end{array}
$$

$sp^3(C) + 1s(H)$

$sp^3(O) + sp^3(C)$

Sixteen of the 20 valence electrons occupy the eight σ-bond orbitals and the remaining four occupy two of the oxygen sp^3 orbitals as lone pairs.

10-23   (a) The Lewis formula for $Cl_2C{=}CH_2$ is

$$
\begin{array}{c}
\ddot{\underset{..}{Cl}} \qquad\qquad H \\
\;\;\;\;\backslash \qquad\quad / \\
\;\;\;\;\;\; C{=}C \\
\;\;\;\;/ \qquad\quad \backslash \\
\ddot{\underset{..}{Cl}} \qquad\qquad H
\end{array}
$$

There are five σ bonds and one π bond.

(b) The Lewis formula for $H_2C{=}CHCH{=}CH_2$ is

$$
\begin{array}{c}
H-C{=}C-C{=}C-H \\
|\quad\; |\quad\; |\quad\; | \\
H\quad H\quad H\quad H
\end{array}
$$

There are nine σ bonds and two π bonds.

(c) The Lewis formula of CH_3COOH is

$$
\begin{array}{c}
\overset{\displaystyle H}{|} \qquad\quad \ddot{O}: \\
\;\;\;\;\;\;\;\;\;\;\;\;\;\; \| \\
H-C-C \\
| \qquad\quad \backslash \\
H \qquad\quad \underset{..}{\ddot{O}}{-}H
\end{array}
$$

There are seven σ bonds and one π bond.

(d) The Lewis formula is

There are 14 σ bonds and two π bonds.

10-25 The Lewis formula for ethylacetylene is

There are nine σ bonds and two π bonds. There are $(6 \times 1) + (4 \times 4) = 22$ valence electrons, which occupy the 11 bond orbitals.

10-27 The Lewis formula of carbon monoxide is

The σ-bond orbital between the carbon and oxygen atoms is formed by combining an sp orbital on the carbon atom and an sp orbital on the oxygen atom. Each of the two π-bond orbitals is formed by combining a $2p$ orbital on the carbon atom and a $2p$ orbital on the oxygen atom. Two of the ten valence electrons occupy the σ-bond orbital, four occupy the two π-bond orbitals, and the remaining four valence electrons are lone-pair electrons. One lone pair occupies an sp orbital on the carbon atom; the other pair occupies an sp orbital on the oxygen atom.

10-29 The Lewis formula for phenol is

The σ-bond framework is

There are six π-bond orbitals that are delocalized over the entire ring. The 13 σ-bond orbitals and three of the delocalized π-bond orbitals are occupied by 32 of the 36 valence electrons. The remaining four valence electrons constitute two lone pairs on the oxygen atom.

10-31 The Lewis formula for naphthalene is

The σ-bond framework is

There are ten π-bond orbitals that are delocalized over the entire two rings as indicated by the circles in the Lewis formula. Thirty-eight of the 48 valence electrons occupy the 19 σ-bond orbitals and the remaining ten valence electrons occupy five of the delocalized π-bond orbitals.

10-33 The resonance hybrid Lewis formula of CO_3^{2-} is

AX_3 (trigonal planar)
24 valence electrons

We use sp^2 orbitals on each of the four atoms and form three localized σ-bond orbitals that lie in the plane of the ion. The remaining p orbital on each atom, which is perpendicular to the plane of the ion, combines with the others to form four delocalized π-bond orbitals. Six of the valence electrons occupy the three localized σ-bond orbitals to form three localized σ bonds, 12 of the valence electrons occupy the two remaining sp^2 orbitals on each oxygen atom to form two lone pairs on each oxygen atom, and the remaining six valence electrons occupy the three delocalized π-bond orbitals of lowest energy. The resulting charge delocalization corresponds to the fact that the Lewis formula of CO_3^{2-} is written as a resonance hybrid.

10-35   There are eight electrons in diatomic beryllium. Using Figure 10-27, we see that the ground-state electron configuration of diatomic beryllium is $(1\sigma)^2(1\sigma^*)^2$ $(2\sigma)^2(2\sigma^*)^2$. There are four electrons in bonding orbitals and four electrons in antibonding orbitals, and so Be_2 has no net bonding. We predict that Be_2 does not exist.

10-37   Using Figure 10-27 and Equation (10-1), we find that the ground-state electron configurations and bond orders of N_2, N_2^+, O_2 and O_2^+ are as follows.

	Ground-state electron configuration	Bond order
N_2	$(1\sigma)^2(1\sigma^*)^2(2\sigma)^2(2\sigma^*)^2(1\pi)^4(3\sigma)^2$	3
N_2^+	$(1\sigma)^2(1\sigma^*)^2(2\sigma)^2(2\sigma^*)^2(1\pi)^4(3\sigma)^1$	2½
O_2	$(1\sigma)^2(1\sigma^*)^2(2\sigma)^2(2\sigma^*)^2(1\pi)^4(3\sigma)^2(1\pi^*)^2$	2
O_2^+	$(1\sigma)^2(1\sigma^*)^2(2\sigma)^2(2\sigma^*)^2(1\pi)^4(3\sigma)^2(1\pi^*)^1$	2½

We find that the bond order of N_2 is 3 while the bond order of N_2^+ is 2½. The bond energy increases as the bond order increases; therefore, the bond energy of N_2 is greater than that of N_2^+. However, we find that the bond order of O_2 is 2, while the bond order of O_2^+ is 2½. Therefore, the bond energy of O_2 is less than that of O_2^+.

10-39   Using Figure 10-27 and Equation (10-1), we find that the ground-state electron configurations and bond orders of C_2 and C_2^{2-} are as follows.

	Ground-state electron configuration	Bond order
C_2	$(1\sigma)^2(1\sigma^*)^2(2\sigma)^2(2\sigma^*)^2(1\pi)^4$	2
C_2^{2-}	$(1\sigma)^2(1\sigma^*)^2(2\sigma)^2(2\sigma^*)^2(1\pi)^4(3\sigma)^2$	3

Because the bond order of C_2^{2-} is greater than that of C_2, we predict that C_2^{2-} has a larger bond energy and a shorter bond length than C_2.

10-41   Carbon monoxide has $6 + 8 = 14$ electrons, and so the ground-state electron configuration of carbon monoxide is $(1\sigma)^2(1\sigma^*)^2(2\sigma)^2(2\sigma^*)^2(1\pi)^4(3\sigma)^2$. The bond order of CO is 3. The Lewis formula for CO is

$$^{\ominus}\!:\!C\!\equiv\!O\!:^{\oplus}$$

Both molecular orbital theory and the Lewis formula predict that there is a triple bond in CO.

10-43 Determine the total number of electrons and use Figure 10-27.

(a) 18 electrons
$(1\sigma)^2(1\sigma^*)^2(2\sigma)^2(2\sigma^*)^2(1\pi)^2(1\pi)^2(3\sigma)^2(1\pi^*)^2(1\pi^*)^2$
bond order $= 1$

(b) 11 electrons
$(1\sigma)^2(1\sigma^*)^2(2\sigma)^2(2\sigma^*)^2(1\pi)^2(1\pi)^1$
bond order $= 1\frac{1}{2}$

(c) 7 electrons
$(1\sigma)^2(1\sigma^*)^2(2\sigma)^2(2\sigma^*)^1$
bond order $= \frac{1}{2}$

(d) 19 electrons
$(1\sigma)^2(1\sigma^*)^2(2\sigma)^2(2\sigma^*)^2(1\pi)^2(1\pi)^2(3\sigma)^2(1\pi^*)^2(1\pi^*)^2(3\sigma^*)^1$
bond order $= \frac{1}{2}$

10-45 If the additional electron occupies a bonding orbital, then a stronger net bonding will result. For example, the ground-state electron configuration of B_2 (ten electrons) is $(1\sigma)^2(1\sigma^*)^2(2\sigma)^2(2\sigma^*)^2(1\pi)^1(1\pi)^1$. The addition of an electron will produce $(1\sigma)^2(1\sigma^*)^2(2\sigma)^2(2\sigma^*)^2(1\pi)^2(1\pi)^1$ with one additional bonding electron.

10-47 Write the ground-state electron configuration and determine if there are unpaired electrons.

(a) $(1\sigma)^2(1\sigma^*)^2(2\sigma)^2(2\sigma^*)^2(1\pi)^2(1\pi)^2$

(b) $(1\sigma)^2(1\sigma^*)^2(2\sigma)^2(2\sigma^*)^2(1\pi)^1(1\pi)^1$

(c) $(1\sigma)^2(1\sigma^*)^2(2\sigma)^2(2\sigma^*)^2(1\pi)^1(1\pi)^1$

(d) $(1\sigma)^2(1\sigma^*)^2(2\sigma)^2(2\sigma^*)^2(1\pi)^2(1\pi)^2(3\sigma)^2(1\pi^*)^1(1\pi^*)^1$

The species B_2, C_2^{2+} and F_2^{2+} have unpaired electrons.

10-49 The Lewis formula of acetaldehyde is

The σ-bond framework in acetaldehyde is

The π-bond orbital is formed by combining the remaining $2p$ orbital on the central carbon atom with the remaining $2p$ orbital on the oxygen atom. Twelve of the 18 valence electrons occupy the six σ-bond orbitals and two of them occupy the π-bond orbital. The two lone electron pairs on the oxygen atom occupy the other two sp^2 orbitals. The shape of acetaldehyde is trigonal planar around the central carbon atom.

10-51 The σ-bond framework of methylacetylene is

The remaining bond orbitals between the two carbon atoms on the right are two π-bond orbitals formed from the $2p$ orbitals on each atom. There are six σ-bond orbitals and two π-bond orbitals. There are $(4 \times 1) + (3 \times 4) = 16$ valence electrons, which occupy the eight bond orbitals.

10-53 A telliurim atom's electron configuration is $[\text{Kr}](5s)^2(4d)^{10}(5p_x)^2(5p_y)^1 (5p_z)^1$, indicating that two of the $5p$ orbitals are occupied by only one electron. To describe the bonding in H_2Te, use the $1s$ orbitals on the hydrogen atom and two of the $5p$ orbitals on the tellurium atom.

10-55 The π-bond constituent of the double bond holds a molecule in place about a double bond. Any rotation about the double bond would require that the π bond be ruptured.

10-57 To describe the bonding in formamide we use sp^2 orbitals on the nitrogen, carbon, and oxygen atoms. The σ-bond framework is

The remaining p orbitals on the nitrogen, carbon, and oxygen atoms combine to form three delocalized π-bond orbitals. Ten of the 16 valence electrons occupy the five localized σ-bond orbitals, four of them occupy the remaining two oxygen sp^2 orbitals as two lone pairs, and the remaining four valence electrons occupy two of the delocalized π-bond orbitals. The resulting charge delocalization is represented by the two Lewis resonance formulas

If either Lewis resonance formula of a molecule indicates that the molecule is planar (see the right-hand formula above), then the molecule will be planar.

E   ANSWERS TO THE SELF-TEST

1 the two $1s$ atomic orbitals

2 combinations of atomic orbitals

3 combining atomic orbitals on the same atom

4 a $2s$ orbital with one $2p$ orbital on the same atom

5 two

6 180° from each other

7 circular

8 two

9 true

10 true

11 two

12 three

13 a $2s$ orbital with two $2p$ orbitals on the same atom

14 the vertices of an equilateral triangle

15 true

16 three

17 a $2s$ orbital and all three $2p$ orbitals on the same atom

18 the vertices of a tetrahedron

19 combining an sp^3 orbital on the carbon atom with a hydrogen $1s$ atomic orbital

20 true

21 an ns orbital, the three np orbitals, and one nd orbital (e.g., $3s$, three $3p$, and one $3d$) on the same atom

22 five

23 the vertices of a trigonal bipyramid

24 an ns orbital, the three np orbitals, and two nd orbitals (e.g., $3s$, three $3p$, and two $3d$ orbitals) on the same atom

25 six

26 vertices of a regular octahedron

27 combining an sp^3 orbital on one carbon atom with an sp^3 orbital on the other carbon atom

28 an sp^3 orbital on the oxygen atom with a hydrogen $1s$ atomic orbital

29 the overlap of p orbitals from different atoms

30 false (It is similar to a p orbital in cross section.)

31 $\sigma \ldots \pi$

32 $(2 \times 4) + (4 \times 1) = 12$ valence electrons . . . five σ bonds and one π bond

33 sp^2; $1s$

34 true

35 false

36 true

37 on opposite sides of the double bond

38 stereo-

39 false

40 σ bond; two π bonds

41 $(3 \times 4) + (4 \times 1) = 16$ valence electrons; six; two

42 sp; $1s$

43 true

44 true

45 planar . . . hexagonal

46 sp^2

47 twelve . . . three

48 delocalized

49 false

50 H_2^+, the hydrogen molecular ion

51 false

52 false

53 is concentrated in the region between the two nuclei

54 is zero in the region between the two nuclei

55 antibonding σ orbital of lowest energy

56 false (The electrons are placed into the molecular orbitals according to the Pauli exclusion principle and Hund's rule.)

57 two

58 four

59 false

60 true

61 one

62 false (Hund's rule)

63 photoelectron spectroscopy

64 each $1\pi^*$ is occupied by one electron, and the electrons have the same spin (two unpaired electrons)

LIQUIDS AND SOLIDS

A   OUTLINE OF CHAPTER 11

11-1   The processes of melting and boiling appear as horizontal lines on a heating curve.

A heating curve for one mole of water starting as ice at $-10°C$ is shown in Figure 11-1.

The molar enthalpy of fusion, ΔH_{fus}, is the heat required to melt one mole of a substance.

The molar enthalpy of vaporization, ΔH_{vap}, is the heat required to vaporize one mole of a substance.

The heat absorbed in raising the temperature of a substance from T_1 to T_2 without a change in phase is given by

$$q_P = nC_P(T_2 - T_1) \qquad (11-1)$$

where C_P is the molar heat capacity at constant pressure and n is the number of moles.

11-2   It requires energy to melt a solid or to vaporize a liquid.

The enthalpy of vaporization of a substance is greater than its enthalpy of fusion, or $\Delta H_{vap} > \Delta H_{fus}$.

The values of the melting point, boiling point, and molar enthalpies of vaporization and fusion of some substances are given in Table 11-1.

Sublimation is the process whereby a solid is converted directly into a gas.

The molar enthalpy of sublimation, ΔH_{sub}, is the energy required to sublime one mole of a substance.

11-3   Van der Waals forces are attractive forces between molecules.

The value of ΔH_{vap} is a measure of how strongly the molecules in a liquid attract each other.

Values of ΔH_{vap} are relatively large for ionic compounds.

Polar molecules attract each other by a dipole-dipole force.

Water and some other compounds have relatively large values of ΔH_{vap} because of hydrogen bonding (Figures 11-3, 11-4, and 11-5).

Hydrogen bonding is the electrostatic attraction between a hydrogen atom and highly electronegative atoms in neighboring molecules.

All molecules attract each other by London forces, which are instantaneous dipole-dipole attractions.

The strengths of London forces depend on the number of electrons in the two molecules.

11-4   A liquid has a unique equilibrium vapor pressure at each temperature.

The equilibrium between a liquid and its vapor is a dynamic equilibrium.

When the rate of evaporation of a liquid is equal to the rate of condensation of its vapor, a liquid-vapor equilibrium is established (Figures 11-10 and 11-11).

The equilibrium vapor pressure is the pressure of the vapor in equilibrium with the liquid.

The equilibrium vapor pressure of a liquid increases with temperature (Figure 11-13 and Table 11-2).

The vapor pressure curve is a plot of the equilibrium vapor pressure of a substance versus temperature.

The normal boiling point of a liquid is the temperature at which its equilibrium vapor pressure is 1 atm.

The boiling point of a liquid decreases with increasing elevation.

11-5   Relative humidity is based upon the vapor pressure of water.

The relative humidity is a measure of the amount of water vapor in the atmosphere:

$$\text{relative humidity} = \frac{P_{H_2O}}{P^{\circ}_{H_2O}} \times 100 \qquad (11\text{-}2)$$

where P_{H_2O} is the partial pressure of the water vapor and $P^{\circ}_{H_2O}$ is the equilibrium vapor pressure at the same temperature (Table 11-2).

The dew point is the air temperature at which the relative humidity reaches 100 percent.

11-6   The temperature dependence of the equilibrium vapor pressure is given by the Clapeyron-Clausius equation.

The Clapeyron-Clausius equation is

$$\log\left(\frac{P_2}{P_1}\right) = \frac{\Delta H_{vap}}{2.30R}\left(\frac{T_2 - T_1}{T_1 T_2}\right) \qquad (11\text{-}3)$$

where P_2 is the equilibrium vapor pressure at the Kelvin temperature T_2, P_1 is the equilibrium vapor pressure at the Kelvin temperature T_1, ΔH_{vap} is the enthalpy of vaporization, and R is the gas constant.

The value of R is $8.314\,\text{J}\cdot\text{mol}^{-1}\cdot\text{K}^{-1}$.

11-7   A phase diagram displays the regions of all the phases of a pure substance simultaneously.

The phase diagrams of water and carbon dioxide are shown in Figures 11-14 and 11-15.

The critical point terminates the vapor pressure curve.

A gas with a temperature above its critical temperature cannot be liquefied.

The sublimation pressure curve gives the temperature at which the solid and gas phases are in equilibrium with each other at a particular pressure.

The melting point curve gives the temperature at which the solid and liquid phases are in equilibrium with each other at a particular pressure.

The vapor pressure curve gives the temperature at which the liquid and gas phases are in equilibrium with each other at a particular pressure.

The triple point is the temperature and pressure at which three phases coexist in equilibrium.

11-8   X-ray diffraction patterns yield information about the structures of crystals.

The X-ray diffraction pattern produced by a crystal is shown in Figure 11-16.

The unit cell is the smallest subunit of a crystal lattice that can be used to generate the entire lattice.

The three cubic unit cells are simple cubic, body-centered cubic, and face-centered cubic, as shown in Figure 11-18.

The unit cell of many metals is one of the three cubic unit cells.

The radii of atoms in a face-centered cubic structure can be calculated when the density is known (Example 11-7).

Avogadro's number can be determined from the density and length of the unit cell of a solid (Example 11-8).

11-9   Crystals can be classified according to the forces between the constituent particles.

The constituent particles of atomic crystals are atoms.

The constituent particles of ionic crystals are ions of opposite charge.

The lattice structure of ionic crystals depends on the sizes of the cations and anions (Figure 11-19).

The high lattice energy of ionic crystals is due to the total electrostatic interaction energy.

The constituent particles of molecular crystals are molecules.

The forces that hold together molecular crystals are weaker than those in ionic crystals.

Molecular crystals have a variety of crystal structures (Figures 11-20 and 11-21).

The structure of a single molecule can be determined by X-ray crystallography (Figures 11-22 and 11-23).

Diamond has a covalently bonded tetrahedral network (Figure 11-24).

Graphite has a layered structure (Figure 11-25).

11-10 The electrons in metals are delocalized throughout the crystal.

A metal can be pictured as an array of fixed ionic cores consisting of the inner-core electrons immersed in a sea of valence electrons.

The valence electrons are easily displaced by an externally applied electric field.

Metals have a high electrical conductivity.

The valence band in a crystal is the lower set of energy levels due to the combination of valence orbitals of all the atoms.

The valence electrons of the atoms occupy the valence band.

The conduction band is the higher set of energy levels, which corresponds to antibonding orbitals.

Electrons in the conduction band can move readily throughout the crystal.

The energy gap between the valence band and the conduction band is small for a metal and large for an insulator (Figure 11-27).

There are essentially no electrons in the conduction band of an insulator.

The energy gap for a semiconductor is intermediate between that of a conductor and an insulator.

B SELF-TEST

1 The molecules in a solid move freely throughout the solid. *True/False*

2 The molecules in a liquid have no rotational motion. *True/False*

3 A liquid is easy to compress to smaller volumes. *True/False*

4 When heat is added to a liquid at a constant rate, the temperature will remain constant for a period of time at _____ .

5 When heat is added to a solid at a constant rate, the temperature will remain constant for a period of time at _____ .

6 The amount of energy as heat required to raise the temperature of a substance is determined by the _____ of the substance.

7 The energy as heat required to melt one mole of a solid is the _____ _____ .

8   Energy as heat is required to melt a solid because _____
_____.

9   The energy as heat required to vaporize one mole of a liquid is the _____
_____.

10 Energy is required to vaporize a liquid because _____
_____.

11 For all substances, ΔH_{vap} is *(greater, smaller)* than ΔH_{fus}.

12 The evaporation of water in perspiration *(adds, removes)* heat from the body.

13 A solid cannot be converted to a gas directly. *True/False*

14 The energy required to sublime one mole of a solid is the _____
_____.

15 There are attractive forces between all molecules or atoms. *True/False*

16 A large value of ΔH_{vap} indicates a strong attraction between the particles in a liquid.
True/False

17 The values of ΔH_{vap} of ionic compounds are smaller than for molecular compounds.
True/False

18 The attractive forces between polar molecules are due to _____
_____ attraction.

19 Ammonia, NH_3, has a lower value of ΔH_{vap} than methane, CH_4. *True/False*

20 Hydrogen bonding is _____
_____.

21 The attractive forces between nonpolar molecules are called _____
_____.

22 The attractive force between nonpolar molecules is due to

_____.

23 When a liquid is placed in a closed container, vapor from the liquid appears in the container. *True/False*

24 When the rate of condensation is equal to the rate of evaporation, the process of evaporation ceases. *True/False*

25 The system of a liquid in a closed container is at equilibrium when the rate

_____.

26 When a system is at equilibrium no net observable change occurs. *True/False*

27 The equilibrium vapor pressure is the pressure _____

_____.

28 The equilibrium vapor pressure of a substance is the same at all temperatures. *True/False*

29 The normal boiling point of a liquid is _____

_____.

30 Water always boils at 100°C. *True/False*

31 Relative humidity is a measure of the amount _____

_____

_____.

32 The dew point is _____

_____.

33 The temperature dependence of the equilibrium vapor pressure of a substance is given by _____.

34 The Clapeyron-Clausius equation is

35 A phase diagram is a diagram that shows _____

_____

_____.

36 A phase diagram can be used to determine the state of a substance at any pressure and temperature. *True/False*

37 The melting point curve separates the _____ phase and the _____ phase.

38   The melting point of water changes markedly with pressure. *True/False*

39   The critical temperature is _____

_____.

40   A triple point is _____

_____.

41   A gas can be liquefied at all temperatures by applying sufficient pressure. *True/False*

42   Liquid carbon dioxide does not exist at any temperature and pressure. *True/False*

43   The melting point of all substances decreases with pressure. *True/False*

44   A substance does not have a normal boiling point when its solid-liquid-gas triple point _____.

45   An X-ray diffraction pattern of a crystal can be used to determine the

_____.

46   The unit cells of all crystals are identical. *True/False*

47   The three types of cubic unit cells are _____

_____.

48   Draw a simple cubic unit cell.

49   Atomic or ionic radii can be calculated from crystal structures. *True/False*

50   The constituent particles of an atomic crystal are _____.

51   A crystal of NaCl is an example of a(n) _____ crystal.

52   The lattice energy of an ionic crystal is *(large, small)*.

53   The different crystal-packing arrangements for NaCl and CsCl are due to

_____.

54   Carbon dioxide crystals are an example of a(n) _____ crystal.

55   Molecular crystals usually have *(higher, lower)* melting points than ionic crystals.

56 All molecular crystals have the same structure. *True/False*

57 The structure of a single molecule can be determined from the crystal structure of the molecular solid. *True/False*

58 Two crystalline forms of solid carbon are _____ and

_____ .

59 The constituent particles in diamond are held together by

_____ .

60 In a crystal, the valence band is _____

_____ .

61 In a crystal, the conduction band is _____

_____ .

62 An electric current is carried in a solid by the electrons in the _____ band.

63 In a metal, the valence electrons are the conduction electrons. *True/False*

64 In an insulator, the band gap is *(large, small)*.

C   CALCULATIONS YOU SHOULD KNOW HOW TO DO

1 Compute the quantity of heat that is absorbed or evolved in vaporization, fusion, or sublimation. See Example 11-1 and Problems 11-1 through 11-8.

2 Construct a heating curve for a substance that is heated at some given rate. You need the values of the heat capacities of the solid, liquid, and gas phases and the values of ΔH_{fus} and ΔH_{vap}. See Problems 11-9 through 11-12.

3 Calculate the relative humidity and the dew point by using Equation (11-2) and the data in Table 11-2. See Example 11-3 and Problems 11-25 through 11-27.

4 Calculate the temperature dependence of the equilibrium vapor pressure by using the Clapeyron-Clausius equation.

$$\log\left(\frac{P_2}{P_1}\right) = \frac{\Delta H_{vap}}{2.30R}\left(\frac{T_2 - T_1}{T_1 T_2}\right) \tag{11-3}$$

See Example 11-4 and Problems 11-29 through 11-32.

5 Calculate ΔH_{vap} given two values of the equilibrium vapor pressure at two different temperatures of a substance by using the Clapeyron-Clausius equation. See Problems 11-33 and 11-34.

6 Calculate the length of an edge of a unit cell. See Example 11-7 and Problems 11-43, 11-44, 11-49, and 11-50.

7 Calculate the density of a substance, given the length of an edge of the unit cell. See Problems 11-45 and 11-46.

8 Calculate Avogadro's number, given the density and length of an edge of the unit cell. See Example 11-8 and Problems 11-47 and 11-48.

A Review of Logarithms

Recall from Appendix A1 of the text that $100 = 10^2$, $1000 = 10^3$, and so on. Also recall that

$$\sqrt{10} = 10^{1/2} = 10^{0.50} = 3.16$$

By taking the square root of both sides of

$$10^{0.50} = 3.16$$

we find that

$$\sqrt{10^{0.50}} = 10^{(1/2)(0.50)} = 10^{0.25} = \sqrt{3.16} = 1.78$$

Furthermore, because

$$(10^x)(10^y) = 10^{x+y}$$

we can write

$$10^{0.25} \times 10^{0.50} = 10^{0.75} = (3.16)(1.78) = 5.62$$

By continuing this process, we would be able to express any number y as

$$y = 10^x \tag{1}$$

The number x to which 10 must be raised to get y is called the *logarithm* of y and is written as

$$x = \log y \tag{2}$$

Equations (1) and (2) are equivalent.
  For example, we have shown above that

$$\log 1.78 = 0.25$$
$$\log 3.16 = 0.50$$
$$\log 5.62 = 0.75$$
$$\log 10.00 = 1.00$$

Logarithms of other numbers may be obtained from tables (Appendix C of the text) or more conveniently with a hand calculator. If you use tables, you must always write the number y in standard scientific notation. Thus, for example, you must write 42,500 as 4.25×10^4, or 0.000465 as 4.65×10^{-4}. To take the logarithm of such numbers, we use the fact that

$$\log(ab) = \log a + \log b \qquad\qquad (3)$$

Thus we write

$$\log 42{,}500 = \log(4.25 \times 10^4) = \log 4.25 + \log 10^4$$
$$= \log 4.25 + 4.000$$

Log tables are set up so that the number a in $\log a$ is between 1 and 10 and the numbers within the tables are between 0 and 1. Thus, for example, from Appendix C we find that

$$\log 5.08 = 0.7059$$
$$\log 8.16 = 0.9117$$

and so on. If we look up $\log 4.25$ in Appendix C, then we find that $\log 4.25 = 0.6284$. Therefore,

$$\log 42{,}500 = 0.6284 + 4.000$$
$$= 4.6284$$

If you use your calculator, you simply enter 42,500 and push a LOG key to get 4.6284 directly. To find $\log 0.000465$, we write

$$\log 0.000465 = \log(4.65 \times 10^{-4}) = \log 4.65 + \log 10^{-4}$$
$$= \log 4.65 - 4.000$$

We find $\log 4.65 = 0.6675$ from Appendix C, and so

$$\log 0.000465 = 0.6675 - 4.000$$
$$= -3.3325$$

If you use your calculator, simply enter 0.000465 and push the LOG key to get -3.3325 directly. Although the use of a hand calculator is much more convenient than a table of logarithms, you should be able to handle logarithms by either method.

> **Example 1** Evaluate
>
> (a) $\log(6.64 \times 10^{-8})$ (b) $\log 0.00476$
>
> **Solution**
>
> (a) $\log(6.64 \times 10^{-8}) = \log 6.64 + \log 10^{-8}$
> $$= 0.8222 - 8$$
> $$= -7.1778$$

(b) $\log 0.00476 = \log(4.76 \times 10^{-3})$
$$= \log 4.76 + \log 10^{-3}$$
$$= 0.6776 - 3$$
$$= -2.3224$$

Both of these results can be obtained directly from your hand calculator by entering the number and pushing the LOG key.

Because logarithms are exponents ($y = 10^x$), logarithms have certain special properties, such as

$$\log ab = \log a + \log b \tag{3}$$

$$\log \frac{a}{b} = \log a - \log b \tag{4}$$

$$\log a^n = n \log a \tag{5}$$

$$\log \sqrt[n]{a} = \log a^{1/n} = \frac{1}{n}\log a \tag{6}$$

If we let $a = 1$ in Equation (4), then we have

$$\log \frac{1}{b} = \log 1 - \log b$$

or, because $\log 1 = 0$,

$$\log \frac{1}{b} = -\log b \tag{7}$$

Thus we change the sign of logarithm by taking the reciprocal of its argument.

Up to this point we have found the value of x in

$$y = 10^x$$

when y is given. It is often necessary to find the value of y when x is given. Because x is called the logarithm of y, y is called the antilogarithm of x. For example, suppose that $x = 6.1303$ and we wish to find y. We write

$$y = 10^{6.1303} = 10^{0.1303} \times 10^6$$

From the log table, we see that the number whose logarithm is 0.1303 is 1.35. Thus we find that

$$10^{6.1303} = 1.35 \times 10^6$$

You can obtain this result directly from your calculator. On a TI calculator, for example, enter 6.1303 and press the INV key (for inverse) and then the LOG key.

To obtain the antilogarithm of y using log tables, you must express y as

$$y = 10^a \times 10^n \tag{8}$$

where n is a positive or negative integer and a is between 0 and 1. The quantity a is found within the log table and the antilog of a is read from the table. As another example, let's find the antilog of -2.3936. We write

$$y = 10^{-2.3936} = 10^{0.6064} \times 10^{-3}$$

Find the value of 0.6064 within the log table and see that its antilog is 4.04. Thus we have

$$y = 10^{-2.3936} = 4.04 \times 10^{-3}$$

You should be able to obtain this result directly from your calculator. If your calculator has a 10^x key, then you can obtain the antilog of -2.3936 by entering -2.3936 and pressing the 10^x key. This operation is equivalent to using the INV key followed by the LOG key.

Exercises

---

1 Find the logarithms of the following numbers, using both the table of logarithms and your calculator:

(a) 3.12×10^{-10} (b) 8.06×10^5

(c) 12.3   (d) 6.63×10^{-12}

(e) 4.23   (f) 0.0000291

(g) 556,000   (h) 1.02×10^{-3}

2 Find the antilogarithms of the following numbers, using both the table of logarithms and your calculator.

(a) 4.316   (b) 0.711

(c) -5.2573 (d) -1.6289

Answers

---

1 (a) -9.5058 (b) 5.9063

(c) 1.0899   (d) -11.1785

(e) 0.6263   (f) -4.5361

(g) 5.7451   (h) -2.9914

2 (a) 2.07×10^4 (b) 5.14

(c) 5.53×10^{-6} (d) 2.35×10^{-2}

D   SOLUTIONS TO THE ODD-NUMBERED PROBLEMS

11-1   The number of moles in 5.00 kg of NH_3 is

$$\text{mol } NH_3 = (5.00 \text{ kg})\left(\frac{10^3 \text{ g}}{1 \text{ kg}}\right)\left(\frac{1 \text{ mol } NH_3}{17.03 \text{ g } NH_3}\right)$$
$$= 294 \text{ mol}$$

The amount of heat absorbed when 294 mol of $NH_3(l)$ is vaporized is

$$\text{heat absorbed} = n\,\Delta H_{vap} = (294 \text{ mol})(23.4 \text{ kJ} \cdot \text{mol}^{-1})$$
$$= 6880 \text{ kJ}$$

11-3   The number of moles in 20.1 g of mercury is

$$n = (20.1 \text{ g})\left(\frac{1 \text{ mol Hg}}{200.6 \text{ g Hg}}\right)$$
$$= 0.1002 \text{ mol}$$

The heat *released* when 0.1002 mol of mercury freezes at its melting point is (Table 11-1)

$$q_P = n\,\Delta H_{fus}$$
$$= (0.1002 \text{ mol})(2.30 \text{ kJ} \cdot \text{mol}^{-1})$$
$$= 0.230 \text{ kJ}$$

The heat *released* when 0.1002 mol of mercury is cooled from 298 K to 234 K (the melting point of mercury) is given by

$$q_P = nC_P(T_2 - T_1)$$
$$= (0.1002 \text{ mol})(28.0 \text{ J} \cdot \text{K}^{-1} \cdot \text{mol}^{-1})(64 \text{ K})$$
$$= 180 \text{ J} = 0.180 \text{ kJ}$$

The total heat released is 0.230 kJ + 0.180 kJ = 0.410 kJ.

11-5   To heat the gallium from 20.0° C to its melting point (29.0°C) requires

$$\text{heat absorbed} = (5.00 \text{ g})(0.37 \text{ J} \cdot \text{K}^{-1} \cdot \text{g}^{-1})(9.0 \text{ K}) = 17 \text{ J}$$

The amount of energy as heat absorbed when it melts is given by

$$\text{heat absorbed} = (5.00 \text{ g})\left(\frac{1 \text{ mol Ga}}{69.72 \text{ g Ga}}\right)(5.59 \text{ kJ} \cdot \text{mol}^{-1})$$
$$= 0.401 \text{ kJ} = 401 \text{ J}$$

The total quantity of heat absorbed is 17 J + 401 J = 418 J.

11-7   The heat absorbed by the sublimation of 100.0 g of $CO_2(s)$ is

$$q_P = (100.0 \text{ g})\left(\frac{1 \text{ mol}}{44.01 \text{ g}}\right)(25.2 \text{ kJ} \cdot \text{mol}^{-1}) = 57.3 \text{ kJ}$$

11-9   Mercury is a solid from 200 K to 234 K. It requires

$$q_P = nC_P(T_2 - T_1) = (7.50 \text{ g})\left(\frac{1 \text{ mol Hg}}{200.6 \text{ g Hg}}\right)(27.2 \text{ J} \cdot \text{K}^{-1} \cdot \text{mol}^{-1})(34 \text{ K})$$
$$= 34.6 \text{ J}$$

to heat the solid mercury from 200 K to its melting point. If heat is supplied at $100 \text{ J} \cdot \text{min}^{-1}$, then the time required is

$$t = \frac{34.6 \text{ J}}{100 \text{ J} \cdot \text{min}^{-1}} = 0.346 \text{ min} = 20.8 \text{ s}$$

The heat required to melt the mercury is given by

$$q_P = n \, \Delta H_{vap} = (7.50 \text{ g})\left(\frac{1 \text{ mol Hg}}{200.6 \text{ g Hg}}\right)(2.30 \text{ kJ} \cdot \text{mol}^{-1})$$
$$= 0.0860 \text{ kJ} = 86.0 \text{ J}$$

At a heating rate of $100 \text{ J} \cdot \text{min}^{-1}$, the time required is

$$t = \frac{86.0 \text{ J}}{100 \text{ J} \cdot \text{min}^{-1}} = 0.860 \text{ min} = 51.6 \text{ s}$$

The heat required to heat the liquid mercury from its melting point (234 K) to its boiling point (630 K) is

$$q_P = nC_P(T_2 - T_1) = (0.0374 \text{ mol})(28.0 \text{ J} \cdot \text{K}^{-1} \cdot \text{mol}^{-1})(630 \text{ K} - 234 \text{ K})$$
$$= 415 \text{ J}$$

and the time required is

$$t = \frac{415 \text{ J}}{100 \text{ J} \cdot \text{min}^{-1}} = 4.15 \text{ min} = 245 \text{ s}$$

The heat required to vaporize the mercury is

$$q_P = n \, \Delta H_{vap} = (0.0374 \text{ mol})(59.1 \text{ kJ} \cdot \text{mol}^{-1})$$
$$= 2.21 \text{ kJ} = 2210 \text{ J}$$

and the time required is

$$t = \frac{2210 \text{ J}}{100 \text{ J} \cdot \text{min}^{-1}} = 22.10 \text{ min} = 1330 \text{ s}$$

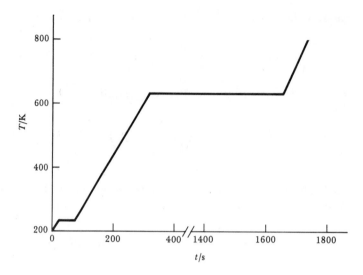

The heat required to heat the mercury vapor from 630 K to 800 K is given by

$$q_P = nC_P(T_2 - T_1) = (0.0374 \text{ mol})(20.8 \text{ J}\cdot\text{K}^{-1}\cdot\text{mol}^{-1})(800 \text{ K} - 630 \text{ K})$$
$$= 132 \text{ J}$$

and the time required is

$$t = \frac{132 \text{ J}}{100 \text{ J}\cdot\text{min}^{-1}} = 1.32 \text{ min} = 79.3 \text{ s}$$

The heating curve is shown at the top of the page.

11-11 The quantity of heat absorbed by the NaCl(s) is

$$q_P = (3.00 \text{ kJ}\cdot\text{min}^{-1})(250 \text{ s})\left(\frac{1 \text{ min}}{60 \text{ s}}\right) = 12.5 \text{ kJ}$$

The number of moles of NaCl(s) is

$$n = (25.0 \text{ g})\left(\frac{1 \text{ mol NaCl}}{58.44 \text{ g NaCl}}\right) = 0.428 \text{ mol}$$

and the molar enthalpy of fusion is

$$\Delta H_{fus} = \frac{12.5 \text{ kJ}}{0.428 \text{ mol}} = 29.2 \text{ kJ}\cdot\text{mol}^{-1}$$

11-13 Cl_2 is a homonuclear diatomic molecule and so is nonpolar.
The Lewis formula for ClF is

$$:\ddot{C}l—\ddot{F}:$$

Fluorine is more electronegative than chlorine; therefore, the fluorine atom has a small negative charge and the chlorine atom has a small positive charge

$$\overset{\delta+}{:\ddot{C}l}—\overset{\delta-}{\ddot{F}:}$$

The molecule is polar.
The Lewis formula for NF_3 is

$$:\ddot{F}—\ddot{N}—\ddot{F}:$$
$$|$$
$$:\ddot{F}:$$

Since fluorine is more electronegative than nitrogen, there is a small negative charge on each fluorine atom and a small positive charge on the nitrogen atom.

$$\overset{\delta-}{:\ddot{F}}—\overset{3\delta+}{\ddot{N}}—\overset{\delta-}{\ddot{F}:}$$
$$|$$
$$:\ddot{F}:$$
$$\delta-$$

The molecule is polar because of its trigonal pyramidal shape.
The molecule F_2, being homonuclear, is nonpolar.

11-15 The only ionic compound is KBr. Thus we predict that KBr has the highest boiling point. The Lewis formulas of C_2H_5OH and C_2H_6 are

We see that liquid C_2H_5OH is hydrogen bonded and C_2H_6 is nonpolar. Helium is a smaller molecule than C_2H_6. Therefore, the predicted order is

$$T_b[\text{He}] < T_b[C_2H_6] < T_b[C_2H_5OH] < T_b[\text{KBr}]$$

11-17 The two nonpolar molecules, CH_4 and C_2H_6, have the lowest molar enthalpies of vaporization. Of the two, the smaller molecule, CH_4, has the lower value of ΔH_{vap}. The two polar molecules, CH_3OH and C_2H_5OH, are hydrogen bonded and have the highest values of molar enthalpies of vaporization. The larger of the two, C_2H_5OH, has the higher value of ΔH_{vap}. Therefore, the order of the molar enthalpies of vaporization is

$$\Delta H_{vap}[CH_4] < \Delta H_{vap}[C_2H_6] < \Delta H_{vap}[CH_3OH] < \Delta H_{vap}[C_2H_5OH]$$

11-19 Using Table 11-2 or Figure 11-13, the vapor pressure of water at 37°C is between 45 and 50 torr. The vapor pressure of water in exhaled air is between 45 and 50 torr.

11-21 Using Figure 11-13, the equilibrium vapor pressure of ethyl alcohol at 60°C is about 0.5 atm. If all the ethyl alcohol (CH_3CH_2OH) were to vaporize, then the pressure would be

$$P = \frac{nRT}{V} = \frac{\left[(0.75\ g)\left(\dfrac{1\ mol}{46.07\ g}\right)\right](0.0821\ L\cdot atm\cdot mol^{-1}\cdot K^{-1})(333\ K)}{0.400\ L}$$

$$= 1.1\ atm$$

This pressure is greater than the equilibrium vapor pressure of ethyl alcohol at 60°C, and so vapor will condense until the vapor pressure is about 0.5 atm. Liquid will be present.

11-23 We use the ideal-gas equation and write

$$P = \frac{nRT}{V} = \left(\frac{nR}{V}\right)T = aT$$

where we have let nR/V be denoted by a constant, a. The value of a can be determined by using the fact that $P = 300$ torr at 75.0°C.

$$a = \frac{P}{T} = \frac{300\ torr}{348\ K} = 0.862\ torr\cdot K^{-1}$$

Thus we have

$$P = (0.862\ torr\cdot K^{-1})T$$

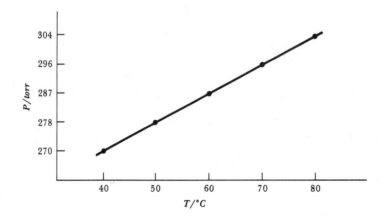

A plot of P versus T from 80.0°C to 40.0°C (assuming no condensation) is shown at the bottom of page 232.

The pressure calculated from the ideal-gas equation exceeds the equilibrium vapor pressure at around 330 K, or around 60°C (Figure 11-13). Thus we expect condensation to occur at around 60°C.

11-25 Set up the following table.

Air temperature/°C	Relative humidity/%	Dew point/°C
20	70	14
30	70	24

The 20°C day is much more comfortable.

11-27 The equilibrium vapor pressure of water at 30°C is 31.6 torr (Table 11-2). We can find the partial pressure of water from the definition of relative humidity

$$\text{relative humidity} = \frac{P_{H_2O}}{P^{\circ}_{H_2O}} \times 100$$

or

$$P_{H_2O} = \frac{(65)(31.6 \text{ torr})}{100} = 20 \text{ torr}$$

The temperature at which the equilibrium vapor pressure is 20 torr is the dew point. From Table 11-2 we see that the dew point is about 23°C.

11-29 The Clapeyron-Clausius equation is

$$\log\left(\frac{P_2}{P_1}\right) = \frac{\Delta H_{vap}}{2.30R}\left(\frac{T_2 - T_1}{T_1 T_2}\right)$$

At the normal boiling point, $P = 760$ torr. Let these values be T_2 and P_2 and let $T_1 = 20.0°C + 273.2°C = 293.2$ K. Then

$$\log\left(\frac{760 \text{ torr}}{P_1}\right) = \frac{(31.97 \times 10^3 \text{ J} \cdot \text{mol}^{-1})}{(2.30)(8.314 \text{ J} \cdot \text{K}^{-1} \cdot \text{mol}^{-1})}\left[\frac{36.2 \text{ K}}{(293.2 \text{ K})(329.4 \text{ K})}\right]$$
$$= 0.627$$

or

$$\frac{760 \text{ torr}}{P_1} = 4.24$$

or

$$P_1 = \frac{760 \text{ torr}}{4.24} = 179 \text{ torr}$$

11-31 Let $P_1 = 387$ torr, $T_1 = 60°C + 273°C = 333$ K, $P_2 = 760$ torr, and write the Clapeyron-Clausius equation as

$$\log\left(\frac{760}{387}\right) = \frac{(32.3 \times 10^3 \text{ J} \cdot \text{mol}^{-1})}{(2.30)(8.314 \text{ J} \cdot \text{K}^{-1} \cdot \text{mol}^{-1})}\left[\frac{T_2 - 333 \text{ K}}{(333 \text{ K})(T_2)}\right]$$

or

$$\frac{T_2 - 333 \text{ K}}{T_2} = \frac{(2.30)(8.314 \text{ J} \cdot \text{mol}^{-1} \cdot \text{K}^{-1})(333 \text{ K})}{(32.3 \times 10^3 \text{ J} \cdot \text{mol}^{-1})}\log\left(\frac{760}{387}\right)$$

Thus

$$T_2 - 333 \text{ K} = 0.0578 T_2$$

$$T_2 = \frac{333 \text{ K}}{0.942} = 352 \text{ K} = 80°C$$

11-33 Let $P_1 = 92.68$ torr, $T_1 = 23.50°C + 273.2°C = 296.7$ K, $P_2 = 221.6$ torr, $T_2 = 45.00°C + 273.2°C = 318.2$ K, and write the Clapeyron-Clausius equation as

$$\log\left(\frac{221.6}{92.68}\right) = \frac{\Delta H_{vap}}{(2.30)(8.314 \text{ J} \cdot \text{K}^{-1} \cdot \text{mol}^{-1})}\left[\frac{318.2 \text{ K} - 296.7 \text{ K}}{(296.7 \text{ K})(318.2 \text{ K})}\right]$$

Solving for ΔH_{vap} gives

$$\Delta H_{vap} = 3.18 \times 10^4 \text{ J} \cdot \text{mol}^{-1} = 31.8 \text{ kJ} \cdot \text{mol}^{-1}$$

11-35 Let P_2 be the vapor pressure of lead at $1300°C$ and P_1 be that at $500°C$. Then the Clapeyron-Clausius equation is

$$\log\left(\frac{P_2}{P_1}\right) = \frac{(178 \times 10^3 \text{ J} \cdot \text{mol}^{-1})}{(2.30)(8.314 \text{ J} \cdot \text{K}^{-1} \cdot \text{mol}^{-1})}\left[\frac{800 \text{ K}}{(773 \text{ K})(1573 \text{ K})}\right]$$

$$= 6.12$$

$$\frac{P_2}{P_1} = 1.32 \times 10^6$$

11-37 (a) gas   (b) solid   (c) liquid   (d) liquid

11-39 The phase diagram (not to scale) of oxygen is shown on the next page.
The melting point curve slopes to the right which means that the melting point increases with pressure. Thus solid oxygen does not melt under an applied pressure.

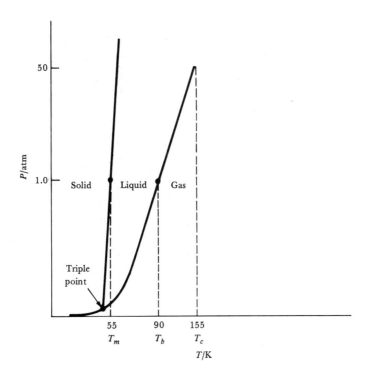

11-41   From Figure 11-18 we see that there is one atom at each corner and one atom at the center of a body-centered cubic lattice. Each of the eight atoms at the corners is shared by seven other unit cells, while the atom at the center belongs entirely to the unit cell. Thus there is a total of two atoms per unit cell.

11-43   The molar volume of silver is given by

$$V = \frac{\text{molar mass}}{\text{density}} = \frac{107.9 \text{ g} \cdot \text{mol}^{-1}}{10.50 \text{ g} \cdot \text{cm}^{-3}} = 10.28 \text{ cm}^3 \cdot \text{mol}^{-1}$$

There are four silver atoms per unit cell (Example 11-6), and so the number of unit cells per mole of silver is

$$\text{unit cells per mole} = \frac{6.022 \times 10^{23} \text{ atoms} \cdot \text{mol}^{-1}}{4 \text{ atoms/unit cell}} = 1.5055 \times 10^{23} \frac{\text{unit cells}}{\text{mol}}$$

The volume of a unit cell is

$$v = \frac{10.28 \text{ cm}^3 \cdot \text{mol}^{-1}}{(1.5055 \times 10^{23} \text{ unit cell} \cdot \text{mol}^{-1})} = 6.828 \times 10^{-23} \frac{\text{cm}^3}{\text{unit cell}}$$

The length of an edge of a unit cell is

$$\text{length} = (6.828 \times 10^{-23} \text{ cm}^3)^{1/3} = 4.087 \times 10^{-8} \text{ cm} = 408.7 \text{ pm}$$

11-45 A unit cell of a simple cubic lattice is shown in Figure 11-18. Each of the eight atoms is shared by eight unit cells, so there is a total of one atom per unit cell for a simple cubic lattice. The volume of a unit cell of a simple cubic lattice is given by

$$v = l^3 = (334.7 \times 10^{-12} \text{ m})^3 = 3.749 \times 10^{-29} \text{ m}^3$$
$$= (3.749 \times 10^{-29} \text{ m}^3)\left(\frac{100 \text{ cm}}{1 \text{ m}}\right)^3 = 3.749 \times 10^{-23} \text{ cm}^3$$

The mass of the unit cell is the mass of one atom of polonium, or

$$\text{mass} = \frac{209 \text{ g} \cdot \text{mol}^{-1}}{6.022 \times 10^{23} \text{ atoms} \cdot \text{mol}^{-1}} = 3.47 \times 10^{-22} \text{ g} \cdot \text{atom}^{-1}$$

and the density is given by

$$d = \frac{m}{v} = \frac{3.47 \times 10^{-22} \text{ g} \cdot \text{atom}^{-1}}{3.749 \times 10^{-23} \text{ cm}^3 \cdot \text{atom}^{-1}} = 9.26 \text{ g} \cdot \text{cm}^{-3}$$

11-47 The molar volume of copper is

$$V = \frac{\text{molar mass}}{\text{density}} = \frac{63.55 \text{ g} \cdot \text{mol}^{-1}}{8.93 \text{ g} \cdot \text{cm}^{-3}} = 7.116 \text{ cm}^3 \cdot \text{mol}^{-1}$$

The volume of a unit cell is

$$v = (361.6 \text{ pm})^3 = (3.616 \times 10^{-8} \text{ cm})^3 = 4.728 \times 10^{-23} \text{ cm}^3$$

The number of unit cells in a molar volume of copper is

$$\text{unit cells per mol} = \frac{V}{v}$$
$$= \frac{7.116 \text{ cm}^3 \cdot \text{mol}^{-1}}{4.728 \times 10^{-23} \text{ cm}^3/\text{unit cell}} = 1.505 \times 10^{23} \frac{\text{unit cells}}{\text{mol}}$$

There are four copper atoms per unit cell, and so

$$\text{Avogadro's number} = \left(\frac{4 \text{ atoms}}{\text{unit cell}}\right)\left(1.505 \times 10^{23} \frac{\text{unit cells}}{\text{mol}}\right)$$
$$= 6.02 \times 10^{23} \text{ atom} \cdot \text{mol}^{-1}$$

11-49 The molar volume of KF is

$$V = \frac{\text{molar mass}}{\text{density}} = \frac{58.10 \text{ g} \cdot \text{mol}^{-1}}{2.481 \text{ g} \cdot \text{cm}^{-3}} = 23.42 \text{ cm}^3 \cdot \text{mol}^{-1}$$

There are four KF formula units per unit cell (Figure 11-19) and so there are

$$\text{unit cells per mole} = \frac{6.022 \times 10^{23} \text{ formula units/mol}}{4 \text{ formula units/unit cell}}$$

$$= 1.506 \times 10^{23} \frac{\text{unit cells}}{\text{mol}}$$

The volume of a unit cell is

$$v = \frac{23.42 \text{ cm}^3 \cdot \text{mol}^{-1}}{1.506 \times 10^{23} \dfrac{\text{unit cells}}{\text{mol}}} = 1.555 \times 10^{-22} \frac{\text{cm}^3}{\text{unit cell}}$$

The length of an edge of a unit cell is

$$l = (1.555 \times 10^{-22} \text{ cm}^3)^{1/3} = 5.377 \times 10^{-8} \text{ cm}$$

From Figure 11-19a we see that the nearest-neighbor distance is $l/2$, or 2.689×10^{-8} cm, or 268.9 pm.

11-51 Your body uses energy to melt the snow. It requires

$$q_P = n \, \Delta H_{fus} = (1.00 \text{ g})\left(\frac{1 \text{ mol}}{18.02 \text{ g}}\right)(6.01 \text{ kJ} \cdot \text{mol}^{-1}) = 0.334 \text{ kJ}$$

to melt one gram of snow if the temperature of the snow is 0°C.

11-53 $\Delta H_{vap} = (85 \text{ J} \cdot \text{K}^{-1} \cdot \text{mol}^{-1}) T_b$
$= (85 \text{ J} \cdot \text{K}^{-1} \cdot \text{mol}^{-1})(373 \text{ K})$
$= 31700 \text{ J} \cdot \text{mol}^{-1} = 31.7 \text{ kJ} \cdot \text{mol}^{-1}$

The actual value of ΔH_{vap} for water is $40.7 \text{ kJ} \cdot \text{mol}^{-1}$. Water is strongly hydrogen bonded, and so has strong specific intermolecular interactions. Therefore, Trouton's rule does not apply to water.

11-55 Near the triple point, we have the relation

$$\Delta H_{sub} = \Delta H_{fus} + \Delta H_{vap}$$

This relation results from Hess's law.

11-57 Both silicon carbide (SiC) and boron nitride (BN) form a diamondlike covalent crystal network.

11-59 The boiling point of water was used to determine the atmospheric pressure of Lhasa. Plots of atmospheric pressure versus altitude were used to find the altitude corresponding to the atmospheric pressure of Lhasa.

11-61 We use the Clapeyron-Clausius equation to estimate the vapor pressure of Cl_2 at 20°C. Using the value of ΔH_{vap} given in Table 11-1 and letting $P_1 = 1.00$ atm, $T_1 = -35°C + 273°C = 238$ K, and $T_2 = 20°C + 273°C = 293$ K, we can write

$$\log\left(\frac{P_2}{1.00\text{ atm}}\right) = \frac{(20.4 \times 10^3\text{ J}\cdot\text{mol}^{-1})}{(2.30)(8.314\text{ J}\cdot\text{K}^{-1}\cdot\text{mol}^{-1})}\left[\frac{293\text{ K} - 238\text{ K}}{(238\text{ K})(293\text{ K})}\right]$$
$$= 0.841$$

or

$$\frac{P_2}{1.00\text{ atm}} = 6.94$$

or

$$P_2 = 6.94\text{ atm}$$

The pressure within the cylinder is greater than this value, and so the chlorine will exist as a liquid.

11-63   The vapor pressure of the solid is equal to the vapor pressure of the liquid at the triple point. Thus we write

$$10.560 - \frac{1640\text{ K}}{T_t} = 7.769 - \frac{1159\text{ K}}{T_t}$$

$$2.791 = \frac{481\text{ K}}{T_t}$$

$$T_t = \frac{481\text{ K}}{2.791} = 172\text{ K}$$

The triple point pressure is given by either

$$\log P_t = 7.769 - \frac{1159\text{ K}}{172\text{ K}}$$
$$= 7.769 - 6.738 = 1.03$$

or

$$\log P_t = 10.560 - \frac{1640\text{ K}}{172\text{ K}} = 1.03$$

and so

$$P_t = 10^{1.03} = 10.7\text{ torr}$$

11-65   We start with the Clapeyron-Clausius equation in the form

$$\log\left(\frac{P_2}{P_1}\right) = \frac{\Delta H_{vap}}{2.30R}\left(\frac{1}{T_1} - \frac{1}{T_2}\right)$$

Now let $P_1 = 760$ torr and $T_1 = 760°C + 273°C = 1033$ K (normal boiling point) and use the fact that

$$\log\left(\frac{P_2}{P_1}\right) = \log P_2 - \log P_1$$

to write

$$\log P_2 = -\frac{\Delta H_{vap}}{2.30RT_2} + \left(\frac{\Delta H_{vap}}{2.30RT_1} + \log P_1\right)$$

By comparing this equation to the one given in the problem, we see that

$$\frac{\Delta H_{vap}}{2.30R} = 4021 \text{ K}$$

or that

$$\Delta H_{vap} = 76.9 \text{ kJ} \cdot \text{mol}^{-1}$$

We could also have used the fact that

$$\frac{\Delta H_{vap}}{2.30R(1033 \text{ K})} + \log(760) = 6.774$$

In this case we obtain $\Delta H_{vap} = 76.9$ kJ·mol^{-1}, in excellent agreement with the previous result.

11-67 The molar volume of CaO is

$$V = \frac{\text{molar mass}}{\text{density}} = \frac{56.08 \text{ g} \cdot \text{mol}^{-1}}{3.25 \text{ g} \cdot \text{cm}^{-3}} = 17.26 \text{ cm}^3 \cdot \text{mol}^{-1}$$

The volume of a unit cell is

$$v = (481 \text{ pm})^3 = (4.81 \times 10^{-8} \text{ cm})^3 = 1.113 \times 10^{-22} \text{ cm}^3$$

The number of unit cells per mole is

$$\frac{V}{v} = \frac{17.26 \text{ cm}^3 \cdot \text{mol}^{-1}}{1.113 \times 10^{-22} \dfrac{\text{cm}^3}{\text{unit cell}}} = 1.551 \times 10^{23} \frac{\text{unit cells}}{\text{mol}}$$

The result says that there are four ($6.02 \times 10^{23}/1.551 \times 10^{23}$) formula units of CaO in a unit cell, and so the unit cell must be the NaCl type.

11-69 The unit cell of cesium chloride is body-centered cubic. The volume of the unit cell of CsCl is

$$v = (412.1 \text{ pm})^3 = (4.121 \times 10^{-8} \text{ cm})^3 = 6.999 \times 10^{-23} \text{ cm}^3$$

A unit cell consists of one chloride ion and one cesium ion (Figure 11-19). The mass of the unit cell is

$$m = \left(\frac{1 \text{ formula unit}}{\text{unit cell}}\right)\left(\frac{168.4 \text{ g}\cdot\text{mol}^{-1}}{6.022 \times 10^{23} \text{ formula units}\cdot\text{mol}^{-1}}\right)$$
$$= 2.796 \times 10^{-22} \text{ g/unit cell}$$

The density is

$$d = \frac{\text{mass}}{\text{volume}}$$
$$= \frac{2.796 \times 10^{-22} \text{ g/unit cell}}{6.999 \times 10^{-23} \text{ cm}^3/\text{unit cell}} = 3.995 \text{ g}\cdot\text{cm}^{-3}$$

11-71 We first convert the data given in the problem to $\log(P/\text{torr})$ and T^{-1}.

$\log(P/\text{torr})$	$T^{-1}/10^{-3} \text{ K}^{-1}$
1.889	3.404
2.096	3.287
2.245	3.202
2.418	3.103
2.605	2.994
2.798	2.880
2.892	2.824

These data are plotted in the graph on the next page. The normal boiling point of benzene occurs when $P = 760$ torr, or $\log(P/\text{torr}) = 2.88$, which corresponds to slightly less than $T^{-1} = 2.85 \times 10^{-3} \text{ K}^{-1}$, or to T slightly greater than 351 K, or slightly greater than 78°C.

The molar heat of vaporization of benzene is related to the slope in the graph by the relation

$$\text{slope} = -\frac{\Delta H_{vap}}{2.30R}$$

The value of the slope can be calculated from the data in the table; for example,

$$\text{slope} = \frac{(2.798 - 2.605)}{(2.880 \times 10^{-3} \text{ K}^{-1}) - (2.994 \times 10^{-3} \text{ K})} = -1693 \text{ K}$$

and so

$$\Delta H_{vap} = -(2.30)(8.314 \text{ J}\cdot\text{K}^{-1}\cdot\text{mol}^{-1})(-1693 \text{ K})$$
$$= 3.24 \times 10^4 \text{ J}\cdot\text{mol}^{-1} = 32.4 \text{ kJ}\cdot\text{mol}^{-1}$$

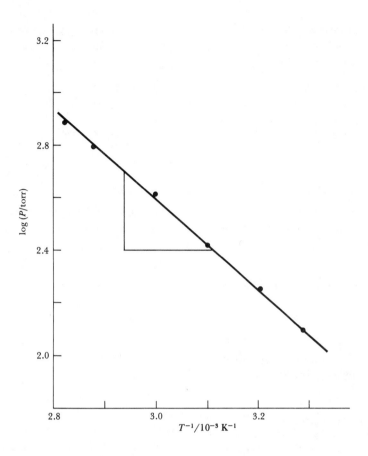

E   ANSWERS TO THE SELF-TEST

1   false

2   false (They have hindered rotational motion.)

3   false

4   the boiling point of the liquid

5   the melting point of the solid

6   heat capacity

7   molar enthalpy of fusion, ΔH_{fus}

8   the forces that hold the crystal into a lattice must be overcome by the thermal motion of the particles

9   molar enthalpy of vaporization, ΔH_{vap}

10   attractive forces between the molecules must be overcome by the thermal motion of the particles

11   greater

12   removes

13   false

14   molar enthalpy of sublimation, ΔH_{sub}

15   true

16   true

17   false

18   dipole-dipole

19   false

20 an electrostatic intermolecular attraction between a hydrogen atom in one molecule and a highly electronegative atom (e.g., O or F) in another molecule

21 London forces

22 instantaneous dipole-dipole interactions

23 true

24 false (There is a dynamic equilibrium.)

25 of evaporation is equal to the rate of condensation

26 true

27 of the vapor that is in equilibrium with a liquid

28 false

29 the temperature at which the equilibrium vapor pressure of the liquid is exactly 1 atm

30 false

31 of water vapor pressure in the air relative to the equilibrium water vapor pressure at that temperature

32 the temperature at which the relative humidity would be 100% for a given vapor pressure of water

33 the Clapeyron-Clausius equation

34 $\log\left(\dfrac{P_2}{P_1}\right) = \dfrac{\Delta H_{vap}}{2.30R}\left(\dfrac{T_2 - T_1}{T_1 T_2}\right)$

35 the regions of the various phases of a pure substance simultaneously

36 true

37 solid . . . liquid

38 false (It changes by a small amount.)

39 the temperature above which a gas cannot be liquefied regardless of the pressure applied

40 a temperature and pressure at

which three phases coexist at equilibrium

41 false

42 false

43 false

44 lies at a pressure greater than 1 atm in the phase diagram

45 structure of the crystal

46 false

47 simple cubic, body-centered cubic, and face-centered cubic

48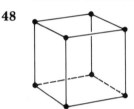

49 true

50 atoms

51 ionic

52 large

53 the different sizes of Cs^+ and Na^+ relative to Cl^-

54 molecular

55 lower

56 false (They have a wide variety of structures.)

57 true

58 diamond . . . graphite

59 covalent bonds

60 the lower set of energy levels due to the combination of valence orbitals of all the atoms

61 the higher set of energy levels

62 conduction

63 true

64 large

PROPERTIES OF SOLUTIONS

A   OUTLINE OF CHAPTER 12

12-1   A solution is a homogeneous mixture of two or more substances.

The solvent is the substance in which other substances are dissolved.

The solute is the dissolved substance.

The various types of solutions are described in Table 12-1.

12-2   Solubility involves a dynamic equilibrium.

Ions in aqueous solutions interact strongly with water molecules.

Dynamic equilibrium between an ionic solid and a solution occurs when the number of ions being deposited onto the surfaces of the crystals is equal to the number of ions entering the solution at any instant (Figure 12-2).

A saturated solution contains the maximum quantity of solute that can be dissolved in the solvent at equilibrium.

An unsaturated solution is able to dissolve additional solute.

The solubility of a solute is the maximum quantity of the solute that can be dissolved in a given quantity of solvent.

Solubility can be expressed in a variety of units.

The solubilities of most solids in liquids increase with increasing temperature (Figure 12-3).

12-3   The solubility of a gas in a liquid is directly proportional to the pressure of the gas over the liquid.

Henry's law states that $P_{gas} = k_h M_{gas}$, where P_{gas} is the equilibrium gas pressure over a solution, M_{gas} is the molarity of the dissolved gas, and k_h is the Henry's law constant for the gas [Equation (12-1)].

The Henry's law constant, k_h, depends on the gas and the solvent (Table 12-2).

The smaller the value of the Henry's law constant, k_h, for a gas, the greater is the solubility of the gas.

Gas solubility decreases with increasing temperature (Figure 12-5).

12-4   The equilibrium vapor pressure of a pure liquid always decreases when a substance is dissolved in the liquid.

Solution properties depend primarily on the ratio of the number of solute particles to the number of solvent particles.

A solute decreases the rate of evaporation of the solvent and thereby lowers the vapor pressure of the solvent (Figure 12-6).

The equilibrium vapor pressure of the solvent over a solution is proportional to the mole fraction of the solvent in the solution.

The mole fraction, X_1, of the solvent in a solution is defined by the relation

$$X_1 = \frac{n_1}{n_1 + n_2} \tag{12-2}$$

where n_1 is the number of moles of solvent and n_2 is the number of moles of solute in the solution.

In an ideal solution the solvent and solute molecules are randomly distributed.

In an ideal solution the vapor pressure of the solvent, P_1, is directly proportional to the mole fraction of the solvent, X_1 (Raoult's law).

Raoult's law states that

$$P_1 = X_1 P_1^\circ \tag{12-4}$$

where P_1° is the vapor pressure of the pure solvent at the temperature of the solution.

The vapor pressure lowering, ΔP_1, is given by

$$\Delta P_1 = X_2 P_1^\circ \tag{12-5}$$

where X_2 is the mole fraction of the solute.

12-5   Colligative properties of solutions depend only on the solute particle concentration.

The major colligative properties are

(a) vapor pressure lowering

(b) boiling point elevation

(c) freezing point depression

(d) osmotic pressure

Molality, m, is the number of moles of solute per kilogram of solvent.

Molarity, M, is the number of moles of solute per liter of solution.

Colligative molality, m_c, is the molality times the number of solute particles per formula unit (Table 12-3).

12-6   Nonvolatile solutes increase the boiling point of a liquid.

The key to understanding colligative properties is the lowering of the solvent vapor pressure by the solute (Figure 12-8).

The boiling point elevation, $T_b - T_b^\circ$, is given by the equation

$$T_b - T_b^\circ = K_b m_c \qquad (12\text{-}7)$$

The boiling point elevation constant, K_b, depends on only the solvent properties (Table 12-4).

12-7   Solutes decrease the freezing point of a liquid.

The freezing point depression, $T_f^\circ - T_f$, is given by the equation

$$T_f^\circ - T_f = K_f m_c \qquad (12\text{-}8)$$

The freezing point depression constant, K_f, depends on only the solvent properties (Table 12-4).

The freezing point depression effect is the basis of the action of antifreeze.

Ethylene glycol is a commonly used antifreeze.

12-8   Osmotic pressure requires a semipermeable membrane.

The escaping tendency of water from pure water is greater than the escaping tendency of water from a solution.

The osmotic pressure is the pressure that must be applied to a solution to raise the escaping tendency of water in the solution to that of pure water (Figure 12-11).

The osmotic pressure π is computed from the expression

$$\pi = RTM_c \qquad (12\text{-}9)$$

where M_c is the colligative molarity.

Reverse osmosis is used to obtain pure water from seawater.

Osmotic pressure is a large effect and is used to determine molecular masses of proteins.

Osmotic pressure plays a major role in living systems by keeping cells inflated.

The net flow of water across cell walls is to the side with the larger colligative molarity.

12-9   Ideal solutions consisting of two liquids obey Raoult's law.

A solution of A and B is ideal if the interaction between A and B molecules is the same as that between A molecules and between B molecules.

In an ideal solution of liquids A and B, $P_A = X_A P_A^\circ$ and $P_B = X_B P_B^\circ$ [Equation (12-10)].

The total pressure over an ideal solution composed of A and B is given by

$$P_{total} = P_B^\circ + X_A(P_A^\circ - P_B^\circ) \qquad (12\text{-}13)$$

A separation of two liquids can be achieved by fractional distillation (Figure 12-16).

There are deviations from Raoult's law if the solution is not ideal.

Positive deviations from ideal behavior occur when the total vapor pressure is greater than that calculated from Equation (12-13) (Figure 12-17b).

Negative deviations from ideal behavior occur when the total vapor pressure is lower than that calculated from Equation (12-13) (Figure 12-17a).

An azeotrope is a solution that distills without a change in composition.

B   SELF-TEST

1   In a saturated solution the rate of crystallization is greater than the rate of dissolution. *True/False*

2   The vapor pressure of a liquid *(increases, decreases)* when a solute is dissolved in the liquid.

3   The solubility of a gas *(increases, decreases)* if the equilibrium pressure of the gas over the solution is increased.

4   Henry's law states that _____

   _____ .

5   The value of a Henry's law constant depends on the gas. *True/False*

6   The solubility of a gas in water *(increases, decreases)* as the temperature increases.

7   The rate of evaporation of the solvent from a solution is the same as the rate of evaporation from the pure solvent at the same temperature. *True/False*

8   A 1.0-m aqueous solution of sucrose has the same equilibrium vapor pressure as a 1.0-m aqueous solution of NaCl at the same temperature. *True/False*

9   Explain why the vapor pressure of a solution containing a nonvolatile solute is less than the vapor pressure of the pure solvent at the same temperature.

   _____

10   The equilibrium vapor pressure of the solvent over a solution is proportional to

   _____ in the solution.

11   Raoult's law states that _____

   _____ .

12 The colligative properties of a solution depend primarily on ⎯⎯⎯⎯⎯

⎯⎯⎯⎯⎯⎯⎯⎯⎯⎯⎯⎯⎯⎯⎯⎯⎯⎯⎯⎯⎯⎯⎯⎯⎯⎯⎯ .

13 The molality of a solution is defined as ⎯⎯⎯⎯⎯⎯⎯⎯⎯⎯⎯⎯⎯

⎯⎯⎯⎯⎯⎯⎯⎯⎯⎯⎯⎯⎯⎯⎯⎯⎯⎯⎯⎯ .

14 The molality of a solution is always the same as the molarity of the solution. *True/False*

15 A 1.0-m aqueous solution of glucose is prepared by dissolving 1.0 mol of glucose in

⎯⎯⎯⎯⎯⎯⎯⎯⎯⎯⎯⎯⎯⎯⎯⎯⎯⎯⎯⎯⎯⎯⎯⎯⎯⎯⎯ .

16 The colligative molality of a 1.0 m aqueous glucose solution is ⎯⎯⎯⎯⎯ m_c.

17 The colligative molality of a 1.0 m aqueous solution of KCl is ⎯⎯⎯⎯⎯ m_c.

18 Nonvolatile solutes *(increase, decrease)* the boiling point of the solvent.

19 Explain why a nonvolatile solute raises the boiling point of the solvent.

⎯⎯⎯⎯⎯⎯⎯⎯⎯⎯⎯⎯⎯⎯⎯⎯⎯⎯⎯⎯⎯⎯⎯⎯⎯⎯⎯⎯⎯⎯⎯

⎯⎯⎯⎯⎯⎯⎯⎯⎯⎯⎯⎯⎯⎯⎯⎯⎯⎯⎯⎯⎯⎯⎯⎯⎯⎯⎯⎯⎯⎯⎯

20 The boiling point elevation due to a dissolved solute is proportional to

⎯⎯⎯⎯⎯⎯⎯⎯⎯⎯⎯⎯⎯⎯⎯⎯⎯⎯⎯⎯⎯⎯⎯⎯⎯⎯⎯⎯⎯ .

21 The boiling point elevation of a solution depends on the number of solute particles dissolved in the solvent. *True/False*

22 The boiling point elevation constant, K_b, depends on the nature of the solute. *True/False*

23 Solutes *(increase, decrease)* the freezing point of the solvent.

24 Explain why a solute lowers the freezing point of the solvent.

⎯⎯⎯⎯⎯⎯⎯⎯⎯⎯⎯⎯⎯⎯⎯⎯⎯⎯⎯⎯⎯⎯⎯⎯⎯⎯⎯⎯⎯⎯⎯

⎯⎯⎯⎯⎯⎯⎯⎯⎯⎯⎯⎯⎯⎯⎯⎯⎯⎯⎯⎯⎯⎯⎯⎯⎯⎯⎯⎯⎯⎯⎯

25 The freezing point depression of a solution due to a solute is proportional to

⎯⎯⎯⎯⎯⎯⎯⎯⎯⎯⎯⎯⎯⎯⎯⎯⎯⎯⎯⎯⎯⎯⎯⎯⎯⎯ in the solution.

26 The freezing point depression of a solution depends primarily on the concentration of solute particles dissolved in the solvent. *True/False*

27 The freezing point depression constant, K_f, depends on the nature of the solute. *True/False*

28 An antifreeze is added to water to _____.

29 An antifreeze mixture cannot freeze regardless of the temperature. *True/False*

30 The freezing point of seawater is 0.0°C. *True/False*

31 If a beaker of water and a beaker of an aqueous solution of NaCl are placed under a Bell jar, then water transfers from the beaker of

_____ to the beaker of

_____.

32 If a 0.1-M aqueous solution of NaCl is separated from a 1.0-M aqueous solution of NaCl by a rigid semipermeable membrane, then water passes spontaneously from

_____ to _____.

33 The osmotic pressure of a solution is _____

_____

_____.

34 The osmotic pressure is given by the equation $\pi =$ _____.

35 The osmotic pressure of a solution is the equilibrium vapor pressure of the solution. *True/False*

36 The osmotic pressure of a solution depends primarily on the concentration of solute particles dissolved in the solvent. *True/False*

37 Pressure can be used to obtain pure water from seawater. *True/False*

38 Red blood cells will rupture when placed in pure water because

_____.

39 Explain why the osmotic pressure of a protein solution can be used to determine the molecular mass of a protein.

_____

_____

40 Boiling point elevation is useful for determining the formula mass of low molecular mass compounds. *True/False*

41 A solution of two liquids is ideal when _____

_____

_____.

42   In an ideal solution of two liquids, each component obeys Raoult's law. *True/False*

43   The total vapor pressure over an ideal solution of two liquids is given by $P_{total} =$

_____.

44   Two volatile liquids cannot be separated by fractional distillation. *True/False*

45   When the total vapor pressure over a solution of two liquids is greater than that calculated, there is a *(negative, positive)* deviation from ideal behavior.

46   A negative deviation from ideal behavior occurs when the total vapor pressure over a solution of two liquids is less than that calculated using Raoult's law. *True/False*

47   A solution of ethyl alcohol and water is an *(ideal, nonideal)* solution.

48   An azeotrope is a solution that _____

_____.

C   CALCULATIONS YOU SHOULD KNOW HOW TO DO

1   Calculate the solubilities of gases in liquids by using Henry's law, Equation (12-1). See Example 12-1 and Problems 12-1 through 12-6.

2   Calculate mole fractions. See Example 12-2 and Problems 12-7 through 12-12.

3   Calculate solvent vapor pressure and vapor pressure lowering by using Raoult's law, Equation (12-4). See Example 12-2 and Problems 12-13 through 12-18.

4   Calculate molality and colligative molality of solutions. See Examples 12-3, 12-4 and 12-5 and Problems 12-19 through 12-26.

5   Calculate the boiling-point elevation of solutions. See Problems 12-27 through 12-32.

6   Calculate the freezing-point depression of solutions and molecular mass from the freezing-point depression. See Example 12-6 and Problems 12-33 through 12-42.

7   Calculate the osmotic pressure of solutions and molecular mass from the osmotic pressure. See Examples 12-7 and 12-8 and Problems 12-45 through 12-50.

8   Calculate the vapor pressure over an ideal solution of two liquids. See Example 12-9 and Problems 12-51 and 12-52.

D   SOLUTIONS TO THE ODD-NUMBERED PROBLEMS

12-1   From Henry's law we have

$$P_{gas} = k_h M_{gas}$$

Thus

$$M_{gas} = \frac{P_{gas}}{k_h}$$

The Henry's law constant for N_2 is 1.6×10^3 atm·M^{-1} (see Table 12-2):

$$M_{N_2} = \frac{0.79 \text{ atm}}{1.6 \times 10^3 \text{ atm} \cdot M^{-1}} = 4.9 \times 10^{-4} \text{ M}$$

12-3   The concentration of CO_2 is given by

$$M_{CO_2} = \frac{P_{CO_2}}{k_h}$$

Using the value of k_h for CO_2 given in Table 12-2, we have

$$M_{CO_2} = \frac{2.0 \text{ atm}}{29 \text{ atm} \cdot M^{-1}} = 6.9 \times 10^{-2} \text{ M} = 0.069 \text{ M}$$

12-5   The partial pressure of O_2 is (Table 12-2)

$$P_{O_2} = k_h M_{O_2} = (7.8 \times 10^2 \text{ atm} \cdot M^{-1})(1.28 \times 10^{-3} \text{ M}) = 1.0 \text{ atm}$$

Air is 20 percent O_2; the air pressure when the partial pressure of O_2 is 1.0 atm is

$$(0.20)P_{air} = P_{O_2}$$

$$P_{air} = \frac{1.0 \text{ atm}}{0.20} = 5.0 \text{ atm}$$

The increase in pressure is 4.0 atm. The depth of the dive is

$$\left(\frac{33 \text{ ft}}{1 \text{ atm}}\right)(4.0 \text{ atm}) = 130 \text{ ft}$$

12-7   The mole fraction of water is given by

$$X_{H_2O} = \frac{n_{H_2O}}{n_{H_2O} + n_{C_2H_5OH}}$$

The mole fraction of water is

$$X_{H_2O} = \frac{(80.0 \text{ g})\left(\dfrac{1 \text{ mol } H_2O}{18.02 \text{ g } H_2O}\right)}{(80.0 \text{ g})\left(\dfrac{1 \text{ mol } H_2O}{18.02 \text{ g } H_2O}\right) + (20.0 \text{ g})\left(\dfrac{1 \text{ mol } C_2H_5OH}{46.07 \text{ g } C_2H_5OH}\right)}$$

$$= \frac{4.440 \text{ mol}}{4.440 \text{ mol} + 0.4341 \text{ mol}} = \frac{4.440 \text{ mol}}{4.874 \text{ mol}}$$

$$= 0.911$$

The mole fraction of ethyl alcohol is

$$X_{C_2H_5OH} = \frac{(20.0\text{ g})\left(\dfrac{1\text{ mol C}_2\text{H}_5\text{OH}}{46.07\text{ g C}_2\text{H}_5\text{OH}}\right)}{4.440\text{ mol} + 0.4341\text{ mol}} = 0.0891$$

12-9 The mole fraction of acetone (A) is given by

$$X_A = \frac{n_A}{n_A + n_{H_2O}} = 0.19$$

In 1.00 kg of solution we have x g of acetone and $(1000 - x)$g of water. The moles of acetone and water are given by

$$n_A = \frac{x}{58.08\text{ g}\cdot\text{mol}^{-1}} \qquad n_{H_2O} = \frac{1000\text{ g} - x}{18.02\text{ g}\cdot\text{mol}^{-1}}$$

Thus

$$\frac{\left(\dfrac{x}{58.08}\right)}{\left(\dfrac{x}{58.08}\right) + \left(\dfrac{1000 - x}{18.02}\right)} = 0.19$$

and

$$\frac{x}{58.08} = \frac{0.19x}{58.08} + \frac{190}{18.02} - \frac{0.19x}{18.02}$$

Multiplying both sides of this equation by 58.08 yields

$$x = 0.19x + 612.4 - 0.612x$$

Solving for x yields

$$x = \frac{612.4}{1.422} = 431$$

The solution is prepared by mixing 431 g of acetone with 569 g of water.

12-11 In a 100.0-mL sample we have 70.0 mL of isopropyl alcohol and 30.0 mL of water. The masses of isopropyl alcohol and water are

$$m_{alc} = (70.0\text{ mL})(0.785\text{ g}\cdot\text{mL}^{-1}) = 55.0\text{ g}$$

$$m_{H_2O} = (30.0\text{ mL})(1.000\text{ g}\cdot\text{mL}^{-1}) = 30.0\text{ g}$$

The mole fraction of isopropyl alcohol is given by

$$X_{alc} = \frac{n_{alc}}{n_{alc} + n_{H_2O}} = \frac{\left(\dfrac{55.0\ g}{60.09\ g \cdot mol^{-1}}\right)}{\left(\dfrac{55.0\ g}{60.09\ g \cdot mol^{-1}}\right) + \left(\dfrac{30.0\ g}{18.02\ g \cdot mol^{-1}}\right)}$$

$$= \frac{0.915\ mol}{0.915\ mol + 1.665\ mol} = 0.354$$

12-13 The mole fraction of water in the solution is

$$X_{H_2O} = \frac{n_{H_2O}}{n_{H_2O} + n_{glucose}}$$

$$= \frac{(500.0\ g)\left(\dfrac{1\ mol\ H_2O}{18.02\ g\ H_2O}\right)}{(500.0\ g)\left(\dfrac{1\ mol\ H_2O}{18.02\ g\ H_2O}\right) + (20.0\ g)\left(\dfrac{1\ mol\ glucose}{180.16\ g\ glucose}\right)}$$

$$= 0.996$$

Raoult's law is

$$P_{H_2O} = X_{H_2O} P^{\circ}_{H_2O}$$

and thus at $37°C$ we have

$$P_{H_2O} = (0.996)(47.1\ torr) = 46.9\ torr$$

The vapor pressure lowering is

$$P^{\circ} - P = 47.1\ torr - 46.9\ torr = 0.2\ torr$$

12-15 The mole fraction of water in the solution is

$$X_{H_2O} = \frac{n_{H_2O}}{n_{H_2O} + n_{sucrose}}$$

$$= \frac{(195\ g)\left(\dfrac{1\ mol\ H_2O}{18.02\ g\ H_2O}\right)}{(195\ g)\left(\dfrac{1\ mol\ H_2O}{18.02\ g\ H_2O}\right) + (20.0\ g)\left(\dfrac{1\ mol\ sucrose}{342.30\ g\ sucrose}\right)}$$

$$= 0.995$$

From Raoult's law we compute

$$P_{H_2O} = X_{H_2O} P^{\circ}_{H_2O} = (0.995)(23.76\ torr) = 23.64\ torr$$

The vapor pressure lowering is

$$P_{H_2O}^\circ - P_{H_2O} = 23.76 \text{ torr} - 23.64 \text{ torr} = 0.12 \text{ torr}$$

12-17 The mole fraction of ethyl alcohol in the solution is given by

$$X_{alc} = \frac{n_{alc}}{n_{alc} + n_{urea}}$$

Thus

$$X_{alc} = \frac{\left(\dfrac{100.0 \text{ g}}{46.07 \text{ g·mol}^{-1}}\right)}{\left(\dfrac{100.0 \text{ g}}{46.07 \text{ g·mol}^{-1}}\right) + \left(\dfrac{20.0 \text{ g}}{60.06 \text{ g·mol}^{-1}}\right)}$$

$$= \frac{2.171 \text{ mol}}{2.171 \text{ mol} + 0.333 \text{ mol}} = 0.867$$

The vapor pressure of ethyl alcohol is calculated by using Raoult's law.

$$P_{alc} = X_{alc}P_{alc}^\circ = (0.867)(59.2 \text{ torr}) = 51.3 \text{ torr}$$

The vapor pressure lowering is

$$P_{alc}^\circ - P_{alc} = 59.2 \text{ torr} - 51.3 \text{ torr} = 7.9 \text{ torr}$$

12-19 A 2.50 m formic-acid-in-acetone solution contains 2.50 mol of formic acid dissolved in 1000 g of acetone. Thus we dissolve

$$(2.50 \text{ mol})(46.03 \text{ g·mol}^{-1}) = 115 \text{ g}$$

of formic acid in 1000 g of acetone.

12-21 The number of moles of I_2 that correspond to 2.603 g is

$$n = (2.603 \text{ g})\left(\frac{1 \text{ mol } I_2}{253.8 \text{ g } I_2}\right) = 0.01026 \text{ mol}$$

Therefore,

$$\text{molality} = \frac{\text{moles of solute}}{\text{kilogram of solvent}}$$

$$= \frac{0.01026 \text{ mol } I_2}{0.1000 \text{ kg } CCl_4} = 0.1026 \text{ m}$$

12-23 (a) There are two ions per $MgSO_4$ formula unit, because $MgSO_4$ dissociates into $Mg^{2+}(aq)$ and $SO_4^{2-}(aq)$ in water. The colligative molality is thus 2.0 m_c.

(b) There are three ions per $Cu(NO_3)_2$ formula unit, because $Cu(NO_3)_2$ dissociates into $Cu^{2+}(aq)$ and $2NO_3^-(aq)$ in water. The colligative molality is thus $3.0\ m_c$.

(c) There is one solute particle per C_2H_5OH formula unit because C_2H_5OH does not dissociate in water. Thus the colligative molality is $1.0\ m_c$.

(d) There are five ions per $Al_2(SO_4)_3$ formula unit, because $Al_2(SO_4)_3$ dissociates into $2Al^{3+}(aq)$ and $3SO_4^{2-}(aq)$ in water. The colligative molality is thus $5.0 m_c$.

12-25 (a) The colligative molality of 0.25 m NaCl is $0.50\ m_c$. Thus there are 0.50 mol of solute particles in 1000 g of water. The mole fraction of water in the solution is

$$X_{H_2O} = \frac{n_{H_2O}}{n_{H_2O} + n_{solute}}$$

$$= \frac{(1000\ g)\left(\dfrac{1\ mol\ H_2O}{18.02\ g\ H_2O}\right)}{(1000\ g)\left(\dfrac{1\ mol\ H_2O}{18.02\ g\ H_2O}\right) + 0.50\ mol}$$

$$= 0.9911$$

The partial pressure of water is computed by using Raoult's law:

$$P_{H_2O} = X_{H_2O}P^{\circ}_{H_2O} = (0.9911)(17.54\ torr) = 17.38\ torr$$

The vapor pressure lowering is

$$P^{\circ}_{H_2O} - P_{H_2O} = 17.54\ torr - 17.38\ torr = 0.16\ torr$$

(b) The colligative molality of 0.25 m $CaCl_2$ is $0.75\ m_c$. Thus there are 0.75 mol of solute particles in 1000 g of water. The mole fraction of water in the solution is

$$X_{H_2O} = \frac{(1000\ g)\left(\dfrac{1\ mol\ H_2O}{18.02\ g\ H_2O}\right)}{(1000\ g)\left(\dfrac{1\ mol\ H_2O}{18.02\ g\ H_2O}\right) + 0.75\ mol}$$

$$= 0.9867$$

The vapor pressure of water is

$$P_{H_2O} = X_{H_2O}P^{\circ}_{H_2O} = (0.9867)(17.54\ torr) = 17.31\ torr$$

The vapor pressure lowering is

$$P^{\circ}_{H_2O} - P_{H_2O} = 17.54\ torr - 17.31\ torr = 0.23\ torr$$

(c) The colligative molality of 0.25 m sucrose is 0.25 m_c. Thus there are 0.25 mol of solute particles in 1000 g of water. The mole fraction of water in the solution is

$$X_{H_2O} = \frac{(1000 \text{ g})\left(\dfrac{1 \text{ mol } H_2O}{18.02 \text{ g } H_2O}\right)}{(1000 \text{ g})\left(\dfrac{1 \text{ mol } H_2O}{18.02 \text{ g } H_2O}\right) + 0.25 \text{ mol}}$$

$$= 0.9955$$

The vapor pressure of water is

$$P_{H_2O} = X_{H_2O}P^\circ_{H_2O} = (0.9955)(17.54 \text{ torr}) = 17.46 \text{ torr}$$

The vapor pressure lowering is

$$P^\circ_{H_2O} - P_{H_2O} = 17.54 \text{ torr} - 17.46 \text{ torr} = 0.08 \text{ torr}$$

(d) The colligative molality of 0.25 m $Al(ClO_4)_3$ is 1.00 m_c. Thus, there is 1.00 mol of solute particles in 1000 g of water. The mole fraction of water in the solution is

$$X_{H_2O} = \frac{(1000 \text{ g})\left(\dfrac{1 \text{ mol } H_2O}{18.02 \text{ g } H_2O}\right)}{(1000 \text{ g})\left(\dfrac{1 \text{ mol } H_2O}{18.02 \text{ g } H_2O}\right) + 1.00 \text{ mol}}$$

$$= 0.9823$$

The vapor pressure of water is computed by using Raoult's law

$$P_{H_2O} = X_{H_2O}P^\circ_{H_2O} = (0.9823)(17.54 \text{ torr}) = 17.23 \text{ torr}$$

The vapor pressure lowering is

$$P^\circ_{H_2O} - P_{H_2O} = 17.54 \text{ torr} - 17.23 \text{ torr} = 0.31 \text{ torr}$$

12-27 The colligative molality of the $Sc(ClO_4)_3(aq)$ solution is

$$m_c = (4)(2.0 \text{ m}) = 8.0 \text{ m}_c$$

The boiling point elevation is

$$T_b - T^\circ_b = K_b m_c$$
$$= (0.52 \text{ K} \cdot \text{m}_c^{-1})(8.0 \text{ m}_c)$$
$$= 4.2 \text{ K} = 4.2°C$$

The boiling point of the solution is

$$T_b = 100.00°C + 4.2°C = 104.2°C$$

12-29 The molality of the solution is

$$m = \frac{(10.0 \text{ g})\left(\dfrac{1 \text{ mol picric acid}}{229.1 \text{ g picric acid}}\right)}{(0.100 \text{ kg cyclohexane})} = 0.436 \text{ m}$$

$$m_c = m = 0.436 \text{ m}_c$$

The boiling point elevation is (Table 12-4)

$$T_b - T_b° = K_b m_c = (2.79 \text{ K} \cdot \text{m}_c^{-1})(0.436 \text{ m}_c) = 1.22 \text{ K} = 1.22°C$$

The boiling point is (Table 12-4)

$$T_b = 80.7°C + 1.22°C = 81.9°C$$

12-31 Urea does not dissociate in solution, and thus the colligative molality of the urea is

$$m_c = \frac{(25.0 \text{ g})\left(\dfrac{1 \text{ mol urea}}{60.06 \text{ g urea}}\right)}{1.500 \text{ kg nitrobenzene}} = 0.278 \text{ m}_c$$

The boiling point elevation is (Table 12-4)

$$T_b - T_b° = K_b m_c = (5.24 \text{ K} \cdot \text{m}_c^{-1})(0.278 \text{ m}_c) = 1.46 \text{ K} = 1.46°C$$

The boiling point of the solution is (Table 12-4)

$$T_b = 210.8°C + 1.46°C = 212.3°C$$

12-33 The molality of the solution is

$$m = \frac{(60.0 \text{ g})\left(\dfrac{1 \text{ mol glucose}}{180.16 \text{ g glucose}}\right)}{0.200 \text{ kg water}} = 1.67 \text{ m} = 1.67 \text{ m}_c$$

The freezing point depression is

$$T_f° - T_f = K_f m_c = (1.86 \text{ K} \cdot \text{m}_c^{-1})(1.67 \text{ m}_c) = 3.11 \text{ K} = 3.11°C$$

The freezing point is

$$T_f = 0.00°C - 3.11°C = -3.11°C$$

12-35 The molality of the solution is

$$m = \frac{(22.0 \text{ g})\left(\dfrac{1 \text{ mol CCl}_4}{153.81 \text{ g CCl}_4}\right)}{0.800 \text{ kg benzene}} = 0.179 \text{ m} = 0.179 \text{ m}_c$$

The freezing point depression is (Table 12-4)

$$T_f^\circ - T_f = K_f m_c = (5.10 \text{ K} \cdot \text{m}_c^{-1})(0.179 \text{ m}_c)$$
$$= 0.913 \text{ K} = 0.913°\text{C}$$

The freezing point is

$$T_f = 5.50°\text{C} - 0.913°\text{C} = 4.59°\text{C}$$

12-37 Diphenyl and naphthalene do not dissociate in solution and thus the colligative molality is

$$m_c = \frac{(5.00 \text{ g})\left(\dfrac{1 \text{ mol diphenyl}}{154.20 \text{ g diphenyl}}\right) + (7.50 \text{ g})\left(\dfrac{1 \text{ mol naphthalene}}{128.16 \text{ g naphthalene}}\right)}{(0.200 \text{ kg benzene})}$$
$$= 0.455 \text{ m}_c$$

The freezing point depression of the solution is (Table 12-4)

$$T_f^\circ - T_f = K_b m_c = (5.10 \text{ K} \cdot \text{m}_c^{-1})(0.455 \text{ m}_c)$$
$$= 2.32 \text{ K} = 2.32°\text{C}$$

The freezing point of the solution is

$$T_f = 5.50°\text{C} - 2.32°\text{C} = 3.18°\text{C}$$

12-39 We can find the molality of the solution from the freezing point depression.

$$T_f^\circ - T_f = K_f m_c$$
$$4.43 \text{ K} = (40.0 \text{ K} \cdot \text{m}_c^{-1})m_c$$
$$m_c = \frac{4.43 \text{ K}}{40.0 \text{ K} \cdot \text{m}_c^{-1}} = 0.111 \text{ m}_c$$

Because the mass is given, we have the correspondence

$$0.111 \text{ mol} \cdot \text{kg}^{-1} \backsimeq \frac{0.500 \text{ g vitamin C}}{0.0100 \text{ kg camphor}} = 50.0 \text{ g} \cdot \text{kg}^{-1}$$

and therefore

$$0.111 \text{ mol} \backsimeq 50.0 \text{ g}$$

Dividing both sides by 0.111, we have

$$1.00 \text{ mol} \approx 450 \text{ g}$$

The molecular mass of vitamin K is 450.

An alternative solution is to use the definition of molality.

$$m_c = \frac{\text{moles of vitamin K}}{\text{kilograms of camphor}}$$

$$0.111 \text{ m} = \frac{(0.500 \text{ g})/(\text{molar mass})}{(0.0100 \text{ kg})}$$

Solving for the molar mass, we have

$$\text{molar mass} = \frac{0.500 \text{ g}}{(0.111 \text{ mol} \cdot \text{kg}^{-1})(0.0100 \text{ kg})} = 450 \text{ g} \cdot \text{mol}^{-1}$$

The molecular mass of vitamin K is 450.

12-41 We can find the colligative molality of the solution from the freezing point depression.

$$T_f^\circ - T_f = K_f m_c$$

$$0.00°C - (-57°C) = (1.86 \text{ K} \cdot \text{m}_c^{-1}) m_c$$

$$m_c = \frac{57 \text{ K}}{1.86 \text{ K} \cdot \text{m}_c^{-1}} = 30.6 \text{ m}_c$$

The concentration of $CaCl_2$ in the pond is

$$\text{molality} = \frac{m_c}{3} = \frac{30.6 \text{ m}_c}{3} = 10 \text{ m}$$

12-43 The molality of the solution is

$$m = \frac{(40.7 \text{ g})\left(\dfrac{1 \text{ mol HgCl}_2}{271.5 \text{ g HgCl}_2}\right)}{0.100 \text{ kg H}_2\text{O}} = 1.50 \text{ m}$$

If $HgCl_2$ were completely dissociated, the colligative molality would be 4.50 m_c. We can find the colligative molality from the freezing point depression.

$$T_f^\circ - T_f = K_f m_c$$

$$2.83 \text{ K} = (1.86 \text{ K} \cdot \text{m}_c^{-1}) m_c$$

$$m_c = \frac{2.83 \text{ K}}{1.86 \text{ K} \cdot \text{m}_c^{-1}} = 1.52 \text{ m}_c$$

This shows that the compound $HgCl_2$ is essentially undissociated.

12-45   The osmotic pressure is given by

$$\pi = RTM_c$$

Thus

$$\pi = (0.0821 \ \text{L} \cdot \text{atm} \cdot \text{K}^{-1} \cdot \text{mol}^{-1})(310 \ \text{K})(0.25 \ \text{mol} \cdot \text{L}^{-1}) = 6.4 \ \text{atm}$$

12-47   The concentration of insulin in the aqueous solution is

$$M_c = \frac{\pi}{RT} = \frac{(6.48 \ \text{torr})\left(\dfrac{1 \ \text{atm}}{760 \ \text{torr}}\right)}{(0.0821 \ \text{L} \cdot \text{atm} \cdot \text{K}^{-1} \cdot \text{mol}^{-1})(298 \ \text{K})}$$
$$= 3.48 \times 10^{-4} \ \text{mol} \cdot \text{L}^{-1}$$

The molecular mass can be calculated from the concentration. We have the correspondence

$$3.48 \times 10^{-4} \ \text{mol} \cdot \text{L}^{-1} \approx \frac{2.00 \times 10^{-2} \ \text{g}}{0.0100 \ \text{L}} = 2.00 \ \text{g} \cdot \text{L}^{-1}$$

and, therefore,

$$3.48 \times 10^{-4} \ \text{mol} \approx 2.00 \ \text{g}$$

Dividing both sides by 3.48×10^{-4}, we have

$$1.00 \ \text{mol} \approx 5.75 \times 10^{3} \ \text{g}$$

The molecular mass of insulin is about 5750.

12-49   The concentration of a solution for which an applied pressure of 100 atm is just sufficient to cause reverse osmosis is

$$M_c = \frac{\pi}{RT} = \frac{100 \ \text{atm}}{(0.0821 \ \text{L} \cdot \text{atm} \cdot \text{K}^{-1} \cdot \text{mol}^{-1})(293 \ \text{K})}$$
$$= 4.16 \ \text{mol} \cdot \text{L}^{-1} = 4.16 \ M_c$$

The concentration of seawater is $1.1 \ M_c$. The number moles of ions in the seawater will remain the same after reverse osmosis:

$$\text{moles of ions before reverse osmosis} = \text{moles of ions after reverse osmosis}$$

$$M_B V_B = M_A V_A$$

$$(1.1 \ M_c)V_B = (4.16 \ M_c)V_A$$

We want 10 L of fresh water, that is, $\Delta V = 10$ L:

$$V_B = 10 \ \text{L} + V_A \qquad \text{or} \qquad V_A = V_B - 10 \ \text{L}$$

$$(1.1 \ M_c)V_B = (4.16 \ M_c)(V_B - 10 \ \text{L})$$

Solving for V_B, we have

$$41.6 \text{ L} = 3.06 V_B$$

$$V_B = \frac{41.6 \text{ L}}{3.06} = 13.6 \text{ L}$$

12-51   (a) The total pressure over the solution is given by

$$P_{tot} = P_B + P_T$$

where P_B and P_T denote the partial pressures of benzene and toluene, respectively. Assuming an ideal solution, we use Raoult's law for both components.

$$
\begin{aligned}
P_{tot} &= X_B P_B^\circ + X_T P_T^\circ \\
&= (0.250)(768 \text{ torr}) + (0.750)(293 \text{ torr}) \\
&= 412 \text{ torr}
\end{aligned}
$$

(b) The mole fraction of benzene in the vapor phase is given by

$$
\begin{aligned}
Y_B &= \frac{n_B}{n_{tot}} = \frac{(P_B V/RT)}{(P_{tot} V/RT)} = \frac{P_B}{P_{tot}} = \frac{X_B P_B^\circ}{P_{tot}} \\
&= \frac{(0.250)(768 \text{ torr})}{412 \text{ torr}} \\
&= 0.466
\end{aligned}
$$

12-53   Recall from Example 4-1 that the height of a column of water is 13.6 times higher than the height of a column of mercury if both columns are supported by the same gas pressure. Thus, the osmotic pressure in units of atm is

$$
\begin{aligned}
\pi &= (8.42 \text{ mmH}_2\text{O})\left(\frac{1 \text{ mmHg}}{13.6 \text{ mmH}_2\text{O}}\right)\left(\frac{1 \text{ torr}}{1 \text{ mmHg}}\right)\left(\frac{1 \text{ atm}}{760 \text{ torr}}\right) \\
&= 8.15 \times 10^{-4} \text{ atm}
\end{aligned}
$$

The concentration of immunoglobulin G in the aqueous solution is

$$
\begin{aligned}
M_c &= \frac{\pi}{RT} = \frac{8.15 \times 10^{-4} \text{ atm}}{(0.0821 \text{ L} \cdot \text{atm} \cdot \text{K}^{-1} \cdot \text{mol}^{-1})(298 \text{ K})} \\
&= 3.33 \times 10^{-5} \text{ mol} \cdot \text{L}^{-1}
\end{aligned}
$$

Thus we have the correspondence

$$3.33 \times 10^{-5} \text{ mol} \cdot \text{L}^{-1} \backsimeq \frac{0.500 \text{ g IgG}}{0.100 \text{ L solution}} = 5.00 \text{ g} \cdot \text{L}^{-1}$$

or

$$3.33 \times 10^{-5} \text{ mol} \backsimeq 5.00 \text{ g}$$

Dividing both sides by 3.33×10^{-5}, we have

$$1.00 \text{ mol} \approx 1.50 \times 10^5 \text{ g}$$

The molecular mass of immunoglobulin G is about 150,000.

12-55 Ethyl alcohol (boiling point, $78°C$) is a temporary antifreeze because its equilibrium vapor pressure is much greater than one atmosphere at $100°C$. Thus ethyl alcohol is much more readily lost by evaporation from the coolant system than a relatively high boiling liquid like ethylene glycol (boiling point, $197°C$).

12-57 The number of moles of sucrose in two teaspoons is

$$n = (2 \text{ teaspoons})\left(\frac{14 \text{ g}}{3 \text{ teaspoons}}\right)\left(\frac{1 \text{ mol sucrose}}{342.3 \text{ g sucrose}}\right)$$

$$= 0.027 \text{ mol}$$

The mass of water in one cup is

$$\text{mass} = dV = (1.00 \text{ g} \cdot \text{mL}^{-1})(1 \text{ cup})\left(\frac{0.946 \text{ L}}{4 \text{ cups}}\right)\left(\frac{1000 \text{ mL}}{1 \text{ L}}\right)$$

$$= 240 \text{ g} = 0.240 \text{ kg}$$

The molality is

$$\text{molality} = \frac{\text{moles of solute}}{\text{kilogram of solvent}}$$

$$= \frac{0.027 \text{ mol sucrose}}{0.240 \text{ kg H}_2\text{O}} = 0.11 \text{ m}$$

12-59 The freezing point is $-36°C$, so the freezing point depression is

$$T_f^{\circ} - T_f = 0.00°C - (-36°C) = 36°C = 36 \text{ K}$$

The colligative molality of the solution is

$$T_f^{\circ} - T_f = K_b m_c$$
$$36 \text{ K} = (1.86 \text{ K} \cdot \text{m}_c^{-1})m_c$$
$$m_c = 19 \text{ m}_c = 19 \text{ m}$$

The boiling point of the 19 m_c solution is given by

$$T_b = T_b^{\circ} + K_b m_c$$
$$= 100.0°C + (0.52 \text{ K} \cdot \text{m}_c^{-1})(19 \text{ m}_c)$$
$$= 110°C$$

12-61 The mole fractions are calculated as follows. For methyl alcohol we have

$$X_{met} = \frac{n_{met}}{n_{met} + n_{eth} + n_{H_2O}}$$

$$= \frac{\left(\dfrac{0.305 \text{ g}}{32.04 \text{ g} \cdot \text{mol}^{-1}}\right)}{\left(\dfrac{0.305 \text{ g}}{32.04 \text{ g} \cdot \text{mol}^{-1}}\right) + \left(\dfrac{0.275 \text{ g}}{46.07 \text{ g} \cdot \text{mol}^{-1}}\right) + \left(\dfrac{10.0 \text{ g}}{18.02 \text{ g} \cdot \text{mol}^{-1}}\right)}$$

$$= \frac{0.00952 \text{ mol}}{0.00952 \text{ mol} + 0.00597 \text{ mol} + 0.5549 \text{ mol}} = 0.0167$$

For ethyl alcohol we have

$$X_{eth} = \frac{0.00597 \text{ mol}}{0.00952 \text{ mol} + 0.00597 \text{ mol} + 0.5549 \text{ mol}} = 0.0104$$

The molalities are calculated as follows

$$m_{met} = \frac{0.00952 \text{ mol CH}_3\text{OH}}{0.0100 \text{ kg H}_2\text{O}} = 0.952 \text{ m}$$

$$m_{eth} = \frac{0.00597 \text{ mol CH}_3\text{CH}_2\text{OH}}{0.0100 \text{ kg H}_2\text{O}} = 0.597 \text{ m}$$

12-63 There will be a net flow of water from the solution with the lower osmotic pressure to the solution with the higher osmotic pressure. Because $\pi = RTM_c$, the net flow of water will be from the solution with the lower value of M_c to the solution with the higher value of M_c.

(a) Because M_c ($=0.20$ M_c) is the same in both cases, there is no net flow.

(b) The values of M_c are

$$M_c \text{ [for 0.10 M Al(NO}_3)_3] = 4 \times 0.10 \text{ M} = 0.40 \text{ M}_c$$
$$M_c \text{ [for 0.20 M NaNO}_3] = 2 \times 0.20 \text{ M} = 0.40 \text{ M}_c$$

Because M_c is the same in both cases, there is no net flow.

(c) Because $M_c = 0.30$ M_c for 0.10 M CaCl$_2$ and $M_c = 1.50$ M_c for 0.50 M CaCl$_2$, the net flow of water will be from the 0.30 M_c solution to the 1.50 M_c solution.

12-65 Consider a 100.0-mL sample of the solution. The total mass of the solution is

$$(100.0 \text{ mL})(1.101 \text{ g} \cdot \text{mL}^{-1}) = 110.1 \text{ g}$$

The mass of glycerol is

$$(110.1 \text{ g})(0.400) = 44.0 \text{ g}$$

The mass of water is

$$(110.1 \text{ g})(0.600) = 66.1 \text{ g}$$

The molarity of glycerol in the solution is

$$M = \frac{(44.0 \text{ g})\left(\dfrac{1 \text{ mol glycerol}}{92.09 \text{ g glycerol}}\right)}{(0.100 \text{ L})} = 4.78 \text{ M}$$

The molality of glycerol in the solution is

$$m = \frac{(44.0 \text{ g})\left(\dfrac{1 \text{ mol glycerol}}{92.09 \text{ g glycerol}}\right)}{(0.0661 \text{ kg})} = 7.23 \text{ m}$$

The molality at $0\,°C$ is the same as at $20\,°C$, because molality is independent of temperature.

12-67 (a) The molality of the $K_2SO_4(aq)$ solution is

$$m = \frac{(5.00 \text{ g})\left(\dfrac{1 \text{ mol } K_2SO_4}{174.26 \text{ g } K_2SO_4}\right)}{(0.250 \text{ kg } H_2O)} = 0.115 \text{ m}$$

In water K_2SO_4 dissociates into $2K^+(aq) + SO_4^{2-}(aq)$; thus the colligative molality is

$$m_c = 3 \text{ m} = 0.345 \text{ m}_c$$

The freezing point of the solution is

$$T_f = T_f^° - K_f m_c$$
$$= 0.00\,°C - (1.86 \text{ K} \cdot \text{m}_c^{-1})(0.345 \text{ m}_c) = -0.642\,°C$$

The boiling point of the solution is

$$T_b = T_b^° + K_b m_c$$
$$= 100.00\,°C + (0.52 \text{ K} \cdot \text{m}_c^{-1})(0.345 \text{ m}_c) = 100.18\,°C$$

(b) The compound C_2H_5OH does not dissociate in aqueous solution, so $m = m_c$ and

$$m_c = \frac{(5.00 \text{ g})\left(\dfrac{1 \text{ mol } C_2H_5OH}{46.07 \text{ g } C_2H_5OH}\right)}{(0.250 \text{ kg } H_2O)} = 0.434 \text{ m}_c$$

The freezing point of the solution is

$$T_f = T_f^\circ - K_f m_c$$
$$= 0.00 - (1.86 \text{ K} \cdot \text{m}_c^{-1})(0.434 \text{ m}_c) = -0.807°C$$

The boiling point of the solution is

$$T_b = T_b^\circ + K_b m_c$$
$$= 100.00 + (0.52 \text{ K} \cdot \text{m}_c^{-1})(0.434 \text{ m}_c) = 100.23°C$$

(c) Aniline does not dissociate in camphor, and thus $m = m_c$.

$$m_c = \frac{(1.00 \text{ g})\left(\dfrac{1 \text{ mol aniline}}{93.13 \text{ g aniline}}\right)}{(0.0500 \text{ kg camphor})} = 0.215 \text{ m}_c$$

The freezing point of the solution is

$$T_f = T_f^\circ - K_f m_c$$
$$= 179.8°C - (40.0 \text{ K} \cdot \text{m}_c^{-1})(0.215 \text{ m}_c) = 171.2°C$$

The boiling point of the solution is

$$T_b = T_b^\circ + K_b m_c$$
$$= 208.0°C + (5.95 \text{ K} \cdot \text{m}_c^{-1})(0.215 \text{ m}_c) = 209.3°C$$

12-69 The colligative molality of phosphorus in the carbon disulfide solution is given by

$$m_c = \frac{\left(\dfrac{2.74 \text{ g}}{P_x}\right)}{\left(\dfrac{100 \text{ mL} \times 1.261 \text{ g} \cdot \text{mL}^{-1}}{1000 \text{ g} \cdot \text{kg}^{-1}}\right)} = \frac{21.73 \text{ g} \cdot \text{kg}^{-1}}{P_x}$$

where P_x is the formula mass of phosphorus. The boiling point elevation is given by

$$T_b - T_b^\circ = K_b m_c$$

Thus

$$46.71°C - 46.30°C = (2.34 \text{ K} \cdot \text{m}_c^{-1})\left(\frac{21.73 \text{ g} \cdot \text{kg}^{-1}}{P_x}\right)$$

Solving for P_x yields

$$P_x = 124 \text{ g} \cdot \text{mol}^{-1}$$

The atomic mass of phosphorus is 30.97 and

$$\frac{124}{30.97} = 4.00$$

Thus there are four phosphorus atoms per formula unit and the molecular formula of phosphorus is P_4.

12-71 The mass of the solution prepared by dissolving 2.00 mol of NaOH in 1000 g of H_2O is

$$\text{mass} = \text{mass}_{\text{NaOH}} + \text{mass}_{H_2O}$$

Thus

$$\text{mass} = (2.00 \text{ mol})\left(\frac{40.00 \text{ g NaOH}}{1 \text{ mol NaOH}}\right) + 1000 \text{ g} = 1080 \text{ g}$$

The volume of the solution can be found from the density

$$d = \frac{\text{mass}}{V} \quad \text{or} \quad V = \frac{\text{mass}}{d}$$

$$V = \frac{1080 \text{ g}}{1.22 \text{ g}\cdot\text{mL}^{-1}} = 885 \text{ mL} = 0.885 \text{ L}$$

The molarity is

$$\text{molarity} = \frac{\text{moles of solute}}{\text{volume of solution}}$$

$$= \frac{2.00 \text{ mol NaOH}}{0.885 \text{ L solution}} = 2.26 \text{ M}$$

12-73 The molality of the solution is

$$\text{molality} = \frac{\text{moles of solute}}{\text{kilograms of solvent}}$$

$$= \frac{(50.0 \text{ g})\left(\dfrac{1 \text{ mol ethylene glycol}}{62.07 \text{ g ethylene glycol}}\right)}{0.0500 \text{ kg water}} = 16.1 \text{ m}$$

$$m_c = 16.1 \text{ m}_c$$

The boiling point elevation is

$$T_b - T_b^\circ = K_b m_c = (0.52 \text{ K}\cdot\text{m}_c^{-1})(16.1 \text{ m}_c)$$
$$= 8.4 \text{ K} = 8.4^\circ\text{C}$$

The boiling point is

$$T_b = 100.00°C + 8.4°C = 108.4°C$$

12-75 In a 100.0-g sample of the sulfuric acid we have 98 g of H_2SO_4 and 2.0 g of water. The volume of the 100.0 g sample is

$$V = \frac{m}{d} = \frac{100.0 \text{ g}}{1.84 \text{ g·mL}^{-1}} = 54.3 \text{ mL}$$

The molarity of H_2SO_4 is equal to the moles of H_2SO_4 per liter of solution; thus

$$M = \frac{(98 \text{ g})\left(\dfrac{1 \text{ mol } H_2SO_4}{98.08 \text{ g } H_2SO_4}\right)}{(0.0543 \text{ L solution})} = 18 \text{ M}$$

E   ANSWERS TO THE SELF-TEST

1 false (The rates are equal.)

2 decreases

3 increases

4 the solubility of a gas is proportional to the partial pressure of that gas over the solution, that is, $P_{gas} = k_h M_{gas}$

5 true

6 decreases

7 false

8 false

9 The solute molecules decrease the rate of evaporation of the solvent relative to that of the pure solvent.

10 the mole fraction of the solvent

11 the vapor pressure of the solvent, P_1, is equal to $X_1 P_1°$

12 the ratio of the number of solute particles to the number of solvent molecules, or to the colligative molality of the solution

13 moles of solute per kilogram of solvent

14 false

15 1000 g (1.000 kg) of water

16 1.0

17 2.0

18 increase

19 The solute lowers the vapor pressure of the solvent, and thus the temperature must be raised to increase the vapor pressure back to 1.0 atm, where the solution boils.

20 the colligative molality

21 true

22 false

23 decrease

24 The solute decreases the rate of crystallization of the solvent (the solute lowers the escaping tendency of the solvent).

25 the colligative molality of the solute

26 true

27 false

28 decrease the freezing point

29 false

30 false

31 pure water; NaCl in solution

32 the 0.1 M solution . . . the 1.0 M solution

33 the pressure required to increase the escaping tendency of the solvent in a solution to a value equal to that of the pure solvent

34 RTM_c

35 false

36 true

37 true

38 of the osmotic pressure that develops in the cells (Water enters the cells, thereby expanding the cell.)

39 Osmotic pressure is a large effect, and only a relatively small protein concentration is necessary for a molecular mass determination.

40 false (Boiling point elevation is a relatively small effect except for high solute concentrations and is not used for molecular mass determinations.)

41 the interactions between the two kinds of molecules are the same as those between like molecules

42 true

43 $P_B^\circ + X_A^\circ(P_A^\circ - P_B^\circ)$ (12-13)

44 false

45 positive

46 true

47 nonideal

48 distills without a change in composition

RATES AND MECHANISMS OF CHEMICAL REACTIONS

A   OUTLINE OF CHAPTER 13

13-1   A rate tells us how fast a quantity is changing with time.

For the reaction $A \rightarrow P$, the rate of formation of product P is defined as

$$\text{rate} = \frac{\Delta[P]}{\Delta t} = \frac{[P]_2 - [P]_1}{t_2 - t_1} \tag{13-1}$$

The rate of consumption of reactant A is defined as

$$\text{rate} = -\frac{\Delta[A]}{\Delta t} = -\left(\frac{[A]_2 - [A]_1}{t_2 - t_1} \right) \tag{13-2}$$

The units of reaction rate are moles per liter per unit time; for example, $\text{mol} \cdot \text{L}^{-1} \cdot \text{s}^{-1}$ or $M \cdot \text{s}^{-1}$.

13-2   The rate law of a reaction can be determined by the method of initial rates.

The rate law of a reaction is the equation that gives the dependence of the reaction rate on the concentrations of the species involved.

The reaction rate constant is the proportionality constant between the reaction rate and the concentration terms on which the rate depends.

A reaction rate is said to be first order in the concentration of a species when the rate is proportional to the first power of the concentration of that species.

A first-order rate law is of the form rate $= k[A]$.

A second-order rate law is of the form rate $= k[A]^2$ or rate $= k[A][B]$.

If a reaction rate law is of the form rate $= k[A]^x[B]^y[C]^z$, then the rate law is x order in [A], y order in [B], and z order in [C]. The overall order is $x + y + z$.

The units of the rate constant depend on the order of the reaction.

Rate laws must be determined experimentally. There is no necessary relationship between the balancing coefficients in a chemical equation and the order of the various species concentrations in the reaction rate law.

The initial reaction rate is the reaction rate measured over a time interval that is short enough that the reactant concentrations do not change appreciably.

If the initial concentration of a reactant is doubled and the initial rate doubles, then the rate law is first order in the concentration of that reactant.

If the initial concentration of a reactant is doubled and the initial rate increases by a factor of 4, then the rate law is second order in the concentration of that reactant.

13-3   The half-life for a first-order rate law is independent of the initial concentration.

If the rate law is rate $= k[A]$, then the dependence of $[A]$ on time is given by

$$\log[A] = \log[A]_0 - \frac{kt}{2.30} \qquad (13\text{-}9)$$

where $[A]_0$ is the concentration of A at time $t = 0$.

For a first-order reaction a plot of $\log[A]$ versus t is linear (Figure 13-2).

The half-life $t_{1/2}$ is the time required for the concentration of a reactant to decrease by a factor of 2.

The half-life for a first-order reaction is related to the rate constant by

$$t_{1/2} = \frac{0.693}{k} \qquad (13\text{-}11)$$

If the half-life for a reactant is independent of the initial concentration of the reactant, then the reaction rate law is first order.

13-4   A rate law cannot be deduced from the reaction stoichiometry.

An elementary process is a chemical reaction that occurs in a single step.

The rate law for an elementary process can be deduced from the stoichiometry of the reaction.

Most chemical reactions are not elementary processes.

A series of elementary processes that add up to give the overall reaction is called a reaction mechanism.

A slow step that controls the overall rate of a reaction is called the rate-determining step.

An intermediate is a species that appears in the reaction mechanism, but does not appear as a reactant or a product in the overall reaction.

13-5   The activation energy is an energy barrier that the reactants must surmount in order to react.

Molecules must collide before they can react.

The collision theory of reaction rates postulates that only the more energetic collisions that occur with the correct relative orientations of the molecules lead to a reaction.

The reaction rate is given by

$$\text{rate} = \begin{pmatrix} \text{fraction of collisions} \\ \text{with the required} \\ \text{relative orientations} \end{pmatrix} \begin{pmatrix} \text{collision} \\ \text{frequency} \end{pmatrix} \begin{pmatrix} \text{fraction of collisions} \\ \text{with the required} \\ \text{energy} \end{pmatrix}$$

The activation energy, E_a, is the minimum energy necessary to achieve a reaction between the colliding molecules (Figure 13-6).

The Arrhenius equation

$$\log\left(\frac{k_2}{k_1}\right) = \frac{E_a}{2.30R}\left(\frac{T_2 - T_1}{T_1 T_2}\right) \tag{13-13}$$

describes the dependence of the reaction rate constant on the Kelvin temperature and the activation energy.

Reaction rate constants increase with increasing temperature because the activation energy is positive.

13-6 A catalyst is a substance that increases the reaction rate but is not consumed as a reactant.

A catalyst is a reaction rate facilitator that acts by providing a different and faster pathway to the products (Figure 13-7).

A catalyst increases the rates of both the forward and reverse reactions.

A catalyst does not affect the equilibrium concentrations of reactants and products.

The rate law for a catalyzed reaction is different from that of the uncatalyzed reaction.

In heterogeneous catalysis the reactants bind to a solid surface and react more rapidly (Figure 13-8).

Enzymes are proteins that catalyze reactions in living systems.

The lock-and-key theory of enzyme activity involves the postulate that the shape of the enzyme at the binding site allows only the substrate to bind to the enzyme (Figure 13-9).

The substrate is the substance that is reacting.

13-7 Chemical reactions reach a state of equilibrium.

When starting with only reactants, the rate of the forward reaction decreases with time.

When starting with only reactants, the rate of the reverse reaction increases with time.

An equilibrium state is a dynamic state in which the forward and the reverse reactions continue to occur but at equal rates.

The equilibrium constant is equal to the ratio of the forward reaction rate constant to the reverse reaction rate constant, $K = k_f/k_r$.

B   SELF-TEST

Questions 1 through 6 refer to the reaction

$$2H_2O_2(aq) \rightleftharpoons 2H_2O(l) + O_2(g)$$

1   The rate at which oxygen is produced is defined as

_____.

2   The reaction rate for the decomposition of hydrogen peroxide is always positive. *True/False*

3   The rate of the decomposition of hydrogen peroxide can be determined by measuring the increase in pressure due to oxygen. *True/False*

4   The rate of the decomposition of hydrogen peroxide can be determined by measuring the concentration of H_2O_2 at various times during the reaction. *True/False*

5   The rate for the decomposition of hydrogen peroxide can be expressed

in terms of the concentration of _____ or of

_____.

6   From the stoichiometry of the decomposition of hydrogen peroxide, the reaction rate law must be rate $= k[H_2O_2]^2$. *True/False*

7   Reaction rates can be expressed in the units $M \cdot min^{-1}$. *True/False*

8   The rate law of a first-order reaction is rate $=$ _____.

9   The units of the rate constant for a first-order reaction are _____.

10   Given that the decomposition of hydrogen peroxide is a first-order reaction in H_2O_2, the rate law is rate $=$ _____.

11   The rate law of a second-order reaction is rate $=$ _____.

12   The units of the rate constant for a second-order reaction are

_____.

13   The reaction $H^+(aq) + OH^-(aq) \rightarrow H_2O(l)$ is first order in both $[H^+]$ and $[OH^-]$. The rate law is rate $=$ _____.

14   The method of initial rates is used to determine _____.

15   If a reaction rate law is first order in reactant A, then the initial reaction rate _____ when the concentration of A is doubled and the concentrations of all other reactants remain the same.

16   If a reaction rate law is second order in reactant B, then the initial reaction rate _____ when the concentration of B is doubled and the concentrations of all other reactants remain the same.

17   If a reaction rate law is zero order in reactant C, then the initial reaction rate _____ when the concentration of C is doubled and the concentrations of all other reactants remain the same.

18   If a reaction is first order, then the dependence of the concentration of A on time is given by $\log[A] =$ _____ .

19   The decomposition of H_2O_2 is a first-order reaction in H_2O_2. A plot of _____ versus time is a straight line.

20   If a plot of the concentration of reactant A versus time is a horizontal straight line, then the reaction is first order. *True/False*

21   The half-life of a reactant is defined as _____
_____
_____ .

22   The half-life for a first-order reaction is *(independent of, dependent on)* the initial concentration of the reactant.

23   If the rate law is rate $= k[H_2O_2]$, then the time it takes for hydrogen peroxide to decrease from 0.50 M to 0.25 M is the same as the time to decrease from 0.25 M to 0.125 M. *True/False*

24   The rate law for the reaction

$$NO_2(g) + CO(g) \longrightarrow NO(g) + CO_2(g)$$

is rate $= k[NO_2]^2$. The time it takes for $[NO_2]$ to decrease from 0.50 M to 0.25 M is the same as the time to decrease from 0.25 M to 0.125 M. *True/False*

25   Most reactions are elementary processes. *True/False*

26   A series of elementary processes that add up to give the overall reaction stoichiometry is called the reaction _____ .

27   The overall reaction rate may be controlled by a rate-determining step, which is the fastest step in the reaction mechanism. *True/False*

28   The reaction mechanism often involves intermediate species that do not appear in the overall reaction. *True/False*

29   The sum of the elementary processes for a reaction need not add up to the overall chemical equation. *True/False*

30   All collisions between reactant molecules lead to reaction. *True/False*

31   The activation energy is the minimum amount of kinetic energy that reactant molecules must have in order to react. *True/False*

32   Rate constants increase as the temperature increases. *True/False*

33   The temperature dependence of a rate constant is given by the Arrhenius equation,

_____ = _____ .

34   A catalyst acts by providing a new reaction pathway with a *(lower, higher)* activation energy.

35   A catalyst increases the rate of production of products without affecting the rate of the reverse reaction. *True/False*

36   Platinum metal is used as a catalyst for the reaction

$$C_2H_4(g) + H_2(g) \longrightarrow C_2H_6(g)$$

In this reaction, platinum is a heterogeneous catalyst. *True/False*

37   The rate law for the catalyzed reaction must be the same as that of the uncatalyzed reaction. *True/False*

38   Enzymes are proteins that enable reactions to take place in living systems. *True/False*

39   The shape of an enzyme is important to its activity as a catalyst. *True/False*

40   Starting with only reactants, the rate of the forward reaction *(increases, decreases)* with time.

41   Starting with only reactants, the rate of the reverse reaction *(increases, decreases)* with time.

42   At equilibrium the net reaction rate is zero. *True/False*

43   The rate constants of the forward and reverse reactions, k_f and k_r, are related to the equilibrium constant. *True/False*

C   CALCULATIONS YOU SHOULD KNOW HOW TO DO

1   Express the reaction rate in terms of changes in the reactant or product concentrations and calculate the reaction rate from the changes in the concentrations of reactants or products. See Example 13-1 and Problems 13-3 through 13-8.

2   Determine the reaction rate law by using the method of initial rates. See Examples 13-3 and 13-4 and Problems 13-9 through 13-18.

3   Determine the amount of reactant remaining after a given amount of time using Equation (13-9) and calculate the reaction rate constant and half-life for first-order reactions. See Examples 13-5 and 13-6 and Problems 13-19 through 13-24.

4   Determine the rate law from the reaction mechanism. See Example 13-7 and Problems 13-27, 13-28 and 13-49 through 13-54.

5   Use the Arrhenius equation to find the rate constant at some other temperature or to find the activation energy given the rate constants at two different temperatures. See Example 13-8 and Problems 13-29 through 13-34.

6   Calculate the rate constant of the reverse reaction given the rate constant of the forward reaction and the equilibrium constant. See Problems 13-43 through 13-48.

D   SOLUTIONS TO THE ODD-NUMBERED PROBLEMS

13-1   (a) Use a spectrophotometer to measure the decrease in the yellow color due to $I_2(aq)$ as a function of time.

(b) Measure the total pressure in the reaction vessel as a function of time. Because there are more moles of gaseous products than reactants, the total pressure increases as the reaction proceeds.

13-3   We have

$$\text{rate} = (3.0 \times 10^6 \text{ M}^{-1} \cdot \text{s}^{-1})[O_3][NO]$$

Thus the rate is

$$\text{rate} = (3.0 \times 10^6 \text{ M}^{-1} \cdot \text{s}^{-1})(6.0 \times 10^{-4} \text{ M})(4.0 \times 10^{-5} \text{ M})$$
$$= 7.2 \times 10^{-2} \text{ M} \cdot \text{s}^{-1}$$

13-5   The rate of production of O_2 is three-halves as great as the rate of loss of O_3 because three O_2 molecules are produced by the consumption of two O_3 molecules. Thus

$$\frac{\Delta P_{O_2}}{\Delta t} = \left(-\frac{3}{2}\right)\left(\frac{\Delta P_{O_3}}{\Delta t}\right) = \left(\frac{3}{2}\right)(5.0 \times 10^{-4} \text{ atm} \cdot \text{s}^{-1})$$
$$= 7.5 \times 10^{-4} \text{ atm} \cdot \text{s}^{-1}$$

13-7   The average reaction rate is given by

$$\text{rate} = \left(-\frac{1}{2}\right)\left(\frac{\Delta[N_2O_5]}{\Delta t}\right) = \left(-\frac{1}{2}\right)\left(\frac{[N_2O_5]_2 - [N_2O_5]_1}{t_2 - t_1}\right)$$

where the factor of $\frac{1}{2}$ arises because of the balancing coefficient of 2 in front of N_2O_5. Application of this equation to the data yields the following results. For the time interval from 0 to 175 s we have

$$\text{rate} = \left(-\frac{1}{2}\right)\left(\frac{1.32 \text{ M} - 1.48 \text{ M}}{175 \text{ s} - 0}\right) = 4.6 \times 10^{-4} \text{ M} \cdot \text{s}^{-1}$$

For the time interval 175 s to 506 s we have

$$\text{rate} = \left(-\frac{1}{2}\right)\left(\frac{1.07 \text{ M} - 1.32 \text{ M}}{506 \text{ s} - 175 \text{ s}}\right) = 3.8 \times 10^{-4} \text{ M} \cdot \text{s}^{-1}$$

For the time interval 506 s to 845 s we have

$$\text{rate} = \left(-\frac{1}{2}\right)\left(\frac{0.87 \text{ M} - 1.07 \text{ M}}{845 \text{ s} - 506 \text{ s}}\right) = 2.9 \times 10^{-4} \text{ M} \cdot \text{s}^{-1}$$

Note that the reaction rate decreases as the reaction proceeds.

13-9   The data indicate that the rate is directly proportional to $[SO_2Cl_2]_0$. The rate doubles as $[SO_2Cl_2]_0$ is doubled. Assuming that the rate law does not vary with time, we deduce that the order of the reaction is first order. The first order reaction rate law is

$$\text{rate} = k[SO_2Cl_2]$$

13-11   The rate law is

$$\text{rate} = k[C_2H_5Cl]_0^x$$

When $[C_2H_5Cl]_0$ is doubled, the initial rate doubles. Assuming that the rate law does not vary with time, we deduce that the rate is first order in $[C_2H_5Cl]$. The rate law is

$$\text{rate} = k[C_2H_5Cl]$$

The value of the rate constant is given by

$$k = \frac{\text{rate}}{[C_2H_5Cl]}$$

We can calculate k by using the data from any of the runs

$$k = \frac{2.40 \times 10^{-30} \text{ M} \cdot \text{s}^{-1}}{0.33 \text{ M}} = 7.3 \times 10^{-30} \text{ s}^{-1}$$

$$k = \frac{4.80 \times 10^{-30} \text{ M} \cdot \text{s}^{-1}}{0.66 \text{ M}} = 7.3 \times 10^{-30} \text{ s}^{-1}$$

$$k = \frac{9.60 \times 10^{-30} \text{ M} \cdot \text{s}^{-1}}{1.32 \text{ M}} = 7.3 \times 10^{-30} \text{ s}^{-1}$$

13-13 The rate law is

$$\text{rate} = k[\text{NOCl}]_0^x$$

When $[\text{NOCl}]_0$ is doubled, the initial rate quadruples, and when $[\text{NOCl}]_0$ is tripled, the initial rate increases by a factor of 9. Assuming that the rate law does not vary with time, we deduce that the rate law is second order in $[\text{NOCl}]$:

$$\text{rate} = k[\text{NOCl}]^2$$

The value of the rate constant is given by

$$k = \frac{\text{rate}}{[\text{NOCl}]^2}$$

We can calculate k by using the data for any one of the three runs.

$$k = \frac{1.75 \times 10^{-6} \text{ M} \cdot \text{s}^{-1}}{(0.25 \text{ M})^2} = 2.8 \times 10^{-5} \text{ M}^{-1} \cdot \text{s}^{-1}$$

$$k = \frac{7.00 \times 10^{-6} \text{ M} \cdot \text{s}^{-1}}{(0.50 \text{ M})^2} = 2.8 \times 10^{-5} \text{ M}^{-1} \cdot \text{s}^{-1}$$

$$k = \frac{1.57 \times 10^{-5} \text{ M} \cdot \text{s}^{-1}}{(0.75 \text{ M})^2} = 2.8 \times 10^{-5} \text{ M}^{-1} \cdot \text{s}^{-1}$$

13-15 When $[\text{Cr}(H_2O)_6^{3+}]_0$ is increased by a factor of 10 and $[\text{SCN}^-]_0$ remains constant, the initial rate increases by a factor of 10. Thus the rate is first order in $[\text{Cr}(H_2O)_6^{3+}]_0$. When $[\text{SCN}^-]$ is increased by a factor of $0.5/0.2 = 2.5$ and $[\text{Cr}(H_2O)_6^{3+}]_0$ remains the same, then the initial rate increases by a factor of

2.5 ($1.5 \times 10^{-9}/6.0 \times 10^{-10}$). Assuming that the rate law does not vary with time, we deduce that the rate is first order in [SCN⁻]. The rate law is

$$\text{rate} = k[\text{Cr(H}_2\text{O)}_6^{3+}][\text{SCN}^-]$$

We can calculate the rate constant by using the data from any of the runs. The value of the rate constant is given by

$$k = \frac{\text{rate}}{[\text{Cr(H}_2\text{O)}_6^{3+}][\text{SCN}^-]}$$

$$k = \frac{2.0 \times 10^{-11} \text{ M} \cdot \text{s}^{-1}}{(1.0 \times 10^{-4} \text{ M})(0.10 \text{ M})} = 2.0 \times 10^{-6} \text{ M}^{-1} \cdot \text{s}^{-1}$$

$$k = \frac{2.0 \times 10^{-10} \text{ M} \cdot \text{s}^{-1}}{(1.0 \times 10^{-3} \text{ M})(0.10 \text{ M})} = 2.0 \times 10^{-6} \text{ M}^{-1} \cdot \text{s}^{-1}$$

$$k = \frac{6.0 \times 10^{-10} \text{ M} \cdot \text{s}^{-1}}{(1.5 \times 10^{-3} \text{ M})(0.20 \text{ M})} = 2.0 \times 10^{-6} \text{ M}^{-1} \cdot \text{s}^{-1}$$

$$k = \frac{1.5 \times 10^{-9} \text{ M} \cdot \text{s}^{-1}}{(1.5 \times 10^{-3} \text{ M})(0.50 \text{ M})} = 2.0 \times 10^{-6} \text{ M}^{-1} \cdot \text{s}^{-1}$$

13-17 When $[\text{NO}_2]_0$ is doubled and $[\text{O}_3]_0$ remains the same, the initial rate doubles. Thus the rate law is first order in $[\text{NO}_2]_0$. When $[\text{O}_3]_0$ is doubled and $[\text{NO}_2]_0$ remains the same, the initial rate doubles. Assuming that the rate law does not vary with time, we deduce that the rate law is first order in $[\text{O}_3]$. The complete rate law is

$$\text{rate} = k[\text{NO}_2][\text{O}_3]$$

The value of the rate constant is given by

$$k = \frac{\text{rate}}{[\text{NO}_2][\text{O}_3]}$$

$$= \frac{5.0 \times 10^4 \text{ M} \cdot \text{s}^{-1}}{(1.00 \text{ M})(1.00 \text{ M})} = 5.0 \times 10^4 \text{ M}^{-1} \cdot \text{s}^{-1}$$

$$= \frac{1.0 \times 10^5 \text{ M} \cdot \text{s}^{-1}}{(2.00 \text{ M})(1.00 \text{ M})} = 5.0 \times 10^4 \text{ M}^{-1} \cdot \text{s}^{-1}$$

$$= \frac{2.0 \times 10^5 \text{ M} \cdot \text{s}^{-1}}{(2.00 \text{ M})(2.00 \text{ M})} = 5.0 \times 10^4 \text{ M}^{-1} \cdot \text{s}^{-1}$$

13-19 The half-life of the reaction is given by

$$t_{1/2} = \frac{0.693}{k}$$

$$= \frac{0.693}{2.2 \times 10^{-5} \text{ s}^{-1}} = 3.15 \times 10^4 \text{ s}$$

The number of half-lives in 5.0 hours is

$$\frac{(5.0 \text{ h})\left(\dfrac{60 \text{ min}}{1 \text{ h}}\right)\left(\dfrac{60 \text{ s}}{1 \text{ min}}\right)}{3.15 \times 10^4 \text{ s/half-life}} = 0.571 \text{ half-life}$$

The fraction of SO_2Cl_2 remaining after 0.571 half-lives is given by

$$\frac{[A]}{[A]_0} = \left(\frac{1}{2}\right)^n$$

Thus

$$\text{fraction remaining} = \frac{[SO_2Cl_2]}{[SO_2Cl_2]_0} = \left(\frac{1}{2}\right)^{0.571}$$
$$= 0.67$$

An alternative solution is to use the equation

$$\log\frac{[A]}{[A]_0} = -\frac{kt}{2.30}$$

where $[A]/[A]_0$ is the fraction of SO_2Cl_2 remaining. Thus

$$\log\frac{[A]}{[A]_0} = -\frac{(2.2 \times 10^{-5} \text{ s}^{-1})\left(\dfrac{60 \text{ s}}{1 \text{ min}}\right)\left(\dfrac{60 \text{ min}}{1 \text{ h}}\right)(5.0 \text{ h})}{2.30}$$
$$= -0.1722$$

Taking antilogarithms, we have

$$\text{fraction remaining} = \frac{[A]}{[A]_0} = 0.67$$

13-21   The fraction of a reactant remaining after time t is given by

$$\log\frac{[A]}{[A]_0} = -\frac{kt}{2.30}$$

Substituting the values of k and t, we have

$$\log\frac{[A]}{[A]_0} = -\frac{(4.0 \times 10^{-4} \text{ s}^{-1})\left(\dfrac{3600 \text{ s}}{1 \text{ h}}\right)(1 \text{ h})}{2.30}$$
$$= -0.626$$

Taking antilogarithms, we have

$$\text{fraction remaining} = \frac{[A]}{[A]_0} = 10^{-0.626} = 0.24$$

13-23 If the reaction rate is first order, then a plot of $\log[S_2O_8^{2-}]$ versus time is a straight line.

t/min	$\log([S_2O_8^{2-}]/M)$
0	-1.00
17	-1.30
34	-1.60
51	-1.92

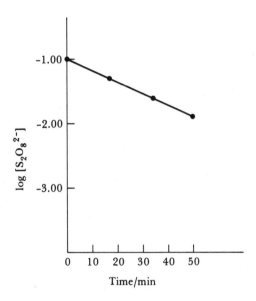

The reaction is first order:

$$\text{rate} = k[S_2O_8^{2-}]$$

The equation for the straight line is

$$\log[S_2O_8^{2-}] = \log[S_2O_8^{2-}]_0 - \frac{kt}{2.30}$$

We can use the data at any of the time points to calculate k. At time $t = 17$ min, we have

$$-1.30 = -1.00 - \frac{k(17 \text{ min})}{2.30}$$

$$k = \frac{(0.30)(2.30)}{17 \text{ min}} = 0.041 \text{ min}^{-1}$$

Another approach is to realize that if the reaction is first order, then the half-life, $t_{1/2}$, is independent of the initial concentration of the reactant.

$[S_2O_8^{2-}]/M$	t/min	$t_{1/2}/\text{min}$
0.100	0	
		17
0.050	17	
		17
0.025	34	
		17
0.012	51	

The $[S_2O_8^{2-}]$ is reduced by a factor of 2 every 17 minutes, so the half-life is 17 minutes. We can calculate k from the expression

$$t_{1/2} = \frac{0.693}{k}$$

$$k = \frac{0.693}{t_{1/2}} = \frac{0.693}{17 \text{ min}} = 0.041 \text{ min}^{-1}$$

13-25   (a) rate $= k[N_2O][O]$

(b) rate $= k[O][O_3]$

(c) rate $= k[ClCO][Cl_2]$

13-27   The rate law is determined by the slow elementary step. The rate law for the slow step is

$$\text{rate} = k[CO_2][OH^-]$$

The experimental rate law is

$$\text{rate} = k[CO_2][OH^-]$$

Thus the mechanism is consistent with the rate equation, because the mechanism leads to the same rate law as is found experimentally.

13-29   The Arrhenius equation is

$$\log\left(\frac{k_2}{k_1}\right) = \frac{E_a}{2.30R}\left(\frac{T_2 - T_1}{T_1 T_2}\right)$$

Thus

$$\log\left(\frac{9.15 \times 10^{-4}\ s^{-1}}{2.35 \times 10^{-4}\ s^{-1}}\right) = \frac{E_a}{(2.30)(8.314\ J\cdot mol^{-1}\cdot K^{-1})}\left(\frac{(303\ K - 293\ K)}{(303\ K)(293\ K)}\right)$$

$$0.590 = E_a(5.89 \times 10^{-6}\ J^{-1}\cdot mol)$$

$$E_a = \frac{0.590}{5.89 \times 10^{-6}\ J^{-1}\cdot mol} = 1.00 \times 10^5\ J\cdot mol^{-1}$$

$$= 100\ kJ\cdot mol^{-1}$$

13-31   The Arrhenius equation is

$$\log\left(\frac{k_2}{k_1}\right) = \frac{E_a}{2.30R}\left(\frac{T_2 - T_1}{T_1 T_2}\right)$$

Thus

$$\log\left(\frac{k_2}{6.07 \times 10^{-8}\ s^{-1}}\right) = \frac{(262 \times 10^3\ J\cdot mol^{-1})}{(2.30)(8.314\ J\cdot mol^{-1}\cdot K^{-1})}\left(\frac{(800\ K - 600\ K)}{(600\ K)(800\ K)}\right)$$

$$= 5.709$$

Taking the antilogarithm of both sides, we have

$$\frac{k_2}{6.07 \times 10^{-8}\ s^{-1}} = 5.12 \times 10^5$$

or

$$k_2 = (5.12 \times 10^5)(6.07 \times 10^{-8}\ s^{-1})$$

$$= 3.11 \times 10^{-2}\ s^{-1}$$

13-33   The Arrhenius equation is

$$\log\left(\frac{k_2}{k_1}\right) = \frac{E_a}{2.30R}\left(\frac{T_2 - T_1}{T_1 T_2}\right)$$

The half-life, $t_{1/2}$, is related to the rate constant of a first order process by

$$t_{1/2} = \frac{0.693}{k}$$

Thus the Arrhenius equation in terms of $t_{1/2}$ is

$$\log\left(\frac{t_{1/2,1}}{t_{1/2,2}}\right) = \frac{E_a}{2.30R}\left(\frac{T_2 - T_1}{T_1 T_2}\right)$$

Thus

$$\log\left(\frac{4.5\text{ h}}{t_{1/2,2}}\right) = \frac{(586 \times 10^3\text{ J}\cdot\text{mol}^{-1})(310.2\text{ K} - 302.8\text{ K})}{(2.30)(8.314\text{ J}\cdot\text{mol}^{-1}\cdot\text{K}^{-1})(310.2\text{ K})(302.8\text{ K})}$$
$$= 2.414$$

Taking the antilogarithm of both sides, we have

$$\frac{4.5\text{ h}}{t_{1/2,2}} = 260$$

or

$$t_{1/2} = \frac{4.5\text{ h}}{260} = 0.017\text{ h at }37°\text{C}$$

13-35   A catalyst cannot affect the equilibrium concentrations in a chemical reaction. A catalyst provides an alternate pathway from the reactants to the products and from the products to the reactants. Thus the rates of the forward and reverse reaction are equally affected, so that the equilibrium concentrations are unaffected.

13-37   (a) The catalysts are $H^+(aq)$ and $Br^-(aq)$. Although neither appears in the overall reaction, both appear in the rate law.

(b) The overall order of the reaction is third order.

(c) The reaction is first order in $[H_2O_2]$:

$$rate = k[H^+]_0[Br^-]_0[H_2O_2]$$

where the zero subscripts indicate that the concentrations of $H^+(aq)$ and $Br^-(aq)$ are constant. The effective first order rate constant is

$$k_{eff} = k[H^+]_0[Br^-]_0$$
$$= (1.0 \times 10^3\text{ M}^{-2}\cdot\text{s}^{-1})(1.00 \times 10^{-3}\text{ M})(1.00 \times 10^{-3}\text{ M})$$
$$= (1.0 \times 10^{-3}\text{ s}^{-1})$$

and the half-life of the $H_2O_2(aq)$ is

$$t_{1/2} = \frac{0.693}{1.0 \times 10^{-3}\text{ M}} = 693\text{ s}$$

A plot of $[H_2O_2]$ versus time looks like Figure 13-3 for $[N_2O_5]$, but with a half-life of 693 s.

13-39   Run the reaction with all initial concentrations held constant in vessels with different amounts of reaction vessel wall area in contact with the reaction mixture. If the reaction rate increases as the wall surface in contact with the reaction mixture increases, then the reaction is catalyzed by the wall.

13-41   The mechanism outlined in Figure 13-8 can be written as

$$O_2(g) \longrightarrow O_2(surface) \qquad \text{fast}$$
$$O_2(surface) \longrightarrow 2O(surface) \qquad \text{slow}$$
$$SO_2(g) + O(surface) \longrightarrow SO_3(g) \qquad \text{fast}$$

Except at very low pressure, the platinum surface will be completely covered with oxygen molecules. Thus, the value of $[O_2(surface)]$ will be essentially constant and the rate-determining step will be independent of the pressure of $O_2(g)$. Furthermore, the oxygen atoms react rapidly with SO_2 molecules except when the number of SO_2 molecules present is very small (when the pressure of SO_2 is very low).

13-43   The equilibrium constant is related to the rate constants by

$$K = \frac{k_f}{k_r}$$

Thus

$$k_r = \frac{k_f}{K}$$
$$= \frac{6.7 \times 10^{-7}\ \text{s}^{-1}}{0.14\ \text{M}} = 4.8 \times 10^{-6}\ \text{M}^{-1} \cdot \text{s}^{-1}$$

13-45   At equilibrium, the rate of the reaction in the forward direction is equal to the rate in the reverse direction:

$$\text{rate}_f = \text{rate}_r$$

Thus

$$\text{rate}_f = k_f[\text{HI}]^2$$

The rate constant of the forward reaction is related to the rate constant of the reverse reaction through the equilibrium constant:

$$K = \frac{k_f}{k_r}$$

or

$$k_f = Kk_r$$

The equilibrium constant expression for the equation is

$$K = \frac{[H_2][I_2]}{[HI]^2}$$

Thus

$$k_f = k_r \frac{[H_2][I_2]}{[HI]^2}$$

and

$$\text{rate}_r = k_f[HI]^2 = \frac{k_r[H_2][I_2]}{[HI]^2}[HI]^2$$
$$= k_r[H_2][I_2]$$

13-47   At equilibrium

$$\text{rate}_f = \text{rate}_r$$

Thus

$$\text{rate}_r = k_f[NO_2][O_3]$$

We also have

$$K = \frac{k_f}{k_r}$$

or

$$k_f = k_r K$$

The equilibrium constant expression for the equation is

$$K = \frac{[N_2O_5][O_2]}{[NO_2]^2[O_3]}$$

Thus

$$\text{rate}_r = k_f[NO_2][O_3] = \frac{k_r[N_2O_5][O_2]}{[NO_2]^2[O_3]}[NO_2][O_3]$$
$$= k_r \frac{[N_2O_5][O_2]}{[NO_2]}$$

13-49   To obtain the overall reaction, we add the three equations to obtain

$$2N_2O_5(g) + NO_2(g) + NO_3(g) + NO(g) + NO_3(g) \rightleftharpoons$$
$$2NO_2(g) + 2NO_3(g) + NO(g) + O_2(g) + NO_2(g) + 2NO_2(g)$$

or, after combining and canceling like terms,

$$2N_2O_5(g) \rightleftharpoons 4NO_2(g) + O_2(g)$$

The rate law is given by the slow elementary step

$$\text{rate} = k[NO_2][NO_3]$$

Both species, NO_2 and NO_3, are intermediate species. The first reaction is fast and equilibrium is attained essentially instantaneously; thus we have

$$K = \frac{[NO_2]^2[NO_3]^2}{[N_2O_5]^2}$$

or

$$[NO_2][NO_3] = K^{1/2}[N_2O_5]$$

Thus the rate law is

$$\text{rate} = kK^{1/2}[N_2O_5]$$

If we let $k_1 = kK^{1/2}$, then we have

$$\text{rate} = k_1[N_2O_5]$$

13-51 The rate law for the elementary slow step is

$$\text{rate} = k[ClCO][Cl_2]$$

The species $ClCO(g)$ is an intermediate and its concentration is not easily measured. Because the reaction in step 2 is fast, the equilibrium adjusts instantaneously:

$$K_2 = \frac{[ClCO]}{[Cl][CO]}$$

The species Cl is also an intermediate. We can eliminate $[Cl]$ by using the fast equilibrium in step 1:

$$K_1 = \frac{[Cl]^2}{[Cl_2]}$$

$$[Cl] = K_1^{1/2}[Cl_2]^{1/2}$$

Substituting the expression for $[Cl]$ into the K_2 expression, we have

$$K_2 = \frac{[ClCO]}{K_1^{1/2}[Cl_2]^{1/2}[CO]}$$

Thus

$$[ClCO] = K_2 K_1^{1/2} [Cl_2]^{1/2} [CO]$$

Substituting the expression for $[ClCO]$ into the rate law, we have

$$\text{rate} = kK_2 K_1^{1/2} [Cl_2]^{1/2} [CO][Cl_2]$$

If we let $k_3 = kK_2 K_1^{1/2}$, then we have

$$\text{rate} = k_3 [Cl_2]^{3/2} [CO]$$

13-53 The rate law of the slow elementary step is

$$\text{rate} = k[NO_3][NO]$$

The species NO_3 is an intermediate. We can eliminate $[NO_3]$ from the rate law by using the equilibrium expression in step 1 because the equilibrium reaction is fast. We have

$$K = \frac{[NO_3]}{[NO][O_2]}$$

or

$$[NO_3] = K[NO][O_2]$$

Substituting the expression for $[NO_3]$ into the rate law, we have

$$\text{rate} = kK[NO][O_2][NO]$$

If we let $k' = kK$, then we have

$$\text{rate} = k'[NO]^2[O_2]$$

13-55 The total pressure in the reaction vessel is

$$P_{total} = P_{CO} + P_{CO_2}$$

If P_{CO}° is the initial pressure of CO, then the partial pressure of CO is equal to

$$P_{CO} = P_{CO}^\circ - 2P_{CO_2}$$

because each mole of CO_2 produced consumes 2 moles of CO. Thus

$$P_{total} = P_{CO}^\circ - P_{CO_2} = 250 \text{ torr} - P_{CO_2}$$

or

$$P_{CO_2} = 250 \text{ torr} - P_{total}$$

Using the data given in the problem and the preceding equation, we obtain

t/s	P_{CO_2}/torr
0	0
398	12
1002	26
1801	40

The average reaction rates for each of these time intervals are as follows:
For 0 to 398 s,

$$\text{rate} = \frac{\Delta P_{CO_2}}{\Delta t} = \frac{12 \text{ torr} - 0 \text{ torr}}{398 \text{ s} - 0 \text{ s}} = 3.0 \times 10^{-2} \text{ torr} \cdot \text{s}^{-1}$$

For 398 s to 1002 s,

$$\text{rate} = \frac{\Delta P_{CO_2}}{\Delta t} = \frac{26 \text{ torr} - 12 \text{ torr}}{1002 \text{ s} - 398 \text{ s}} = 2.3 \times 10^{-2} \text{ torr} \cdot \text{s}^{-1}$$

For 1002 s to 1801 s,

$$\text{rate} = \frac{\Delta P_{CO_2}}{\Delta t} = \frac{40 \text{ torr} - 26 \text{ torr}}{1801 \text{ s} - 1002 \text{ s}} = 1.8 \times 10^{-2} \text{ torr} \cdot \text{s}^{-1}$$

The reaction rate law is assumed to be of the form

$$\text{rate} = kP_{CO}^x$$

We can find x and k by dividing the rate by P_{CO}^x for various values of x. The value of x for which k is the same for all time intervals is the correct value of x. We take the value of P_{CO} as the average value over the time interval for which we know the average rate. Thus with $x = 2$ we have for the three time intervals above ($P_{CO} = P_{CO}^\circ - 2P_{CO_2}$)

$$k = \frac{3.0 \times 10^{-2} \text{ torr} \cdot \text{s}^{-1}}{[250 \text{ torr} - 2(6 \text{ torr})]^2} = 5.3 \times 10^{-7} \text{ torr}^{-1} \cdot \text{s}^{-1}$$

$$k = \frac{2.3 \times 10^{-2} \text{ torr} \cdot \text{s}^{-1}}{[250 \text{ torr} - 2(19 \text{ torr})]^2} = 5.1 \times 10^{-7} \text{ torr}^{-1} \cdot \text{s}^{-1}$$

$$k = \frac{1.8 \times 10^{-2} \text{ torr} \cdot \text{s}^{-1}}{[250 \text{ torr} - 2(33 \text{ torr})]^2} = 5.3 \times 10^{-7} \text{ torr} \cdot \text{s}^{-1}$$

The constancy of the calculated k values shows that the rate law is

$$\text{rate} = (5.2 \times 10^{-7} \text{ torr}^{-1} \cdot \text{s}^{-1}) P_{CO}^2$$

where we have averaged the three k values to obtain the final value of k.

13-57 (a) The initial rate is

$$\begin{aligned}\text{rate} &= (2.99 \times 10^6 \text{ M}^{-1} \cdot \text{s}^{-1})(2.0 \times 10^{-6} \text{ M})(6.0 \times 10^{-5} \text{ M}) \\ &= 3.6 \times 10^{-4} \text{ M} \cdot \text{s}^{-1}\end{aligned}$$

(b) The rate of production of NO_2 is

$$\text{rate} = \frac{\Delta[NO_2]}{\Delta t} = 3.6 \times 10^{-4} \text{ M} \cdot \text{s}^{-1}$$

The amount of NO_2 produced in one hour is

$$[NO_2] = \text{rate} \times \text{time}$$
$$= (3.6 \times 10^{-4} \text{ M} \cdot \text{s}^{-1}) \left(\frac{60 \text{ min}}{1 \text{ h}}\right)\left(\frac{60 \text{ s}}{1 \text{ min}}\right)(1 \text{ h})$$
$$= 1.3 \text{ mol} \cdot \text{L}^{-1}$$

13-59 We see from the data that the number of bacteria doubles every 15 min. The doubling time is independent of the number of bacteria; thus the rate law is first order (see also the plot of log(number of bacteria) versus t on the next page).

$$\text{rate of production} = k(\text{number of bacteria})$$

The half-life is equal to 15 min. There are

$$\frac{120 \text{ min}}{15 \text{ min/half-life}} = 8.0 \text{ half-lives}$$

in 2 hours. The number of bacteria after n half-lives is given by

$$\text{number of bacteria} = (\text{initial number of bacteria})(2)^n$$

or after 8 half-lives

$$\text{number of bacteria} = (100)(2)^8 = 2.56 \times 10^4 \text{ bacteria}$$

The rate constant is

$$k = \frac{0.693}{t_{1/2}} = \frac{0.693}{15 \text{ min}} = 4.6 \times 10^{-2} \text{ min}^{-1}$$

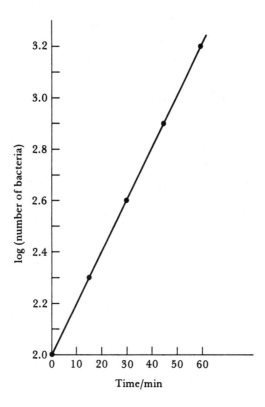

13-61 The fraction of a reactant remaining after time t is given by

$$\log\frac{[A]}{[A]_0} = -\frac{kt}{2.30}$$

The fraction of material retained is $0.10 = 1.00 - 0.90$. The value of the rate constant is given by

$$k = \frac{0.693}{t_{1/2}} = \frac{0.693}{70 \text{ day}} = 0.0099 \text{ day}^{-1}$$

Thus

$$\log(0.10) = -\frac{(0.0099 \text{ day}^{-1})t}{2.30}$$

$$t = \frac{(-1.00)(2.30)}{-0.0099 \text{ day}^{-1}} = 230 \text{ day}$$

13-63 The formation of a covalent bond from two radicals does not involve any bond-breaking process. For example, for two $CH_3 \cdot$ radicals,

$$2H_3C \cdot \longrightarrow H_3C{-}CH_3$$

Thus $E_a \approx 0$. The only limitation to a reaction would be the orientations of the two radicals as they collide.

13-65 The reaction rate is given by

$$\text{rate} = \frac{-\Delta P_{SO_2Cl_2}}{\Delta t} = \frac{-P_{SO_2Cl_2,2} + P_{SO_2Cl_2,1}}{t_2 - t_1}$$

Thus the rate over the interval 0 to 5000 s is

$$\text{rate} = \frac{-680 \text{ torr} + 760 \text{ torr}}{5000 \text{ s} - 0 \text{ s}} = 1.6 \times 10^{-2} \text{ torr} \cdot \text{s}^{-1}$$

The rate over the interval 5000 s to 10,000 s is

$$\text{rate} = \frac{-610 \text{ torr} + 680 \text{ torr}}{10,000 \text{ s} - 5000 \text{ s}} = 1.4 \times 10^{-2} \text{ torr} \cdot \text{s}^{-1}$$

We assume that the rate law is of the form

$$\text{rate} = kP_{SO_2Cl_2}^x$$

We can find x and k by dividing the rate by $P_{SO_2Cl_2}^x$ for various values of x. The value of x for which k is the same for all time intervals is the correct value of x. We take the value of $P_{SO_2Cl_2}$ as the average value over the time interval for which we know the average rate. Thus with $x = 1$, we have for the two time intervals

$$k = \frac{\text{rate}}{P_{SO_2Cl_2}} = \frac{1.6 \times 10^{-2} \text{ torr} \cdot \text{s}^{-1}}{720 \text{ torr}} = 2.2 \times 10^{-5} \text{ s}^{-1}$$

$$k = \frac{\text{rate}}{P_{SO_2Cl_2}} = \frac{1.4 \times 10^{-2} \text{ torr} \cdot \text{s}^{-1}}{645 \text{ torr}} = 2.2 \times 10^{-5} \text{ s}^{-1}$$

The agreement between the k values tells us the rate law is first order in the pressure of SO_2Cl_2, that is,

$$\text{rate} = kP_{SO_2Cl_2}$$

13-67 From the rate law we compute the initial rate for run 1

$$\text{rate} = (5.0 \times 10^{-3} \text{ M}^{-1} \cdot \text{s}^{-1})(0.20 \text{ M})(0.20 \text{ M})$$
$$= 2.0 \times 10^{-4} \text{ M} \cdot \text{s}^{-1}$$

For run 2 we have

$$4.0 \times 10^{-4} \text{ M} \cdot \text{s}^{-1} = (5.0 \times 10^{-3} \text{ M}^{-1} \cdot \text{s}^{-1})(0.20 \text{ M})[\text{I}^-]_0$$

Thus

$$[\text{I}^-]_0 = \frac{4.0 \times 10^{-4} \text{ M} \cdot \text{s}^{-1}}{(5.0 \times 10^{-3} \text{ M}^{-1} \cdot \text{s}^{-1})(0.20 \text{ M})} = 0.40 \text{ M}$$

For run 3 we have

$$8.0 \times 10^{-4} \text{ M} \cdot \text{s}^{-1} = (5.0 \times 10^{-3} \text{ M}^{-1} \cdot \text{s}^{-1})[\text{C}_2\text{H}_4\text{Br}_2]_0(0.20 \text{ M})$$

Thus

$$[\text{C}_2\text{H}_4\text{Br}_2]_0 = \frac{8.0 \times 10^{-4} \text{ M} \cdot \text{s}^{-1}}{(5.0 \times 10^{-3} \text{ M}^{-1} \cdot \text{s}^{-1})(0.20 \text{ M})} = 0.80 \text{ M}$$

13-69 The production of bacteria is a first order reaction with a certain doubling time. Thus the number of bacteria present after n doubling times is given by

$$\text{number of bacteria} = (\text{number of bacteria})_0(2)^n$$

The number of doubling times in 10 days is

$$\frac{(10 \text{ day})\left(\dfrac{24 \text{ h}}{1 \text{ day}}\right)}{39 \text{ h}} = 6.15$$

Thus if there are 20,000 bacteria per milliliter present initially, after 10 days at 40°F

$$\text{number of bacteria} = (20,000)(2)^{6.15}$$
$$= 1.4 \times 10^6 \text{ bacteria/mL}$$

13-71 The rate of loss of neurons is given as constant; thus the rate law is

$$\text{rate} = k = 2 \times 10^5 \text{ neurons} \cdot \text{day}^{-1}$$

Notice that the rate law is independent of the number of neurons. That is, the rate law is zero order in the concentration of neurons. The number of days required for $2 \times 10^{10} \times 0.20 = 4 \times 10^9$ neurons to be lost is

$$\left(2 \times 10^5 \frac{\text{neurons}}{\text{day}}\right)(\text{number of days}) = 4 \times 10^9 \text{ neurons}$$

Thus, the number of days is

$$\frac{4 \times 10^9 \text{ neurons}}{2 \times 10^5 \text{ neurons} \cdot \text{day}^{-1}} = 2 \times 10^4 \text{ days}$$

$$(2 \times 10^4 \text{ days})\left(\frac{1 \text{ year}}{365 \text{ days}}\right) = 55 \text{ years}$$

Thus, the age in years at which the number of neurons is 80% of the original value is

$$55 \text{ years} + 30 \text{ years} = 85 \text{ years}$$

13-73   We first must calculate $\log k$ and $1/T$.

$(1/T)/10^{-3} \text{ K}^{-1}$	$\log (k/s^{-1})$
3.66	−6.10
3.36	−4.46
3.14	−3.30
2.96	−2.31

A plot of $\log (k/s^{-1})$ versus $1/T$ is a straight line (see next page). To estimate k at 50°C, we read the value of $\log (k/s^{-1})$ at $1/323 \text{ K} = 3.10 \times 10^{-3} \text{ K}^{-1}$ from the plot. We see that

$$\log (k/s^{-1}) = -3.2$$
$$k = 10^{-3.2} \text{ s}^{-1} = 6 \times 10^{-4} \text{ s}^{-1}$$

We can calculate E_a by using the Arrhenius equation and any pair of data.

$$\log\left(\frac{k_2}{k_1}\right) = \frac{E_a}{2.30R}\left(\frac{T_2 - T_1}{T_1 T_2}\right)$$

$$\log\left(\frac{49.8 \times 10^{-5} \text{ s}^{-1}}{3.46 \times 10^{-5} \text{ s}^{-1}}\right) = \frac{E_a(318 \text{ K} - 298 \text{ K})}{(2.30)(8.314 \text{ J} \cdot \text{mol}^{-1} \cdot \text{K}^{-1})(318 \text{ K})(298 \text{ K})}$$

$$1.158 = (1.104 \times 10^{-5} \text{ J}^{-1} \cdot \text{mol})E_a$$

$$E_a = \frac{1.158}{1.104 \times 10^{-5} \text{ J}^{-1} \cdot \text{mol}} = 1.05 \times 10^5 \text{ J} \cdot \text{mol}^{-1}$$

$$= 105 \text{ kJ} \cdot \text{mol}^{-1}$$

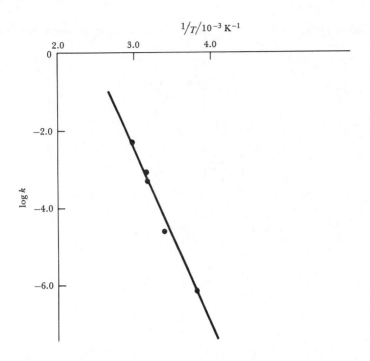

13-75 The rate constant at 700 K is calculated from the log k expression.

$$\log (k/\text{min}^{-1}) = 14.58 - \frac{99.96 \times 10^3 \, \text{J} \cdot \text{mol}^{-1}}{RT}$$

$$= 14.58 - \frac{99.96 \times 10^3 \, \text{J} \cdot \text{mol}^{-1}}{(8.314 \, \text{J} \cdot \text{mol}^{-1} \cdot \text{K}^{-1})(700 \, \text{K})} = -2.596$$

Thus

$$k = 10^{-2.596} \, \text{min}^{-1} = 2.54 \times 10^{-3} \, \text{min}^{-1}$$

The half-life for the reaction is

$$t_{1/2} = \frac{0.693}{k} = \frac{0.693}{2.54 \times 10^{-3} \, \text{min}^{-1}} = 273 \, \text{min}$$

The fraction remaining after 30.0 min is

$$\frac{[CH_2CH_2Br]}{[CH_3CH_2Br]_0} = \left(\frac{1}{2}\right)^{(30.0/273)} = 0.927$$

13-77 We have $t = t_{1/2}$ when $[A] = [A]_0/2$; substitution of these relations into the expression

$$\frac{1}{[A]} = \frac{1}{[A]_0} + kt$$

yields

$$\frac{2}{[A]_0} = \frac{1}{[A]_0} + kt_{1/2}$$

Thus

$$kt_{1/2} = \frac{1}{[A]_0}$$

or

$$t_{1/2} = \frac{1}{k[A]_0}$$

13-79 The half-life of a second-order reaction is given by (see Problem 13-77)

$$t_{1/2} = \frac{1}{k[A]_0}$$

Since $[OH^-]_0 = [H^+]_0$, we can use either OH^- or H^+ as A. Thus

$$t_{1/2} = \frac{1}{(1.3 \times 10^{11} \ M^{-1} \cdot s^{-1})(1.0 \times 10^{-3} \ M)} = 7.7 \times 10^{-9} \ s$$

E   ANSWERS TO THE SELF-TEST

1   $\dfrac{\Delta[O_2]}{\Delta t}$

2   true

3   true

4   true

5   reactant, H_2O_2; product, O_2

6   false

7   true

8   $k[A]$

9   s^{-1} (more generally, reciprocal time)

10   $k[H_2O_2]$

11   $k[A]^2$ or $k[A][B]$

12   $M^{-1} \cdot s^{-1}$

13   $k[H^+][OH^-]$

14   the reaction rate law

15   doubles

16 quadruples

17 does not change

18 $\log[A]_0 - \dfrac{kt}{2.30}$

19 $\log[H_2O_2]$

20 false (In such a case the rate law is zero order in [A].)

21 the time it takes for the concentration of the reactant to decrease by a factor of 2

22 independent of

23 true

24 false

25 false

26 mechanism

27 false (The rate-determining step is the slowest step.)

28 true

29 false

30 false (Colliding molecules must have the proper orientations and sufficient energy to react.)

31 true

32 true

33 $\log\left(\dfrac{k_2}{k_1}\right) = \dfrac{E_a}{2.30R}\left(\dfrac{T_2 - T_1}{T_1 T_2}\right)$

34 lower

35 false (The catalyst also increases the reverse reaction rate.)

36 true

37 false

38 true

39 true

40 decreases

41 increases

42 true

43 true

CHEMICAL EQUILIBRIUM

A OUTLINE OF CHAPTER 14

14-1 A chemical equilibrium is dynamic.

An equilibrium state is attained when the rates of the forward and reverse processes are equal.

Double arrows, $\rightleftharpoons$, denote a reaction equilibrium.

A state of equilibrium can be attained from either direction.

Chemical equilibrium is attained when the forward reaction rate equals the reverse reaction rate.

14-2 A chemical equilibrium is approachable from either direction.

Initial concentrations are denoted by the subscript zero, as in $[N_2O_4]_0$.

At equilibrium the reactant and the product concentrations remain constant (Figure 14-2).

The same equilibrium is attained starting from either the reactant side (left) or the product side (right) of the reaction (Table 14-1).

14-3 The equilibrium-constant expression for a chemical equation is equal to the ratio of product concentration terms to reactant concentration terms.

The equilibrium constant expression for the general equation

$$aA(g) + bB(soln) + cC(s) \rightleftharpoons xX(g) + yY(soln) + zZ(l)$$

is given by the law of concentration action (Guldberg and Waage) as

$$K_c = \frac{[X]^x[Y]^y}{[A]^a[B]^b} \tag{14-3}$$

The law of concentration action states that the equilibrium constant expression for a chemical reaction is formulated as the ratio of product concentrations to reactant concentrations, with each concentration factor raised to a power equal to the stoichiometric coefficient of that species in the balanced equation for the reaction. Pure liquids and solids, whose concentrations cannot be varied, do not appear in the equilibrium constant expression.

The subscript c in K_c denotes that the equilibrium constant is expressed in terms of concentrations.

The law of concentration action tells us how to write the equilibrium constant expression for any balanced chemical equation.

The key point is that at equilibrium the particular algebraic combination of concentration terms given by the law of concentration action for a reaction is equal to a constant called the equilibrium constant.

Equilibrium constants can be expressed in terms of pressures for gas-phase reactions.

The relation between K_c and K_p for a gas reaction is obtained by using the K_c expression and the relation $P = [gas]RT$.

14-4 Equilibrium constants are used in a variety of calculations.

The reaction stoichiometry is used to find the relationship between the equilibrium concentration and the initial concentration of a reactant or a product.

The solutions to the quadratic equation $ax^2 + bx + c = 0$ are

$$x = \frac{-b \pm \sqrt{b^2 - 4ac}}{2a}$$

14-5 Equilibrium constants for chemical equations can be combined to obtain equilibrium constants for other equations.

The equilibrium constant for the reverse equation is equal to the reciprocal of the equilibrium constant for the forward equation, $K_r = 1/K_f$ [Equation (14-5)].

If we add two chemical equations, then the equilibrium constant for the resulting equation is equal to the product of the equilibrium constants for the two equations that are added together, $K_3 = K_1 K_2$ [Equation (14-6)].

14-6 Le Châtelier's principle is used to predict the direction of shift in a reaction displaced from equilibrium.

Le Châtelier's principle states that a chemical reaction displaced from equilibrium proceeds toward a new equilibrium state in the direction that at least partially offsets the change in conditions.

The conditions whose change can affect a reaction equilibrium are

(a) the concentration of a reactant or product

(b) the reaction volume or the applied pressure

(c) the temperature

A decrease in volume (or increase in applied pressure) shifts a reaction equilibrium toward the side with fewer moles of gas.

To predict the effect of a volume change on an equilibrium, it is important to focus on only the gaseous species in the reaction.

The allotropic form of a substance with the lower molar volume is the stable form at high pressure.

14-7 An increase in temperature shifts a reaction equilibrium in the direction in which heat is absorbed.

Endothermic reactions ($\Delta H^\circ_{rxn} > 0$) shift to the right with increasing temperature.

Exothermic reactions ($\Delta H^\circ_{rxn} < 0$) shift to the left with increasing temperature.

A change in temperature changes the value of the equilibrium constant. The van't Hoff equation governs how the value of the equilibrium constant, K, varies with temperature, T

$$\log\left(\frac{K_2}{K_1}\right) = \frac{\Delta H^\circ_{rxn}}{2.30R}\left(\frac{T_2 - T_1}{T_1 T_2}\right) \tag{14-7}$$

The value of K increases with increasing temperature for an endothermic reaction. The value of K decreases with increasing temperature for an exothermic reaction.

14-8 Chemical reactions always proceed toward equilibrium.

The reaction quotient, Q_c, has the same algebraic form as the equilibrium constant expression, K_c, but the concentration values inserted in Q_c need not be equilibrium values.

The value of Q_c depends on how the system is prepared.

The value of the ratio Q_c/K_c is used to determine the direction in which a reaction system proceeds toward equilibrium.

If $Q_c/K_c < 1$, then the reaction proceeds left to right to equilibrium. If $Q_c/K_c > 1$, then the reaction proceeds right to left to equilibrium.

A reaction that is not at equilibrium proceeds to equilibrium in the direction such that Q_c approaches K_c in magnitude.

At equilibrium, $Q_c = K_c$.

B SELF-TEST

1 Chemical equilibrium is attained when the rates of the forward reaction and the reverse reaction are zero. *True/False*

2 At equilibrium, the concentrations of reactants increase and the concentrations of the products decrease. *True/False*

3 A chemical equilibrium is a dynamic equilibrium. *True/False*

4 A chemical equilibrium can be approached from the reactant side or from the product side of a reaction. *True/False*

5 At equilibrium the rate of the forward reaction equals _____

_____ .

6 If we start a reaction with only reactants, then in time the concentrations of the reactants will *(decrease, increase, stay the same)*.

7 If we start a reaction with only reactants, then in time the concentrations of products will *(decrease, increase, stay the same)*.

8 At equilibrium the concentrations of the reactants and products are _____ .

9 The value of the equilibrium constant of a reaction depends on the initial values of the concentrations of the reactants. *True/False*

10 The value of the equilibrium constant of a reaction depends on the direction in which the equilibrium is approached. *True/False*

11 The law of concentration action states that _____

_____

_____ .

12 For the balanced chemical equation

$$aA(g) + bB(soln) + cC(s) \rightleftharpoons xX(g) + yY(soln) + zZ(l)$$

the equilibrium constant expression is given by

$$K_c = \text{————————————————}$$

13 The equilibrium constant of a gas-phase reaction can be expressed in terms of

_____ or _____ .

14 For reactions involving gases, the equilibrium constant cannot be expressed in terms of pressure. *True/False*

15 Pure solid reactants and products do not appear in the K_p expression. *True/False*

16 An equilibrium constant cannot have a negative value. *True/False*

17   The K_c expression for the equation

$$C(s) + CO_2(g) \rightleftharpoons 2CO(g)$$

is _____ .

18   The K_p expression for the equation

$$C(s) + H_2O(g) \rightleftharpoons CO(g) + H_2(g)$$

is _____ .

19   If the equilibrium constant for a forward reaction is K_f, then the equilibrium constant for the reverse reaction is given by $K_r = $ _____ .

20   If a chemical equation can be written as the sum of two equations whose equilibrium constants are K_1 and K_2, then the equilibrium constant of the new equation is given by $K_3 = $ _____ .

21   A change in the conditions of a reaction at equilibrium can cause the chemical system to shift to a new equilibrium state. *True/False*

22   Le Châtelier's principle states that _____

_____

_____ .

23   The conditions that can affect a reaction equilibrium are _____ ,

_____ , and _____ .

24   A decrease in the volume of a reaction vessel at equilibrium shifts the equilibrium toward the side of the reaction with _____ .

25   An increase in temperature always shifts the reaction equilibrium toward the product side of a reaction. *True/False*

26   The reaction equilibrium

$$H_2(g) + I_2(g) \rightleftharpoons 2HI(g)$$

is unaffected by a change in the volume in which the reaction takes place. *True/False*

27   If the value of ΔH°_{rxn} is zero, then a chemical equilibrium is unaffected by a change in temperature. *True/False*

28 The equilibrium for an exothermic reaction shifts to the left with increasing temperature. *True/False*

29 A change in temperature has no effect on the value of the equilibrium constant. *True/False*

30 The van't Hoff equation is

31 The value of *K (increases, decreases)* with increasing temperature for an endothermic reaction.

32 Ammonia is produced commercially by the _____.

33 The ammonia production reaction is _____.

34 Chemical reactions always proceed toward _____.

35 The reaction quotient has the same algebraic form as the equilibrium constant expression for the reaction. *True/False*

36 For the balanced chemical equation

$$aA(g) + bB(soln) + cC(s) \rightleftharpoons xX(g) + yY(soln) + zZ(l)$$

the value of the reaction quotient is given by

$$Q_c = \underline{\hspace{4cm}}$$

where the subscript zeros denote _____.

37 The value of the ratio Q_c/K_c can be used to predict the direction in which a system will proceed spontaneously toward equilibrium. *True/False*

38 When the value of Q/K is less than 1, the reaction proceeds from _____ to _____ toward equilibrium.

39 Suppose that for the reaction represented by the equation

$$H_2(g) + I_2(g) \rightleftharpoons 2HI(g)$$

we take $[H_2]_0 = [I_2]_0 = 0.010$ M and $[HI]_0 = 0$. The value of Q_c is

_____.

40 For the reaction system described in Question 39, which of the following relations is valid at equilibrium?

(a) $[H_2] = [I_2] = 0.010 - [HI]$

(b) $[H_2] = [I_2] = 0.010 - 2[HI]$

(c) $[H_2] = [I_2] = 0.010 - [HI]/2$

(d) $[HI] = 2[H_2]$

41 For the reaction system described in Question 39, which of the following relations is *not* valid at equilibrium?

(a) $[HI]^2 = K_c[I_2]^2$

(b) $[HI] = \sqrt{K_c}[H_2]$

(c) $\dfrac{(2x)^2}{(0.010 \text{ M} - x)^2} = K_c$, where $2x = [HI]$

(d) $2[HI]^2 = K_c[H_2]^2$

C   CALCULATIONS YOU SHOULD KNOW HOW TO DO

1 Use the law of concentration action to write expressions for K_c and K_p. See Examples 14-2 and 14-3 and Problems 14-1 through 14-6.

2 Calculate the values of equilibrium constants from initial or equilibrium concentrations. See Example 14-3 and Problems 14-7 through 14-12.

3 Compute equilibrium concentrations (or pressures) using K_c (or K_p) expressions together with initial concentrations. See Examples 14-4 through 14-6 and Problems 14-13 through 14-26.

4 Calculate an equilibrium constant for an equation from other equilibrium constants. See Examples 14-7 and 14-8 and Problems 14-41 through 14-44.

5 Use Le Châtelier's principle. See Examples 14-9 through 14-11 and Problems 14-27 through 14-34.

6 Use the van't Hoff equation to calculate equilibrium constants at different temperatures. See Example 14-12 and Problems 14-45 through 14-50.

7 Use Q_c/K_c to determine the direction in which a reaction proceeds toward equilibrium. See Example 14-13 and Problems 14-35 through 14-40.

The Quadratic Formula

The standard form for a quadratic equation in x is

$$ax^2 + bx + c = 0 \tag{1}$$

where a, b, and c are constants. The two solutions to the quadratic equation are

$$x = \frac{-b \pm \sqrt{b^2 - 4ac}}{2a} \tag{2}$$

Equation (2) is called the quadratic formula. The quadratic formula is used to obtain the solutions to a quadratic equation in the standard form, that is, $ax^2 + bx + c = 0$. For example, let's find the solutions to the quadratic equation

$$2x^2 - 2x - 3 = 0$$

In this case $a = 2$, $b = -2$, and $c = -3$, and Equation (2) gives

$$x = \frac{-(-2) \pm \sqrt{(-2)^2 - 4(2)(-3)}}{2(2)}$$
$$= \frac{2 \pm \sqrt{4 + 24}}{4}$$
$$= \frac{2 \pm 5.292}{4}$$
$$= 1.823 \text{ and } -0.823$$

To use the quadratic formula to solve a quadratic equation, it is first necessary to put the quadratic equation in the standard form so that we know the values of the constants a, b, and c to use in Equation (2). For example, consider the problem of solving for x in the quadratic equation

$$\frac{x^2}{0.35 - x} = 0.100$$

To identify the constants a, b, and c, we must write this equation in the standard form of the quadratic equation. Multiplying both sides by $0.35 - x$ yields

$$x^2 = (0.35 - x)(0.100)$$

or

$$x^2 = 0.035 - 0.100x$$

Rearrangement to the standard quadratic form yields

$$x^2 + 0.100x - 0.035 = 0$$

Thus $a = 1$, $b = 0.100$, and $c = -0.035$. Using Equation (2) we have

$$x = \frac{-0.100 \pm \sqrt{(0.10)^2 - 4(1)(-0.035)}}{2(1)}$$

from which we compute

$$x = \frac{-0.100 \pm \sqrt{0.15}}{2}$$
$$= \frac{-0.100 \pm 0.387}{2}$$

Thus the solutions for x are

$$x = \frac{-0.100 + 0.387}{2} = 0.144$$

and

$$x = \frac{-0.100 - 0.387}{2} = -0.244$$

If x represents a concentration or gas pressure, then the only physically possible value of x is $+0.144$ because concentrations and pressures cannot have negative values.

Exercises

Solve the following equations for x.

1 $x^2 - 2x - 1 = 0$

2 $0.600x^2 - x - 0.450 = 0$

3 $x^2 + 2x - 0.285 = 0$

4 $\dfrac{x^2}{0.020 - x} = 0.0100$

5 $\dfrac{x^2}{0.150 - x} = 0.0250$

Answers

1 $1 \pm \sqrt{2}$ or 2.414; -0.414

2 2.04; -0.369

3 $0.134; -2.13$

4 $0.010; -0.020$

5 $0.0500; -0.0750$

D   SOLUTIONS TO THE ODD-NUMBERED PROBLEMS

14-1   Each product concentration factor, raised to a power equal to its balancing coefficient, appears in the numerator of the K_c expression, and each reactant concentration factor, raised to a power equal to its balancing coefficient, appears in the denominator of the K_c expression. Pure solids and liquids do not appear in the K_c expression.

   (a) $K_c = \dfrac{[CO_2]}{[CO]}$ (b) $K_c = \dfrac{[O_2]^3}{[O_3]^2}$

   (c) $K_c = \dfrac{[C_{10}H_{12}]}{[C_5H_6]^2}$ (d) $K_c = \dfrac{[NO_2]^4[O_2]}{[N_2O_5]^2}$

14-3   (a) $K_c = \dfrac{[SO_2][Cl_2]}{[SO_2Cl_2]}$ (b) $K_c = \dfrac{[O_2]}{[H_2O_2]^2}$

   (c) $K_c = \dfrac{1}{[H_2O]^3}$

14-5   (a) $K_p = \dfrac{P_{SO_2}P_{Cl_2}}{P_{SO_2Cl_2}}$ (b) $K_p = \dfrac{P_{O_2}}{P_{H_2O_2}^2}$

   (c) $K_p = \dfrac{1}{P_{H_2O}^3}$

14-7   The K_c expression for the equation is

$$K_c = \frac{[CO][Cl_2]}{[COCl_2]}$$

We now set up a table of initial and equilibrium concentrations.

	$COCl_2(g)$	$\rightleftharpoons CO(g)$	$+ \; Cl_2(g)$
initial concentrations	0.500 M	0	0
equilibrium concentrations	0.500 M $-$ 0.046 M	0.046 M	0.046 M

Note that at equilibrium $[CO] = [Cl_2]$ because CO and Cl_2 are formed in a $1:1$ ratio on decomposition of $COCl_2$. Substitution of the equilibrium concentrations into the K_c expression yields

$$K_c = \frac{(0.046 \text{ M})(0.046 \text{ M})}{(0.454 \text{ M})} = 4.7 \times 10^{-3} \text{ M at } 527°C$$

14-9   The equilibrium constant expression for the reaction is

$$K_p = P_{NH_3}^2$$

The equilibrium pressure of $NH_3(g)$ in atmospheres is

$$P_{NH_3} = (62 \text{ torr})\left(\frac{1 \text{ atm}}{760 \text{ torr}}\right) = 8.2 \times 10^{-2} \text{ atm}$$

Substituting this value of P_{NH_3} into K_p yields

$$K_p = (8.2 \times 10^{-2} \text{ atm})^2 = 6.7 \times 10^{-3} \text{ atm}^2$$

14-11   The equilibrium constant expression for the reaction is

$$K_c = \frac{[HI]^2}{[H_2][I_2]}$$

We now set up a table of the initial concentrations and the equilibrium concentrations. For every H_2 (or I_2) molecule that reacts, two molecules of HI are produced. The decrease in the concentration of H_2 (or I_2) is therefore one half the increase in the concentration of HI.

	$H_2(g)$	$+$ $I_2(g)$	$\rightleftharpoons$ $2HI(g)$
Initial concentration	$\dfrac{1.00 \text{ mol}}{2.00 \text{ L}} = 0.500$ M	0.500 M	0
Equilibrium concentration	$0.500 \text{ M} - \left(\dfrac{0.780}{2}\right)$ M $= 0.110$ M	$0.500 \text{ M} - \left(\dfrac{0.780}{2}\right)$ M $= 0.110$ M	$\dfrac{1.56 \text{ mol}}{2.00 \text{ L}} = 0.780$ M

Substituting the values of the equilibrium concentrations into the K_c expression, we find that

$$K_c = \frac{[HI]^2}{[H_2][I_2]} = \frac{(0.780 \text{ M})^2}{(0.110 \text{ M})^2} = 50.3$$

14-13 The K_c expression for the equation is

$$K_c = \frac{[\text{Ni(CO)}_4]}{[\text{CO}]^4} = 5.0 \times 10^4 \text{ M}^{-3}$$

At equilibrium we have

$$\frac{(0.85 \text{ M})}{[\text{CO}]^4} = 5.0 \times 10^4 \text{ M}^{-3}$$

Solving for [CO] yields

$$[\text{CO}] = \left(\frac{0.85 \text{ M}}{5.0 \times 10^4 \text{ M}^{-3}}\right)^{1/4} = 0.064 \text{ M}$$

14-15 From the law of concentration action we have

$$K_c = \frac{[\text{PCl}_3][\text{Cl}_2]}{[\text{PCl}_5]}$$

We set up a table of initial concentrations and equilibrium concentrations. Let x be the number of moles per liter of PCl_3 that is produced by the decomposition of PCl_5. From the reaction stoichiometry $[\text{PCl}_3] = [\text{Cl}_2] = x$ and $[\text{PCl}_5] = 0.25 \text{ M} - x$ at equilibrium.

	$\text{PCl}_5(g)$	$\rightleftharpoons \text{PCl}_3(g)$ +	$\text{Cl}_2(g)$
Initial concentrations	$\dfrac{0.50 \text{ mol}}{2.0 \text{ L}} = 0.25 \text{ M}$	0	0
Equilibrium concentrations	$0.25 - x$	x	x

Substituting the equilibrium concentration expressions into the K_c expression, we have

$$K_c = \frac{(x)(x)}{0.25 \text{ M} - x} = \frac{x^2}{0.25 \text{ M} - x} = 1.8 \text{ M}$$

or

$$x^2 = (1.8 \text{ M})(0.25 \text{ M} - x) = 0.45 \text{ M}^2 - (1.8 \text{ M})x$$

We rearrange this equation to the standard quadratic form.

$$x^2 + (1.8 \text{ M})x - 0.45 \text{ M}^2 = 0$$

Using the quadratic formula, we have

$$x = \frac{-1.8 \text{ M} \pm \sqrt{(1.8 \text{ M})^2 - (4)(1)(-0.45 \text{ M}^2)}}{(2)(1)}$$

Taking the positive root, we obtain

$$x = 0.22 \text{ M}$$

Therefore, at equilibrium $[PCl_3] = 0.22$ M, $[Cl_2] = 0.22$ M, and $[PCl_5] = 0.25$ M $- 0.22$ M $= 0.03$ M.

14-17 From the law of concentration action we have

$$K_c = 2.5 \times 10^4 = \frac{[HCl]^2}{[H_2][Cl_2]}$$

Let x be the number of moles of H_2 or of Cl_2 that react. From the reaction stoichiometry, the number of moles of HCl produced is $2x$. Let V be the reaction volume. Thus the initial and equilibrium concentrations are:

	H₂(g)	**+**	**Cl₂(g)**	**⇌ 2HCl(g)**
Initial concentration	$\dfrac{0.50 \text{ mol}}{V}$		$\dfrac{0.50 \text{ mol}}{V}$	0
Equilibrium concentration	$\dfrac{0.50 \text{ mol} - x}{V}$		$\dfrac{0.50 \text{ mol} - x}{V}$	$\dfrac{2x}{V}$

Substituting the equilibrium concentrations into the K_c expression yields

$$\frac{\left(\dfrac{2x}{V}\right)^2}{\left(\dfrac{0.50 \text{ mol} - x}{V}\right)^2} = 2.5 \times 10^4$$

Taking the square root of both sides yields

$$\frac{\left(\dfrac{2x}{V}\right)}{\left(\dfrac{0.50 \text{ mol} - x}{V}\right)} = 1.58 \times 10^2$$

or after canceling V, the volume, in the denominator and the numerator, we have

$$2x = 158(0.50 \text{ mol} - x)$$

Collecting like terms yields

$$160x = 79 \text{ mol}$$

and solving for x gives

$$x = 0.49 \text{ mol}$$

The number of moles of HCl at equilibrium is $2x$, or 0.98 mol.

14-19   From the law of concentration action, we have

$$K_c = [\text{NH}_3][\text{H}_2\text{S}] = 1.81 \times 10^{-4} \text{ M}^2$$

We need K_p in order to calculate equilibrium pressures. The relation between K_c and K_p is

$$K_c = \left(\frac{P_{\text{NH}_3}}{RT}\right)\left(\frac{P_{\text{H}_2\text{S}}}{RT}\right) = \left(\frac{1}{RT}\right)^2 K_p$$

or

$$K_p = (RT)^2 K_c$$

Thus

$$K_p = [(0.0821 \text{ L} \cdot \text{atm} \cdot \text{K}^{-1} \cdot \text{mol}^{-1})(298 \text{ K})]^2 (1.81 \times 10^{-4} \text{ mol}^2 \cdot \text{L}^{-2})$$
$$= 0.108 \text{ atm}^2$$

From the reaction stoichiometry we have $P_{\text{NH}_3} = P_{\text{H}_2\text{S}}$ at equilibrium. Let x be the equilibrium pressure of NH_3. Thus

$$K_p = (x)(x) = x^2 = 0.108 \text{ atm}^2$$

Taking the square root yields

$$x = 0.329 \text{ atm}$$

At equilibrium $P_{\text{H}_2\text{S}} = P_{\text{NH}_3} = 0.329$ atm. The total pressure is the sum of the partial pressures of H_2S and NH_3

$$P_{tot} = P_{\text{H}_2\text{S}} + P_{\text{NH}_3} = 0.329 \text{ atm} + 0.329 \text{ atm} = 0.658 \text{ atm}$$

14-21   From the law of concentration action we have

$$K_c = \frac{[\text{Cl}_2][\text{I}_2]}{[\text{ICl}]^2} = 0.11$$

We set up a table of initial concentrations and equilibrium concentrations. Let x be the number of moles per liter of I_2 or of Cl_2 that react. From the reaction stoichiometry the number of moles per liter of ICl produced is $2x$. (Each mole of I_2 or Cl_2 that reacts produces two moles of ICl.)

	2ICl(g) $\rightleftharpoons$	**$I_2(g)$**	**+**	**$Cl_2(g)$**
Initial concentration	0	$\dfrac{0.65 \text{ mol}}{1.5 \text{ L}} = 0.43 \text{ M}$		$\dfrac{0.33 \text{ mol}}{1.5 \text{ L}} = 0.22 \text{ M}$
Equilibrium concentration	$2x$	$0.43 \text{ M} - x$		$0.22 \text{ M} - x$

Substituting the equilibrium concentration expressions in the K_c expression yields

$$\frac{(0.43 \text{ M} - x)(0.22 \text{ M} - x)}{(2x)^2} = 0.11$$

Multiplying out and collecting terms yields

$$0.56x^2 - (0.65 \text{ M})x + (0.0946 \text{ M}^2) = 0$$

The solutions of this quadratic equation are

$$x = \frac{+0.65 \text{ M} \pm \sqrt{(0.65 \text{ M})^2 - (4)(0.56)(0.0946 \text{ M}^2)}}{2(0.56)}$$

The two roots are $x = 0.17$ M and $x = 0.99$ M. We reject the 0.99 M root as physically impossible because it gives negative values for $[I_2]$ and $[Cl_2]$. Thus, we have at equilibrium

$$[Cl_2] = 0.22 \text{ M} - 0.17 \text{ M} = 0.05 \text{ M}$$

$$[I_2] = 0.43 \text{ M} - 0.17 \text{ M} = 0.26 \text{ M}$$

$$[ICl] = 2(0.17 \text{ M}) = 0.34 \text{ M}$$

14-23 From the law of concentration action we have

$$K_p = \frac{P_{NO_2}^2}{P_{N_2O_4}} = 4.90 \text{ atm}$$

We know from Dalton's law of partial pressures that

$$P_{total} = P_{NO_2} + P_{N_2O_4} = 1.45 \text{ atm}$$

Solving for P_{NO_2}, we have

$$P_{NO_2} = 1.45 \text{ atm} - P_{N_2O_4}$$

Substituting this expression for P_{NO_2} into the K_p expression, we have

$$\frac{(1.45 \text{ atm} - P_{N_2O_4})^2}{P_{N_2O_4}} = \frac{2.10 \text{ atm}^2 - (2.90 \text{ atm})P_{N_2O_4} + P_{N_2O_4}^2}{P_{N_2O_4}} = 4.90 \text{ atm}$$

or

$$2.10 \text{ atm}^2 - (2.90 \text{ atm})P_{N_2O_4} + P_{N_2O_4}^2 = (4.90 \text{ atm})P_{N_2O_4}$$

Rearranging to the standard form of a quadratic equation, we have

$$P_{N_2O_4}^2 - (7.80 \text{ atm})P_{N_2O_4} + 2.10 \text{ atm}^2 = 0$$

The solutions to the above equation from the quadratic formula are

$$P_{N_2O_4} = \frac{7.80 \text{ atm} \pm \sqrt{60.84 \text{ atm}^2 - (4)(1)(2.10 \text{ atm}^2)}}{2}$$

$$P_{N_2O_4} = \frac{7.80 \text{ atm} \pm 7.24 \text{ atm}}{2} = 7.52 \text{ atm and } 0.28 \text{ atm}$$

We can rule out the value 7.52 atm, because it is larger than the total pressure. At equilibrium $P_{N_2O_4} = 0.28$ atm and $P_{NO_2} = 1.45$ atm $- 0.28$ atm $= 1.17$ atm.

14-25 From the law of concentration action we have

$$K_p = \frac{P_{CO_2}}{P_{CO}} = 600$$

The total pressure is equal to the sum of the partial pressures of $CO(g)$ and $CO_2(g)$:

$$P_{total} = P_{CO} + P_{CO_2} = 1.80 \text{ atm}$$

Solving for P_{CO_2}, we have

$$P_{CO_2} = 1.80 \text{ atm} - P_{CO}$$

Substituting the expression for P_{CO_2} into the K_p expression, we have that

$$\frac{1.80 \text{ atm} - P_{CO}}{P_{CO}} = 600$$

Thus

$$P_{CO} = \frac{1.80 \text{ atm}}{601} = 3.00 \times 10^{-3} \text{ atm}$$

The partial pressure of CO_2 is

$$P_{CO_2} = 1.80 \text{ atm} - P_{CO} = 1.80 \text{ atm} - 0.0030 \text{ atm} = 1.80 \text{ atm}$$

14-27 (a) An increase in P_{H_2O} will cause a shift in the reaction equilibrium from right to left, because this is the direction in which P_{H_2O} will decrease. Thus P_{CO} will decrease and P_{CO_2} will increase.

(b) The number of moles of gas is the same on both sides of the equation, and thus an increase in the reaction volume will not change the equilibrium pressures of the reactants or products.

14-29 (a) $\rightarrow$ The reaction is exothermic. A decrease in temperature shifts the equilibrium to the right.

(b) $\rightarrow$ A decrease in reaction volume leads to an increase in the total number of moles per unit volume in the reaction mixture. A shift to the right causes a decrease in the number of moles per unit volume.

(c) $\leftarrow$ A shift in equilibrium to the left will increase the pressure of H_2.

(d) $\leftarrow$ A shift in equilibrium to the left will decrease the pressure of CH_4.

(e) no change   The concentration of $C(s)$ is independent of the amount of $C(s)$, and thus the equilibrium concentrations are independent of the amount of $C(s)$.

14-31 (a) $\leftarrow$ The reaction is exothermic, and thus an increase in temperature makes the evolution of heat less favorable and shifts the equilibrium to the left.

(b) $\leftarrow$ There are more moles of gas on the left than on the right, and thus a shift to the left will partially offset the decrease in the number of moles per unit volume.

(c) $\leftarrow$ The decrease of $[O_2]$ will be offset partially by a shift to the left.

(d) $\rightarrow$ The increase of $[SO_2]$ will be partially offset by a shift to the right.

14-33 (1) $$K_c = \frac{[CO][H_2]}{[H_2O]}$$

An increase in temperature shifts the reaction equilibrium to the right (endothermic reaction). A decrease in reaction volume shifts the reaction equilibrium to the left ($\Delta n_{gas} = +1$).

(2) $$K_c = \frac{[CO_2][H_2]}{[CO][H_2O]}$$

An increase in temperature shifts the reaction equilibrium to the left (exothermic reaction). A decrease in reaction volume has no effect ($\Delta n_{gas} = 0$).

(3) $$K_c = \frac{[H_2O][CH_4]}{[CO][H_2]^3}$$

An increase in temperature shifts the equilibrium to the left (exothermic reaction). A decrease in the reaction volume shifts the equilibrium to the right ($\Delta n_{gas} = -2$).

14-35 The equilibrium constant expression is

$$K_c = \frac{[SO_3]^2}{[SO_2]^2[O_2]} = 13 \text{ M}^{-1}$$

The Q_c expression is

$$Q_c = \frac{[SO_3]_0^2}{[SO_2]_0^2[O_2]_0}$$

The value of Q_c is calculated from the given initial concentrations:

Q_c		Q_c/K_c	Direction that the reaction proceeds toward equilibrium
(a)	$\dfrac{(0.10 \text{ M})^2}{(0.40 \text{ M})^2(0.20 \text{ M})} = 0.31 \text{ M}^{-1}$	$\dfrac{0.31 \text{ M}^{-1}}{13 \text{ M}^{-1}} = 0.024 < 1$	$\longrightarrow$
(b)	$\dfrac{(0.30 \text{ M})^2}{(0.05 \text{ M})^2(0.10 \text{ M})} = 360 \text{ M}^{-1}$	$\dfrac{360 \text{ M}^{-1}}{13 \text{ M}^{-1}} = 28 > 1$	$\longleftarrow$

14-37 The Q_p expression is

$$Q_p = \frac{(P_{CO})_0(P_{H_2O})_0}{(P_{H_2})_0(P_{CO_2})_0}$$

Thus

$$Q_p = \frac{(1.25 \text{ atm})(0.10 \text{ atm})}{(0.55 \text{ atm})(0.20 \text{ atm})} = 1.1$$

Because Q_p does not equal K_p, the reaction is not at equilibrium

$$\frac{Q_p}{K_p} = \frac{1.1}{1.59} = 0.69 < 1$$

Because the value of Q_p/K_p is less than 1, the reaction proceeds from left to right toward equilibrium.

14-39 The Q_p expression for the reaction is

$$Q_p = \frac{(P_{SO_3})_0^2}{(P_{SO_2})_0^2 (P_{O_2})_0}$$

Thus

$$Q_p = \frac{(0.20 \text{ atm})^2}{(0.30 \text{ atm})^2 (0.50 \text{ atm})} = 0.89 \text{ atm}^{-1}$$

$$\frac{Q_p}{K_p} = \frac{0.89 \text{ atm}^{-1}}{0.14 \text{ atm}^{-1}} = 6.4$$

Because $Q_p/K_p > 1$, the reaction proceeds from right to left toward equilibrium.

14-41 The equation

$$CH_4(g) + 2H_2O(g) \rightleftharpoons CO_2(g) + 4H_2(g)$$

is the sum of the two given equations. Thus the equilibrium constant is given by

$$K = K_1 K_2 = (1.44)(25.6 \text{ atm}^2) = 36.9 \text{ atm}^2$$

14-43 For the reverse of Equation (1) multiplied through by 2,

(3) $\qquad\qquad 2Cl_2(g) + 2MgO(s) \rightleftharpoons 2MgCl_2(s) + O_2(g)$

we have

$$K_3 = \frac{1}{K_1^2} = \left(\frac{1}{2.95 \text{ atm}^{1/2}}\right)^2 = 0.115 \text{ atm}^{-1}$$

Adding Equation (3) to Equation (2) multiplied by 2,

(4) $\qquad\qquad 2MgCl_2(s) + 2H_2O(g) \rightleftharpoons 2MgO(s) + 4HCl(g)$

$$K_4 = (8.40 \text{ atm})^2 = 70.6 \text{ atm}^2$$

yields

(5) $\qquad\qquad 2Cl_2(g) + 2H_2O(g) \rightleftharpoons 4HCl(g) + O_2(g)$

Thus

$$K_5 = K_3 K_4 = (0.115 \text{ atm}^{-1})(70.6 \text{ atm}^2) = 8.12 \text{ atm}$$

14-45 The van't Hoff equation is

$$\log\left(\frac{K_2}{K_1}\right) = \frac{\Delta H_{rxn}^\circ}{2.30R}\left(\frac{T_2 - T_1}{T_1 T_2}\right)$$

Substituting the values of K_1, T_1, T_2, and ΔH°_{rxn} into the van't Hoff equation, we obtain

$$\log\left(\frac{K_2}{1.78 \text{ atm}}\right) = \frac{(92.9 \text{ kJ}\cdot\text{mol}^{-1})(1000 \text{ J}\cdot\text{kJ}^{-1})(673 \text{ K} - 523 \text{ K})}{(2.30)(8.314 \text{ J}\cdot\text{K}^{-1}\cdot\text{mol}^{-1})(523 \text{ K})(673 \text{ K})}$$
$$= 2.070$$

Taking the antilogarithm of both sides yields

$$\frac{K_2}{1.78 \text{ atm}} = 117.5$$

Thus

$$K_2 = (117.5)(1.78 \text{ atm}) = 209 \text{ atm}$$

14-47   Substituting in the values of K_1, T_1, T_2 and ΔH°_{rxn} into the van't Hoff equation (Problem 14-45), we have

$$\log\left(\frac{K_2}{0.14 \text{ atm}^{-1}}\right) = \frac{(-198 \text{ kJ}\cdot\text{mol}^{-1})(1000 \text{ J}\cdot\text{kJ}^{-1})(1273 \text{ K} - 900 \text{ K})}{(2.30)(8.314 \text{ J}\cdot\text{mol}^{-1}\cdot\text{K}^{-1})(1273 \text{ K})(900 \text{ K})}$$
$$= -3.371$$

Taking the antilogarithm of both sides, we have

$$\frac{K_2}{0.14 \text{ atm}^{-1}} = 4.26 \times 10^{-4}$$

$$K_2 = (4.26 \times 10^{-4})(0.14 \text{ atm}^{-1}) = 6.0 \times 10^{-5} \text{ atm}^{-1}$$

14-49   Using the property $\log a/b = \log a - \log b$, the van't Hoff equation can be written

$$\log\left(\frac{K_2}{K_1}\right) = \log K_2 - \log K_1 = \frac{\Delta H^\circ_{rxn}}{2.30R}\left(\frac{T_2 - T_1}{T_1 T_2}\right)$$

Substituting the values of K_1, T_1, K_2, and T_2 into the van't Hoff equation yields

$$\frac{\Delta H^\circ_{rxn}(873 \text{ K} - 723 \text{ K})}{(2.30)(8.314 \text{ J}\cdot\text{mol}^{-1}\cdot\text{K}^{-1})(723 \text{ K})(873 \text{ K})} = -0.002 - (-0.706)$$

Thus

$$(1.243 \times 10^{-5} \text{ J}^{-1}\cdot\text{mol})\, \Delta H^\circ_{rxn} = 0.704$$

Solving for ΔH°_{rxn}, we have

$$\Delta H^\circ_{rxn} = \frac{0.704}{1.243 \times 10^{-5} \text{ J}^{-1}\cdot\text{mol}}$$
$$= 5.66 \times 10^4 \text{ J}\cdot\text{mol}^{-1} = 56.6 \text{ kJ}\cdot\text{mol}^{-1}$$

14-51   The K_p expression for the equation is

$$K_p = P_{NH_3}^2 = 6.66 \times 10^{-3} \text{ atm}^2 \qquad \text{(at } 20°\text{C)}$$

Thus the equilibrium partial pressure of $NH_3(g)$ at $20°C$ is

$$P_{NH_3} = (6.66 \times 10^{-3} \text{ atm}^2)^{1/2} = 8.16 \times 10^{-2} \text{ atm}$$

14-53   From the law of concentration action we have

$$K_c = \frac{[I_2][H_2]}{[HI]^2}$$

Let x be the number of moles per liter of H_2 that are produced from the decomposition of HI. Each mole of H_2 produced requires that two moles of HI decompose. We will set up a table of initial concentrations and equilibrium concentrations:

	2HI(*g*)	⇌	H₂(*g*)	+	I₂(*g*)
Initial concentrations	3.52 M + 1.00 M = 4.52 M		0.42 M		0.42 M
Equilibrium concentrations	4.52 M − 2x		0.42 M + x		0.42 M + x

Notice that the initial concentration of HI is the equilibrium concentration plus the concentration of the added HI. Substituting the equilibrium concentration expressions in the K_c expression, we have

$$K_c = \frac{(0.42 \text{ M} + x)(0.42 \text{ M} + x)}{(4.52 \text{ M} - 2x)^2}$$

We can calculate the value of K_c from the initial equilibrium concentrations.

$$K_c = \frac{(0.42 \text{ M})(0.42 \text{ M})}{(3.52 \text{ M})^2} = 0.014$$

We now have

$$\frac{(0.42 \text{ M} + x)^2}{(4.52 \text{ M} - 2x)^2} = 0.014$$

Taking the square root of both sides, we obtain

$$\frac{0.42 \text{ M} + x}{4.52 \text{ M} - 2x} = 0.12$$

or

$$0.42 \text{ M} + x = (0.12)(4.52 \text{ M} - 2x) = 0.54 \text{ M} - 0.24x$$

$$1.24x = 0.12 \text{ M}$$

$$x = \frac{0.12 \text{ M}}{1.24} = 0.097 \text{ M}$$

Thus in the new equilibrium state we have

$$[\text{HI}] = 4.52 \text{ M} - 2x = 4.33 \text{ M}$$

$$[\text{H}_2] = 0.42 \text{ M} + x = 0.52 \text{ M}$$

$$[\text{I}_2] = 0.42 \text{ M} + x = 0.52 \text{ M}$$

14-55 (a) No change: There are the same number of moles of gaseous species on each side of the reaction.

(b) ← The reaction is exothermic.

(c) → A shift to the right will decrease P_{NO_2}.

(d) → A shift to the right will increase P_{SO_3} and P_{NO}.

14-57 From the law of concentration action we have

$$K_c = \frac{[\text{H}_2\text{O}]^2}{[\text{H}_2]^2}$$

We can find the value of K_c by substituting the values of the equilibrium concentrations.

$$K_c = \frac{(0.25 \text{ M})^2}{(0.25 \text{ M})^2} = 1.0$$

We set up a table of initial concentrations and equilibrium concentrations. Let x be the number of moles per liter of H_2O produced by the reaction of SnO_2 and H_2. One mole of H_2 reacts to produce one mole of H_2O.

	$\text{SnO}_2(s)$	+	$2\text{H}_2(g)$	$\rightleftharpoons$	$\text{Sn}(s)$	+	$2\text{H}_2\text{O}(g)$
Initial Concentration	—		0.50 M		—		0.25 M
Equilibrium Concentration	—		0.50 M − x		—		0.25 M + x

Substituting the equilibrium concentration expressions in the K_c expression, we have

$$K_c = \frac{(0.25 \text{ M} + x)^2}{(0.50 \text{ M} - x)^2} = 1.0$$

Taking the square root of both sides, we have that

$$\frac{0.25 \text{ M} + x}{0.50 \text{ M} - x} = 1.0$$

or

$$0.25 \text{ M} + x = (1.0)(0.50 \text{ M} - x) = 0.50 \text{ M} - x$$

$$2x = 0.25 \text{ M}$$

$$x = \frac{0.25 \text{ M}}{2} = 0.13 \text{ M}$$

Thus at the new equilibrium state we have

$$[H_2O] = 0.25 \text{ M} + 0.13 \text{ M} = 0.38 \text{ M}$$

$$[H_2] = [H_2O] = 0.38 \text{ M}$$

14-59   The K_p expression for the equation is

$$K_p = P_{NH_3}^2 P_{CO_2}$$

The total pressure is given by

$$P_{total} = P_{NH_3} + P_{CO_2}$$

but from the reaction stoichiometry

$$P_{NH_3} = 2P_{CO_2}$$

Thus

$$P_{total} = 3P_{CO_2}$$

or

$$P_{CO_2} = \frac{1}{3}P_{tot}$$

Therefore

$$K_p = (2P_{CO_2})^2 P_{CO_2} = 4P_{CO_2}^3$$

$$= 4\left(\frac{1}{3}P_{total}\right)^3$$

$$= \frac{4}{27}P_{total}^3$$

14-61 For the general equation

$$a\mathrm{A}(g) + b\mathrm{B}(g) \rightleftharpoons c\mathrm{C}(g) + d\mathrm{D}(g)$$

we have for K_c

$$K_c = \frac{[\mathrm{C}]^c[\mathrm{D}]^d}{[\mathrm{A}]^a[\mathrm{B}]^b} \tag{1}$$

From the ideal-gas equation,

$$P_iV = n_iRT$$

we have

$$P_i = \left(\frac{n_i}{V}\right)RT = [i]RT \tag{2}$$

where $[i]$ is the concentration of the gas i in $\mathrm{mol \cdot L^{-1}}$. Substitution of Equation (2) into Equation (1) yields

$$K_c = \frac{\left(\dfrac{P_C}{RT}\right)^c\left(\dfrac{P_D}{RT}\right)^d}{\left(\dfrac{P_A}{RT}\right)^a\left(\dfrac{P_B}{RT}\right)^b}$$

$$= \frac{P_C^c P_D^d}{P_A^a P_B^b}(RT)^{a+b-c-d} = K_p(RT)^{-\Delta n}$$

where $\Delta n = c + d - a - b$. Solving for K_p, we obtain

$$K_p = K_c(RT)^{\Delta n}$$

14-63 (a) The K_c expression for the equation is

$$K_c = \frac{[\mathrm{HI}]^2}{[\mathrm{H_2}][\mathrm{I_2}]} = 85$$

With $[\mathrm{HI}] = [\mathrm{I_2}] = [\mathrm{H_2}]$ we have

$$Q_c = 1 \neq K_c$$

and thus equilibrium is not possible with these concentrations.

(b) The initial value of $[\mathrm{HI}]$ is

$$[\mathrm{HI}] = \frac{(5.0\ \mathrm{g})\left(\dfrac{1\ \mathrm{mol}}{127.9\ \mathrm{g}}\right)}{(2.00\ \mathrm{L})} = 0.0195\ \mathrm{M}$$

The initial and equilibrium concentrations are as follows.

	$H_2(g)$ + $I_2(g)$ ⇌ 2HI(g)		
initial concentrations	0	0	0.0195 M
equilibrium concentrations	x	x	0.0195 M − 2x

Thus

$$\frac{(0.0195 \text{ M} - 2x)^2}{x^2} = 85$$

Take the square root of both sides of this equation to get

$$\frac{0.0195 \text{ M} - 2x}{x} = 9.22$$

and solve for x

$$x = \frac{0.0195 \text{ M}}{11.22} = 0.00174 \text{ M}$$

Thus at equilibrium we have

$$[H_2] = [I_2] = 1.74 \times 10^{-3} \text{ M}$$
$$[HI] = 0.0195 \text{ M} - 2(0.00174 \text{ M}) = 0.0160 \text{ M}$$

14-65 The initial number of moles of O_2 is computed by using the ideal-gas equation.

$$n = \frac{PV}{RT} = \frac{(1.00 \text{ atm})(2.00 \text{ L})}{(0.0821 \text{ L} \cdot \text{atm} \cdot \text{K}^{-1} \cdot \text{mol}^{-1})(298 \text{ K})}$$
$$= 0.0817 \text{ mol}$$

The number of moles of $MgCl_2$ is

$$\frac{50 \text{ g}}{95.21 \text{ g} \cdot \text{mol}^{-1}} = 0.525 \text{ mol}$$

Thus O_2 is the limiting reactant. The K_p expression is

$$K_p = \frac{P_{Cl_2}}{P_{O_2}^{1/2}} = 1.75 \text{ atm}^{1/2}$$

The initial pressure of O_2 at 823 K is

$$P_{O_2} = (1.00 \text{ atm})\left(\frac{823 \text{ K}}{298 \text{ K}}\right) = 2.76 \text{ atm}$$

If we let $x = P_{Cl_2}$ at equilibrium, then we have

$$\frac{x}{\left(2.76 \text{ atm} - \dfrac{x}{2}\right)^{1/2}} = 1.75 \text{ atm}^{1/2}$$

Squaring both sides of the equation yields

$$\frac{x^2}{2.76 \text{ atm} - \dfrac{x}{2}} = 3.06 \text{ atm}$$

or

$$x^2 + (1.53 \text{ atm})x - 8.45 \text{ atm}^2 = 0$$

The solutions to the quadratic equation are

$$x = \frac{-1.53 \text{ atm} \pm \sqrt{(1.53 \text{ atm})^2 + 4(8.45 \text{ atm}^2)}}{2}$$

$$x = 2.24 \text{ atm}$$

Thus at equilibrium

$$P_{Cl_2} = 2.24 \text{ atm}$$

$$P_{O_2} = 2.76 \text{ atm} - \frac{2.24 \text{ atm}}{2} = 1.64 \text{ atm}$$

14-67 High pressure favors the more dense form. Thus the brown form is more stable at high pressure.

14-69 The value of K_p at 900 K is calculated using the van't Hoff equation

$$\log\left(\frac{K_2}{K_1}\right) = \frac{\Delta H_{rxn}^\circ}{2.30R}\left(\frac{T_2 - T_1}{T_1 T_2}\right)$$

Substituting in the values of K_1, T_1, T_2 and ΔH_{rxn}° gives

$$\log\left(\frac{K_2}{5.50 \times 10^{25} \text{ atm}^{-1/2}}\right) = \frac{(-167 \times 10^3 \text{ J} \cdot \text{mol}^{-1})}{(2.30)(8.314 \text{ J} \cdot \text{mol}^{-1} \cdot \text{K}^{-1})}\left(\frac{900 \text{ K} - 300 \text{ K}}{(900 \text{ K})(300 \text{ K})}\right)$$

$$= -19.41$$

Thus

$$K_2 = (5.50 \times 10^{25} \text{ atm}^{-1/2})(10^{-19.41}) = (5.50 \times 10^{25} \text{ atm}^{-1/2})(3.89 \times 10^{-20})$$
$$= 2.14 \times 10^6 \text{ atm}^{-1/2}$$

The pressure of $O_2(g)$ at equilibrium at 900 K is calculated from the equilibrium constant expression

$$K = \frac{1}{P_{O_2}^{1/2}} = 2.14 \times 10^6 \text{ atm}^{-1/2}$$

from which we obtain

$$P_{O_2} = \frac{1}{(2.14 \times 10^6 \text{ atm}^{-1/2})^2} = 2.18 \times 10^{-13} \text{ atm}$$

E   ANSWERS TO THE SELF-TEST

1 false (Forward and reverse rates are equal at equilibrium.)

2 false

3 true

4 true

5 the rate of the reverse reaction

6 decrease

7 increase

8 constant

9 false

10 false

11 the equilibrium constant expression for a reaction is given by the ratio of product equilibrium concentrations to reactant equilibrium concentrations, with each concentration factor raised to a power equal to the stoichiometric coefficient of that species in the balanced equation for the reaction

12 $K_c = \dfrac{[X]^x [Y]^y}{[A]^a [B]^b}$

13 concentrations (K_c) . . . pressures (K_p)

14 false

15 true

16 true

17 $K_c = \dfrac{[CO]^2}{[CO_2]}$

18 $K_p = \dfrac{P_{CO} P_{H_2}}{P_{H_2O}}$

19 $1/K_f$

20 $K_1 K_2$

21 true

22 if a change in conditions displaces a reaction equilibrium, then the reaction proceeds toward equilibrium in the direction that at least partially offsets the change in conditions

23 temperature . . . reaction volume . . . concentrations of reactants and products.

24 the smaller number of moles of gaseous species

25 false (true only for endothermic reactions)

26 true

27 true

28 true

29 false

30 $\log\left(\dfrac{K_2}{K_1}\right) = \dfrac{\Delta H^{\circ}_{rxn}}{2.30R}\left(\dfrac{T_2 - T_1}{T_1 T_2}\right)$

31 increases

32 Haber process

33 $N_2(g) + 3H_2(g) \xrightarrow{\text{500°C, catalyst}} 2NH_3(g)$

34 equilibrium

35 true

36 $\dfrac{[X]_0^x [Y]_0^y}{[A]_0^a [B]_0^b}$, initial or arbitrary values of the concentrations

37 true

38 left . . . right

39 0

40 (c)

41 (d)

ACIDS AND BASES, I

A OUTLINE OF CHAPTER 15

15-1 An acid is a proton donor and a base is a proton acceptor.

In the Arrhenius acid-base classification, an acid produces $H^+(aq)$ and a base produces $OH^-(aq)$ in aqueous solution.

In the Brönsted-Lowry acid-base classification, an acid is a proton donor and a base is a proton acceptor.

In aqueous solution an acid donates a proton to water, which can act as a base, to produce the hydronium ion $H_3O^+(aq)$.

The hydronium ion is a hydrated proton (Figure 15-1).

$$HCl(aq) \rightarrow H^+(aq) + Cl^-(aq) \qquad \text{(Arrhenius)}$$
$$HCl(aq) + H_2O(l) \rightarrow H_3O^+(aq) + Cl^-(aq) \qquad \text{(Brönsted-Lowry)}$$

15-2 In an aqueous solution the ion concentration product $[H_3O^+][OH^-]$ is a constant

The equilibrium constant expression for the equation

$$H_2O(l) + H_2O(l) \rightleftharpoons H_3O^+(aq) + OH^-(aq)$$

is given by

$$K_w = [H_3O^+][OH^-] = 1.00 \times 10^{-14} \text{ M}^2 \text{ at } 25\,°C \qquad (15\text{-}3)$$

K_w is called the ion product constant of water:

In a neutral solution, $\quad [H_3O^+] = [OH^-]$

In an acidic solution, $\quad [H_3O^+] > [OH^-]$

In a basic solution, $\quad [OH^-] > [H_3O^+]$

15-3 Strong acids and bases are completely dissociated in aqueous solutions.

Some strong acids and bases are given in Table 15-1.

Acids and bases that are incompletely dissociated in water are called weak acids and weak bases.

Most acids and bases are weak.

Carboxylic acids have the general formula RCOOH. The carboxylate ion, RCOO⁻, is stabilized by charge delocalization.

15-4 pH is a measure of the acidity of an aqueous solution.

$$\text{pH} = -\log[\text{H}_3\text{O}^+] \tag{15-4}$$

The pH of most aqueous solutions lies in the range 0 to 14, although pH values outside this range are occasionally encountered (Figure 15-2).

In a neutral aqueous solution at 25°C, pH = 7.0.

In an acidic aqueous solution at 25°C, pH < 7.0.

In a basic aqueous solution at 25°C, pH > 7.0.

The value of $[\text{H}_3\text{O}^+]$ can be found from a pH measurement.

$$[\text{H}_3\text{O}^+] = 10^{-\text{pH}} \tag{15-7}$$

By definition

$$\text{pOH} = -\log[\text{OH}^-] \tag{15-5}$$

At 25°C the pH and pOH are related by the expression

$$\text{pH} + \text{pOH} = 14.00 \tag{15-6}$$

15-5 Weak acids and weak bases react only partially with water.

The percent dissociation of an acid is given by

$$\text{percent dissociation} = \frac{[\text{H}_3\text{O}^+]}{[\text{acid}]_0} \times 100$$

where $[\text{acid}]_0$ is the stoichiometric concentration of the acid.

15-6 The larger the value of K_a, the stronger is the acid.

For the acid-dissociation equilibrium

$$\text{HB}(aq) + \text{H}_2\text{O}(l) \rightleftharpoons \text{H}_3\text{O}^+(aq) + \text{B}^-(aq)$$

the acid-dissociation constant is given by

$$K_a = \frac{[\text{H}_3\text{O}^+][\text{B}^-]}{[\text{HB}]}$$

Some K_a values are given in Table 15-2.

The pH of an aqueous solution of a weak acid can be found from the value of K_a and the K_a expression.

The percent dissociation of an acid increases as the concentration of the acid decreases (Figure 15-4).

By definition

$$pK_a = -\log K_a \qquad (15\text{-}9)$$

The smaller the pK_a value for an acid, the stronger is the acid.

Some pK_a values are given in Table 15-2.

15-7 The method of successive approximations is often used in solving acid-base equilibrium problems.

In the first approximation, it is assumed that the value of $[H_3O^+]$ is small relative to the initial concentration of a weak acid, that is

$$[\text{acid}]_0 - [H_3O^+] \approx [\text{acid}]_0$$

In the second approximation, the value of $[H_3O^+]$ found in the first approximation is used in the $[\text{acid}]_0 - [H_3O^+]$ expression.

15-8 The larger the value of K_b, the stronger is the base.

For the base-protonation equilibrium

$$B(aq) + H_2O(l) \rightleftharpoons HB^+(aq) + OH^-(aq)$$

the base-protonation constant is given by

$$K_b = \frac{[HB^+][OH^-]}{[B]}$$

Some K_b values are given in Table 15-3.

The pH of an aqueous solution of a weak base can be found from the value of K_b and the K_b expression.

By definition

$$pK_b = -\log K_b \qquad (15\text{-}12)$$

The smaller the value of pK_b, the stronger is the base.

Some pK_b values are given in Table 15-3.

15-9 Polyprotic acids can donate more than one proton per formula unit.

A diprotic acid has two distinct acid dissociation equilibria.

Each successive acid-dissociation constant of a polyprotic acid is about 10^{-5} times the value of the preceding one.

The successive acid-dissociation constants for some polyprotic acids are given in Table 15-4.

A good approximation in calculating the pH of most solutions of polyprotic acids is to ignore the second dissociation equilibrium.

15-10   The acid-base pair HB, B^- is called a conjugate acid-base pair.

For the dissociation of an acid in water

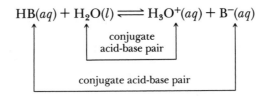

For

$$HB(aq) + H_2O(l) \rightleftharpoons H_3O^+(aq) + B^-(aq)$$

$$K_a = \frac{[H_3O^+][B^-]}{[HB]} \tag{15-14}$$

For

$$B^-(aq) + H_2O(l) \rightleftharpoons HB(aq) + OH^-(aq)$$

$$K_b = \frac{[HB][OH^-]}{[B^-]} \tag{15-15}$$

Therefore,

$$K_a K_b = K_w \tag{15-16}$$

or at 25°C

$$pK_a + pK_b = 14.00 \tag{15-17}$$

The anion of a weak acid is itself a weak base.

The values of K_a, K_b, pK_a, and pK_b for a number of conjugate acid-base pairs are listed in Table 15-5.

15-11   Aqueous solutions of many salts are either acidic or basic.

Various ions react with water to produce hydronium ions or hydroxide ions.

The acidic, neutral, or basic properties of a number of ions are given in Table 15-6.

The pH of aqueous salt solutions can be found from K_a or K_b expressions.

15-12   A Lewis acid is an electron-pair acceptor.

In the Lewis acid-base classification, an acid is an electron-pair acceptor and a base is an electron-pair donor.

In general, an electron-deficient species can act as a Lewis acid and a species with a lone pair of electrons can act as a Lewis base.

B SELF-TEST

1 In the Brönsted-Lowry acid-base classification, an acid is _____.

2 In the Brönsted-Lowry acid-base classification, a base is _____.

3 Ammonia, NH_3, is an example of an acid. *True/False*

4 The hydronium ion is _____.

5 In aqueous solution the proton exists as a bare proton. *True/False*

6 In aqueous solution the concentration of $OH^-(aq)$ does not depend on the concentration of $H_3O^+(aq)$. *True/False*

7 The concentration of $OH^-(aq)$ in a neutral aqueous solution at 25°C is 1.0×10^{-14} M. *True/False*

8 The ion-product constant of water is given by the expression $K_w =$ _____.

9 The value of K_w at 25°C is _____.

10 The concentration of OH^- in an aqueous solution is 2.5×10^{-3} M; the solution is *(acidic, basic, neutral)*.

11 The concentration of $H_3O^+(aq)$ in an aqueous solution is 2.5×10^{-11} M; the solution is *(acidic, basic, neutral)*.

12 An aqueous solution of HBr contains the species HBr, Br^-, and $H_3O^+(aq)$. *True/False*

13 An aqueous solution of KOH contains the ionic species _____.

14 A carboxylic acid has the general formula _____.

15 Most carboxylic acids are *(weak, strong)* acids.

16 A carboxylic acid reacts with water to form a hydronium ion and a _____ ion.

17 The negative charge on a carboxylate ion is distributed over both oxygen atoms. *True/False*

18 The concentration of $H_3O^+(aq)$ in an aqueous solution that is 0.032 M in HCl is _____.

19   The pH of a solution is defined as _____ .

20   The pH scale compresses the wide range of the _____ scale.

21   The pH of a 0.010 M aqueous solution of HCl is _____ .

22   Measurement of the pH of a solution can be used to find the concentration of $H_3O^+(aq)$ in the solution. *True/False*

23   The concentration of OH^- in an aqueous solution cannot be determined from pH measurements. *True/False*

24   The pH of pure water or of a neutral aqueous solution at 25°C is _____ .

25   Acidic solutions have pH values less than _____ .

26   Basic solutions have pH values greater than _____ .

27   A weak acid is *(completely, partially)* dissociated in water.

28   A 0.10 M aqueous solution of the weak acid, HF, has the same pH as a 0.10 M aqueous solution of HCl. *True/False*

29   An aqueous solution of acetic acid, $HC_2H_3O_2$, contains no undissociated acid. *True/False*

30   An acid dissociation reaction is an example of a _____ reaction.

31   The equation for the acid dissociation reaction of hydrofluoric acid, HF(*aq*), is

_____ .

32   The acid dissociation constant expression for hydrofluoric acid, HF(*aq*), is $K_a =$

_____ .

33   The value of K_a indicates the extent of an acid's dissociation in water. *True/False*

34   An aqueous solution of nitrous acid, HNO_2, contains the species _____

_____ .

35   A weak base is a base that does not react completely with water. *True/False*

36   A 0.10 M aqueous solution of ammonia, NH_3, has the same pH as a 0.10 M aqueous solution of sodium hydroxide, NaOH. *True/False*

37   The protonation equation for ammonia, NH_3, in water is _____

_____ .

38   The base protonation equilibrium constant expression for ammonia, NH_3, is given by $K_b = $ _____.

39   The value of the pK_a of an acid is given by p$K_a = $ _____.

40   The stronger the acid, the *(smaller, larger)* is the pK_a value of the acid.

41   The value of the pK_b of a base is given by p$K_b = $ _____.

42   The larger the value of pK_b, the *(stronger, weaker)* is the base.

43   A diprotic acid has _____ dissociable protons per formula unit.

44   A triprotic acid has _____ dissociable protons per formula unit.

45   The two successive acid dissociation constants of a diprotic acid are approximately equal. *True/False*

46   In calculating the pH of a solution of a diprotic acid, the second acid-dissociation constant usually may be ignored. *True/False*

47   Label the conjugate acid-base pairs in the proton transfer equation

$$HNO_2(aq) + H_2O(l) \rightleftharpoons H_3O^+(aq) + NO_2^-(aq)$$

48   The conjugate _____ of $NH_3(aq)$ is $NH_4^+(aq)$.

49   The conjugate _____ of $HF(aq)$ is $F^-(aq)$.

50   The conjugate base of acetic acid, $HC_2H_3O_2$, reacts with water according to the equation _____.

51   The conjugate acid of NH_3 reacts with water according to the equation

_____.

52   The base protonation constant K_b for the conjugate base of an acid is related to the acid dissociation constant K_a of the acid by the relation $K_b = $

_____.

53   The aqueous solution of a salt is always neutral. *True/False*

54   The anion of a weak acid is a *(neutral, acidic, basic)* anion.

55   The cation of a strong base is a *(neutral, acidic, basic)* cation.

56   An aqueous solution of NH_4Cl is *(neutral, acidic, basic)*.

57   An aqueous solution of $NaNO_2$ is *(neutral, acidic, basic)*.

58   An aqueous solution of $FeCl_3$ is *(neutral, acidic, basic)*.

59   In the Lewis acid-base classification an acid is —————————————————.

60   In the Lewis acid-base classification a base is —————————————————.

61   An electron-deficient species can act as a Lewis —————————————.

62   A species with a lone pair of electrons can act as a Lewis —————————.

C   CALCULATIONS YOU SHOULD KNOW HOW TO DO

1   Calculate the concentrations of various ionic species in solutions of strong acids or strong bases. See Examples 15-1 and 15-2 and Problems 15-1 through 15-4.

2   Calculate the pH of a solution of a strong base or a strong acid. See Example 15-5 and Problems 15-5 through 15-10. (The use of logarithms is explained in Chapter 11 of this Study Guide.)

3   Calculate $[H_3O^+]$ or $[OH^-]$ from the pH. See Example 15-6 and Problems 15-11 through 15-16.

4   Given the pH, calculate the percentage of weak-acid molecules that are dissociated or the percentage of weak-base molecules that are protonated. See Example 15-7 and Problems 15-21 and 15-22.

5   Calculate the value of K_a or K_b from the pH. See Problems 15-17 through 15-20.

6   Calculate the pH of an acidic solution given the value of K_a. See Example 15-9 and Problems 15-23 through 15-28.

7   Calculate the pH of a basic solution given the value of K_b. See Example 15-10 and Problems 15-29 through 15-34.

8   Calculate K_a given K_b or calculate K_b given K_a for conjugate acid-base pairs. See Example 15-11 and Problems 15-51 through 15-54.

9   Calculate the pH of aqueous salt solutions. See Example 15-14 and Problems 15-61 through 15-70.

D   SOLUTIONS TO THE ODD-NUMBERED PROBLEMS

15-1   Because $HClO_4$ is a strong acid in water (see Table 15-1), it is completely dissociated and thus

$$[H_3O^+] = 0.150 \text{ M} \quad \text{and} \quad [ClO_4^-] = 0.150 \text{ M}$$

We can calculate $[OH^-]$ from the K_w expression.

$$K_w = [H_3O^+][OH^-] = 1.00 \times 10^{-14} \text{ M}^2$$

Solving for $[OH^-]$, we get

$$[OH^-] = \frac{1.00 \times 10^{-14} \text{ M}^2}{[H_3O^+]} = \frac{1.00 \times 10^{-14} \text{ M}^2}{0.150 \text{ M}} = 6.67 \times 10^{-14} \text{ M}$$

Because $[H_3O^+] > [OH^-]$, the solution is acidic.

15-3   We first must find the number of moles in 2.00 g of TlOH.

$$n = (2.00 \text{ g})\left(\frac{1 \text{ mol}}{221.4 \text{ g}}\right) = 0.00903 \text{ mol}$$

The molarity of the solution is

$$\text{molarity} = \frac{\text{moles of solute}}{\text{volume of solution}} = \frac{0.00903 \text{ mol}}{0.500 \text{ L}} = 0.0181 \text{ M}$$

Because TlOH is a strong base (Table 15-1), it is completely dissociated in aqueous solution, and thus

$$[OH^-] = 1.81 \times 10^{-2} \text{ M} \qquad \text{and} \qquad [Tl^+] = 1.81 \times 10^{-2} \text{ M}$$

We can calculate $[H_3O^+]$ from the K_w expression

$$K_w = [H_3O^+][OH^-] = 1.00 \times 10^{-14} \text{ M}^2$$

to get

$$[H_3O^+] = \frac{1.00 \times 10^{-14} \text{ M}^2}{[OH^-]} = \frac{1.00 \times 10^{-14} \text{ M}^2}{1.81 \times 10^{-2} \text{ M}} = 5.52 \times 10^{-13} \text{ M}$$

15-5   Because HNO_3 is a strong acid in solution, it is completely dissociated, and thus

$$[H_3O^+] = 0.020 \text{ M}$$

The pH is given by

$$\text{pH} = -\log[H_3O^+] = -\log(0.020) = 1.70$$

Because pH < 7, the solution is acidic.

15-7   Because both HCl and HBr are strong acids, they are completely dissociated in water. Thus from HCl

$$[H_3O^+] = 0.035 \text{ M}$$

and from HBr

$$[H_3O^+] = 0.045 \text{ M}$$

The total concentration of $H_3O^+(aq)$ is

$$[H_3O^+] = 0.035 \text{ M} + 0.045 \text{ M} = 0.080 \text{ M}$$

The pH of the solution is

$$pH = -\log[H_3O^+] = -\log(0.080) = 1.10$$

The solution is acidic because the pH < 7.
The pOH of the solution is

$$pOH = 14.00 - pH = 14.00 - 1.10 = 12.90$$

15-9 We first calculate the number of moles of KOH in 2.00 g:

$$n = (2.00 \text{ g})\left(\frac{1 \text{ mol}}{56.11 \text{ g}}\right) = 3.56 \times 10^{-2} \text{ mol}$$

The molarity of the solution is

$$\text{molarity} = \frac{\text{moles of solute}}{\text{volume of solution}} = \frac{3.56 \times 10^{-2} \text{ mol}}{0.500 \text{ L}} = 7.12 \times 10^{-2} \text{ M}$$

Because KOH is a strong base, it is completely dissociated, and thus

$$[OH^-] = 7.12 \times 10^{-2} \text{ M}$$

The pOH of the solution is

$$pOH = -\log[OH^-] = -\log(7.12 \times 10^{-2}) = 1.15$$

The pH of the solution is

$$pH = 14.00 - pOH = 14.00 - 1.15 = 12.85$$

15-11 We calculate the value of $[H_3O^+]$ using the relation

$$[H_3O^+] = 10^{-pH} \tag{15-7}$$

The pH of the muscle fluids is given as 6.8, and so

$$[H_3O^+] = 10^{-6.8} = 1.6 \times 10^{-7} \text{ M}$$

If you do not use a calculator to find $10^{-6.8}$, then write

$$[H_3O^+] = 10^{-6.8} = 10^{0.20} \times 10^{-7} = 1.6 \times 10^{-7} \text{ M}$$

15-13 We use the relation

$$[H_3O^+] = 10^{-pH} \tag{15-7}$$

The pH is 1.0 and so

$$[H_3O^+] = 10^{-1.0} = 0.10 \text{ M}$$

Because HCl is a strong acid, the concentration of HCl in the stomach when the pH = 1.0 is

$$[HCl] = [H_3O^+] = 0.10 \text{ M}$$

15-15 We use the relation

$$[H_3O^+] = 10^{-pH} \qquad (15\text{-}7)$$

The pH of human blood is 7.4 and so

$$[H_3O^+] = 10^{-7.4} = 4.0 \times 10^{-8} \text{ M}$$

We can calculate $[OH^-]$ from the K_w expression.

$$[OH^-] = \frac{1.00 \times 10^{-14} \text{ M}^2}{[H_3O^+]} = \frac{1.00 \times 10^{-14} \text{ M}^2}{4.0 \times 10^{-8} \text{ M}} = 2.5 \times 10^{-7} \text{ M}$$

15-17 The equation for the reaction is

$$HC_3H_5O_2(aq) + H_2O(l) \rightleftharpoons H_3O^+(aq) + C_3H_5O_2^-(aq)$$

The acid dissociation constant expression is

$$K_a = \frac{[H_3O^+][C_3H_5O_2^-]}{[HC_3H_5O_2]}$$

We can find the value of $[H_3O^+]$ from the pH of the solution. We have

$$[H_3O^+] = 10^{-pH} = 10^{-3.09} = 8.13 \times 10^{-4} \text{ M}$$

From the reaction stoichiometry at equilibrium, $[H_3O^+] = [C_3H_5O_2^-]$, because we started with only $HC_3H_5O_2$. At equilibrium

$$[HC_3H_5O_2] = 0.050 \text{ M} - [H_3O^+] = 0.050 \text{ M} - 0.000813 \text{ M} = 0.049 \text{ M}$$

Substituting the values of the concentrations of H_3O^+, $C_3H_5O_2^-$, and $HC_3H_5O_2$ into the K_a expression, we have

$$K_a = \frac{(8.13 \times 10^{-4} \text{ M})(8.13 \times 10^{-4} \text{ M})}{(0.049 \text{ M})}$$
$$= 1.3 \times 10^{-5} \text{ M}$$

15-19 The equation for the reaction is

$$HC_2H_3O_2(aq) + H_2O(l) \rightleftharpoons H_3O^+(aq) + C_2H_3O_2^-(aq)$$

The acid dissociation constant expression is

$$K_a = \frac{[H_3O^+][C_2H_3O_2^-]}{[HC_2H_3O_2]}$$

We can find the value of $[H_3O^+]$ from the pH:

$$[H_3O^+] = 10^{-pH} = 10^{-3.39} = 4.07 \times 10^{-4} \text{ M}$$

We can set up a table of initial concentrations and equilibrium concentrations.

	$HC_2H_3O_2(aq)$	$+ H_2O(l) \rightleftharpoons H_3O^+(aq)$	$+ C_2H_3O_2^-(aq)$
initial concentration	1.00×10^{-2} M	— 0	0
equilibrium concentration	1.00×10^{-2} M $- [H_3O^+]$ $= 0.96 \times 10^{-2}$ M	— 4.07×10^{-4} M	$[C_2H_3O_2^-] = [H_3O^+]$ $= 4.07 \times 10^{-4}$ M

Substituting in the values of the equilibrium concentrations in the K_a expression, we have

$$K_a = \frac{(4.07 \times 10^{-4} \text{ M})(4.07 \times 10^{-4} \text{ M})}{0.96 \times 10^{-2} \text{ M}}$$
$$= 1.7 \times 10^{-5} \text{ M}$$

15-21   The reaction is

$$\text{acetylsalicylic acid}(aq) + H_2O(l) \rightleftharpoons H_3O^+(aq) + \text{acetylsalicylate}^-(aq)$$

or

$$\text{acid}(aq) + H_2O(l) \rightleftharpoons H_3O^+(aq) + \text{anion}^-(aq)$$

The acid dissociation constant expression is

$$K_a = \frac{[\text{anion}^-][H_3O^+]}{[\text{acid}]} = 2.75 \times 10^{-5} \text{ M}$$

The ratio of the dissociated acid to the undissociated acid is given by

$$\frac{[\text{anion}^-]}{[\text{acid}]} = \frac{K_a}{[H_3O^+]} = \frac{2.75 \times 10^{-5} \text{ M}}{[H_3O^+]}$$

The concentration of $H_3O^+(aq)$ is

$$[H_3O^+] = 10^{-pH} = 10^{-1.5} = 3.2 \times 10^{-2} \text{ M}$$

and so

$$\frac{[anion^-]}{[acid]} = \frac{2.75 \times 10^{-5} \text{ M}}{3.2 \times 10^{-2} \text{ M}} = 8.6 \times 10^{-4}$$

15-23   The equation is

$$HC_7H_5O_2(aq) + H_2O(l) \rightleftharpoons H_3O^+(aq) + C_7H_5O_2^-(aq)$$

We can set up a table of initial and equilibrium concentrations.

	$HC_7H_5O_2(aq)$	$+ \; H_2O(l) \rightleftharpoons$	$H_3O^+(aq) \; +$	$C_7H_5O_2^-(aq)$
initial concentration	0.020 M	—	0	0
equilibrium concentration	$0.020 \text{ M} - [H_3O^+]$	—	$[H_3O^+]$	$[C_7H_5O_2^-] = [H_3O^+]$

Substituting the equilibrium concentration expressions in the K_a expression, we have

$$K_a = \frac{[H_3O^+][C_7H_5O_2^-]}{[HC_7H_5O_2]} = \frac{[H_3O^+]^2}{0.020 \text{ M} - [H_3O^+]} = 6.46 \times 10^{-5} \text{ M}$$

or

$$[H_3O^+]^2 + 6.46 \times 10^{-5} \text{ M } [H_3O^+] - 1.29 \times 10^{-6} \text{ M}^2 = 0$$

The quadratic formula (reviewed in Section C of Chapter 14 in this Study Guide) gives

$$[H_3O^+] = \frac{-6.46 \times 10^{-5} \text{ M} \pm \sqrt{4.17 \times 10^{-9} \text{ M}^2 - (4)(1)(-1.29 \times 10^{-6} \text{ M}^2)}}{(2)(1)}$$

$$= \frac{-6.46 \times 10^{-5} \text{ M} \pm 2.27 \times 10^{-3} \text{ M}}{2}$$

$$= 1.10 \times 10^{-3} \text{ M} \quad \text{and} \quad -1.17 \times 10^{-3} \text{ M}$$

We reject the negative root because concentrations are positive quantities. The pH of the solution is

$$pH = -\log[H_3O^+] = -\log(1.10 \times 10^{-3}) = 2.96$$

15-25 The equation is

$$HC_2Cl_3O_2(aq) + H_2O(l) \rightleftharpoons H_3O^+(aq) + C_2Cl_3O_2^-(aq)$$

We can set up a table of initial and equilibrium concentrations.

	$HC_2Cl_3O_2(aq)$	$+ H_2O(l) \rightleftharpoons$	$H_3O^+(aq)$	$+ C_2Cl_3O_2^-(aq)$
initial concentration	0.030 M	—	0	0
equilibrium concentration	$0.030 \text{ M} - [H_3O^+]$	—	$[H_3O^+]$	$[C_2Cl_3O_2^-] = [H_3O^+]$

Substituting the equilibrium concentration expressions in the K_a expression, we have

$$K_a = \frac{[H_3O^+][C_2Cl_3O_2^-]}{[HC_2Cl_3O_2]} = \frac{[H_3O^+]^2}{0.030 \text{ M} - [H_3O^+]} = 2.3 \times 10^{-1} \text{ M}$$

or

$$[H_3O^+]^2 + 2.3 \times 10^{-1} \text{ M } [H_3O^+] - 6.9 \times 10^{-3} \text{ M}^2 = 0$$

The quadratic formula gives

$$[H_3O^+] = \frac{-2.3 \times 10^{-1} \text{ M} \pm \sqrt{5.29 \times 10^{-2} \text{ M}^2 - (4)(1)(-6.9 \times 10^{-3} \text{ M}^2)}}{(2)(1)}$$

$$= \frac{-2.3 \times 10^{-1} \text{ M} \pm 2.8 \times 10^{-1} \text{ M}}{2}$$

$$= 2.5 \times 10^{-2} \text{ M} \quad \text{and} \quad -0.26 \text{ M}$$

We reject the negative root and write

$$pH = -\log[H_3O^+] = -\log(2.5 \times 10^{-2}) = 1.6$$

15-27 We can set up a table of initial and equilibrium concentrations.

	$HO_3SNH_2(aq)$	$+ H_2O(l) \rightleftharpoons$	$H_3O^+(aq)$	$+ O_3SNH_2^-(aq)$
initial concentration	0.040 M	—	0	0
equilibrium concentration	$0.040 \text{ M} - [H_3O^+]$	—	$[H_3O^+]$	$[O_3SNH_2^-] = [H_3O^+]$

Substituting the equilibrium concentration expressions in the K_a expression, we have

$$K_a = \frac{[H_3O^+][O_3SNH_2^-]}{[HO_3SNH_2]} = \frac{[H_3O^+]^2}{0.040 \text{ M} - [H_3O^+]} = 0.10 \text{ M}$$

or

$$[H_3O^+]^2 + 0.10 \text{ M } [H_3O^+] - 0.0040 \text{ M}^2 = 0$$

The quadratic formula gives

$$[H_3O^+] = \frac{-0.10 \text{ M} \pm \sqrt{0.010 \text{ M}^2 - (4)(1)(-0.0040 \text{ M}^2)}}{(2)(1)}$$

$$= \frac{-0.10 \text{ M} \pm 0.16 \text{ M}}{2}$$

$$= 0.03 \text{ M} \quad \text{and} \quad -0.13 \text{ M}$$

We reject the negative root and write

$$pH = -\log[H_3O^+] = -\log(0.03) = 1.5$$

15-29   The equation for the reaction is

$$NH_3(aq) + H_2O(l) \rightleftharpoons NH_4^+(aq) + OH^-(aq)$$

The pOH of the solution is given by

$$pOH = 14.00 - pH = 14.00 - 11.12 = 2.88$$

and the concentration of $OH^-(aq)$ is

$$[OH^-] = 10^{-pOH} = 10^{-2.88} = 1.32 \times 10^{-3} \text{ M}$$

We can set up a table of initial and equilibrium concentrations

	$NH_3(aq)$	$+ H_2O(l) \rightleftharpoons NH_4^+(aq)$	$+ OH^-(aq)$
initial concentration	0.100 M	— $\qquad$ 0	0
equilibrium concentration	0.100 M $-$ [OH$^-$] $=$ 9.9 $\times$ 10^{-2} M	— $\qquad$ [NH$_4^+$] $=$ [OH$^-$] $=$ 1.32 $\times$ 10^{-3} M	[OH$^-$] $=$ 1.32 $\times$ 10^{-3} M

The base protonation constant expression is

$$K_b = \frac{[NH_4^+][OH^-]}{[NH_3]} = \frac{(1.32 \times 10^{-3} \text{ M})(1.32 \times 10^{-3} \text{ M})}{9.9 \times 10^{-2} \text{ M}}$$

$$= 1.8 \times 10^{-5} \text{ M}$$

15-31   The equation is

$$C_5H_5N(aq) + H_2O(l) \rightleftharpoons C_5H_5NH^+(aq) + OH^-(aq)$$

We can set up a table of initial and equilibrium concentrations.

	$C_5H_5N(aq)$	$+ \ H_2O(l) \rightleftharpoons C_5H_5NH^+(aq)$		$+ \ OH^-(aq)$
initial concentration	0.300 M	—	0	0
equilibrium concentration	0.300 M $-$ [OH$^-$]	—	[C$_5$H$_5$NH$^+$] = [OH$^-$]	[OH$^-$]

The expression for K_b is

$$K_b = \frac{[C_5H_5NH^+][OH^-]}{[C_5H_5N]} = \frac{[OH^-]^2}{0.300 \ M - [OH^-]} = 1.46 \times 10^{-9} \ M$$

Because K_b is so small, we expect that [OH$^-$] will be small and thus negligible compared with 0.300 M. The expression for K_b becomes

$$\frac{[OH^-]^2}{0.300 \ M} \approx 1.46 \times 10^{-9} \ M$$

$$[OH^-]^2 \approx 4.38 \times 10^{-10} \ M^2$$

$$[OH^-] \approx 2.09 \times 10^{-5} \ M$$

We can see that [OH$^-$] is much smaller than 0.300 M. The method of successive approximations also confirms this result. The pOH of the solution is given by

$$pOH = -\log[OH^-] = -\log(2.09 \times 10^{-5}) = 4.68$$

and the pH is

$$pH = 14.00 - pOH = 14.00 - 4.68 = 9.32$$

15-33   We can set up a table of initial and equilibrium concentrations.

	$(CH_3)_2NH(aq)$	$+ \ H_2O(l) \rightleftharpoons (CH_3)_2NH_2^+(aq)$		$+ \ OH^-(aq)$
initial concentration	0.060 M	—	0	0
equilibrium concentration	0.060 M $-$ [OH$^-$]	—	[(CH$_3$)$_2$NH$_2^+$] = [OH$^-$]	[OH$^-$]

The expression for K_b is

$$K_b = \frac{[(CH_3)_2NH_2^+][OH^-]}{[(CH_3)_2NH]} = \frac{[OH^-]^2}{0.060\ M - [OH^-]} = 5.81 \times 10^{-4}\ M$$

The value of K_b is not small enough to ignore $[OH^-]$ in the denominator, and so we use the quadratic formula.

$$[OH^-]^2 + 5.81 \times 10^{-4}\ M\ [OH^-] - 3.49 \times 10^{-5}\ M^2 = 0$$

The quadratic formula gives

$$[OH^-] = \frac{-5.81 \times 10^{-4}\ M \pm \sqrt{3.38 \times 10^{-7}\ M^2 - (4)(1)(-3.49 \times 10^{-5}\ M^2)}}{(2)(1)}$$

$$= \frac{-5.81 \times 10^{-4}\ M \pm 1.18 \times 10^{-2}\ M}{2}$$

$$= 5.61 \times 10^{-3}\ M \qquad (\text{and} -0.00619\ M)$$

We could also have used the method of successive approximations. The pOH of the solution is given by

$$pOH = -\log[OH^-] = -\log(5.61 \times 10^{-3}) = 2.25$$

and so the pH is

$$pH = 14.00 - pOH = 14.00 - 2.25 = 11.75$$

15-35 (a) The equilibrium is shifted from right to left.

(b) The equilibrium is shifted from left to right.

(c) The equilibrium is shifted from left to right.

(d) The equilibrium is shifted from left to right, because there are more solute particles on the right than on the left.

15-37 (a) The equilibrium shifts from right to left.

(b) The equilibrium is not affected. Because $\Delta H_{rxn}^\circ \approx 0$, the equilibrium constant does not change with temperature.

(c) The equilibrium shifts from right to left.

(d) The equilibrium shifts from left to right because the added $NH_3(aq)$ reacts with $H_3O^+(aq)$ according to

$$NH_3(aq) + H_3O^+(aq) \rightleftharpoons NH_4^+(aq) + H_2O(l)$$

(e) The equilibrium is shifted from right to left because $[H_3O^+]$ has increased.

15-39 Because oxalic acid is a diprotic acid (Table 15-4), it takes two moles of NaOH to neutralize one mole of oxalic acid. We have

$$\text{moles of OH}^-(aq) = \text{moles of H}_3\text{O}^+(aq)$$

$$\text{moles of NaOH} = \left(\frac{2 \text{ mol NaOH}}{1 \text{ mol oxalic acid}}\right)(\text{moles of oxalic acid})$$

$$M_b V_b = 2M_a V_a$$

$$V_b = \frac{2M_a V_a}{M_b} = \frac{(2)(0.10 \text{ M})(25.0 \text{ mL})}{(0.10 \text{ M})} = 50.0 \text{ mL}$$

15-41 The number of moles of NaOH(aq) used to neutralize the oxalic acid is

$$\text{moles of NaOH} = MV = (0.250 \text{ mol} \cdot \text{L}^{-1})(0.0444 \text{ L}) = 0.0111 \text{ mol}$$

Because oxalic acid is a diprotic acid, it takes two moles of NaOH to neutralize one mole of oxalic acid. Thus the number of moles of oxalic acid is

$$\text{moles of oxalic acid} = \left(\frac{1 \text{ mol oxalic acid}}{2 \text{ mol NaOH}}\right)(0.0111 \text{ mol NaOH})$$
$$= 5.55 \times 10^{-3} \text{ mol}$$

Thus we have the correspondence

$$0.500 \text{ g oxalic acid} \backsimeq 0.00555 \text{ mol oxalic acid}$$

Dividing both sides by 0.00555, we have

$$90.1 \text{ g oxalic acid} \backsimeq \text{one mole of oxalic acid}$$

The molecular mass of oxalic acid is 90.1.

15-43 The reaction is

$$\text{H}_3\text{AsO}_4(aq) + \text{H}_2\text{O}(l) \rightleftharpoons \text{H}_3\text{O}^+(aq) + \text{H}_2\text{AsO}_4^-(aq)$$

The value of K_{a1} is

$$K_{a1} = 10^{-pK_{a1}} = 10^{-2.22} = 6.03 \times 10^{-3} \text{ M}$$

The K_{a1} expression is

$$K_{a1} = \frac{[\text{H}_3\text{O}^+][\text{H}_2\text{AsO}_4^-]}{[\text{H}_3\text{AsO}_4]} = \frac{[\text{H}_3\text{O}^+]^2}{0.100 \text{ M} - [\text{H}_3\text{O}^+]} = 6.03 \times 10^{-3} \text{ M}$$

or

$$[\text{H}_3\text{O}^+]^2 + 6.03 \times 10^{-3} \text{ M } [\text{H}_3\text{O}^+] - 6.03 \times 10^{-4} \text{ M}^2 = 0$$

The quadratic formula gives

$$[H_3O^+] = \frac{-6.03 \times 10^{-3}\ M \pm \sqrt{3.64 \times 10^{-5}\ M^2 - (4)(1)(-6.03 \times 10^{-4}\ M^2)}}{(2)(1)}$$

$$= \frac{-6.03 \times 10^{-3}\ M \pm 4.95 \times 10^{-2}\ M}{2}$$

$$= 2.17 \times 10^{-2}\ M \quad (\text{and} -0.0278\ M)$$

The pH of the solution is

$$pH = -\log[H_3O^+] = -\log(2.17 \times 10^{-2}) = 1.66$$

15-45 (a) $HC_7H_5O_2(aq) + H_2O(l) \rightleftharpoons H_3O^+(aq) + C_7H_5O_2^-(aq)$

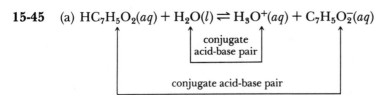

(b) $CH_3NH_2(aq) + H_2O(l) \rightleftharpoons CH_3NH_3^+(aq) + OH^-(aq)$

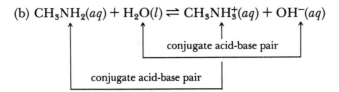

(c) $HCHO_2(aq) + H_2O(l) \rightleftharpoons H_3O^+(aq) + CHO_2^-(aq)$

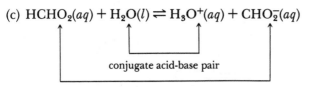

15-47 (a) $ClO^-(aq)$ (b) $NH_3(aq)$

(c) $N_3^-(aq)$ (d) $S^{2-}(aq)$

15-49 (a) Acid; conjugate base is $CNO^-(aq)$.

(b) Base; conjugate acid is $HOBr(aq)$.

(c) Acid; conjugate base is $ClO_3^-(aq)$.

(d) Acid; conjugate base is $CH_3NH_2(aq)$.

(e) Base; conjugate acid is $ClNH_3^+(aq)$.

(f) Base; conjugate acid is $HONH_3^+(aq)$.

15-51 We have that $K_b = \dfrac{K_w}{K_a}$.

(a) $K_b = \dfrac{1.00 \times 10^{-14} \text{ M}^2}{1.34 \times 10^{-5} \text{ M}} = 7.46 \times 10^{-10}$ M for $C_3H_5O_2^-$

(b) $K_b = \dfrac{1.00 \times 10^{-14} \text{ M}^2}{6.76 \times 10^{-4} \text{ M}} = 1.48 \times 10^{-11}$ M for F^-

(c) $K_b = \dfrac{1.00 \times 10^{-14} \text{ M}^2}{5.71 \times 10^{-10} \text{ M}} = 1.75 \times 10^{-5}$ M for NH_3

(d) $K_b = \dfrac{1.00 \times 10^{-14} \text{ M}^2}{6.32 \times 10^{-8} \text{ M}} = 1.58 \times 10^{-7}$ M for HPO_4^{2-}

15-53 (a) The equation is the sum of two equations:

(1) $HCNO(aq) + H_2O(l) \rightleftharpoons H_3O^+(aq) + CNO^-(aq)$

$$K_1 = K_a = 2.19 \times 10^{-4} \text{ M}$$

(2) $NO_2^-(aq) + H_3O^+(aq) \rightleftharpoons HNO_2(aq) + H_2O(l)$

$$K_2 = \frac{1}{K_a} = \frac{1}{4.47 \times 10^{-4} \text{ M}}$$

The equilibrium constant for an equation that is equal to the sum of two other equations is equal to the product of the equilibrium constants for the two equations. Thus

$$K = K_1 K_2 = \frac{2.19 \times 10^{-4} \text{ M}}{4.47 \times 10^{-4} \text{ M}} = 0.490$$

(b) Proceeding as in part (a), we have

(1) $NH_4^+(aq) + H_2O(l) \rightleftharpoons NH_3(aq) + H_3O^+(aq)$

$$K_1 = K_a = 5.71 \times 10^{-10} \text{ M}$$

(2) $HCO_3^-(aq) + H_3O^+(aq) \rightleftharpoons H_2O(l) + H_2CO_3(aq)$

$$K_2 = \frac{1}{K_{a1}} = \frac{1}{4.46 \times 10^{-7} \text{ M}}$$

and thus

$$K = K_1 K_2 = \frac{5.71 \times 10^{-10} \text{ M}}{4.46 \times 10^{-7} \text{ M}} = 1.28 \times 10^{-3}$$

15-55 (a) acidic (acidic cation, neutral anion)

$$Al(H_2O)_6^{3+}(aq) + H_2O(l) \rightleftharpoons Al(OH)(H_2O)_5^{2+}(aq) + H_3O^+(aq)$$

(b) acidic (acidic cation, neutral anion)

$$NH_4^+(aq) + H_2O(l) \rightleftharpoons NH_3(aq) + H_3O^+(aq)$$

(c) basic (neutral cation, basic anion)

$$HCO_3^-(aq) + H_2O(l) \rightleftharpoons H_2CO_3(aq) + OH^-(aq)$$

(d) basic (neutral cation, basic anion)

$$CNO^-(aq) + H_2O(l) \rightleftharpoons HCNO(aq) + OH^-(aq)$$

15-57 (a) neutral cation, basic anion; basic solution

(b) neutral cation, neutral anion; neutral solution

(c) neutral cation, basic anion; basic solution

(d) acidic cation, neutral anion; acidic solution

15-59 The reaction that takes place in producing certain soaps is

$$NaOH(aq) + HC_{18}H_{35}O_2(s) \rightleftharpoons \underset{\text{soap}}{NaC_{18}H_{35}O_2(s)} + H_2O(l)$$

Soap is made up of a neutral cation and a basic anion. The anion is the conjugate base of a weak acid and is a weak base. The soap solution is basic.

15-61 The salt NaClO dissociates completely in water to yield $Na^+(aq)$ and $ClO^-(aq)$. The reaction of the anion with water is

$$ClO^-(aq) + H_2O(l) \rightleftharpoons HClO(aq) + OH^-(aq)$$

The value of the equilibrium constant is $K_b = 3.33 \times 10^{-7}$ M (Table 15-5) We can set up a table of initial and equilibrium concentrations.

	$ClO^-(aq)$	$+$ $H_2O(l)$ $\rightleftharpoons$	$HClO(aq)$	$+$ $OH^-(aq)$
initial concentration	0.030 M	—	0	0
equilibrium concentration	0.030 M − [OH⁻]	—	[HClO] = [OH⁻]	[OH⁻]

The expression for K_b is

$$K_b = \frac{[HClO][OH^-]}{[ClO^-]} = \frac{[OH^-]^2}{0.030 \text{ M} - [OH^-]} = 3.33 \times 10^{-7} \text{ M}$$

We can neglect [OH⁻] relative to 0.050 M because K_b is very small. We have

$$\frac{[OH^-]^2}{0.030 \text{ M}} \approx 3.33 \times 10^{-7} \text{ M}$$

Solving for $[OH^-]$, we have

$$[OH^-] = 9.99 \times 10^{-5} \text{ M}$$

The method of successive approximations yields $[OH^-] = 9.98 \times 10^{-5}$ M, and so

$$[HClO] = 9.98 \times 10^{-5} \text{ M}$$

Using the ion product constant of water, we obtain

$$[H_3O^+] = \frac{1.00 \times 10^{-14} \text{ M}^2}{[OH^-]} = \frac{1.00 \times 10^{-14} \text{ M}^2}{9.98 \times 10^{-5} \text{ M}} = 1.00 \times 10^{-10} \text{ M}$$

The pH of the solution is

$$pH = -\log[H_3O^+] = -\log(1.00 \times 10^{-10}) = 10.00$$

15-63 The equation is

$$CNO^-(aq) + H_2O(l) \rightleftharpoons HCNO(aq) + OH^-(aq)$$

The value of the equilibrium constant is $K_b = 4.57 \times 10^{-11}$ M (Table 15-5) We can set up a table of the initial and equilibrium concentrations.

	$CNO^-(aq)$	$+$ $H_2O(l)$ $\rightleftharpoons$	$HCNO(aq)$	$+$ $OH^-(aq)$
initial concentration	0.20 M	—	0	0
equilibrium concentration	0.20 M $-$ [OH$^-$]	—	[HCNO] = [OH$^-$]	[OH$^-$]

The K_b expression is

$$K_b = \frac{[HCNO][OH^-]}{[CNO^-]} = \frac{[OH^-]^2}{0.20 \text{ M} - [OH^-]} = 4.57 \times 10^{-11} \text{ M}$$

Neglecting $[OH^-]$ with respect to 0.20 M, we have

$$\frac{[OH^-]^2}{0.20 \text{ M}} = 4.57 \times 10^{-11} \text{ M}$$

$$[OH^-] = 3.02 \times 10^{-6} \text{ M}$$

and

$$[HCNO] = 3.02 \times 10^{-6} \text{ M}$$

and

$$[CNO^-] = 0.20 \text{ M} - [OH^-] = 0.20 \text{ M} - 3.02 \times 10^{-6} \text{ M} = 0.20 \text{ M}$$

Using the ion product constant of water, we obtain

$$[H_3O^+] = \frac{1.00 \times 10^{-14} \text{ M}^2}{[OH^-]} = \frac{1.00 \times 10^{-14} \text{ M}^2}{3.02 \times 10^{-6} \text{ M}} = 3.31 \times 10^{-9} \text{ M}$$

$$pH = -\log[H_3O^+] = -\log(3.31 \times 10^{-9}) = 8.48$$

15-65 The equation for the reaction is

$$C_5H_5NH^+(aq) + H_2O(l) \rightleftharpoons H_3O^+(aq) + C_5H_5N(aq)$$

We can set up a table of initial and equilibrium concentrations.

	$C_5H_5NH^+(aq)$	$+ H_2O(l) \rightleftharpoons$	$H_3O^+(aq)$	$+ C_5H_5N(aq)$
initial concentration	0.30 M	—	0	0
equilibrium concentration	0.30 M $- [H_3O^+]$	—	$[H_3O^+]$	$[C_5H_5N] = [H_3O^+]$

The K_a expression is (Table 15-5)

$$K_a = \frac{[H_3O^+][C_5H_5N]}{[C_5H_5NH^+]} = \frac{[H_3O^+]^2}{0.30 \text{ M} - [H_3O^+]} = 6.84 \times 10^{-6} \text{ M}$$

Neglecting $[H_3O^+]$ with respect to 0.30 M, we have

$$\frac{[H_3O^+]^2}{0.30 \text{ M}} = 6.84 \times 10^{-6} \text{ M}$$

$$[H_3O^+] = 1.43 \times 10^{-3} \text{ M}$$

This value of $[H_3O^+]$ is confirmed by successive approximations. The pH of the solution is

$$pH = -\log[H_3O^+] = -\log(1.43 \times 10^{-3}) = 2.84$$

15-67 The number of moles in 23.7 g of NH_4ClO_4 is

$$n = (23.7 \text{ g})\left(\frac{1 \text{ mol}}{117.49 \text{ g}}\right) = 0.202 \text{ mol}$$

The molarity of a saturated $NH_4ClO_4(aq)$ solution is

$$\text{molarity} = \frac{0.202 \text{ mol}}{0.100 \text{ L}} = 2.02 \text{ M}$$

The equation is

$$NH_4^+(aq) + H_2O(l) \rightleftharpoons H_3O^+(aq) + NH_3(aq)$$

We have the following:

	$NH_4^+(aq)$	$+ \ H_2O(l) \ \rightleftharpoons \ H_3O^+(aq)$	$+ \ NH_3(aq)$
initial concentration	2.02 M	— 0	0
equilibrium concentration	$2.02 \text{ M} - [H_3O^+]$	— $[H_3O^+]$	$[NH_3] = [H_3O^+]$

The K_a expression is (Table 15-5)

$$K_a = \frac{[H_3O^+][NH_3]}{[NH_4^+]} = \frac{[H_3O^+]^2}{2.02 \text{ M} - [H_3O^+]} = 5.71 \times 10^{-10} \text{ M}$$

Neglecting $[H_3O^+]$ relative to 2.02 M, we have

$$\frac{[H_3O^+]^2}{2.02 \text{ M}} \approx 5.71 \times 10^{-10} \text{ M}$$

$$[H_3O^+] = 3.40 \times 10^{-5} \text{ M}$$

The pH of the solution is

$$pH = -\log[H_3O^+] = -\log(3.40 \times 10^{-5}) = 4.47$$

15-69   In aqueous solution Fe^{3+} exists as $Fe(H_2O)_6^{3+}(aq)$.

	$Fe(H_2O)_6^{3+}(aq)$	$+ \ H_2O(l) \ \rightleftharpoons \ H_3O^+(aq)$	$+ \ Fe(OH)(H_2O)_5^{2+}(aq)$
initial concentration	0.20 M	— 0	0
equilibrium concentration	$0.20 \text{ M} - [H_3O^+]$	— $[H_3O^+]$	$[Fe(OH)(H_2O)_5^{2+}]$ $= [H_3O^+]$

The K_a expression is

$$K_a = \frac{[H_3O^+][Fe(OH)(H_2O)_5^{2+}]}{[Fe(H_2O)_6^{3+}]} = \frac{[H_3O^+]^2}{0.20\ M - [H_3O^+]} = 1.0 \times 10^{-3}\ M$$

The value of K_a is not small enough to neglect $[H_3O^+]$ in the denominator, and so we use the quadratic equation.

$$[H_3O^+]^2 + 1.0 \times 10^{-3}\ M\ [H_3O^+] - 2.0 \times 10^{-4}\ M^2 = 0$$

The quadratic formula gives

$$[H_3O^+] = \frac{-1.0 \times 10^{-3}\ M \pm \sqrt{1.0 \times 10^{-6}\ M^2 - (4)(1)(-2.0 \times 10^{-4}\ M^2)}}{(2)(1)}$$

$$= \frac{-1.0 \times 10^{-3}\ M \pm 2.8 \times 10^{-2}\ M}{2}$$

$$= 1.35 \times 10^{-2}\ M \qquad (\text{and } -1.45 \times 10^{-2}\ M)$$

The pH of the solution is

$$pH = -\log[H_3O^+] = -\log(1.35 \times 10^{-2}) = 1.87$$

15-71 (a) HCl yields $H^+(aq)$ in aqueous solution and thus is an Arrhenius acid. HCl is a proton donor and thus is a Brönsted-Lowry acid.

(b) $AlCl_3$ yields $H^+(aq)$ in aqueous solution and thus is an Arrhenius acid. $Al(H_2O)_6^{3+}(aq)$ is a proton donor and thus is a Brönsted-Lowry acid. $AlCl_3$ is an electron-deficient species and is a Lewis acid.

(c) BCl_3 is neither an Arrhenius acid nor a Brönsted-Lowry acid. BCl_3 can act as an electron-pair acceptor and hence is a Lewis acid.

15-73 (a) CH_3OCH_3 has two lone pairs of electrons and so can act as an electron-pair donor.

$$H-\overset{\overset{\displaystyle H}{|}}{\underset{\underset{\displaystyle H}{|}}{C}}-\overset{..}{\underset{..}{O}}-\overset{\overset{\displaystyle H}{|}}{\underset{\underset{\displaystyle H}{|}}{C}}-H$$

CH_3OCH_3 is a Lewis base.

(b) $GaCl_3$ is an electron-deficient species and thus is a Lewis acid.

(c) H_2O has two lone pairs of electrons and so can act as an electron-pair donor. H_2O is a Lewis base.

15-75 The acid dissociation constant expression is

$$K_a = \cfrac{[H_3O^+]\left[\begin{array}{c} O^- \\ NO_2 \\ NO_2 \end{array}\right]}{\left[\begin{array}{c} OH \\ NO_2 \\ NO_2 \end{array}\right]} = 1.1 \times 10^{-4}\ M$$

The ratio of the concentrations of the anion to the undissociated acid is

$$\text{ratio} = \cfrac{\left[\begin{array}{c} O^- \\ NO_2 \\ NO_2 \end{array}\right]}{\left[\begin{array}{c} OH \\ NO_2 \\ NO_2 \end{array}\right]} = \frac{K_a}{[H_3O^+]} = \frac{1.1 \times 10^{-4}\ M}{[H_3O^+]}$$

We can find the value of $[H_3O^+]$ from the pH of the solution.

$$[H_3O^+] = 10^{-pH} = 10^{-7.4} = 4.0 \times 10^{-8}\ M$$

The value of the ratio is

$$\text{ratio} = \frac{1.1 \times 10^{-4}\ M}{4.0 \times 10^{-8}\ M} = 2.8 \times 10^3$$

Most of the acid is dissociated at this pH.

15-77   The number of moles of benzoic acid in 6.15 g is

$$n = (6.15\ \text{g})\left(\frac{1\ \text{mol}}{122.12\ \text{g}}\right) = 0.05036\ \text{mol}$$

The molarity of the solution is

$$\text{molarity} = \frac{\text{moles of solute}}{\text{volume of solution}} = \frac{0.05036 \text{ mol}}{0.600 \text{ L}} = 0.0839 \text{ M}$$

We can set up a table of initial and equilibrium concentrations.

	$HC_7H_5O_2(aq)$	$+ H_2O(l) \rightleftharpoons H_3O^+(aq) + C_7H_5O_2^-(aq)$		
initial concentration	0.0839 M	—	0	0
equilibrium concentration	0.0839 M $- [H_3O^+]$	—	$[H_3O^+]$	$[C_7H_5O_2^-] = [H_3O^+]$

Substituting the equilibrium concentration expressions in the K_a expression, we have

$$K_a = \frac{[H_3O^+][C_7H_5O_2^-]}{[HC_7H_5O_2]} = \frac{[H_3O^+]^2}{0.0839 \text{ M} - [H_3O^+]} = 6.46 \times 10^{-5} \text{ M}$$

or

$$[H_3O^+]^2 + 6.46 \times 10^{-5} \text{ M} [H_3O^+] - 5.42 \times 10^{-6} \text{ M}^2 = 0$$

The quadratic formula gives

$$[H_3O^+] = \frac{-6.46 \times 10^{-5} \text{ M} \pm \sqrt{4.17 \times 10^{-9} \text{ M}^2 - (4)(1)(-5.42 \times 10^{-6} \text{ M}^2)}}{(2)(1)}$$

$$= \frac{-6.46 \times 10^{-5} \text{ M} \pm 4.66 \times 10^{-3} \text{ M}}{2}$$

$$= 2.30 \times 10^{-3} \text{ M} \quad (\text{and} -0.00236 \text{ M})$$

and the pH of the solution is

$$pH = -\log[H_3O^+] = -\log(2.30 \times 10^{-3}) = 2.64$$

15-79 The pOH of the solution is given by

$$pOH = 14.00 - pH = 14.00 - 10.52 = 3.48$$

and the value of $[OH^-]$ is given by

$$[OH^-] = 10^{-pOH} = 10^{-3.48} = 3.31 \times 10^{-4} \text{ M}$$

Because one mole of $Mg(OH)_2$ yields two moles of OH^- in water, the concentration of $Mg(OH)_2$ is

$$[Mg(OH)_2] = \tfrac{1}{2}[OH^-] = 1.655 \times 10^{-4} \text{ M}$$

Solubility often is expressed as the number of grams per 100 mL of solution. The number of moles in 100 mL of solution is

$$n = \text{molarity} \times \text{volume} = (1.655 \times 10^{-4} \text{ mol} \cdot L^{-1})(0.100 \text{ L})$$
$$= 1.655 \times 10^{-5} \text{ mol}$$

The mass in 1.655×10^{-5} mol of $Mg(OH)_2$ is

$$\text{mass} = (1.655 \times 10^{-5} \text{ mol})\left(\frac{58.33 \text{ g}}{1 \text{ mol}}\right) = 9.66 \times 10^{-4} \text{ g}$$

The solubility of $Mg(OH)_2$ is 9.66×10^{-4} g per 100 mL of solution.

15-81 The number of moles in two 5-grain aspirin tablets is

$$n = (2)(324 \text{ mg})\left(\frac{1 \text{ g}}{1000 \text{ mg}}\right)\left(\frac{1 \text{ mol}}{180.15 \text{ g}}\right) = 0.00360 \text{ mol}$$

The molarity of the solution is

$$\text{molarity} = \frac{\text{moles of solute}}{\text{volume of solution}} = \frac{0.00360 \text{ mol}}{0.500 \text{ L}} = 0.00720 \text{ M}$$

We can set up a table of initial and equilibrium concentrations.

Acetylsalicylic acid		Acetylsalicylate	
$+ H_2O(l) \rightleftharpoons H_3O^+(aq) +$			
Initial Concentration	0.00720 M	———	0	0
Equilibrium Concentration	0.00720 M $- [H_3O^+]$	———	$[H_3O^+]$	$[H_3O^+]$

Substituting the equilibrium concentration expression in the K_a expression, we have

$$K_a = \frac{[H_3O^+]^2}{0.00720 \text{ M} - [H_3O^+]} = 2.75 \times 10^{-5} \text{ M}$$

Write this equation in the form of a quadratic equation:

$$[H_3O^+]^2 + 2.75 \times 10^{-5} \text{ M } [H_3O^+] - 1.98 \times 10^{-7} \text{ M}^2 = 0$$

The quadratic formula gives

$$[H_3O^+] = \frac{-2.75 \times 10^{-5} \text{ M} \pm \sqrt{7.56 \times 10^{-10} \text{ M}^2 - (4)(1)(-1.98 \times 10^{-7} \text{ M}^2)}}{(2)(1)}$$

$$= \frac{-2.75 \times 10^{-5} \text{ M} \pm 8.90 \times 10^{-4} \text{ M}}{2}$$

$$= 4.31 \times 10^{-4} \text{ M} \quad (\text{and} -4.59 \times 10^{-4} \text{ M})$$

The pH of the solution is

$$\text{pH} = -\log[H_3O^+] = -\log(4.31 \times 10^{-4}) = 3.37$$

15-83   If we take $[H_3O^+] = 2.60 \times 10^{-8}$ M, then we calculate for the pH:

$$\text{pH} = -\log(2.60 \times 10^{-8}) = 7.58$$

But this answer is wrong, because an acidic solution at 25 °C has pH < 7.00. The given concentration of HCl(aq) is so low that we cannot neglect the dissociation of water as an important source of $H_3O^+(aq)$. Thus we have

$$2H_2O(l) \rightleftharpoons H_3O^+(aq) + OH^-(aq)$$

At equilibrium $[H_3O^+] = 2.60 \times 10^{-8}$ M + $[OH^-]$. Using the K_w expression we have

$$K_w = 1.00 \times 10^{-14} \text{ M}^2 = [H_3O^+][OH^-]$$

$$= (2.60 \times 10^{-8} \text{ M} + [OH^-])[OH^-]$$

We have a quadratic equation in $[OH^-]$:

$$[OH^-]^2 + (2.60 \times 10^{-8} \text{ M})[OH^-] - 1.00 \times 10^{-14} \text{ M}^2 = 0$$

and

$$[OH^-] = \frac{-2.60 \times 10^{-8} \text{ M} \pm \sqrt{6.76 \times 10^{-16} \text{ M}^2 + 4.00 \times 10^{-14} \text{ M}^2}}{2}$$

$$= 8.78 \times 10^{-8} \text{ M} \quad (\text{and} -1.13 \times 10^{-7} \text{ M})$$

Thus we have

$$[H_3O^+] = 2.60 \times 10^{-8} \text{ M} + 8.78 \times 10^{-8} \text{ M}$$

$$= 1.13 \times 10^{-7} \text{ M}$$

and

$$pH = -\log(1.13 \times 10^{-7} \text{ M}) = 6.94$$

Note that the pH $<$ 7.00; the solution is acidic.

15-85 Consider this problem by analogy with water, for which we have

$$2H_2O(l) \rightleftharpoons H_3O^+(aq) + OH^-(aq)$$

The strongest acid that can exist in appreciable concentrations in water is $H_3O^+(aq)$, because any stronger acid, for example, HNO_3, will be deprotonated essentially completely by $H_2O(l)$. The strongest base that can exist in appreciable concentrations in water is $OH^-(aq)$, because any stronger base, for example, O^{2-}, will be protonated essentially completely by $H_2O(l)$. Thus, in liquid ammonia, the strongest acid that can exist in appreciable concentrations is $NH_4^+(amm)$, and the strongest base that can exist in appreciable concentrations is $NH_2^-(amm)$. It is of interest to note, for example, that acetic acid is a strong acid in $NH_3(l)$.

15-87 The acid dissociation constant expression for uric acid is

$$\frac{[H_3O^+][\text{urate}^-]}{[\text{uric acid}]} = 1.3 \times 10^{-4} \text{ M}$$

from which we obtain

$$\frac{[\text{urate}^-]}{[\text{uric acid}]} = \frac{1.3 \times 10^{-4} \text{ M}}{[H_3O^+]}$$

Thus [urate$^-$] $>$ [uric acid] if 1.3×10^{-4} M $>$ [H_3O^+] or if

$$pH > -\log(1.3 \times 10^{-4}) = 3.9$$

15-89 The pOH of the solution is given by

$$pOH = 14.00 - pH = 14.00 - 13.50 = 0.50$$

and so

$$[OH^-] = 10^{-pOH} = 10^{-0.50} = 0.32 \text{ M}$$

Because one mole of $Sr(OH)_2$ dissociates and yields two moles of OH^-, the concentration of $Sr(OH)_2$ is

$$[Sr(OH)_2] = \tfrac{1}{2}[OH^-] = 0.16 \text{ M}$$

That is, 0.16 mol of $Sr(OH)_2$ dissolves per 1.00 L of solution. Solubility is often expressed as the number of grams per 100 mL of solution. The number of moles in 100 mL is

$$n = \text{molarity} \times \text{volume} = (0.16 \text{ mol} \cdot \text{L}^{-1})(0.100 \text{ L})$$
$$= 1.6 \times 10^{-2} \text{ mol}$$

The mass corresponding to 1.6×10^{-2} mol of $Sr(OH)_2$ is

$$\text{g } Sr(OH)_2 = (1.6 \times 10^{-2} \text{ mol})\left(\frac{121.64 \text{ g}}{1 \text{ mol}}\right) = 1.9 \text{ g}$$

The solubility of $Sr(OH)_2$ is 1.9 g per 100 mL of solution.

E ANSWERS TO THE SELF-TEST

1 a proton donor

2 a proton acceptor

3 false

4 a hydrated proton and is designated by $H_3O^+(aq)$

5 false (Protons are hydrated in aqueous solution.)

6 false ($[H_3O^+][OH^-] = 1.0 \times 10^{-14} \text{ M}^2$ at 25°C.)

7 false ($[OH^-] = 1.0 \times 10^{-7}$ M in a neutral aqueous solution at 25°C.)

8 $[H_3O^+][OH^-]$

9 $1.00 \times 10^{-14} \text{ M}^2$

10 basic

11 basic

12 false (HBr is completely dissociated.)

13 $K^+(aq)$, $OH^-(aq)$, and $H_3O^+(aq)$

14 RCOOH, where R is a hydrocarbon group such as methyl ($-CH_3$) or ethyl ($-CH_2CH_3$).

15 weak

16 carboxylate ($RCOO^-$)

17 true

18 0.032 M

19 $pH = -\log[H_3O^+]$

20 $[H_3O^+]$, or hydronium ion concentration

21 2.0

22 true

23 false

24 7.0

25 less than 7.0 (at 25°C)

26 greater than 7.0 (at 25°C)

27 partially

28 false

29 false

30 proton-transfer

31 $HF(aq) + H_2O \rightleftharpoons H_3O^+(aq) + F^-(aq)$

32 $\dfrac{[H_3O^+][F^-]}{[HF]}$

33 true

34 $HNO_2(aq)$, $H_3O^+(aq)$, $NO_2^-(aq)$, and $OH^-(aq)$

35 true

36 false

37 $NH_3(aq) + H_2O(l) \rightleftharpoons$
$NH_4^+(aq) + OH^-(aq)$

38 $\dfrac{[NH_4^+][OH^-]}{[NH_3]}$

39 $-\log K_a$

40 smaller

41 $-\log K_b$

42 weaker

43 two

44 three

45 false

46 true

47 $HNO_2(aq) + H_2O(l) \rightleftharpoons H_3O^+(aq) + NO_2^-(aq)$

conjugate acid-base pair

conjugate acid-base pair

48 acid

49 base

50 $C_2H_3O_2^-(aq) + H_2O(l) \rightleftharpoons$
$HC_2H_3O_2(aq) + OH^-(aq)$

51 $NH_4^+(aq) + H_2O(l) \rightleftharpoons$
$H_3O^+(aq) + NH_3(aq)$

52 $\dfrac{K_w}{K_a}$

53 false

54 basic

55 neutral

56 acidic

57 basic

58 acidic

59 an electron-pair acceptor

60 an electron-pair donor

61 acid

62 base

ACIDS AND BASES, II

A   OUTLINE OF CHAPTER 16

16-1   An indicator is a weak organic acid whose color varies with pH.

The acid dissociation equation of an indicator is represented as

$$HIn(aq) + H_2O(l) \rightleftharpoons H_3O^+(aq) + In^-(aq)$$

one color   another color

The acid-dissociation constant expression is

$$K_{ai} = \frac{[H_3O^+][In^-]}{[HIn]} \tag{16-2}$$

$pH \approx pK_{ai}$ at the color transition point.

The colors of some indicators at various pH values are given in Figure 16-2.

16-2   At the equivalence point the number of moles of acid is equal to the number of moles of base.

The titration of an acid with a base involves the addition of the base to a given volume of the acid until all the acid has reacted. (Figure 16-4).

The equivalence point is signaled by the change in color of the indicator added to the acid solution.

The end point of a titration is the point at which the indicator changes color.

The end point is the experimental estimate of the equivalence point.

Calculations of pH for solutions at various stages of titration are presented.

A titration curve of a **strong acid** with a **strong base** is shown in Figure 16-5.

16-3   Weak acids can be titrated with strong bases.

A titration curve of a weak acid with a strong base is shown in Figure 16-6.

The equivalence point in the titration of a weak acid with a strong base occurs at a pH greater than 7.

Calculations of points on a titration curve of a weak acid with a strong base are presented.

16-4   Weak bases can be titrated with strong acids.

A titration curve of a weak base with a strong acid is shown in Figure 16-7.

The equivalence point in the titration of a weak base with a strong acid occurs at a pH less than 7.

Calculations of points on a titration curve of a weak base with a strong acid are presented.

16-5   The pH of a buffer solution can be computed using the Henderson-Hasselbalch equation.

A solution that is resistant to changes in pH upon the addition of an acid or a base is called a buffer.

A solution of a conjugate acid and its conjugate base can act as a buffer.

The pH of a buffer is estimated by the Henderson-Hasselbalch equation:

$$pH \approx pK_a + \log\frac{[\text{base}]_0}{[\text{acid}]_0} \qquad (16\text{-}17)$$

where the subscript zero indicates stoichiometric concentrations.

16-6   A buffer solution suppresses pH changes when acid or base is added.

The capacity of a buffer to resist changes in pH is not unlimited.

Buffers resist changes in pH upon dilution with solvent.

The resistance of a buffer to change in pH is shown in Table 16-2.

Buffers control the pH of blood.

The effective pH range of a buffer is $pH = pK_a \pm 1$.

B   SELF-TEST

1   An indicator is a weak organic _____ that changes color with pH.

2   Indicators come in a variety of colors. *True/False*

3   Indicators can be used to estimate the _____ of a solution from the colors of the indicators.

4   The pH at which an indicator changes color is approximately equal to _____ of the indicator.

5   Methyl orange is red in the acid form and yellow in the base form. Methyl orange is _____ in the pH transition region.

6   The color of litmus paper is _____ in basic solution.

7   Explain how you would use litmus paper to test whether a solution is acidic or basic.

_____

_____ .

8   In a titration of a solution of HCl(aq) with a solution of NaOH(aq), the solution of _____ is added slowly to the solution of _____ .

9   In a titration of a solution of HCl(aq) with a solution of KOH(aq), the titrant is

_____ .

10   The titration curve of a titration of a solution of HCl(aq) with a solution of NaOH(aq) is a plot of _____ versus _____ .

11   The equivalence point of a titration of a solution of HCl(aq) with a solution of NaOH(aq) is the point _____

_____ .

12   The equivalence point of a titration always occurs at pH = 7.0. *True/False*

13   In the titration of a solution of HCl(aq) with a solution of NaOH(aq), phenol-phthalein is added to the solution of HCl(aq) to signal _____ .

14   The end point of a titration is indicated by _____

_____ .

15   In the titration of a solution of HCl(aq) with a solution of NaOH(aq), the pH changes very little around the equivalence point. *True/False*

16   In the titration of a solution of acetic acid, $HC_2H_3O_2(aq)$, with a solution of NaOH(aq), the equivalence point occurs at a pH greater than 7.0. *True/False*

17   Explain why the equivalence point of a titration of a solution of $HC_2H_3O_2(aq)$ with a solution of NaOH(aq) does not occur at pH = 7.0. _____

_____

18 The equilibrium constant for the reaction of a weak acid such as acetic acid with a strong base is very large. *True/False*

19 In the titration of a solution of ammonia, $NH_3(aq)$, with a solution of $HCl(aq)$, the equivalence point occurs at a pH greater than 7.0. *True/False*

20 Explain why the equivalence point of a titration of a solution of $NH_3(aq)$ with a solution of $HCl(aq)$ does not occur at pH $= 7.0$ _____

_____ .

21 A solution that contains a mixture of a weak acid and its conjugate base can be used as a buffer. *True/False*

22 A buffer is resistant to changes in pH upon the addition of an acid but not upon the addition of a base. *True/False*

23 The pH of a buffer can be estimated by using the _____

_____ equation.

24 The Henderson-Hasselbalch equation cannot be used to calculate the pH of a

buffer   when   _____

_____ .

25 The pH of a buffer is resistant to change upon addition of solvent. *True/False*

26 A buffer can resist changes in pH regardless of the amount of acid or base added. *True/False*

27 The pH of a buffer solution *(decreases, increases, remains the same)* when the solution is diluted.

C   CALCULATIONS YOU SHOULD KNOW HOW TO DO

1 Calculate the points on a titration curve of a strong acid with a strong base. See text pages 516 through 518 and Problems 16-9 through 16-16.

2 Calculate certain points on a titration curve of a weak acid with a strong base. You should be able to calculate the initial pH and the pH at the equivalence point. See Section 16-3 and Problems 16-17 through 16-20.

3 Calculate certain points on a titration curve of a weak base with a strong acid. You should be able to calculate the initial pH and the pH at the equivalence point. See Section 16-4 and Problems 16-21, 16-22, 16-27, and 16-28.

4 Determine the molecular mass of an unknown acid or base by titrating to the equivalence point. See Problems 16-23 through 16-26.

5   Estimate the pH of a buffer by using the Henderson-Hasselbalch equation. See Examples 16-9 and 16-10 and Problems 16-29 through 16-36, 16-43, 16-44, 16-47, and 16-48.

6   Use the Henderson-Hasselbalch equation to calculate the pH of a buffer before and after the addition of small amounts of strong acid or base. See Example 16-11 and Problems 16-39 through 16-42, 16-45, and 16-46.

D   SOLUTIONS TO THE ODD-NUMBERED PROBLEMS

16-1   Inspection of Figure 16-2 shows that the pH at which both Nile blue and thymol blue are both blue is about 9.5 ± 0.5.

16-3   From Figure 16-2 we see that the pH at which bromcresol purple is yellow and bromcresol green is green is about 4.5 ± 0.5.

16-5   We see from Figure 16-2 that the middle of the transition color range of bromcresol green is pH = 5. When bromcresol green is added to the medium, a green color indicates that the pH is around 5. When the color changes, the pH is either too high or too low. Methyl red would also be suitable.

16-7   At the middle of the color change the two forms HIn(aq) and In$^-$(aq) are present in equal amounts. At this pH

$$K_{ai} \approx [H_3O^+]$$

In the case of bromcresol green, the middle of the color change occurs at pH ≈ 4.5. The concentration of H_3O^+(aq) is

$$[H_3O^+] = 10^{-pH} = 10^{-4.5} = 3 \times 10^{-5} \text{ M}$$
$$K_{ai} \approx 3 \times 10^{-5} \text{ M}$$

16-9   (a) The net ionic equation for the reaction is

$$H_3O^+(aq) + OH^-(aq) \longrightarrow 2H_2O(l)$$

The millimoles of base available is

$$(25.0 \text{ mL})(0.200 \text{ M}) = 5.00 \text{ mmol}$$

The millimoles of acid added is

$$(20.0 \text{ mL})(0.200 \text{ M}) = 4.00 \text{ mmol}$$

Thus the base is in excess; the excess millimoles of base is

$$(5.00 \text{ mmol}) - (4.00 \text{ mmol}) = 1.00 \text{ mmol}$$

The concentration of $OH^-(aq)$ in the final solution is

$$[OH^-] = \frac{1.00 \text{ mmol}}{(20.0 \text{ mL} + 25.0 \text{ mL})} = 0.0222 \text{ M}$$

The pOH of the solution is

$$pOH = -\log[OH^-] = 1.65$$

The pH of the solution is

$$pH = 14.00 - pOH$$
$$= 14.00 - 1.65 = 12.35$$

(b) Proceeding as in part (a), we have

$$\left(\begin{matrix}\text{mmol of } OH^-(aq) \\ \text{available}\end{matrix}\right) = (30.0 \text{ mL})(0.350 \text{ M}) = 10.50 \text{ mmol}$$

$$\left(\begin{matrix}\text{mmol of } H_3O^+(aq) \\ \text{added}\end{matrix}\right) = (20.0 \text{ mL})(0.200 \text{ M}) = 4.00 \text{ mmol}$$

$$[OH^-] = \frac{(10.50 \text{ mmol} - 4.00 \text{ mmol})}{(20.0 \text{ mL} + 30.0 \text{ mL})} = 0.13 \text{ M}$$

The pOH of the solution is

$$pOH = -\log(0.13) = 0.89$$

The pH of the solution is

$$pH = 14.00 - pOH$$
$$= 14.00 - 0.89 = 13.11$$

16-11 (a) The equivalence point is the point at which the number of moles of base added is equal to the number of moles of acid initially present.

$$\left(\begin{matrix}\text{mmol of } H_3O^+(aq) \\ \text{available}\end{matrix}\right) = (50.0 \text{ mL})(0.200 \text{ M}) = 10.0 \text{ mmol}$$

The volume in milliliters of 0.100 M $NaOH(aq)$ that contains 10.0 mmol of $OH^-(aq)$ is $(MV = n)$

$$(0.100 \text{ M})V = 10.0 \text{ mmol}$$
$$V = 100 \text{ mL}$$

(b) Proceeding as in part (a), we have

$$\left(\begin{matrix}\text{mmol of } H_3O^+(aq) \\ \text{available}\end{matrix}\right) = (30.0 \text{ mL})(0.150 \text{ M}) = 4.50 \text{ mmol}$$

The volume of 0.100 M NaOH(aq) that contains 4.50 mmol is

$$V(0.100 \text{ M}) = 4.50 \text{ mmol}$$
$$V = 45.0 \text{ mL}$$

16-13   The OH$^-$(aq) concentration in a 0.100 M NaOH(aq) solution is

$$[\text{OH}^-] = 0.100 \text{ M}$$

The pOH of the solution is

$$\text{pOH} = -\log[\text{OH}^-] = -\log(0.100) = 1.00$$

and the pH is

$$\text{pH} = 14.00 - \text{pOH} = 13.00$$

Because NaOH is a strong base and HCl is a strong acid, the pH at the equivalence point [50.0 mL of HCl(aq) added] is 7.0. The pH when 100.0 mL of HCl(aq) is added can be obtained by realizing that once the equivalence point is reached, any additional HCl(aq) remains as H_3O^+(aq). Thus when 100.0 mL of HCl(aq) is added there are

$$\text{mol } H_3O^+(aq) = MV_{\text{excess}}$$
$$= (0.10 \text{ mol} \cdot \text{L}^{-1})(0.050 \text{ L})$$
$$= 5.0 \times 10^{-3} \text{ mol}$$

The total volume of the solution is 50.0 mL + 100.0 mL = 150.0 mL, and so $[H_3O^+]$ is given by

$$[\text{H}_3\text{O}^+] = \frac{5.0 \times 10^{-3} \text{ mol}}{0.1500 \text{ L}} = 0.033 \text{ M}$$

The pH is

$$\text{pH} = -\log(0.033) = 1.48$$

The titration curve is shown at the top of page 363.

16-15   At the equivalence point we have the condition

$$\text{moles of acid} = \text{moles of base}$$

or

$$M_a V_a = M_b V_b$$

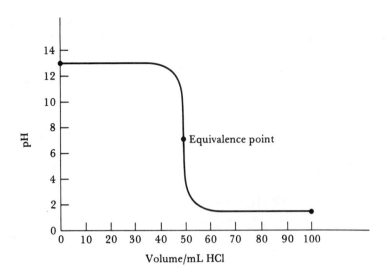

Therefore

$$M_a = \frac{M_b V_b}{V_a} = \frac{(0.165 \text{ M})(35.6 \text{ mL})}{25.0 \text{ mL}} = 0.235 \text{ M}$$

Note that we can use the units mL because the volume units cancel.

16-17 The reaction is

$$\text{HC}_2\text{H}_6\text{AsO}_2(aq) + \text{OH}^-(aq) \rightleftharpoons \text{C}_2\text{H}_6\text{AsO}_2^-(aq) + \text{H}_2\text{O}(l)$$

cacodylic acid   cacodylate

The volume of NaOH(aq) added to reach the equivalence point is given by

$$V_b = \frac{M_a V_a}{M_b} = \frac{(0.100 \text{ M})(25.0 \text{ mL})}{(0.095 \text{ M})} = 26.3 \text{ mL}$$

At the equivalence point

moles of $\text{C}_2\text{H}_6\text{AsO}_2^-$ = initial moles of $\text{HC}_2\text{H}_6\text{AsO}_2$
$$= MV = (0.100 \text{ M})(0.0250 \text{ L}) = 2.50 \times 10^{-3} \text{ mol}$$

The volume of the solution at the equivalence point is 25.0 mL + 26.3 mL = 51.3 mL. The concentration of cacodylate is

$$[\text{C}_2\text{H}_6\text{AsO}_2^-] = \frac{2.50 \times 10^{-3} \text{ mol}}{0.0513 \text{ L}} = 4.87 \times 10^{-2} \text{ M}$$

The cacodylate ion is a weak base because it is the conjugate base of a weak acid. The reaction of the cacodylate ion with water is described by the equation

$$C_2H_6AsO_2^-(aq) + H_2O(l) \rightleftharpoons HC_2H_6AsO_2(aq) + OH^-(aq)$$

The value of K_b is

$$K_b = \frac{K_w}{K_a} = \frac{1.00 \times 10^{-14} \ M^2}{5.4 \times 10^{-7} \ M} = 1.85 \times 10^{-8} \ M$$

At equilibrium we have

$$[HC_2H_6AsO_2] = [OH^-]$$
$$[C_2H_6AsO_2^-] = 4.87 \times 10^{-2} \ M - [OH^-]$$

We shall calculate the value of $[OH^-]$ using the expression for K_b. The expression for K_b is

$$K_b = \frac{[HC_2H_6AsO_2][OH^-]}{[C_2H_6AsO_2^-]} = \frac{[OH^-]^2}{4.87 \times 10^{-2} \ M - [OH^-]} = 1.85 \times 10^{-8} \ M$$

Neglecting $[OH^-]$ compared to 4.87×10^{-2} M, we have

$$\frac{[OH^-]^2}{4.87 \times 10^{-2} \ M} = 1.85 \times 10^{-8} \ M$$
$$[OH^-]^2 = 9.01 \times 10^{-10} \ M^2$$
$$[OH^-] = 3.00 \times 10^{-5} \ M$$

The pOH of the solution is

$$pOH = -\log[OH^-] = -\log(3.00 \times 10^{-5}) = 4.52$$

and the pH is

$$pH = 14.00 - pOH = 14.00 - 4.52 = 9.48$$

Referring to Figure 16-2, we see that thymolphthalein or phenolphthalein is a suitable indicator.

16-19 (a) The reaction equilibrium is

$$HC_2H_3O_2(aq) + H_2O(l) \rightleftharpoons H_3O^+(aq) + C_2H_3O_2^-(aq)$$

The K_a expression is (Table 15-5)

$$K_a = \frac{[H_3O^+][C_2H_3O_2^-]}{[HC_2H_3O_2]} = 1.74 \times 10^{-5} \ M$$

Before any base is added we have

$$[H_3O^+] = [C_2H_3O_2^-]$$

and

$$[HC_2H_3O_2] = 0.200 \text{ M} - [H_3O^+]$$

Substituting these expressions into the K_a expression yields

$$\frac{[H_3O^+]^2}{0.200 \text{ M} - [H_3O^+]} = 1.74 \times 10^{-5} \text{ M}$$

Assuming $[H_3O^+] \ll 0.200$ M yields

$$[H_3O^+] = 1.86 \times 10^{-3} \text{ M}$$

This value is confirmed by the method of successive approximations. The pH of the solution is

$$pH = -\log(1.86 \times 10^{-3}) = 2.73$$

(b) The equation for the reaction is

$$HC_2H_3O_2(aq) + OH^-(aq) \longrightarrow H_2O(l) + C_2H_3O_2^-(aq)$$

The millimoles of base added is

$$\left(\begin{array}{c} \text{mmol } OH^-(aq) \\ \text{added} \end{array}\right) = (5.00 \text{ mL})(0.200 \text{ M}) = 1.00 \text{ mmol}$$

The millimoles of acid available is

$$\left(\begin{array}{c} \text{mmol } HC_2H_3O_2(aq) \\ \text{available} \end{array}\right) = (25.00 \text{ mL})(0.200 \text{ M}) = 5.00 \text{ mmol}$$

The millimoles of $C_2H_3O_2^-(aq)$ is equal to the millimoles of $OH^-(aq)$ added because the acid is in excess. Thus we have for the stoichiometric concentrations

$$[C_2H_3O_2^-]_0 = \frac{1.00 \text{ mmol}}{(25.00 \text{ mL} + 5.00 \text{ mL})} = 0.0333 \text{ M}$$

$$[HC_2H_3O_2]_0 = \frac{(5.00 \text{ mmol} - 1.00 \text{ mmol})}{(25.00 \text{ mL} + 5.00 \text{ mL})} = 0.133 \text{ M}$$

The acid dissociation equilibrium is

$$HC_2H_3O_2(aq) + H_2O(l) \rightleftharpoons H_3O^+(aq) + C_2H_3O_2^-(aq)$$
$$0.133 \text{ M} - [H_3O^+] \qquad\qquad [H_3O^+] \qquad 0.0333 \text{ M} + [H_3O^+]$$

Substituting these values into the K_a expression yields

$$\frac{[H_3O^+](0.0333 \text{ M} + [H_3O^+])}{0.133 \text{ M} - [H_3O^+]} = 1.74 \times 10^{-5} \text{ M}$$

As a first approximation we assume $[H_3O^+]$ is small relative to 0.0333 and 0.133, thus

$$[H_3O^+] \approx \frac{1.74 \times 10^{-5} \text{ M}(0.133 \text{ M})}{(0.0333 \text{ M})}$$
$$\approx 6.95 \times 10^{-5} \text{ M}$$

A second approximation using this value of $[H_3O^+]$ yields

$$[H_3O^+] \approx \frac{(1.74 \times 10^{-5} \text{ M})(0.133 \text{ M} - 6.95 \times 10^{-5} \text{ M})}{(0.0333 \text{ M} + 6.95 \times 10^{-5} \text{ M})}$$
$$\approx 6.93 \times 10^{-5} \text{ M}$$

Successive approximations confirm this value for $[H_3O^+]$. The pH of the solution is

$$pH = -\log[H_3O^+]$$
$$= -\log(6.93 \times 10^{-5}) = 4.16$$

(c) Proceeding as in part (b), we have for the stoichiometric concentrations

$$[C_2H_3O_2^-]_0 = \frac{(12.50 \text{ mL})(0.200 \text{ M})}{(25.00 \text{ mL} + 12.50 \text{ mL})} = 0.0667 \text{ M}$$

$$[HC_2H_3O_2]_0 = \frac{(25.00 \text{ mL})(0.200 \text{ M}) - (12.50 \text{ mL})(0.200 \text{ M})}{(25.00 \text{ mL} + 12.50 \text{ mL})} = 0.0667 \text{ M}$$

Using the K_a expression we have

$$\frac{[H_3O^+][C_2H_3O_2^-]}{[HC_2H_3O_2]} = \frac{[H_3O^+](0.0667 \text{ M} + [H_3O^+])}{0.0667 \text{ M} - [H_3O^+]} = 1.74 \times 10^{-5} \text{ M}$$

As a first approximation we assume $[H_3O^+]$ is small relative to 0.0667 M; thus

$$[H_3O^+] \approx 1.74 \times 10^{-5} \text{ M}$$

Successive approximations confirm this value of $[H_3O^+]$. The pH of the solution is

$$pH = -\log[H_3O^+] = -\log(1.74 \times 10^{-5}) = 4.76$$

(d) The millimoles of base added is

$$(25.00 \text{ mL})(0.200 \text{ M}) = 5.00 \text{ mmol}$$

which is equal to the millimoles of acid originally present; thus the solution is at the equivalence point. The stoichiometric concentration of acetate ion at the equivalence point is equal to the original millimoles of $HC_2H_3O_2(aq)$ divided by the total solution volume

$$[C_2H_3O_2^-]_0 = \frac{5.00 \text{ mmol}}{50.00 \text{ mL}} = 0.100 \text{ M}$$

At the equivalence point we have a 0.100 M solution of $NaC_2H_3O_2(aq)$. The relevant equilibrium is the $C_2H_3O_2^-(aq)$ protonation reaction

$$C_2H_3O_2^-(aq) + H_2O(l) \rightleftharpoons HC_2H_3O_2(aq) + OH^-(aq)$$

The value of K_b is (Table 15-5)

$$K_b = \frac{[HC_2H_3O_2][OH^-]}{[C_2H_3O_2^-]} = 5.75 \times 10^{-10} \text{ M}$$

At equilibrium we have from the equation stoichiometry

$$[HC_2H_3O_2] = [OH^-]$$

and

$$[C_2H_3O_2^-] = 0.100 \text{ M} - [OH^-]$$

Substituting these expressions into the K_b expression yields

$$\frac{[OH^-]^2}{0.100 \text{ M} - [OH^-]} = 5.75 \times 10^{-10} \text{ M}$$

Neglecting $[OH^-]$ relative to 0.100 M yields

$$[OH^-]^2 = 5.75 \times 10^{-11} \text{ M}^2$$

and

$$[OH^-] = 7.58 \times 10^{-6} \text{ M}$$

The pOH is

$$pOH = -\log(7.58 \times 10^{-6}) = 5.12$$

and the pH is

$$pH = 14.00 - pOH = 14.00 - 5.12 = 8.88$$

(e) In this case, the solution is beyond the equivalence point [see part (d)]. The stoichiometric concentration of $C_2H_3O_2^-(aq)$ is

$$[C_2H_3O_2^-]_0 = \frac{(25.00 \text{ mL})(0.200 \text{ M})}{(25.00 \text{ mL} + 26.00 \text{ mL})}$$
$$= 0.0980 \text{ M}$$

The stoichiometric concentration of $OH^-(aq)$ is equal to

$$[OH^-]_0 = \frac{(\text{total mmol base added}) - (\text{total mmol acid initially})}{\text{total volume}}$$
$$= \frac{(26.00 \text{ mL})(0.200 \text{ M}) - (25.00 \text{ mL})(0.200 \text{ M})}{(51.00 \text{ mL})}$$
$$= 0.00392 \text{ M}$$

The equilibrium is

$$C_2H_3O_2^-(aq) \quad + \quad H_2O(l) \rightleftharpoons HC_2H_3O_2(aq) \quad + \quad OH^-(aq)$$
$$\text{0.0980 M} - [HC_2H_3O_2] \qquad\qquad\qquad [HC_2H_3O_2] \quad \text{0.00392 M} + [HC_2H_3O_2]$$

Using the K_b expression we have

$$\frac{[HC_2H_3O_2](0.00392 \text{ M} + [HC_2H_3O_2])}{(0.0980 \text{ M} - [HC_2H_3O_2])} = 5.75 \times 10^{-10} \text{ M}$$

Neglecting $[HC_2H_3O_2]$ relative to 0.00392 and 0.0980 yields

$$[HC_2H_3O_2] \approx \frac{5.75 \times 10^{-10} \text{ M}(0.0980 \text{ M})}{(0.00392 \text{ M})}$$
$$= 1.44 \times 10^{-8} \text{ M}$$

Thus we have

$$[OH^-] = 0.00392 \text{ M} + 1.44 \times 10^{-8} \text{ M} = 0.00392 \text{ M}$$

The pOH of the solution is

$$pOH = -\log(0.00392) = 2.41$$

The pH of the solution is

$$pH = 14.00 - 2.41 = 11.59$$

16-21   (a) Before any $HBr(aq)$ is added we have a 0.150 M solution of pyridine.

$$C_5H_5N(aq) + H_2O(l) \rightleftharpoons C_5H_5NH^+(aq) + OH^-(aq)$$

The K_b expression is (Table 15-5)

$$K_b = \frac{[C_5H_5NH^+][OH^-]}{[C_5H_5N]} = 1.46 \times 10^{-9} \text{ M}$$

At equilibrium we have, from the reaction stoichiometry,

$$[C_5H_5NH^+] = [OH^-]$$
$$[C_5H_5N] = 0.150 \text{ M} - [OH^-]$$

Substituting these expressions into the K_b expression yields

$$\frac{[OH^-]^2}{0.150 \text{ M} - [OH^-]} = 1.46 \times 10^{-9} \text{ M}$$

Assuming $[OH^-] \ll 0.150$ M we have

$$[OH^-]^2 \approx (1.46 \times 10^{-9} \text{ M})(0.150 \text{ M})$$

and

$$[OH^-] \approx 1.48 \times 10^{-5} \text{ M}$$

The pOH is

$$pOH = -\log[OH^-]$$
$$= -\log(1.48 \times 10^{-5}) = 4.83$$

and the pH is

$$pH = 14.00 - pOH = 14.00 - 4.83 = 9.17$$

(b) The equation for the reaction that occurs is

$$C_5H_5N(aq) + H_3O^+(aq) \longrightarrow C_5H_5NH^+(aq) + H_2O(l)$$

After the addition of 10.0 mL of 0.150 M HBr we have the following stoichiometric concentrations.

$$[C_5H_5NH^+]_0 = \frac{(10.0 \text{ mL})(0.150 \text{ M})}{25.0 \text{ mL} + 10.0 \text{ mL}} = 0.0429 \text{ M}$$

$$[C_5H_5N]_0 = \frac{(25.0 \text{ mL})(0.150 \text{ M}) - (10.0 \text{ mL})(0.150 \text{ M})}{(25.0 \text{ mL} + 10.0 \text{ mL})} = 0.0643 \text{ M}$$

Thus we have at equilibrium

$$\begin{array}{ccccc} C_5H_5N(aq) & + H_2O(l) \rightleftharpoons & C_5H_5NH^+(aq) & + OH^-(aq) \\ 0.0643 \text{ M} - [OH^-] & & 0.0429 \text{ M} + [OH^-] & [OH^-] \end{array}$$

and

$$K_b = \frac{[OH^-](0.0429 \text{ M} + [OH^-])}{0.0643 \text{ M} - [OH^-]} = 1.46 \times 10^{-9} \text{ M}$$

Assuming $[OH^-] \ll 0.0429$ or 0.0643 yields

$$[OH^-] \approx \frac{(1.46 \times 10^{-9} \text{ M})(0.0643 \text{ M})}{(0.0429 \text{ M})} = 2.19 \times 10^{-9} \text{ M}$$

This result for $[OH^-]$ confirms the above assumption. The pOH of the solution is

$$pOH = -\log[OH^-] = -\log(2.19 \times 10^{-9}) = 8.66$$

and the pH is

$$pH = 14.00 - pOH = 14.00 - 8.66 = 5.34$$

(c) The problem is similar to part (b), thus

$$[C_5H_5NH^+]_0 = \frac{(24.0 \text{ mL})(0.150 \text{ M})}{(25.0 \text{ mL} + 24.0 \text{ mL})} = 0.0735 \text{ M}$$

and

$$[C_5H_5N]_0 = \frac{(25.0 \text{ mL})(0.150 \text{ M}) - (24.0 \text{ mL})(0.150 \text{ M})}{(25.0 \text{ mL} + 24.0 \text{ mL})} = 0.00306 \text{ M}$$

The K_b expression is

$$K_b = \frac{[OH^-](0.0735 \text{ M} + [OH^-])}{0.00306 \text{ M} - [OH^-]} = 1.46 \times 10^{-9} \text{ M}$$

Assuming $[OH^-] \ll 0.00306$ M or 0.0735 M we have

$$[OH^-] \approx \frac{(1.46 \times 10^{-9} \text{ M})(3.06 \times 10^{-3} \text{ M})}{(7.35 \times 10^{-2} \text{ M})}$$
$$\approx 6.08 \times 10^{-11} \text{ M}$$

The pH of the solution is

$$pH = 14.00 - pOH = 14.00 + \log(6.08 \times 10^{-11}) = 3.78$$

(d) The millimoles of HBr(aq) added is

$$(25.0 \text{ mL})(0.150 \text{ M}) = 3.75 \text{ mmol}$$

The total millimoles of C_5H_5N available initially is

$$(25.0 \text{ mL})(0.150 \text{ M}) = 3.75 \text{ mmol}$$

Thus the resulting solution is at the equivalence point. The solution consists of $C_5H_5NH^+Br^-$. The stoichiometric concentration of $C_5H_5NH^+$ is

$$[C_5H_5NH^+]_0 = \frac{3.75 \text{ mmol}}{50.0 \text{ mL}} = 0.0750 \text{ M}$$

At equilibrium we have

$$C_5H_5NH^+(aq) + H_2O(l) \rightleftharpoons C_5H_5N(aq) + H_3O^+(aq)$$
$$0.0750 \text{ M} - [H_3O^+] \qquad\qquad [H_3O^+] \qquad [H_3O^+]$$

Substitution of these values into the K_a expression (Table 15-5) yields

$$K_a = \frac{[C_5H_5N][H_3O^+]}{[C_5H_5NH^+]} = \frac{[H_3O^+]^2}{0.0750 \text{ M} - [H_3O^+]} = 6.84 \times 10^{-6} \text{ M}$$

Assuming that $[H_3O^+] \ll 0.0750$ M we have

$$[H_3O^+]^2 \approx (6.84 \times 10^{-6} \text{ M})(0.0750 \text{ M})$$

and

$$[H_3O^+] = 7.16 \times 10^{-4} \text{ M}$$

Successive approximations yields 7.13×10^{-4} M.
The pH of the solution is

$$pH = -\log[H_3O^+] = -\log(7.13 \times 10^{-4}) = 3.15$$

(e) The resulting solution is beyond the equivalence point [see part (d)]. The stoichiometric concentrations are

$$[C_5H_5NH^+]_0 = \frac{(25.0 \text{ mL})(0.150 \text{ M})}{(25.0 \text{ mL} + 26.0 \text{ mL})} = 0.0735 \text{ M}$$

$$[H_3O^+]_0 = \frac{(26.0 \text{ mL})(0.150 \text{ M}) - (25.0 \text{ mL})(0.150 \text{ M})}{(25.0 \text{ mL} + 26.0 \text{ mL})} = 0.00294 \text{ M}$$

Thus we have

$$C_5H_5NH^+(aq) + H_2O(l) \rightleftharpoons C_5H_5N(aq) + H_3O^+(aq)$$
$$0.0735 \text{ M} - [C_5H_5N] \qquad\qquad [C_5H_5N] \qquad 0.00294 \text{ M} + [C_5H_5N]$$

Substitution of these values into the K_a expression yields

$$\frac{[H_3O^+][C_5H_5N]}{[C_5H_5NH^+]} = \frac{(0.00294 \text{ M} + [C_5H_5N])[C_5H_5N]}{0.0735 \text{ M} - [C_5H_5N]} = 6.84 \times 10^{-6} \text{ M}$$

Assuming $[C_5H_5N] \ll 0.00294$ M or 0.0735 M we obtain

$$[C_5H_5N] \approx \frac{(6.84 \times 10^{-6} \text{ M})(0.0735 \text{ M})}{(0.00294 \text{ M})}$$
$$\approx 1.71 \times 10^{-4} \text{ M}$$

Because this value of $[C_5H_5N]$ is not small compared to 0.00294 M, we use the method of successive approximations. Thus

$$[C_5H_5N] \approx \frac{(6.84 \times 10^{-6} \text{ M})(0.0735 \text{ M} - 1.71 \times 10^{-4} \text{ M})}{(0.00294 \text{ M} + 1.71 \times 10^{-4} \text{ M})}$$
$$\approx 1.61 \times 10^{-4} \text{ M}$$

The next approximation is

$$[C_5H_5N] \approx \frac{(6.84 \times 10^{-6} \text{ M})(0.0735 \text{ M} - 1.61 \times 10^{-4} \text{ M})}{(0.00294 \text{ M} + 1.61 \times 10^{-4} \text{ M})}$$
$$\approx 1.62 \times 10^{-4} \text{ M}$$

Further approximations confirm this value of $[C_5H_5N]$; thus we have

$$[H_3O^+] = 0.00294 \text{ M} + 1.62 \times 10^{-4} \text{ M} = 0.00310 \text{ M}$$

The pH of the solution is

$$pH = -\log[H_3O^+] = -\log(0.00310) = 2.51$$

16-23 At the equivalence point

$$\text{moles of acid} = \text{moles of base added}$$

The number of moles of acid is given by

$$\text{moles of acid} = M_b V_b = (0.250 \text{ mol} \cdot \text{L}^{-1})(0.0341 \text{ L})$$
$$= 0.00853 \text{ mol}$$

We have the correspondence

$$1.50 \text{ g ascorbic acid} \backsimeq 0.00853 \text{ mol ascorbic acid}$$

Dividing by 0.00853, we have

$$176 \text{ g ascorbic acid} \leftrightharpoons \text{one mole ascorbic acid}$$

Thus the molecular mass of ascorbic acid, Vitamin C, is 176.

16-25   At the equivalence point

$$\text{moles of acid} = \text{moles of base}$$

The concentration of acetic acid in the vinegar solution is given by

$$M_a = \frac{M_b V_b}{V_a} = \frac{(0.400 \text{ M})(38.5 \text{ mL})}{(21.0 \text{ mL})} = 0.733 \text{ M}$$

We now calculate the mass percentage of the acetic acid. For convenience, consider a 100-mL sample of vinegar. The number of moles of acetic acid in 100 mL of vinegar is

$$n = MV = (0.733 \text{ mol} \cdot \text{L}^{-1})(0.100 \text{ L}) = 0.0733 \text{ mol}$$

The mass of acetic acid in 100 mL of vinegar is

$$\text{g HC}_2\text{H}_3\text{O}_2 = (0.0733 \text{ mol}) \left(\frac{60.05 \text{ g HC}_2\text{H}_3\text{O}_2}{1 \text{ mol HC}_2\text{H}_3\text{O}_2} \right) = 4.40 \text{ g}$$

The mass of 100 mL of vinegar solution is

$$\text{mass of vinegar} = dV = (1.060 \text{ g} \cdot \text{mL}^{-1})(100 \text{ mL}) = 106.0 \text{ g}$$

The mass percentage of acetic acid is

$$\text{mass \%} = \frac{\text{mass of acetic acid}}{\text{mass of vinegar solution}} \times 100$$

$$= \frac{4.40 \text{ g}}{106.0 \text{ g}} \times 100 = 4.15\%$$

16-27   The titration reaction is

$$\text{NH}_3(aq) + \text{H}_3\text{O}^+(aq) \longrightarrow \text{NH}_4^+(aq) + \text{H}_2\text{O}(l)$$

The volume of acid required to reach the equivalence point is calculated as follows

$$M_a V_a = M_b V_b$$

$$V_a = \frac{(0.125 \text{ M})(50.0 \text{ mL})}{(0.175 \text{ M})} = 35.7 \text{ mL}$$

The total volume at the equivalence point is

$$50.0 \text{ mL} + 35.7 \text{ mL} = 85.7 \text{ mL}$$

The stoichiometric concentration of $NH_4^+(aq)$ at the equivalence point is

$$[NH_4^+]_0 = \frac{(50.0 \text{ mL})(0.125 \text{ M})}{(85.7 \text{ mL})} = 0.0729 \text{ M}$$

The reaction equilibrium at the equivalence point is

$$\underset{0.0729 \text{ M} - [H_3O^+]}{NH_4^+(aq)} + H_2O(l) \rightleftharpoons \underset{[H_3O^+]}{NH_3(aq)} + \underset{[H_3O^+]}{H_3O^+(aq)}$$

Substitution of these values into the K_a expression (Table 15-5) yields

$$K_a = \frac{[H_3O^+][NH_3]}{[NH_4^+]} = \frac{[H_3O^+]^2}{0.0729 \text{ M} - [H_3O^+]} = 5.71 \times 10^{-10} \text{ M}$$

Assuming $[H_3O^+] \ll 0.0729$ M yields

$$[H_3O^+]^2 \approx (5.71 \times 10^{-10} \text{ M})(0.0729 \text{ M})$$

and

$$[H_3O^+] \approx 6.45 \times 10^{-6} \text{ M}$$

The pH of the solution is

$$pH = -\log[H_3O^+] = -\log(6.45 \times 10^{-6}) = 5.19$$

16-29 We first identify the acid and the base:

acid: $HC_2H_3O_2(aq)$ base: $C_2H_3O_2^-(aq)$ (from $NaC_2H_3O_2(aq)$)

The stoichiometric concentrations of the acid and base forms are

$$[acid]_0 = 0.050 \text{ M} \qquad [base]_0 = 0.050 \text{ M}$$

The pK_a of acetic acid is

$$pK_a = -\log K_a = -\log(1.74 \times 10^{-5}) = 4.76$$

From the Henderson-Hasselbalch equation we have

$$pH = pK_a + \log \frac{[base]_0}{[acid]_0} = 4.76 + \log \left(\frac{0.050 \text{ M}}{0.050 \text{ M}} \right)$$
$$= 4.76 + 0.00 = 4.76$$

16-31 The stoichiometric concentrations of the acid and base forms are

$$[acid]_0 = [HCHO_2]_0 = 0.15 \text{ M}$$
$$[base]_0 = [CHO_2^-]_0 = 0.25 \text{ M}$$

The pK_a of formic acid is

$$pK_a = -\log K_a = -\log(1.78 \times 10^{-4}) = 3.75$$

From the Henderson-Hasselbalch equation we have

$$pH = pK_a + \log \frac{[\text{base}]_0}{[\text{acid}]_0} = 3.75 + \log\left(\frac{0.25 \text{ M}}{0.15 \text{ M}}\right)$$
$$= 3.75 + 0.22 = 3.97$$

16-33 The stoichiometric concentrations of the acid and base forms are

$$[\text{acid}]_0 = [C_5H_5NH^+]_0 = 0.250 \text{ M} \qquad [\text{base}]_0 = [C_5H_5N]_0 = 0.200 \text{ M}$$

The pK_a of pyridinium chloride is given

$$pK_a = -\log(6.84 \times 10^{-6}) = 5.16$$

From the Henderson-Hasselbalch equation we have

$$pH = pK_a + \log \frac{[\text{base}]_0}{[\text{acid}]_0} = 5.16 + \log\left(\frac{0.200 \text{ M}}{0.250 \text{ M}}\right)$$
$$= 5.16 - 0.097 = 5.06$$

16-35 We shall estimate the pH of the solution by using the Henderson-Hasselbalch equation.

$$pH = pK_a + \log \frac{[\text{base}]_0}{[\text{acid}]_0}$$

The equation in each case is

$$H_2PO_4^-(aq) + H_2O(l) \rightleftharpoons H_3O^+(aq) + HPO_4^{2-}(aq)$$

Thus we see that $H_2PO_4^-(aq)$ is the conjugate acid and $HPO_4^{2-}(aq)$ is the conjugate base. The value of pK_a for $H_2PO_4^-$ is

$$pK_a = -\log K_a = -\log(6.32 \times 10^{-8}) = 7.20$$

We can now do each part in turn:

(a) $[\text{acid}]_0 = 0.050 \text{ M} \qquad [\text{base}]_0 = 0.050 \text{ M}$

$$pH = 7.20 + \log\left(\frac{0.050 \text{ M}}{0.050 \text{ M}}\right) = 7.20 + 0.00 = 7.20$$

(b) $[\text{acid}]_0 = 0.050 \text{ M} \qquad [\text{base}]_0 = 0.10 \text{ M}$

$$pH = 7.20 + \log\left(\frac{0.10 \text{ M}}{0.050 \text{ M}}\right) = 7.20 + 0.30 = 7.50$$

(c) $[\text{acid}]_0 = 0.10$ M $\qquad$ $[\text{base}]_0 = 0.050$ M

$$pH = 7.20 + \log\left(\frac{0.050\ \text{M}}{0.10\ \text{M}}\right) = 7.20 - 0.30 = 6.90$$

16-37 If we use equal concentrations of conjugate acid and base, then

$$pH = pK_a + \log\frac{[\text{base}]_0}{[\text{acid}]_0}$$
$$= pK_a$$

To obtain a pH buffered at 3.70, we want $pK_a \approx 3.70$. From Table 15-5 we find that $pK_a = 3.75$ for formic acid, and so a solution of equal concentrations of $HCHO_2(aq)$ and $NaCHO_2(aq)$ would act as a buffer at pH = 3.70.

16-39 The number of moles in 1.00 g of KOH is

$$n = (1.00\ \text{g})\left(\frac{1\ \text{mol KOH}}{56.11\ \text{g KOH}}\right) = 0.0178\ \text{mol}$$

The $OH^-(aq)$ reacts with $NH_4^+(aq)$ in the buffer via the reaction

$$NH_4^+(aq) + OH^-(aq) \longrightarrow NH_3(aq) + H_2O(l)$$

(a) The number of moles of ammonium ion in the buffer solution before adding KOH is

$$\text{moles of } NH_4^+ = MV = (0.10\ \text{mol}\cdot\text{L}^{-1})(0.500\ \text{L}) = 0.050\ \text{mol}$$

The number of moles of NH_4^+ after the addition of 0.0178 mol of KOH is

$$\text{moles of } NH_4^+ = \text{moles of } NH_4^+ \text{ before} - \text{moles of } OH^- \text{ added}$$
$$= 0.050\ \text{mol} - 0.0178\ \text{mol} = 0.032\ \text{mol}$$

The number of moles of ammonia in the buffer solution before adding KOH is

$$\text{moles of } NH_3 = MV = (0.10\ \text{M})(0.500\ \text{L}) = 0.050\ \text{mol}$$

The number of moles of NH_3 after the addition of 0.0178 mol of KOH is

$$\text{moles of } NH_3 = \text{moles of } NH_3 \text{ before} + \text{moles of } OH^- \text{ added}$$
$$= 0.050\ \text{mol} + 0.0178\ \text{mol} = 0.068\ \text{mol}$$

The initial pH of the buffer is

$$pH = pK_a + \log\frac{[\text{base}]_0}{[\text{acid}]_0} = 9.24 + \log\left(\frac{0.10\ \text{M}}{0.10\ \text{M}}\right) = 9.24$$

The final pH of the buffer is

$$pH = pK_a + \log \frac{[\text{base}]_0}{[\text{acid}]_0} = 9.24 + \log\left(\frac{0.068 \text{ mol}}{0.032 \text{ mol}}\right) = 9.57$$

The change in pH is $9.57 - 9.24 = 0.33$.

(b) The number of moles of ammonium ion in the buffer solution before adding KOH is

$$\text{moles of NH}_4^+ = MV = (1.00 \text{ mol} \cdot \text{L}^{-1})(0.500 \text{ L}) = 0.500 \text{ mol}$$

The number of moles of $NH_4^+(aq)$ after the addition of 0.0178 mol of KOH is

$$\text{moles of NH}_4^+ = \text{moles of NH}_4^+ \text{ before} - \text{moles of OH}^- \text{ added}$$
$$= 0.500 \text{ mol} - 0.0178 \text{ mol} = 0.482 \text{ mol}$$

The number of moles of ammonia in the buffer solution before adding KOH is

$$\text{moles of NH}_3 = MV = (1.00 \text{ mol} \cdot \text{L}^{-1})(0.500 \text{ L}) = 0.500 \text{ mol}$$

The number of moles of $NH_3(aq)$ after the addition of 0.0178 mol of KOH is

$$\text{moles of NH}_3 = \text{moles of NH}_3 \text{ before} + \text{moles of KOH added}$$
$$= 0.500 \text{ mol} + 0.0178 \text{ mol} = 0.518 \text{ mol}$$

The final pH of the buffer is

$$pH = pK_a + \log \frac{[\text{base}]_0}{[\text{acid}]_0} = 9.24 + \log\left(\frac{0.518 \text{ mol}}{0.482 \text{ mol}}\right) = 9.27$$

The change in pH is $9.27 - 9.24 = 0.03$. The pH change in the more concentrated buffer solution is much less than the pH change in the more dilute buffer solution.

16-41 The buffer equilibrium is

$$HC_3H_5O_2(aq) + H_2O(l) \rightleftharpoons H_3O^+(aq) + C_3H_5O_2^-(aq)$$

The pH before addition of the HCl is calculated by using the Henderson-Hasselbalch equation.

$$pH \approx pK_a + \log \frac{[\text{base}]_0}{[\text{acid}]_0}$$
$$\approx -\log(1.30 \times 10^{-5}) + \log\left(\frac{0.0150 \text{ M}}{0.0200 \text{ M}}\right)$$
$$\approx 4.89 - 0.12 = 4.77$$

The equation for the reaction upon addition of acid is

$$C_3H_5O_2^-(aq) + H_3O^+(aq) \rightleftharpoons HC_3H_5O_2(aq) + H_2O(l)$$

The pH after the addition of 2.0 mmol of HCl is computed as follows.

$$\text{mmol of acid} = (1000 \text{ mL})(0.0200 \text{ M}) + 2.0 \text{ mmol} = 22.0 \text{ mmol}$$
$$\text{mmol of base} = (1000 \text{ mL})(0.0150 \text{ M}) - 2.0 \text{ mmol} = 13.0 \text{ mmol}$$

Thus the pH is

$$pH \approx 4.87 + \log\left[\frac{(13.0 \text{ mmol}/V)}{(22.0 \text{ mmol}/V)}\right]$$
$$\approx 4.89 - 0.23 = 4.66$$

and the change in pH is

$$\Delta(pH) = 4.66 - 4.77 = -0.11$$

16-43   The total initial number of moles of acid is

$$\left(\begin{array}{c}\text{mol acid}\\\text{available}\end{array}\right) = (2.16 \text{ g})\left(\frac{1 \text{ mol } HC_3H_5O_2}{74.08 \text{ g } HC_3H_5O_2}\right) = 0.0292 \text{ mol}$$

The number of moles of base added is

$$\left(\begin{array}{c}\text{mol base}\\\text{added}\end{array}\right) = (0.56 \text{ g})\left(\frac{1 \text{ mol NaOH}}{40.0 \text{ g NaOH}}\right) = 0.014 \text{ mol}$$

The NaOH reacts with the propionic acid to produce sodium propionate, $NaC_3H_5O_2$; thus the stoichiometric concentrations of propionic acid and propionate ion are as follows.

$$[HC_3H_5O_2]_0 = \frac{0.0292 \text{ mol} - 0.014 \text{ mol}}{0.100 \text{ L}} = 0.152 \text{ M}$$

$$[C_3H_5O_2^-]_0 = \frac{0.014 \text{ mol}}{0.100 \text{ L}} = 0.14 \text{ M}$$

The pH of the resulting buffer is calculated by using the Henderson-Hasselbalch equation.

$$pH \approx pK_a + \log\frac{[\text{base}]_0}{[\text{acid}]_0}$$
$$\approx 4.89 + \log\left(\frac{0.14 \text{ M}}{0.152 \text{ M}}\right) = 4.85$$

16-45 The equation for the reaction is

$$HC_2H_3O_2(aq) + OH^-(aq) \longrightarrow C_2H_3O_2^-(aq) + H_2O(l)$$

Because $OH^-(aq)$ is a strong base, this reaction goes essentially to completion. The number of millimoles of $HC_2H_2O_2(aq)$ initially is

$$n = MV = (0.050 \text{ M})(100 \text{ mL}) = 5.0 \text{ mmol}$$

The volume of 0.10 M $NaOH(aq)$ that contains 5.0 mmol is

$$5.0 \text{ mmol} = (0.10 \text{ M})V$$

or

$$V = \frac{5.0 \text{ mmol}}{0.10 \text{ M}} = 50 \text{ mL}$$

Thus the buffering capacity of the buffer solution is lost when 50 mL of 0.10 M $NaOH(aq)$ is added.

16-47 For $NH_4^+(aq)$, $pK_a = 9.24$ (Table 15-5). Using the Henderson-Hasselbalch equation,

$$pH \approx pK_a + \log \frac{[\text{base}]_0}{[\text{acid}]_0}$$

we have

$$\log \frac{[\text{base}]_0}{[\text{acid}]_0} = 9.50 - 9.24 = 0.26$$

But

$$[\text{base}]_0 = [NH_3]_0 \quad \text{and} \quad [\text{acid}]_0 = [NH_4^+]_0$$

thus

$$\frac{[NH_3]_0}{[NH_4^+]_0} = 10^{0.26} = 1.82$$

and

$$[NH_4^+]_0 = \frac{[NH_3]_0}{1.82} = \frac{0.200 \text{ M}}{1.82} = 0.110 \text{ M}$$

The number of moles of NH_4Cl required is

$$n = MV = (0.110 \text{ M})(1.00 \text{ L}) = 0.110 \text{ mol}$$

and the mass of NH_4Cl is

$$g\ NH_4Cl = (0.110\ \text{mol})\left(\frac{53.49\ g\ NH_4Cl}{1\ \text{mol}\ NH_4Cl}\right) = 5.88\ g$$

16-49   The number of moles in 1.00 g of $Mg(OH)_2$ is

$$mol\ Mg(OH)_2 = (1.00\ g)\left(\frac{1\ \text{mol}\ Mg(OH)_2}{58.33\ g\ Mg(OH)_2}\right) = 0.0171\ \text{mol}$$

At neutralization (the equivalence point)

$$\text{moles of}\ OH^-(aq) = \text{moles of}\ H_3O^+(aq)$$

There are two moles of $OH^-(aq)$ per mole of $Mg(OH)_2(aq)$, and so we have

$$\text{moles of}\ OH^-(aq) = \left(\frac{2\ \text{mol}\ OH^-}{1\ \text{mol}\ Mg(OH)_2}\right)(0.0171\ \text{mol}\ Mg(OH)_2)$$
$$= M_a V_a = (0.10\ \text{mol}\cdot L^{-1})(V_a)$$

Solving for V_a, we get

$$V_a = \frac{0.0342\ \text{mol}}{0.10\ \text{mol}\cdot L^{-1}} = 0.34\ L = 340\ mL$$

16-51   Both acids have only one dissociable proton per molecule. Thus, at the equivalence point

$$\text{moles of acid} = \text{moles of base} = M_b V_b$$
$$= (1.00\ \text{mol}\cdot L^{-1})(0.01549\ L) = 0.01549\ \text{mol}$$

We have the correspondence

$$1.89\ g\ \text{acid} \approx 0.01549\ \text{mol acid}$$

Dividing both sides by 0.01549, we have

$$122\ g \approx \text{one mole}$$

Thus the molecular mass of the acid is 122. The molecular mass of benzoic acid, $HC_7H_5O_2$, is 122.12; the molecular mass of chlorobenzoic acid, $HC_7H_4ClO_2$, is 156.56. The acid must be benzoic acid.

16-53   One equilibrium that is established in the solution is

$$HC_2H_3O_2(aq) + H_2O(l) \rightleftharpoons H_3O^+(aq) + C_2H_3O_2^-(aq)$$
$$K_a = \frac{[C_2H_3O_2^-][H_3O^+]}{[HC_2H_3O_2]} = 1.74 \times 10^{-5}\ M$$

We can set up a table of initial and equilibrium concentrations.

	$HC_2H_3O_2(aq)$	$+ \ H_2O(l) \rightleftharpoons C_2H_3O_2^-(aq)$	$+ \ H_3O^+(aq)$
initial concentration	0.100 M	—	0.100 M	0
equilibrium concentration	$0.100 \ M - [H_3O^+]$	—	$0.100 \ M + [H_3O^+]$	$[H_3O^+]$

Note that $[C_2H_3O_2^-]$ is not equal to $[H_3O^+]$ in this case. The K_a expression is

$$K_a = \frac{(0.100 \ M + [H_3O^+])[H_3O^+]}{0.100 \ M - [H_3O^+]} = 1.74 \times 10^{-5} \ M$$

If we neglect $[H_3O^+]$ with respect to 0.100 M, then we find that

$$[H_3O^+] = 1.74 \times 10^{-5} \ M$$

The equilibrium concentrations are

$$[HC_2H_3O_2] = 0.100 \ M - 1.74 \times 10^{-5} \ M = 0.100 \ M$$
$$[C_2H_3O_2^-] = 0.100 \ M + 1.74 \times 10^{-5} \ M = 0.100 \ M$$

and so we see that

$$[HC_2H_3O_2] \approx [HC_2H_3O_2]_0$$
$$[C_2H_3O_2^-] \approx [C_2H_3O_2^-]_0$$

These relations arise because $[H_3O^+]$ is negligible compared to either $[HC_2H_3O_2]$ or $[C_2H_3O_2^-]$.

16-55 (a) The two equations corresponding to K_{a1} and K_{a2} are

$$H_2CO_3(aq) + H_2O(l) \rightleftharpoons H_3O^+(aq) + HCO_3^-(aq) \qquad K_{a1}$$
$$HCO_3^-(aq) + H_2O(l) \rightleftharpoons H_3O^+(aq) + CO_3^{2-}(aq) \qquad K_{a2}$$

Add these two equations to get

$$H_2CO_3(aq) + 2H_2O(l) \rightleftharpoons 2H_3O^+(aq) + CO_3^{2-}(aq) \qquad K = K_{a1}K_{a2}$$

and

$$K = \frac{[H_3O^+]^2[CO_3^{2-}]}{[H_2CO_3]} = K_{a1}K_{a2}$$

But according to the stoichiometry of the equation

$$2HCO_3^-(aq) \rightleftharpoons CO_3^{2-}(aq) + H_2CO_3(aq)$$

We have $[CO_3^{2-}] = [H_2CO_3]$, and so

$$\frac{[H_3O^+]^2[\cancel{CO_3^{2-}}]}{[\cancel{H_2CO_3}]} = K_{a1}K_{a2}$$

$$[H_3O^+]^2 = K_{a1}K_{a2}$$

$$[H_3O^+] = (K_{a1}K_{a2})^{1/2}$$

Taking the negative logarithm of both sides of this equation yields

$$-\log[H_3O^+] = \frac{1}{2}(-\log K_{a1} - \log K_{a2})$$

or

$$pH = \frac{1}{2}(pK_{a1} + pK_a)$$

From Table 15-4 we have

$$pH = \frac{1}{2}(6.35 + 10.33) = 8.34$$

(b) An $NaHCO_3(aq)$ solution acts as a buffer through the reactions described by the following equations.

$NaHCO_3$ acting as a base:

$$HCO_3^-(aq) + H_3O^+(aq) \rightleftharpoons H_2CO_3(aq) + H_2O(l)$$

$NaHCO_3$ acting as an acid:

$$HCO_3^-(aq) + OH^-(aq) \rightleftharpoons CO_3^{2-}(aq) + H_2O(l)$$

16-57 $3HCO_3^-(aq) + H_3C_6H_5O_7(aq) \rightleftharpoons 3H_2CO_3(aq) + C_6H_5O_7^{3-}(aq)$
$$\Updownarrow$$
$$3CO_2(aq) + 3H_2O(l)$$
$$\Updownarrow$$
$$3CO_2(g)$$

or

$$3HCO_3^-(aq) + H_3C_6H_5O_7(aq) \rightleftharpoons 3CO_2(g) + C_6H_5O_7^{3-}(aq) + 3H_2O(l)$$

16-59 The number of moles in 500 mg of $Al(OH)_3$ is

$$\text{mol } Al(OH)_3 = (0.500 \text{ g})\left(\frac{1 \text{ mol } Al(OH)_3}{78.00 \text{ g } Al(OH)_3}\right) = 0.00641 \text{ mol}$$

At neutralization

$$\text{moles of } OH^-(aq) = \text{moles of } H_3O^+(aq)$$

There are three moles of $OH^-(aq)$ per mole of $Al(OH)_3(s)$, and so

$$\left(\frac{3 \text{ mol } OH^-}{1 \text{ mol } Al(OH)_3}\right)(0.00641 \text{ mol } Al(OH)_3) = M_a V_a = (0.10 \text{ mol} \cdot L^{-1})V_a$$

$$V_a = \frac{0.0192 \text{ mol}}{0.10 \text{ mol} \cdot L^{-1}} = 0.19 \text{ L} = 190 \text{ mL}$$

16-61 At the equivalence point

$$\text{moles of acid} = \text{moles of base} = M_b V_b$$
$$= (0.100 \text{ mol} \cdot L^{-1})(0.0624 \text{ L}) = 0.00624 \text{ mol}$$

We have the correspondence

$$0.550 \text{ g butyric acid} \eqcirc 0.00624 \text{ mol butyric acid}$$

Dividing both sides by 0.00624, we have

$$88.1 \text{ g butyric acid} \eqcirc 1 \text{ mol butyric acid}$$

The molecular mass of butyric acid is 88.1.

16-63 Measure the pH of the original solution. Dilute the solution and measure the pH of the diluted solution. The pH of a buffer would not be affected by dilution.

16-65 The acid is a monoprotic acid (one dissociable proton per molecule); therefore, the number of moles of acid present is equal to the number of moles of base required to reach the equivalence point. Thus

$$\text{mol acid} = MV = (0.150 \text{ M})(0.0690 \text{ L}) = 0.01035 \text{ mol}$$

Thus

$$0.01035 \text{ mol acid} \eqcirc 1.20 \text{ g acid}$$

and

$$1 \text{ mol acid} \eqcirc \frac{1.20 \text{ g acid}}{0.01035 \text{ acid}} = 116 \text{ g acid}$$

16-67 The number of moles of base used is

$$n = MV = (0.135 \text{ M})(0.1472 \text{ L}) = 0.0199 \text{ mol}$$

The number of moles of citric acid available is

$$(1.270 \text{ g C}_6\text{H}_8\text{O}_7)\left(\frac{1 \text{ mol C}_6\text{H}_8\text{O}_7}{192.12 \text{ g C}_6\text{H}_8\text{O}_7}\right) = 0.006611 \text{ mol}$$

Thus

$$\frac{\text{mol of OH}^-}{\text{mol of C}_6\text{H}_8\text{O}_7} = \frac{0.0199 \text{ mol}}{0.006611 \text{ mol}} = 3.01$$

There are three dissociable protons per molecule of citric acid. We normally write the formula of citric acid as $H_3C_6H_5O_7$.

16-69 Because the pH is greater than the pK_{a2}, the relevant equilibrium is

$$\underset{0.125 \text{ M} - [\text{C}_2\text{O}_4^{2-}]}{\text{HC}_2\text{O}_4^-(aq)} + \text{H}_2\text{O}(l) \rightleftharpoons \underset{[\text{H}_3\text{O}^+]}{\text{H}_3\text{O}^+(aq)} + \underset{[\text{C}_2\text{O}_4^{2-}]}{\text{C}_2\text{O}_4^{2-}(aq)}$$

Thus

$$K_{a2} = 10^{-pK_{a2}} = 10^{-4.27} = 5.37 \times 10^{-5} \text{ M} = \frac{[\text{H}_3\text{O}^+][\text{C}_2\text{O}_4^{2-}]}{[\text{HC}_2\text{O}_4^-]}$$

At pH = 5.00 we have

$$[\text{H}_3\text{O}^+] = 10^{-\text{pH}} = 10^{-5.00} = 1.00 \times 10^{-5} \text{ M}$$

Combining this result with the K_{a2} expression yields

$$\frac{(1.00 \times 10^{-5} \text{ M})[\text{C}_2\text{O}_4^{2-}]}{0.125 \text{ M} - [\text{C}_2\text{O}_4^{2-}]} = 5.37 \times 10^{-5} \text{ M}$$

Thus

$$(1.00 \times 10^{-5} \text{ M})[\text{C}_2\text{O}_4^{2-}] = 6.71 \times 10^{-6} \text{ M}^2 - (5.37 \times 10^{-5} \text{ M})[\text{C}_2\text{O}_4^{2-}]$$

and

$$[\text{C}_2\text{O}_4^{2-}] = \frac{6.71 \times 10^{-6} \text{ M}^2}{6.37 \times 10^{-5} \text{ M}} = 0.105 \text{ M}$$

Neglecting $[\text{H}_2\text{C}_2\text{O}_4]$, we have for the value of $[\text{HC}_2\text{O}_4^-]$

$$[\text{HC}_2\text{O}_4^-] = 0.125 \text{ M} - 0.105 \text{ M} = 0.020 \text{ M}$$

We now calculate the value of $[\text{H}_2\text{C}_2\text{O}_4]$ from the K_{a1} expression

$$H_2C_2O_4(aq) + H_2O(l) \rightleftharpoons HC_2O_4^-(aq) + H_3O^+(aq)$$

$$K_{a1} = 10^{-pK_{a1}} = 10^{-1.27} = 5.37 \times 10^{-2} \text{ M} = \frac{[HC_2O_4^-][H_3O^+]}{[H_2C_2O_4]}$$

We know that $[H_3O^+] = 1.00 \times 10^{-5}$ M and $[HC_2O_4^-] = 0.020$ M; thus

$$5.37 \times 10^{-2} \text{ M} = \frac{(0.020 \text{ M})(1.00 \times 10^{-5} \text{ M})}{[H_2C_2O_4]}$$

from which we compute

$$[H_2C_2O_4] = 3.7 \times 10^{-6} \text{ M}$$

which is negligible compared to $[HC_2O_4^-]$ and $[C_2O_4^{2-}]$ and thus confirms our earlier assumption that $[H_2C_2O_4]$ is negligible compared to $[HC_2O_4^-]$ and $[C_2O_4^{2-}]$.

E   ANSWERS TO THE SELF-TEST

1   acid

2   true

3   pH

4   the pK_a

5   orange

6   blue

7   Litmus is red in acidic solutions and blue in basic solutions.

8   NaOH(aq); HCl(aq)

9   KOH(aq)

10   pH . . . the volume of NaOH(aq) added

11   at which the number of moles of NaOH(aq) that has been added is exactly equal to the number of moles of HCl(aq) initially present

12   false

13   the end point of the titration

14   a change in color of the indicator

15   false

16   true

17   The salt, sodium acetate (NaC$_2$H$_3$O$_2$), present at the equivalence point is a basic salt because Na$^+$(aq) is a neutral cation and C$_2$H$_3$O$_2^-$(aq) is basic anion.

18   true

19   false

20   The salt, NH$_4$Cl(aq), present at the equivalence is acidic because NH$_4^+$(aq) is an acidic cation and Cl$^-$(aq) is a neutral anion.

21   true

22   false

23   Henderson-Hasselbalch

24   the stoichiometric concentrations of buffer components are not essentially equal to their actual concentrations, as when a large quantity of acid or base is added

25   true

26   false (See Question 24.)

27   remains the same

SOLUBILITY AND PRECIPITATION REACTIONS

A OUTLINE OF CHAPTER 17

17-1 The driving force of a double replacement reaction is the formation of an insoluble product.

> If the solubility is less than 0.01 M, then we say that the salt is insoluble.
>
> If the solubility is between 0.01 M and 0.1 M, then we say that the salt is slightly soluble.
>
> If the solubility is greater than 0.1 M, then we say that the salt is soluble.
>
> Solubility rules are used to predict the solubilities of salts in water.
>
> The solubility rules for salts in water are given on text page 543. The rules must be applied in the order given. The rule with the lower number supersedes in case of a conflict.

17-2 The law of concentration action governs the equilibrium between an ionic solid and its constituent ions in solution.

> Application of the law of concentration action yields the equilibrium constant expression for the solubility product constant, K_{sp}. For example, for the salt $PbCl_2(s)$

$$PbCl_2(s) \underset{H_2O(l)}{\rightleftharpoons} Pb^{2+}(aq) + 2Cl^-(aq)$$

$$K_{sp} = [Pb^{2+}][Cl^-]^2$$

> The values of K_{sp} for various salts are given in Table 17-1.
>
> The solubility of an ionic solid can be computed by using the K_{sp} expression.
>
> The solubility of a salt is the quantity of the salt that can be dissolved in a given volume of solution.

17-3   The solubility of an ionic solid is decreased when a common ion is present in the solution.

At equilibrium, the K_{sp} expression for an ionic solid must always hold if the solid phase is in contact with the solution.

The decrease in salt solubility arising from the presence of a common ion in the solution is understood readily in terms of Le Châtelier's principle.

17-4   The solubility of a solid is increased by the formation of a soluble complex ion.

A complex ion is a metal ion with small molecules or ions attached to it.

17-5   Salts of weak acids are more soluble in acidic solutions than in neutral or basic solutions.

The increase in solubility of a salt of a weak acid with increased $[H_3O^+]$ is a consequence of the formation of the conjugate acid of the anion of the salt.

17-6   Insoluble sulfides are separated by adjustment of solution pH.

Because $S^{2-}(aq)$ is a conjugate base of a weak acid, HS^-, the solubility of a metal sulfide is greater the greater the value of $[H_3O^+]$.

The solubility of $H_2S(aq)$ in a saturated solution is 0.10 M at 25°C.

The value of $[S^{2-}]$ in a solution is controlled by controlling the pH of the solution with suitable buffers.

The value of $[S^{2-}]$ when $[H_2S] = 0.10$ M is given by

$$[S^{2-}] = \frac{1.1 \times 10^{-21} \text{ M}^3}{[H_3O^+]^2} \qquad \text{at } 25°C \qquad (17\text{-}18)$$

17-7   Some metal cations can be separated from a mixture by the formation of an insoluble hydroxide of one of them.

The solubility of a metal hydroxide depends on both the value of K_{sp} and the pH of the solution (Figure 17-4).

17-8   Amphoteric hydroxides dissolve in both highly acidic and highly basic solutions.

Amphoteric hydroxides dissolve in highly basic solutions by the formation of soluble hydroxy complexes; for example,

$$Al(OH)_3(s) + OH^-(aq) \rightleftharpoons Al(OH)_4^-(aq)$$

The values of the equilibrium constants for the formation of hydroxy complexes of some amphoteric hydroxides are given in Table 17-3.

17-9   The magnitude of the ratio Q_{sp}/K_{sp} is used to predict whether an ionic solid will precipitate.

The Q_{sp} expression has the same algebraic form as the K_{sp} expression, but the concentration values used in the Q_{sp} expression need not be equilibrium values.

If $Q_{sp}/K_{sp} > 1$, then precipitation will occur.

If $Q_{sp}/K_{sp} < 1$, then dissolution will occur.

If $Q_{sp} = K_{sp}$, then the ionic solid is in equilibrium with the solution.

17-10 Qualitative analysis is the identification of the species present in a sample.

The sample to be analyzed is called the unknown.

Precipitation reactions are used to separate mixtures of ions.

A reagent is added that precipitates certain cations but not others.

Many cations are precipitated as insoluble sulfides by adding H_2S to the solution.

Selective precipitation of the metal sulfides is achieved by adjusting the pH of the solution.

Separations of certain cations are achieved by the formation of insoluble hydroxides at controlled pH values.

An essential feature of a qualitative analysis scheme is the successive removal of subgroups of ions by precipitation reactions.

B   SELF-TEST

1 All Na^+, K^+, and NH_4^+ salts are *(soluble, insoluble)* in water.

2 The salt $AgClO_4(s)$ is *(soluble, insoluble)* in water.

3 The salt $Hg_2(NO_3)_2(s)$ is *(soluble, insoluble)* in water.

4 The salt $Pb(NO_3)_2(s)$ is *(soluble, insoluble)* in water.

5 The salt $CaSO_4(s)$ is *(soluble, insoluble)* in water.

6 The salt $PbF_2(s)$ is *(soluble, insoluble)* in water.

7 The salt $FeSO_4$ is *(soluble, insoluble)* in water.

8 The driving force for some double replacement reactions is the formation of an insoluble product. *True/False*

9 The solubility product constant expression for calcium carbonate, $CaCO_3$, is $K_{sp} =$ _____.

10 The solubility product constant expression for magnesium hydroxide, $Mg(OH)_2$, is $K_{sp} =$ _____.

11 The value of K_{sp} determines the solubility of an ionic solid in pure water. *True/False*

12   The solubility of $PbCl_2(s)$ in water is equal to the concentration of $Pb^{2+}(aq)$. *True/ False*

13   The solubility of $Fe(OH)_2(s)$ in water is equal to the concentration of $OH^-(aq)$. *True/False*

14   The solubility of $CaSO_4(s)$ is greater in a 0.10 M $Na_2SO_4(aq)$ solution than in water. *True/False*

15   The solubility product constant expression for $AgCl(s)$ is not $K_{sp} = [Ag^+][Cl^-]$ when $AgCl(s)$ is in equilibrium with a 0.25 M $NaCl(aq)$ solution. *True/False*

16   The common-ion effect is _____

_____ .

17   The solubility of $AgCl(s)$ is *(increased, decreased)* by the addition of $AgNO_3$ to the solution.

18   The solubility of $AgCl(s)$ is *(increased, decreased)* by the addition of $NH_3(aq)$ to the solution.

19   The increased solubility of $AgCl(s)$ in $NH_3(aq)$ relative to the solubility of $AgCl(s)$ in

pure water is a result of the reaction _____

_____ .

20   Addition of $HNO_3(aq)$ to an aqueous solution of $Ag(NH_3)_2Cl(aq)$ results in the

formation of a precipitate of _____ .

21   Salts of weak acids are more soluble the higher the pH of the solution. *True/False*

22   The salt $BaCO_3(s)$ is *(more, less)* soluble when the pH of the solution is 2.0 than when the pH of the solution is 7.0.

23   Using a chemical equation, explain why the solubility of silver benzoate, $AgC_7H_5O_2$,

increases as the pH of the solution decreases. _____

_____

_____ .

24   Water-insoluble metal carbonates, such as $CaCO_3(s)$, dissolve in $HCl(aq)$ with evolu-

tion of the gas _____ .

25   The solubility of a metal sulfide depends on the pH of the solution. *True/False*

26   The net equation for $FeS(s)$ dissolving in a buffered solution with pH $= 2$ is

_____ .

27 For the equation

$$2H_2O(l) + H_2S(aq) \rightleftharpoons 2H_3O^+(aq) + S^{2-}(aq)$$

$K = 1.1 \times 10^{-20}$ M^2 at 25°C. The value of $[S^{2-}]$ in a buffered solution with $[H_3O^+] = 0.010$ M and $[H_2S] = 0.10$ M is 1.1×10^{-17} M. *True/False*

28 For ZnS(s), $K_{sp} = 1.6 \times 10^{-24}$ M^2. If a solution with $[Zn^{2+}] = 0.01$ M is buffered and treated with H$_2$S such that $[S^{2-}] = 1.1 \times 10^{-17}$ M, then ZnS(s) will precipitate. *True/False*

29 For PbS(s), $K_{sp} = 8.0 \times 10^{-28}$ M^2 and for ZnS(s), $K_{sp} = 1.6 \times 10^{-24}$ M^2; ZnS(s) is more soluble than PbS(s) in an acidic solution. *True/False*

30 The solubility of a metal hydroxide depends on the pH of the solution. *True/False*

31 Amphoteric hydroxides are more soluble in both strongly acidic and basic solutions than in water. *True/False*

32 Aluminum hydroxide, Al(OH)$_3$, is insoluble at any pH. *True/False*

33 The equation for the solubility reaction for Al(OH)$_3$(s) in water is _____

_____.

34 The equation for the reaction for Al(OH)$_3$(s) dissolving in a highly acidic aqueous solution is _____.

35 The equation for the reaction for Al(OH)$_3$(s) dissolving in a highly basic solution is

_____.

36 Zinc hydroxide, Zn(OH)$_2$, is soluble when the pH of the solution is 14.0 because of the reaction

_____.

37 If the value of the ratio Q_{sp}/K_{sp} for the equation Cu(OH)$_2$(s) $\rightleftharpoons$ Cu^{2+}(aq) + 2OH$^-$(aq) is 10 when a solution of NaOH(aq) is mixed with a solution of Cu(NO$_3$)$_2$(aq), then a precipitate of _____ *(will, will not)* form.

38 The value of the ratio Q_{sp}/K_{sp} for the equation Ag$_2$SO$_4$(s) $\rightleftharpoons$ 2Ag$^+$(aq) + SO$_4^{2-}$(aq) is 0.032 when a solution of AgNO$_3$(aq) is added to a solution of K$_2$SO$_4$(aq). A precipitate of _____ *(will, will not)* form.

39 Qualitative analysis is the determination of the _____

_____ in a sample.

40 In a solution of $AgNO_3(aq)$ and $KNO_3(aq)$, $Ag^+(aq)$ can be separated from $K^+(aq)$ by adding $HCl(aq)$ to precipitate _____ as _____.

41 In a solution containing both $Ag^+(aq)$ and $K^+(aq)$, $Ag^+(aq)$ must be removed before testing for the presence of $K^+(aq)$ with $Na_3Co(NO_2)_6(aq)$. *True/False*

42 Many metal cations form insoluble metal sulfides. *True/False*

43 The metal sulfides FeS and SnS may be separated by adjusting the _____ of the solution.

44 All metal sulfides are insoluble when $[H_3O^+] = 0.3$ M. *True/False*

45 The insoluble hydroxide $Al(OH)_3$ can be made soluble by adjusting the _____ of the solution.

46 The steps in a qualitative analysis scheme may be carried out in any order. *True/False*

47 A qualitative analysis scheme often utilizes the differences in solubilities at various pH values. *True/False*

C CALCULATIONS YOU SHOULD KNOW HOW TO DO

1 Calculate the value of K_{sp} for a salt given the solubility of the salt. See Example 17-5 and Problems 17-15, 17-16, 17-19, and 17-20.

2 Calculate the solubility of a salt given the value of K_{sp} of the salt. See Examples 17-3 and 17-4 and Problems 17-13, 17-14, 17-17, 17-18, 17-21, and 17-22.

3 Calculate the solubility of a salt in an aqueous solution containing a common ion. See Example 17-6 and Problems 17-23 through 17-28.

4 Calculate the solubility of certain salts at a given pH. See Example 17-7 and Problems 17-37 through 17-40, 17-43, 17-44, 17-49, and 17-50.

5 Calculate the solubilities of metal sulfides at a given pH. See Problems 17-45 through 17-48.

6 Calculate the solubility of amphoteric hydroxides at a given pH. See Example 17-8 and Problems 17-51 and 17-52.

7 Use Q_{sp}/K_{sp} to determine whether precipitation will occur. See Example 17-9 and Problems 17-53 through 17-58.

D   SOLUTIONS TO THE ODD-NUMBERED PROBLEMS

17-1   (a) insoluble, rule 3   (b) soluble, rule 2

(c) soluble, rule 1   (d) soluble, rule 1

(e) insoluble, rule 5

17-3   (a) insoluble, rule 5   (b) soluble, rule 2

(c) soluble, rule 4   (d) insoluble, rule 5

(e) insoluble, rule 6

17-5   (a) CuS is insoluble by rule 5.

$$CuCl_2(aq) + Na_2S(aq) \longrightarrow CuS(s) + 2NaCl(aq)$$
$$Cu^{2+}(aq) + S^{2-}(aq) \longrightarrow CuS(s)$$

(b) $MgCO_3$ is insoluble by rule 5.

$$MgBr_2(aq) + K_2CO_3(aq) \longrightarrow MgCO_3(s) + 2KBr(aq)$$
$$Mg^{2+}(aq) + CO_3^{2-}(aq) \longrightarrow MgCO_3(s)$$

(c) $BaSO_4$ is insoluble by rule 6.

$$BaCl_2(aq) + K_2SO_4(aq) \longrightarrow BaSO_4(s) + 2KCl(aq)$$
$$Ba^{2+}(aq) + SO_4^{2-}(aq) \longrightarrow BaSO_4(s)$$

(d) Hg_2Cl_2 is insoluble by rule 3.

$$Hg_2(NO_3)_2(aq) + 2KCl(aq) \longrightarrow Hg_2Cl_2(s) + 2KNO_3(aq)$$
$$Hg_2^{2+}(aq) + 2Cl^-(aq) \longrightarrow Hg_2Cl_2(s)$$

17-7   (a) $Hg_2(ClO_4)_2(aq) + 2NaBr(aq) \rightarrow 2NaClO_4(aq) + Hg_2Br_2(s)$ (rule 3)

(b) $Fe(ClO_4)_3(aq) + 3NaOH(aq) \rightarrow 3NaClO_4(aq) + Fe(OH)_3(s)$ (rule 5)

(c) $Pb(NO_3)_2(aq) + 2LiIO_3(aq) \rightarrow 2LiNO_3(aq) + Pb(IO_3)_2(s)$ (rule 3)

(d) $H_2SO_4(aq) + Pb(NO_3)_2(aq) \rightarrow 2HNO_3(aq) + PbSO_4(s)$ (rule 3)

17-9   (a) soluble, rule 1   (b) insoluble, rule 3

(c) insoluble, rule 3   (d) insoluble, rule 5

17-11   (a) soluble, rule 2   (b) insoluble, rule 3

(c) soluble, rule 6   (d) insoluble, rule 5

(e) soluble, rule 2

17-13   The solubility equilibrium is

$$PbCrO_4(s) \rightleftharpoons Pb^{2+}(aq) + CrO_4^{2-}(aq)$$

The K_{sp} expression is

$$K_{sp} = [Pb^{2+}][CrO_4^{2-}] = 2.8 \times 10^{-13} \text{ M}^2$$

If $PbCrO_4$ is equilibrated with pure water, then at equilibrium we have

$$[Pb^{2+}] = [CrO_4^{2-}] = s$$

where s is the solubility of $PbCrO_4$ in pure water. Thus

$$K_{sp} = (s)(s) = s^2 = 2.8 \times 10^{-13} \text{ M}^2$$
$$s = 5.3 \times 10^{-7} \text{ M}$$

The solubility in grams per liter is

$$s = (5.3 \times 10^{-7} \text{ mol} \cdot \text{L}^{-1})\left(\frac{323.2 \text{ g PbCrO}_4}{1 \text{ mol PbCrO}_4}\right) = 1.7 \times 10^{-4} \text{ g} \cdot \text{L}^{-1}$$

17-15   The solubility equilibrium is

$$AgBr(s) \rightleftharpoons Ag^+(aq) + Br^-(aq)$$

The solubility of AgBr is

$$(1.33 \times 10^{-4} \text{ g} \cdot \text{L}^{-1})\left(\frac{1 \text{ mol AgBr}}{187.8 \text{ g AgBr}}\right) = 7.08 \times 10^{-7} \text{ M}$$

From the reaction stoichiometry, we have

$$\text{solubility of AgBr} = [Ag^+] = [Br^-] = 7.08 \times 10^{-7} \text{ M}$$

Using the K_{sp} expression, we compute

$$K_{sp} = [Ag^+][Br^-] = (7.08 \times 10^{-7} \text{ M})^2$$
$$= 5.01 \times 10^{-13} \text{ M}^2$$

17-17   The solubility equilibrium is

$$Mg(OH)_2(s) \rightleftharpoons Mg^{2+}(aq) + 2OH^-(aq)$$

The solubility product constant expression is

$$K_{sp} = [Mg^{2+}][OH^-]^2 = 1.8 \times 10^{-11} \text{ M}^3$$

When $Mg(OH)_2(s)$ is in equilibrium with pure water, we have

$$[OH^-] = 2[Mg^{2+}]$$

The solubility of $Mg(OH)_2(s)$ in pure water is equal to $[Mg^{2+}]$ because each mole of $Mg(OH)_2$ that dissolves yields one mole of $Mg^{2+}(aq)$. The solubility of $Mg(OH)_2(s)$ is

$$s = [Mg^{2+}] = \frac{[OH^-]}{2}$$

or $[OH^-] = 2s$ where we have neglected the $[OH^-]$ arising from the dissociation of $H_2O(l)$.

Combining these results with the K_{sp} expression, we have

$$K_{sp} = (s)(2s)^2 = 4s^3 = 1.8 \times 10^{-11} \text{ M}^3$$

$$s = \left(\frac{1.8 \times 10^{-11} \text{ M}^3}{4}\right)^{1/3} = 1.7 \times 10^{-4} \text{ M}$$

The solubility in grams per liter is

$$s = (1.7 \times 10^{-4} \text{ mol} \cdot \text{L}^{-1})\left(\frac{58.33 \text{ g Mg(OH)}_2}{1 \text{ mol Mg(OH)}_2}\right) = 9.9 \times 10^{-3} \text{ g} \cdot \text{L}^{-1}$$

17-19 The solubility equilibrium is

$$KClO_4(s) \rightleftharpoons K^+(aq) + ClO_4^-(aq)$$

The K_{sp} expression is

$$K_{sp} = [K^+][ClO_4^-]$$

From the reaction stoichiometry, at equilibrium $[K^+] = [ClO_4^-] =$ solubility of $KClO_4$. The solubility of $KClO_4$ is

$$s = \frac{0.75 \text{ g}}{0.100 \text{ L}} = (7.5 \text{ g} \cdot \text{L}^{-1})\left(\frac{1 \text{ mol KClO}_4}{138.55 \text{ g KClO}_4}\right) = 0.054 \text{ M}$$

Substituting the values of $[K^+]$ and $[ClO_4^-]$ into the K_{sp} expression, we have

$$K_{sp} = (0.054 \text{ M})(0.054 \text{ M}) = 2.9 \times 10^{-3} \text{ M}^2$$

17-21 The solubility equilibrium is

$$Zn(OH)_2(s) \rightleftharpoons Zn^{2+}(aq) + 2OH^-(aq)$$

The K_{sp} expression is

$$K_{sp} = [Zn^{2+}][OH^-]^2 = 1.0 \times 10^{-15} \text{ M}^3$$

From the reaction stoichiometry, at equilibrium we have

$$[OH^-] = 2[Zn^{2+}] \quad \text{or} \quad [Zn^{2+}] = \frac{1}{2}[OH^-]$$

Substituting $[Zn^{2+}] = \frac{1}{2}[OH^-]$ in the K_{sp} expression, we have

$$K_{sp} = \frac{1}{2}[OH^-][OH^-]^2 = \frac{1}{2}[OH^-]^3 = 1.0 \times 10^{-15} \text{ M}^3$$

$$[OH^-] = (2.0 \times 10^{-15} \text{ M}^3)^{1/3} = 1.3 \times 10^{-5} \text{ M}$$

The pOH of the solution is

$$\text{pOH} = -\log[OH^-] = -\log(1.3 \times 10^{-5}) = 4.89$$

and the pH is

$$\text{pH} = 14.00 - \text{pOH} = 14.00 - 4.89 = 9.11$$

17-23   The equilibrium expression that describes the solubility of silver sulfate is

$$Ag_2SO_4(s) \rightleftharpoons 2Ag^+(aq) + SO_4^{2-}(aq)$$

and the solubility product expression is

$$K_{sp} = [Ag^+]^2[SO_4^{2-}] = 1.4 \times 10^{-5} \text{ M}^3 \qquad \text{(Table 17-1)}$$

The only source of $SO_4^{2-}(aq)$ is from the $Ag_2SO_4(s)$ that dissolves. If we let s be the solubility of $Ag_2SO_4(s)$ in 0.55 M $AgNO_3(aq)$, then

$$[SO_4^{2-}] = s$$

The $Ag^+(aq)$ is due to the 0.55 M $AgNO_3(aq)$ and the $Ag_2SO_4(s)$ that dissolves. Because each $Ag_2SO_4(s)$ that dissolves yields two $Ag^+(aq)$, we have at equilibrium

$$[Ag^+] = \underset{\substack{\text{from} \\ \text{AgNO}_3}}{0.55 \text{ M}} + \underset{\substack{\text{from} \\ \text{Ag}_2\text{SO}_4}}{2s}$$

If we substitute the expressions for $[Ag^+]$ and $[SO_4^{2-}]$ into the K_{sp} expression, then we obtain

$$K_{sp} = (0.55 \text{ M} + 2s)^2(s) = 1.4 \times 10^{-5} \text{ M}^3$$

Because Ag_2SO_4 is a slightly soluble salt, we expect the value of s to be small. Therefore, we neglect $2s$ compared to 0.55 M, and we write

$$(0.55 \text{ M})^2(s) \approx 1.4 \times 10^{-5} \text{ M}^3$$

$$s \approx \frac{1.4 \times 10^{-5} \text{ M}^3}{(0.55 \text{ M})^2} = 4.6 \times 10^{-5} \text{ M}$$

Note that s is small relative to 0.55 M, and so our approximation $0.55 \text{ M} + 2s \approx$ 0.55 M is acceptable. The solubility of $Ag_2SO_4(s)$ in $g \cdot L^{-1}$ is

$$s = (4.6 \times 10^{-5} \text{ mol} \cdot L^{-1}) \left(\frac{311.9 \text{ g } Ag_2SO_4}{1 \text{ mol } Ag_2SO_4} \right) = 1.4 \times 10^{-2} \text{ g} \cdot L^{-1}$$

17-25   The equation that describes the solubility of $TlCl(s)$ is

$$TlCl(s) \rightleftharpoons Tl^+(aq) + Cl^-(aq)$$

The solubility product expression is

$$K_{sp} = [Tl^+][Cl^-] = 1.7 \times 10^{-4} \text{ M}^2$$

The only source of $Tl^+(aq)$ is from the $TlCl(s)$ that dissolves. If we let s be the solubility of $TlCl(s)$ in the solution, then

$$[Tl^+] = s$$

and

$$[Cl^-] = 0.25 \text{ M} + s$$

Substituting these expressions into the K_{sp} expression yields

$$s(0.25 \text{ M} + s) = 1.7 \times 10^{-4} \text{ M}^2$$

Assuming $s \ll 0.25 \text{ M}$ because we expect s to be small yields

$$s \approx \frac{1.7 \times 10^{-4} \text{ M}^2}{0.25 \text{ M}} = 6.8 \times 10^{-4} \text{ M}$$

The solubility in grams per liter is

$$s = (6.8 \times 10^{-4} \text{ M}) \left(\frac{239.9 \text{ g } TlCl}{1 \text{ mol } TlCl} \right) = 0.16 \text{ g} \cdot L^{-1}$$

17-27   The equilibrium expression that describes the solubility of $AgI(s)$ is

$$AgI(s) \rightleftharpoons Ag^+(aq) + I^-(aq)$$

The solubility product expression is

$$K_{sp} = [Ag^+][I^-] = 8.3 \times 10^{-17} \text{ M}^2 \qquad \text{(Table 17-1)}$$

The only source of $Ag^+(aq)$ is $AgI(s)$; thus the solubility s is equal to

$$s = [Ag^+]$$

The $I^-(aq)$ in solution is due to 0.20 M $CaI_2(aq)$ plus the dissolved AgI. Because CaI_2 dissociates completely, we have

$$[I^-] = (2 \times 0.20 \text{ M}) + s$$

Substitution of the above expressions for $[Ag^+]$ and $[I^-]$ into the K_{sp} expression yields

$$s(0.40 \text{ M} + s) = 8.3 \times 10^{-17} \text{ M}^2$$

Assuming that s is small compared to 0.40 M yields

$$s = \frac{8.3 \times 10^{-17} \text{ M}^2}{0.40 \text{ M}} = 2.1 \times 10^{-16} \text{ M}$$

The solubility in grams per liter is

$$s = (2.1 \times 10^{-16} \text{ M})\left(\frac{234.8 \text{ g AgI}}{1 \text{ mol AgI}}\right) = 4.7 \times 10^{-14} \text{ g} \cdot \text{L}^{-1}$$

17-29 The equilibrium constant expression is

$$K = \frac{[Ag(S_2O_3)_2^{3-}][Cl^-]}{[S_2O_3^{2-}]^2} = 5.20 \times 10^3$$

If we let s be the solubility of AgCl(s) in $S_2O_3^{2-}(aq)$, then we have

$$[Cl^-] = s$$

The K_{sp} for AgCl(s) is 1.8×10^{-10} M^2, which is very small compared to the K value above; thus $[Ag^+] \ll [Ag(S_2O_3)_2^{3-}]$ and therefore

$$[Ag(S_2O_3)_2^{3-}] \simeq [Cl^-] = s$$

Substituting the expressions for $[Cl^-]$ and $[Ag(S_2O_3)_2^{3-}]$ into the K expression, we have

$$K = \frac{(s)(s)}{[S_2O_3^{2-}]^2} = \frac{s^2}{(0.010 \text{ M})^2} = 5.20 \times 10^3$$

$$s^2 = 0.52 \text{ M}^2$$

and

$$s = 0.72 \text{ M}$$

17-31 (a) Solubility is increased; an increase in the concentration of $S_2O_3^{2-}$ shifts the equilibrium from left to right.

(b) Solubility remains unchanged; the amount of a solid reactant has no effect on the equilibrium concentrations.

(c) Solubility is decreased; an increase in the concentration of $Br^-(aq)$ shifts the equilibrium from right to left.

(d) Solubility remains unchanged; neither $Na^+(aq)$ nor $NO_3^-(aq)$ reacts with the species involved.

17-33   The equilibrium expression is

$$PbF_2(s) \rightleftharpoons Pb^{2+}(aq) + 2F^-(aq)$$

Recall that HF is a weak acid, and a saturated PbF_2 solution would contain some $HF(aq)$.

(a) The solubility is increased; a decrease in pH is an increase in $[H_3O^+]$. The added $H_3O^+(aq)$ reacts with $F^-(aq)$ to form HF, thereby reducing the concentration of $F^-(aq)$ and causing a shift in the equilibrium from left to right.

(b) The solubility is decreased, an increase in $[Pb^{2+}]$ shifts the equilibrium from right to left (common-ion effect).

17-35   The following compounds are more soluble at lower pH for the reasons stated.

(a) $CaCO_3$; $CO_3^{2-}(aq)$ is the conjugate base of the weak acid $HCO_3^-(aq)$.

(b) CaF_2; $F^-(aq)$ is the conjugate base of the weak acid $HF(aq)$.

(c) $PbSO_3$; $SO_3^{2-}(aq)$ is the conjugate base of the weak acid $HSO_3^-(aq)$.

(e) $Fe(OH)_3$; $OH^-(aq)$ reacts with $H_3O^+(aq)$ so that $[OH^-]$ is decreased.

(f) ZnS; $S^{2-}(aq)$ is the conjugate base of the weak acid $HS^-(aq)$.

17-37   The equilibrium expression is

$$Mg(OH)_2(s) \rightleftharpoons Mg^{2+}(aq) + 2OH^-(aq)$$

The K_{sp} expression is

$$K_{sp} = [Mg^{2+}][OH^-]^2 = 1.8 \times 10^{-11} \ M^3 \qquad \text{(Table 17-1)}$$

At pH = 8.5

$$[H_3O^+] = 10^{-8.5} = 3.2 \times 10^{-9} \ M$$

Thus

$$[OH^-] = \frac{K_w}{[H_3O^+]} = \frac{1.00 \times 10^{-14} \ M^2}{3.2 \times 10^{-9} \ M} = 3.1 \times 10^{-6} \ M$$

Let s be the solubility of $Mg(OH)_2$. Then

$$[Mg^{2+}] = s$$

$$K_{sp} = (s)(3.1 \times 10^{-6} \text{ M})^2 = 1.8 \times 10^{-11} \text{ M}^3$$

$$s = \frac{1.8 \times 10^{-11} \text{ M}^3}{9.6 \times 10^{-12} \text{ M}^2} = 1.9 \text{ M}$$

17-39 The equilibrium expression is

$$Cu(OH)_2(s) \rightleftharpoons Cu^{2+}(aq) + 2OH^-(aq)$$

The K_{sp} expression is

$$K_{sp} = [Cu^{2+}][OH^-]^2 = 2.2 \times 10^{-20} \text{ M}^3 \qquad \text{(Table 17-1)}$$

At pH = 7.0

$$[H_3O^+] = 10^{-pH} = 10^{-7.0} = 1.0 \times 10^{-7} \text{ M}$$

and thus

$$[OH^-] = \frac{K_w}{[H_3O^+]} = \frac{1.00 \times 10^{-14} \text{ M}^2}{1.0 \times 10^{-7} \text{ M}} = 1.0 \times 10^{-7} \text{ M}$$

Let s be the solubility of $Cu(OH)_2$. We have

$$[Cu^{2+}] = s$$

Therefore,

$$K_{sp} = (s)(1.0 \times 10^{-7} \text{ M})^2 = 2.2 \times 10^{-20} \text{ M}^3$$

and

$$s = 2.2 \times 10^{-6} \text{ M}$$

17-41 (a) $ZnS(s) \rightleftharpoons Zn^{2+}(aq) + S^{2-}(aq)$
The solubility increases. The $H_3O^+(aq)$ from the added HNO_3 reacts with S^{2-} to form HS^-, thereby decreasing the concentration of $S^{2-}(aq)$. A decrease in $[S^{2-}]$ shifts the equilibrium from left to right.

(b) $AgI(s) \rightleftharpoons Ag^+(aq) + I^-(aq)$
The solubility increases. Ammonia, NH_3, reacts with Ag^+ to form the soluble ion $Ag(NH_3)_2^+$, thereby reducing the amount of $Ag^+(aq)$. A decrease in $[Ag^+]$ shifts the equilibrium from left to right.

17-43 The solubility product expression of $Cr(OH)_3(s)$ is

$$K_{sp} = [Cr^{3+}][OH^-]^3 = 6.3 \times 10^{-31} \text{ M}^4 \qquad \text{(Table 17-1)}$$

$$\text{solubility of } Cr(OH)_3 = s = [Cr^{3+}] = \frac{6.3 \times 10^{-31} \text{ M}^4}{[OH^-]^3}$$

$$= \frac{6.3 \times 10^{-31} \text{ M}^4[H_3O^+]^3}{K_w^3}$$

At pH $= 5.0$

$$[H_3O^+] = 10^{-pH} = 10^{-5.0} = 1.0 \times 10^{-5} \text{ M}$$

Thus the solubility of $Cr(OH)_3$ is

$$s = \frac{(6.3 \times 10^{-31} \text{ M}^4)(1.0 \times 10^{-5} \text{ M})^3}{(1.00 \times 10^{-14} \text{ M}^2)^3} = 6.3 \times 10^{-4} \text{ M}$$

The solubility product expression of $Ni(OH)_2$ is

$$K_{sp} = [Ni^{2+}][OH^-]^2 = 2.0 \times 10^{-15} \text{ M}^3$$

$$\text{solubility of } Ni(OH)_2 = s = [Ni^{2+}] = \frac{2.0 \times 10^{-15} \text{ M}^3}{[OH^-]^2}$$

$$= \frac{2.0 \times 10^{-15} \text{ M}^3[H_3O^+]^2}{K_w^2}$$

Thus at pH $= 5.0$

$$s = \frac{(2.0 \times 10^{-15} \text{ M}^3)(1.0 \times 10^{-5} \text{ M})^2}{(1.00 \times 10^{-14} \text{ M}^2)^2} = 2.0 \times 10^3 \text{M}$$

Of course, a solubility of 2000 M is physically unrealistic, but this result means that $Ni(OH)_2(s)$ is very soluble. Thus, at pH $= 5.0$, $Ni(OH)_2(s)$ is very soluble, while $Cr(OH)_3(s)$ is only slightly soluble; thus a separation of $Ni^{2+}(aq)$ and $Cr^{3+}(aq)$ can be achieved by buffering the solution at pH $= 5$, where the $Cr(OH)_3(s)$ will precipitate and the $Ni^{2+}(aq)$ will remain in solution.

17-45 The K_{sp} expression for $CuS(s)$ is

$$K_{sp} = [Cu^{2+}][S^{2-}] = 6.3 \times 10^{-36} \text{ M}^2 \qquad \text{(Table 17-1)}$$

The solubility of CuS is

$$s = [Cu^{2+}] = \frac{6.3 \times 10^{-36} \text{ M}^2}{[S^{2-}]}$$

From Equation (17-18)

$$[S^{2-}] = \frac{1.1 \times 10^{-21} \text{ M}^3}{[H_3O^+]^2} \qquad (17\text{-}18)$$

At pH $= 2.0$

$$[H_3O^+] = 10^{-2.0} = 1.0 \times 10^{-2} \text{ M}$$

and thus

$$[S^{2-}] = \frac{1.1 \times 10^{-21} \text{ M}^3}{(1.0 \times 10^{-2} \text{ M})^2} = 1.1 \times 10^{-17} \text{ M}$$

Therefore, the solubility of CuS is

$$s = \frac{6.3 \times 10^{-36} \text{ M}^2}{1.1 \times 10^{-17} \text{ M}} = 5.7 \times 10^{-19} \text{ M}$$

17-47   The solubility product expression for PbS is

$$K_{sp} = [Pb^{2+}][S^{2-}] = 8.0 \times 10^{-28} \text{ M}^2 \qquad \text{(Table 17-1)}$$

Thus the solubility of PbS is

$$s = [Pb^{2+}] = \frac{8.0 \times 10^{-28} \text{ M}^2}{[S^{2-}]}$$

Substituting Equation (17-18) for $[S^{2-}]$ into the above equation for s, we obtain

$$s = \frac{8.0 \times 10^{-28} \text{ M}^2[H_3O^+]^2}{1.1 \times 10^{-21} \text{ M}^3} = 7.3 \times 10^{-7} \text{ M}^{-1}[H_3O^+]^2$$

Proceeding in an analogous manner, we find for the solubility of MnS as a function of $[H_3O^+]$

$$K_{sp} = [Mn^{2+}][S^{2-}] = 2.5 \times 10^{-13} \text{ M}^2 \qquad \text{(Table 17-1)}$$

$$s = [Mn^{2+}] = \frac{2.5 \times 10^{-13} \text{ M}^2}{[S^{2-}]} = \frac{2.5 \times 10^{-13} \text{ M}^2[H_3O^+]^2}{1.1 \times 10^{-21} \text{ M}^3}$$

$$= 2.3 \times 10^8 \text{ M}^{-1}[H_3O^+]^2$$

The $[H_3O^+]$ at which the solubility of PbS is 1×10^{-6} M is given by

$$1 \times 10^{-6} \text{ M} = 7.3 \times 10^{-7} \text{ M}^{-1}[H_3O^+]^2$$

Thus

$$[H_3O^+]^2 = \frac{1 \times 10^{-6} \text{ M}}{7.3 \times 10^{-7} \text{ M}^{-1}} = 1.37 \text{ M}^2$$

$$[H_3O^+] = 1.2 \text{ M}$$

or

$$pH = -0.08$$

The solubility of MnS at $[H_3O^+] = 1.2$ M is

$$s = (2.3 \times 10^8 \text{ M}^{-1})(1.2 \text{ M})^2 = 3.3 \times 10^8 \text{ M}$$

which is much greater than 0.025 M. At a pH of -0.08, essentially all of the $Pb^{2+}(aq)$ precipitates as $PbS(s)$, and essentially all the $Mn^{2+}(aq)$ remains in solution.

17-49 The solution is basic and thus the equation is

$$Sn(OH)_2(s) + OH^-(aq) \rightleftharpoons Sn(OH)_3^-(aq)$$

From Table 17-3, the equilibrium constant expression for this equation is

$$K = \frac{[Sn(OH)_3^-]}{[OH^-]} = 0.01 = \frac{s}{[OH^-]}$$

where we have used the fact that the solubility of $Sn(OH)_2$ is essentially equal to $[Sn(OH)_3^-]$. At pH = 13.0, $[H_3O^+] = 1.0 \times 10^{-13}$ M, and

$$[OH^-] = \frac{K_w}{[H_3O^+]} = \frac{1.00 \times 10^{-14} \text{ M}^2}{1.0 \times 10^{-13} \text{ M}} = 1.0 \times 10^{-1} \text{ M}$$

Thus

$$s = (0.01)[OH^-] = (0.01)(0.10 \text{ M}) = 1 \times 10^{-3} \text{ M}$$

17-51 The equation for the complexation equilibrium is

$$Al(OH)_3(s) + OH^-(aq) \rightleftharpoons Al(OH)_4^-(aq)$$

and the equilibrium constant expression is

$$K = \frac{[Al(OH)_4^-]}{[OH^-]} = 40$$

The solubility of $Al(OH)_3(s)$ in basic solution is

$$s = [Al(OH)_4^-] = 40[OH^-]$$

which is derived from the equilibrium expression. At pH = 12.0, pOH = 2.0, and

$$[OH^-] = 10^{-2.0} = 1.0 \times 10^{-2} \text{ M}$$

Thus

$$s = (40)(1.0 \times 10^{-2} \text{ M}) = 0.40 \text{ M}$$

17-53 The initial concentration of $Cl^-(aq)$ after mixing is

$$[Cl^-]_0 = \frac{(0.25 \text{ M})(0.100 \text{ L})}{(0.100 \text{ L} + 0.0050 \text{ L})} = 0.24 \text{ M}$$

The initial concentration of $Ag^+(aq)$ after mixing is

$$[Ag^+]_0 = \frac{(0.10 \text{ M})(0.0050 \text{ L})}{0.105 \text{ L}} = 4.8 \times 10^{-3} \text{ M}$$

and NO_3^- is a spectator ion. The value of Q_{sp} is

$$Q_{sp} = [Ag^+]_0[Cl^-]_0 = (4.8 \times 10^{-3} \text{ M})(0.24 \text{ M}) = 1.2 \times 10^{-3} \text{ M}^2$$

The value of K_{sp} for $AgCl(s)$ is $1.8 \times 10^{-10} \text{ M}^2$ (Table 17-1); thus,

$$\frac{Q_{sp}}{K_{sp}} = \frac{1.2 \times 10^{-3} \text{ M}^2}{1.8 \times 10^{-10} \text{ M}^2} = 6.7 \times 10^6 > 1$$

Thus $AgCl(s)$ will precipitate from the solution.

17-55 The initial concentration of $Pb^{2+}(aq)$ after mixing is

$$[Pb^{2+}]_0 = \frac{(3.00 \text{ M})(0.0400 \text{ L})}{0.060 \text{ L}} = 2.00 \text{ M}$$

The initial concentration of $I^-(aq)$ after mixing is

$$[I^-]_0 = \frac{(2.00 \times 10^{-3} \text{ M})(0.0200 \text{ L})}{0.060 \text{ L}} = 6.67 \times 10^{-4} \text{ M}$$

The value of Q_{sp} is

$$Q_{sp} = [Pb^{2+}]_0[I^-]_0^2 = (2.00 \text{ M})(6.67 \times 10^{-4} \text{ M})^2 = 8.90 \times 10^{-7} \text{ M}^3$$

The value of K_{sp} is $7.1 \times 10^{-9} \text{ M}^3$ (Table 17-1); thus

$$\frac{Q_{sp}}{K_{sp}} = \frac{8.90 \times 10^{-7} \text{ M}^3}{7.1 \times 10^{-9} \text{ M}^3} = 130 > 1$$

Because $Q_{sp}/K_{sp} > 1$, $PbI_2(s)$ will precipitate from the solution. Because $[Pb^{2+}]_0 \gg [I^-]_0$, essentially all of the $I^-(aq)$ is precipitated as $PbI_2(s)$, and the final equilibrium value of $[Pb^{2+}]$ will still be 2.00 M. Thus we have at equilibrium following the precipitation of $PbI_2(s)$

$$[Pb^{2+}]_0[I^-]^2 \simeq K_{sp} = 7.1 \times 10^{-9} \text{ M}^3$$

Therefore,

$$[I^-] = \left(\frac{7.1 \times 10^{-9} \text{ M}^3}{2.00 \text{ M}}\right)^{1/2} = 6.0 \times 10^{-5} \text{ M}$$

The moles of I^- that precipitates is given by

$$\left(\begin{array}{c}\text{moles of } I^- \\ \text{precipitated}\end{array}\right) = \left(\begin{array}{c}\text{initial} \\ \text{moles of } I^-\end{array}\right) - \left(\begin{array}{c}\text{final moles} \\ \text{of } I^-\end{array}\right)$$

$$= (6.67 \times 10^{-4} \text{ M} - 6.0 \times 10^{-5} \text{ M})(0.060 \text{ L})$$
$$= 3.64 \times 10^{-5} \text{ mol } I^-$$

The moles of $PbI_2(s)$ that precipitates is equal to one half the moles of I^- that precipitates because each mole of $PbI_2(s)$ contains two moles of I^-. Thus

$$\text{moles of } PbI_2(s) = \tfrac{1}{2}(3.64 \times 10^{-5} \text{ mol}) = 1.82 \times 10^{-5} \text{ mol}$$

The equilibrium concentrations following the precipitation of $PbI_2(s)$ are

$$[Pb^{2+}] = 2.00 \text{ M} \qquad\qquad [NO_3^-] = 2[Pb^{2+}]_0 = 4.00 \text{ M}$$
$$[Na^+] = [I^-]_0 = 6.67 \times 10^{-4} \text{ M} \qquad [I^-] = 6.0 \times 10^{-5} \text{ M}$$

17-57   The initial concentration of $Cl^-(aq)$ after mixing is

$$[Cl^-]_0 = \frac{(2.00 \text{ M})(0.100 \text{ L})}{0.200 \text{ L}} = 1.00 \text{ M}$$

The initial concentration of $Ag^+(aq)$ after mixing is

$$[Ag^+]_0 = \frac{(0.020 \text{ M})(0.100 \text{ L})}{0.200 \text{ L}} = 0.010 \text{ M}$$

Thus

$$Q_{sp} = [Ag^+]_0[Cl^-]_0 = (0.010 \text{ M})(1.00 \text{ M}) = 0.010 \text{ M}^2$$

and

$$\frac{Q_{sp}}{K_{sp}} = \frac{0.010 \text{ M}^2}{1.8 \times 10^{-10} \text{ M}^2} = 5.5 \times 10^7 > 1$$

Thus $AgCl(s)$ will precipitate. Because $AgCl(s)$ is insoluble, essentially all of the $Ag^+(aq)$ will precipitate from the solution. The number of moles of $AgCl(s)$ that precipitates is equal to the number of moles of $Ag^+(aq)$ initially present.

(a) moles of $AgCl(s) = $ moles of $Ag^+(aq) = (0.010 \text{ M})(0.200 \text{ L})$
$$= 2.0 \times 10^{-3} \text{ mol}$$

The number of grams of AgCl in 2.0×10^{-3} mol is

$$\text{g AgCl} = (2.0 \times 10^{-3} \text{ mol})\left(\frac{143.4 \text{ g AgCl}}{1 \text{ mol AgCl}}\right) = 0.29 \text{ g}$$

(b) The concentration of $Cl^-(aq)$ at equilibrium is

$$[Cl^-] = 1.00 \text{ M} - 0.010 \text{ M} = 0.99 \text{ M}$$

The concentration of Ag^+ at equilibrium can be found from the K_{sp} expression.

$$K_{sp} = [Ag^+][Cl^-] = [Ag^+][0.99 \text{ M}] = 1.8 \times 10^{-10} \text{ M}^2$$
$$[Ag^+] = \frac{1.8 \times 10^{-10} \text{ M}^2}{0.99 \text{ M}} = 1.8 \times 10^{-10} \text{ M}$$

This confirms the statement that essentially all the $Ag^+(aq)$ is precipitated as $AgCl(s)$.

17-59 The $Pb^{2+}(aq)$ is removed from solution by the formation of insoluble $PbSO_4(s)$, which passes out of the body through the large intestine.

17-61 The equation for the precipitation reaction is

$$Pb(NO_3)_2(aq) + 2NaOH(aq) \rightleftharpoons Pb(OH)_2(s) + 2NaNO_3(aq)$$

The precipitate dissolves via the process

$$Pb(OH)_2(s) + OH^-(aq) \rightleftharpoons Pb(OH)_3^-(aq)$$

17-63 Calcium ion forms an insoluble oxalate, $CaC_2O_4(s)$, which is removed by vomiting. The excess Ca^{2+} is removed by adding $MgSO_4(aq)$ to form $CaSO_4(s)$, which is insoluble in water and in stomach acid. Vomiting of the $CaC_2O_4(s)$ is necessary because the solubility of $CaC_2O_4(s)$ in stomach acid is sufficiently high to permit toxic levels of oxalic acid (a weak acid) to pass through the stomach walls into the bloodstream.

17-65 The equation for the precipitation reaction is

$$Zn(ClO_4)_2(aq) + 2KOH(aq) \rightleftharpoons Zn(OH)_2(s) + 2KClO_4(aq)$$

The precipitate dissolves via the formation of the $Zn(OH)_4^{2-}(aq)$ complex ion

$$Zn(OH)_2(s) + 2OH^-(aq) \rightleftharpoons Zn(OH)_4^{2-}(aq)$$

17-67 The fraction by mass of Cl in a sample of AgCl is equal to the ratio of the atomic mass of Cl to the formula mass of AgCl. Thus for the 4.188-g sample we have

$$(4.188 \text{ g}) \left(\frac{\text{atomic mass of Cl}}{\text{formula mass of AgCl}} \right) = (4.188 \text{ g}) \left(\frac{35.45}{143.4} \right)$$
$$= 1.035 \text{ g Cl}^-$$

Therefore the mass percentage of chloride in the original sample is

$$\left(\frac{1.035 \text{ g}}{2.000 \text{ g}} \right) \times 100 = 51.75\%$$

17-69 We have for the value of K_{sp} (Table 17-1) for the equilibrium

$$(1) \ AgCl(s) \rightleftharpoons Ag^+(aq) + Cl^-(aq) \qquad K_{sp} = 1.8 \times 10^{-10} \text{ M}^2$$

Addition of the K_{sp} equilibrium equation to the complexation equation

$$(2) \ Ag^+(aq) + 2NH_3(aq) \rightleftharpoons Ag(NH_3)_2^+(aq) \qquad K_{comp} = 2.0 \times 10^7 \text{ M}^{-2}$$

yields

$$(3) \ AgCl(s) + 2NH_3(aq) \rightleftharpoons Ag(NH_3)_2^+(aq) + Cl^-(aq)$$

for which we have

$$K_3 = K_{sp}K_{comp}$$
$$= (1.8 \times 10^{-10} \text{ M}^2)(2.0 \times 10^7 \text{ M}^{-2}) = 3.6 \times 10^{-3}$$

Because $K_3 \gg K_{sp}$ we have

$$[Ag(NH_3)_2^+] \gg [Ag^+]$$

and thus the solubility, s, is equal to

$$s = [Ag(NH_3)_2^+] = [Cl^-]$$

A concentration of 250 mg of AgCl in 100 mL of solution corresponds to a solubility of

$$s = \frac{(0.250 \text{ g})\left(\dfrac{1 \text{ mol AgCl}}{143.4 \text{ g AgCl}}\right)}{(0.100 \text{ L})} = 0.0174 \text{ M}$$

Substituting this value of s into the K_3 expression yields

$$3.6 \times 10^{-3} = \frac{[Ag(NH_3)_2^+][Cl^-]}{[NH_3]^2} = \frac{s^2}{[NH_3]^2}$$

or

$$[NH_3]^2 = \frac{(0.0174 \text{ M})^2}{3.6 \times 10^{-3}}$$

Thus

$$[NH_3] = 0.29 \text{ M}$$

17-71 (a) We have from Table 17-1

(1) $Ag_2CrO_4(s) \rightleftharpoons 2Ag^+(aq) + CrO_4^{2-}(aq)$ $\qquad K_{sp1} = 1.1 \times 10^{-12} \text{ M}^3$

(2) $AgBr(s) \rightleftharpoons Ag^+(aq) + Br^-(aq)$ $\qquad K_{sp2} = 5.0 \times 10^{-13} \text{ M}^2$

If we reverse Equation (2), multiply through by 2, and then add the result to Equation (1), we obtain Equation (a):

(a) $Ag_2CrO_4(s) + 2Br^-(aq) \rightleftharpoons 2AgBr(s) + CrO_4^{2-}(aq)$

Thus

$$K_{(a)} = \frac{K_{sp1}}{K_{sp2}^2}$$
$$= \frac{1.1 \times 10^{-12} \text{ M}^3}{(5.0 \times 10^{-13} \text{ M}^2)^2} = 4.4 \times 10^{12} \text{ M}^{-1}$$

(b) We have from Table 17-1

$$(1)\ PbCO_3(s) \rightleftharpoons Pb^{2+}(aq) + CO_3^{2-}(aq) \qquad K_{sp1} = 7.4 \times 10^{-14}\ M^2$$
$$(2)\ CaCO_3(s) \rightleftharpoons Ca^{2+}(aq) + CO_3^{2-}(aq) \qquad K_{sp2} = 2.8 \times 10^{-9}\ M^2$$

If we reverse Equation (2) and add the result to Equation (1), then we obtain Equation (b):

$$(b)\ PbCO_3(s) + Ca^{2+}(aq) \rightleftharpoons CaCO_3(s) + Pb^{2+}(aq)$$

Thus

$$K_{(b)} = \frac{K_{sp1}}{K_{sp2}}$$
$$= \frac{7.4 \times 10^{-14}\ M^2}{2.8 \times 10^{-9}\ M^2} = 2.6 \times 10^{-5}$$

17-73   The mass of $Pb(NO_3)_2$ present is given by

$$\binom{\text{mass of}}{Pb(NO_3)_2} = (12.79\ \text{g}\ PbCl_2)\left(\frac{1\ \text{mol}\ PbCl_2}{278.1\ \text{g}\ PbCl_2}\right)$$
$$\times \left(\frac{1\ \text{mol}\ Pb(NO_3)_2}{1\ \text{mol}\ PbCl_2}\right)\left(\frac{331.2\ \text{g}\ Pb(NO_3)_2}{1\ \text{mol}\ Pb(NO_3)_2}\right)$$
$$= 15.23\ \text{g}$$

The molarity of the solution is

$$[Pb(NO_3)_2] = \frac{(15.23\ \text{g})\left(\dfrac{1\ \text{mol}\ Pb(NO_3)_2}{331.2\ \text{g}\ Pb(NO_3)_2}\right)}{(0.200\ \text{L})} = 0.230\ M$$

E   ANSWERS TO THE SELF-TEST

1	soluble	**9**	$[Ca^{2+}][CO_3^{2-}]$
2	soluble	**10**	$[Mg^{2+}][OH^-]^2$
3	soluble	**11**	true
4	soluble	**12**	true
5	insoluble	**13**	false ($s = [OH^-]/2$)
6	insoluble	**14**	false (common-ion effect)
7	soluble	**15**	false ($[Ag^+][Cl^-] = K_{sp}$ in any aqueous solution in contact with solid AgCl.)
8	true		

16 the decrease in the solubility of an ionic solid that results when one of the constituent ions of the salt is added to the solution

17 decreased

18 increased [due to $Ag(NH_3)_2^+(aq)$ formation]

19 $AgCl(s) + 2NH_3(aq) \rightleftharpoons$
$Ag(NH_3)_2^+(aq) + Cl^-(aq)$

20 $AgCl(s)$ [The reaction is $Ag(NH_3)_2^+(aq) + 2H_3O^+(aq) + Cl^-(aq) \rightleftharpoons AgCl(s) + 2NH_4^+(aq) + 2H_2O(l)$.]

21 false

22 more (because CO_3^{2-} is the conjugate base of a weak acid)

23 because of the equilibrium $AgC_7H_5O_2(s) + H_3O^+(aq) \rightleftharpoons Ag^+(aq) + HC_7H_5O_2(aq) + H_2O(l)$

24 CO_2

25 true

26 $FeS(s) + 2H_3O^+(aq) \rightleftharpoons Fe^{2+}(aq) + H_2S(aq) + 2H_2O(l)$

27 true

28 true

29 true

30 true

31 true

32 false ($Al(OH)_3$ is soluble in strong acids and strong bases.)

33 $Al(OH)_3(s) \rightleftharpoons Al^{3+}(aq) + 3OH^-(aq)$

34 $Al(OH)_3(s) + 3H_3O^+(aq) \rightleftharpoons$
$Al^{3+}(aq) + 6H_2O(l)$

35 $Al(OH)_3(s) + OH^-(aq) \rightleftharpoons$
$Al(OH)_4^-(aq)$

36 $Zn(OH)_2(s) + 2OH^-(aq) \rightleftharpoons$
$Zn(OH)_4^{2-}(aq)$

37 $Cu(OH)_2(s)$ will

38 $Ag_2SO_4(s)$ will not

39 species present; that is, the anions and cations

40 $Ag^+(aq)$ . . . $AgCl(s)$

41 true

42 true

43 pH

44 false (e.g., FeS is soluble)

45 pH

46 false

47 true

OXIDATION-REDUCTION REACTIONS

A   OUTLINE OF CHAPTER 18

18-1   An oxidation state can be assigned to each atom in a chemical species.

The rules for the assignment of oxidation states to the elements in a chemical species are given on page 568.

Elements not covered by the rules can be assigned oxidation states by analogy with other elements in the periodic table.

18-2   Oxidation-reduction reactions involve the transfer of electrons from one reactant to another.

A decrease in oxidation state is called reduction.

An increase in oxidation state is called oxidation.

The reactant that contains the element that is reduced is called the oxidizing agent.

The reactant that contains the element that is oxidized is called the reducing agent.

An oxidizing agent acts as an electron acceptor.

A reducing agent acts as an electron donor.

18-3   Electron-transfer reactions can be separated into two half-reactions.

Electron-transfer reactions can be written as the sum of two half-reactions.

The half-reaction in which electrons appear on the right-hand side is the oxidation half-reaction.

The half-reaction in which electrons appear on the left-hand side is the reduction half-reaction. For example,

$$Zn(s) \longrightarrow Zn^{2+}(aq) + 2e^- \quad \text{(oxidation half-reaction)}$$
$$Cu^{2+}(aq) + 2e^- \longrightarrow Cu(s) \quad \text{(reduction half-reaction)}$$

18-4 Equations for oxidation-reduction reactions can be balanced by balancing each half-reaction separately.

> The procedure for balancing equations by the method of half-reactions is discussed in detail (pages 574 through 578).

> The procedure also applies to balancing half-reactions (Example 18-7).

18-5 Chemical equations for reactions occurring in basic solution are balanced slightly differently than reactions that take place in acidic solution.

> The procedure for balancing equations that occur in basic solution differs in step IV, in which OH^- is used instead of H^+.

18-6 Oxidation-reduction reactions are used in chemical analyses.

> A quantitative reaction is a reaction for which the equilibrium constant is very large.

B   SELF-TEST

1 The oxidation state of a free element is _____.

2 The alkali metals in compounds are always assigned an oxidation state of _____.

3 The alkaline earth metals in compounds are always assigned an oxidation state of _____.

4 Oxygen in compounds usually is assigned an oxidation state of _____ _____.

5 Hydrogen in compounds usually is assigned an oxidation state of _____ _____.

6 The sum of the oxidation states of each atom in a chemical species is equal to the charge on the species. *True/False*

7 The oxidation state of hydrogen in NaH is _____.

8 The oxidation state of chlorine is $NaCl$ is _____.

9 The oxidation state of sulfur in K_2S is _____.

10 The oxidation state of oxygen in Na_2O_2 is _____.

11 The oxidation state of sulfur in SO_4^{2-} is _____.

12 The oxidation state of an element in a compound is always equal to the actual charge on the atom. *True/False*

13 Oxidation states can be assigned by analogy with another element in the periodic table. *True/False*

14 The most electronegative element is ———————.

15 Fluorine in compounds is always assigned an oxidation state of ————.

16 The oxidation state of chlorine in ClF_3 is ————.

17 Oxidation-reduction reactions involve the transfer of ———————— between reactants.

18 Oxidation is an *(increase, decrease)* in oxidation state.

19 An oxidizing agent is the reactant that contains ————————————————————————.

20 An oxidizing agent acts as an electron *(donor, acceptor)*.
Consider the following chemical equation for Questions 21 through 26.

$$2AgNO_3(aq) + Ni(s) \longrightarrow Ni(NO_3)_2(aq) + 2Ag(s)$$

21 The element oxidized is ——————.

22 The element reduced is ——————.

23 The oxidizing agent is ——————.

24 The reducing agent is ——————.

25 The electron donor is ——————.

26 The electron acceptor is ——————.
Consider the following chemical equation for Questions 27 through 32.

$$FeCl_2(aq) + CeCl_4(aq) \longrightarrow FeCl_3(aq) + CeCl_3(aq)$$

27 The element oxidized is ——————.

28 The element reduced is ——————.

29 The oxidizing agent is ——————.

30 The reducing agent is ——————.

31 The oxidation half-reaction is ————————————.

32 The reduction half-reaction is ————————————.

Consider the following unbalanced half-reaction equation for Questions 33 through 36.

$$NO_3^-(aq) \longrightarrow N_2(g)$$

33 The equation when balanced with respect to nitrogen is _____

_____ .

34 Now balance the equation with respect to oxygen.

_____ .

35 Now balance the equation with respect to hydrogen in an acidic solution.

_____ .

36 The equation balanced with respect to charge is _____

_____ .

37 In a balanced oxidation-reduction equation, the number of electrons donated by the oxidation half-reaction must equal _____

_____ .

38 Reactions occurring in basic solutions may contain $H^+(aq)$ in the final balanced equation. *True/False*

39 Oxidation-reduction reactions can be used in chemical analysis. *True/False*

40 The equilibrium constant for a quantitative reaction is very *(large, small)*.

C CALCULATIONS YOU SHOULD KNOW HOW TO DO

1 Assign oxidation states to each atom in a molecule or an ion. This is done either

  (a) by applying the rules given in Section 18-1. See Examples 18-1 and 18-2 and Problems 18-1 through 18-10; or

  (b) by analogy with elements in the same group the periodic table. See Example 18-3 and Problem 18-9.

2 Use the method of half-reactions to balance oxidation-reduction equations. See Examples 18-6 and 18-8 and Problems 18-19 through 18-30.

3 Balance half-reactions. See Example 18-7 and Problems 18-31 through 18-36.

4 Carry out stoichiometric calculations involving oxidation-reduction reactions. See Example 18-9 and Problems 18-37 through 18-44.

D   SOLUTIONS TO THE ODD-NUMBERED PROBLEMS

18-1   (a) CaC_2. We assign calcium an oxidation state of $+2$ (rule 5).

(b) Al_2O_3. We assign aluminum an oxidation state of $+3$ (rule 6).

(c) VO_2^+. We assign oxygen an oxidation state of -2 (rule 8). The oxidation state, x, of vanadium is (rule 2)

$$x + 2(-2) = +1 \quad \text{or} \quad x = +5$$

(d) Co_3O_4. We assign oxygen an oxidation state of -2 (rule 8). The oxidation state, x, of cobalt is (rule 2)

$$3x + 4(-2) = 0 \quad \text{or} \quad x = \frac{8}{3}$$

18-3   (a) $LiAlH_4$. We assign lithium an oxidation state of $+1$ (rule 3) and aluminum an oxidation state of $+3$ (rule 6).
The oxidation state, x, of hydrogen is (rule 2)

$$+1 + (+3) + 4x = 0 \quad \text{or} \quad x = -1.$$

(b) ClO_2. We assign oxygen an oxidation state of -2 (rule 8). The oxidation state, x, of chlorine is (rule 2)

$$x + 2(-2) = 0 \quad \text{or} \quad x = +4$$

(c) $NaBrO_3$. We assign sodium an oxidation state of $+1$ (rule 3) and oxygen an oxidation state of -2 (rule 8). The oxidation state, x, of bromine is (rule 2)

$$+1 + x + 3(-2) = 0 \quad \text{or} \quad x = +5$$

(d) $HAsO_2$. We assign hydrogen an oxidation state of $+1$ (rule 7) and oxygen an oxidation state of -2 (rule 8). The oxidation state, x, of arsenic is (rule 2)

$$+1 + x + 2(-2) = 0 \quad \text{or} \quad x = +3$$

18-5   In each case we assign oxygen an oxidation state of -2 (rule 8) and calculate the oxidation state of nitrogen by rule 2. Thus

(a) NO_2; $x + 2(-2) = 0$, or $x = +4$.

(b) N_2O; $2x + (-2) = 0$, or $x = +1$.

(c) N_2O_5; $2x + 5(-2) = 0$, or $x = +5$.

(d) N_2O_3; $2x + 3(-2) = 0$, or $x = +3$.

18-7   (a) H_2CO. We assign oxygen an oxidation state of -2 (rule 8) and hydrogen an oxidation state of $+1$ (rule 7). The oxidation state, x, of carbon is (rule 2)

$$2(+1) + x + 1(-2) = 0 \quad \text{or} \quad x = 0$$

(b) CH_4. We assign hydrogen an oxidation state of $+1$ (rule 7). The oxidation state, x, of carbon is (rule 2)

$$x + 4(+1) = 0 \quad \text{or} \quad x = -4$$

(c) CH_3OH. We assign oxygen an oxidation state of -2 (rule 8) and hydrogen an oxidation state of $+1$ (rule 7). The oxidation state, x, of carbon is (rule 2)

$$x + 3(+1) + 1(-2) + 1(+1) = 0 \quad \text{or} \quad x = -2$$

(d) HCOOH. We assign oxygen an oxidation state of -2 (rule 8) and hydrogen an oxidation state of $+1$ (rule 7). The oxidation state, x, of carbon is (rule 2)

$$2(+1) + x + 2(-2) = 0 \quad \text{or} \quad x = +2$$

18-9   (a) $SbCl_3$. Because chlorine is more electronegative than antimony, we assign chlorine an oxidation state of -1, by analogy with fluorine (rule 4). Thus the oxidation state of antimony is (rule 2)

$$x + 3(-1) = 0 \quad \text{or} \quad x = +3$$

(b) Sb_4O_6. We assign oxygen an oxidation state of -2 (rule 8), and so the oxidation state of the antimony is (rule 2)

$$4x + 6(-2) = 0 \quad \text{or} \quad x = +3$$

(c) SbF_5^{2-}. We assign fluorine an oxidation state of -1 (rule 4), and so the oxidation state of the antimony is (rule 2)

$$x + 5(-1) = -2 \quad \text{or} \quad x = +3$$

(d) $SbCl_6^{3-}$. We assign chlorine an oxidation state of -1 [part (a)], and so the oxidation state of the antimony is (rule 2)

$$x + 6(-1) = -3 \quad \text{or} \quad x = +3$$

18-11   The oxidation state of iodine decreases from 0 in I_2 to -1 in NaI. Thus iodine is reduced and I_2 acts as the oxidizing agent. The oxidation state of sulfur increases from $+2$ in $Na_2S_2O_3$ to $+\frac{10}{4}$ in $Na_2S_4O_6$. Thus sulfur is oxidized and $Na_2S_2O_3$ acts as the reducing agent.

18-13   The oxidation state of nitrogen decreases from $+5$ in $NaNO_3$ to $+3$ in $NaNO_2$. Thus nitrogen is reduced; $NaNO_3$ is the oxidizing agent. The oxidation state of lead increases from 0 in Pb to $+2$ in PbO. Thus lead is oxidized; Pb is the reducing agent.

18-15   (a) The oxidation state of iodine increases from -1 in I^- to 0 in I_2. Thus iodine is oxidized and I^- acts as the reducing agent. The oxidation state of iron decreases from $+3$ in Fe^{3+} to $+2$ in Fe^{2+}. The iron is reduced and Fe^{3+} is the oxidizing agent. The half-reactions **are**

$$2I^-(aq) \longrightarrow I_2(s) + 2e^- \qquad \text{(oxidation half-reaction)}$$

$$Fe^{3+}(aq) + e^- \longrightarrow Fe^{2+}(aq) \qquad \text{(reduction half-reaction)}$$

(b) The oxidation state of titanium increases from $+2$ in Ti^{2+} to $+3$ in Ti^{3+}. Thus Ti^{2+} is oxidized and acts as the reducing agent. The oxidation state of cobalt decreases from $+2$ in Co^{2+} to 0 in Co. Thus $Co^{2+}(aq)$ is reduced and acts as the oxidizing agent. The half-reaction are

$$Ti^{2+}(aq) \longrightarrow Ti^{3+}(aq) + e^- \qquad \text{(oxidation half-reaction)}$$

$$Co^{2+}(aq) + 2e^- \longrightarrow Co(s) \qquad \text{(reduction half-reaction)}$$

18-17   The oxygen in KO_2 is in an unusual oxidation state $(-\frac{1}{2})$. The common oxidation state of oxygen is -2, and so the oxygen in KO_2 is easily reduced from $-\frac{1}{2}$ to -2, thus making KO_2 a strong oxidizing agent.

18-19   (a) The two half-reactions are

$$MnO \longrightarrow MnO_4^- \qquad \text{(oxidation)}$$

$$PbO_2 \longrightarrow Pb^{2+} \qquad \text{(reduction)}$$

The various steps are

$$MnO + 3H_2O \longrightarrow MnO_4^- + 6H^+ \qquad \text{(oxidation)}$$

$$PbO_2 + 4H^+ \longrightarrow Pb^{2+} + 2H_2O \qquad \text{(reduction)}$$

$$MnO + 3H_2O \longrightarrow MnO_4^- + 6H^+ + 5e^- \qquad \text{(oxidation)}$$

$$PbO_2 + 4H^+ + 2e^- \longrightarrow Pb^{2+} + 2H_2O \qquad \text{(reduction)}$$

$$2MnO + 6H_2O \longrightarrow 2MnO_4^- + 12H^+ + 10e^- \qquad \text{(oxidation)}$$

$$5PbO_2 + 20H^+ + 10e^- \longrightarrow 5Pb^{2+} + 10H_2O \qquad \text{(reduction)}$$

Thus the complete balanced equation is

$$2MnO(s) + 5PbO_2(s) + 8H^+(aq) \longrightarrow 2MnO_4^-(aq) + 5Pb^{2+}(aq) + 4H_2O(l)$$

electron donor	MnO
electron acceptor	PbO_2
oxidizing agent	PbO_2
reducing agent	MnO
species oxidized	Mn
species reduced	Pb

(b) The oxidation state of arsenic does not change in this reaction. The two half-reactions, balanced with respect to the elements other than oxygen and hydrogen are

$$As_2S_5 \longrightarrow 5HSO_4^- + 2H_3AsO_4 \qquad \text{(oxidation)}$$
$$NO_3^- \longrightarrow NO_2 \qquad \text{(reduction)}$$

The various steps are

$$As_2S_5 + 28H_2O \longrightarrow 5HSO_4^- + 2H_3AsO_4 + 45H^+ \qquad \text{(oxidation)}$$
$$NO_3^- + 2H^+ \longrightarrow NO_2 + H_2O \qquad \text{(reduction)}$$

$$As_2S_5 + 28H_2O \longrightarrow 5HSO_4^- + 2H_3AsO_4 + 45H^+ + 40e^- \qquad \text{(oxidation)}$$
$$NO_3^- + 2H^+ + e^- \longrightarrow NO_2 + H_2O \qquad \text{(reduction)}$$

$$As_2S_5 + 28H_2O \longrightarrow 5HSO_4^- + 2H_3AsO_4 + 45H^+ + 40e^- \qquad \text{(oxidation)}$$
$$40NO_3^- + 80H^+ + 40e^- \longrightarrow 40NO_2 + 40H_2O \qquad \text{(reduction)}$$

Thus the complete balanced equation is

$$As_2S_5(s) + 40NO_3^-(aq) + 35H^+(aq) \longrightarrow$$
$$5HSO_4^-(aq) + 2H_3AsO_4(aq) + 40NO_2(g) + 12H_2O(l)$$

electron donor	As_2S_5
electron acceptor	NO_3^-
oxidizing agent	NO_3^-
reducing agent	As_2S_5
species oxidized	S
species reduced	N

18-21 (a) The two half-reactions are

$$NH_4^+ \longrightarrow N_2O \qquad \text{(oxidation)}$$
$$NO_3^- \longrightarrow N_2O \qquad \text{(reduction)}$$

The various steps are

$$2NH_4^+ \longrightarrow N_2O \qquad \text{(oxidation)}$$
$$2NO_3^- \longrightarrow N_2O \qquad \text{(reduction)}$$

$$2NH_4^+ + H_2O \longrightarrow N_2O + 10H^+ \qquad \text{(oxidation)}$$
$$2NO_3^- + 10H^+ \longrightarrow N_2O + 5H_2O \qquad \text{(reduction)}$$

$$2NH_4^+ + H_2O \longrightarrow N_2O + 10H^+ + 8e^- \qquad \text{(oxidation)}$$
$$2NO_3^- + 10H^+ + 8e^- \longrightarrow N_2O + 5H_2O \qquad \text{(reduction)}$$

Thus the complete balanced equation is

$$2NH_4^+(aq) + 2NO_3^-(aq) \longrightarrow 2N_2O(g) + 4H_2O(l)$$

or

$$NH_4^+(aq) + NO_3^-(aq) \longrightarrow N_2O(g) + 2H_2O(l)$$

(b) The notation $\cdot 3H_3O$ signifies three waters of hydration. The two half-reactions are

$$Fe \longrightarrow Fe_2O_3 \cdot 3H_2O \qquad \text{(oxidation)}$$

$$O_2 \longrightarrow OH^- \quad \text{(basic solution)} \quad \text{(reduction)}$$

The various steps are

$$2Fe \longrightarrow Fe_2O_3 \cdot 3H_2O \qquad\qquad \text{(oxidation)}$$
$$O_2 \longrightarrow OH^- \qquad\qquad \text{(reduction)}$$

$$2Fe + 6H_2O \longrightarrow Fe_2O_3 \cdot 3H_2O \qquad \text{(oxidation)}$$
$$O_2 \longrightarrow OH^- + H_2O \qquad\qquad \text{(reduction)}$$

$$2Fe + 6H_2O + 6OH^- \longrightarrow Fe_2O_3 \cdot 3H_2O + 6H_2O \qquad \text{(oxidation)}$$
$$O_2 + 3H_2O \longrightarrow 4OH^- + H_2O \qquad\qquad \text{(reduction)}$$

$$2Fe + 6OH^- \longrightarrow Fe_2O_3 \cdot 3H_2O + 6e^- \qquad \text{(oxidation)}$$
$$O_2 + 2H_2O + 4e^- \longrightarrow 4OH^- \qquad\qquad \text{(reduction)}$$

$$4Fe + 12OH^- \longrightarrow 2Fe_2O_3 \cdot 3H_2O + 12e^- \qquad \text{(oxidation)}$$
$$3O_2 + 6H_2O + 12e^- \longrightarrow 12OH^- \qquad\qquad \text{(reduction)}$$

Thus the complete balanced equation is

$$4Fe(s) + 3O_2(g) + 6H_2O(l) \longrightarrow 2Fe_2O_3 \cdot 3H_2O(s)$$

18-23 (a) The two half-reactions are

$$Fe(OH)_2 \longrightarrow Fe(OH)_3 \quad \text{(oxidation)}$$
$$O_2 \longrightarrow OH^- \qquad \text{(basic solution) (reduction)}$$

The various steps are

$$Fe(OH)_2 \longrightarrow Fe(OH)_3 \qquad\qquad \text{(oxidation)}$$
$$O_2 \longrightarrow OH^- \qquad\qquad \text{(reduction)}$$

$$Fe(OH)_2 + H_2O \longrightarrow Fe(OH)_3 \qquad \text{(oxidation)}$$
$$O_2 \longrightarrow OH^- + H_2O \qquad\qquad \text{(reduction)}$$

$$Fe(OH)_2 + H_2O + OH^- \longrightarrow Fe(OH)_3 + H_2O \qquad \text{(oxidation)}$$

$$O_2 + 3H_2O \longrightarrow 4OH^- + H_2O \qquad \text{(reduction)}$$

$$Fe(OH)_2 + OH^- \longrightarrow Fe(OH)_3 + e^- \qquad \text{(oxidation)}$$

$$O_2 + 2H_2O + 4e^- \longrightarrow 4OH^- \qquad \text{(reduction)}$$

$$4Fe(OH)_2 + 4OH^- \longrightarrow 4Fe(OH)_3 + 4e^- \qquad \text{(oxidation)}$$

$$O_2 + 2H_2O + 4e^- \longrightarrow 4OH^- \qquad \text{(reduction)}$$

The complete balanced equation is

$$4Fe(OH)_2(s) + O_2(g) + 2H_2O(l) \longrightarrow 4Fe(OH)_3(s)$$

(b) The two half-reactions are

$$Cu \longrightarrow Cu^{2+} \qquad \text{(oxidation)}$$

$$NO_3^- \longrightarrow NO \qquad \text{(reduction)}$$

The various steps are

$$Cu \longrightarrow Cu^{2+} \qquad \text{(oxidation)}$$

$$NO_3^- + 4H^+ \longrightarrow NO + 2H_2O \qquad \text{(reduction)}$$

$$Cu \longrightarrow Cu^{2+} + 2e^- \qquad \text{(oxidation)}$$

$$NO_3^- + 4H^+ + 3e^- \longrightarrow NO + 2H_2O \qquad \text{(reduction)}$$

$$3Cu \longrightarrow 3Cu^{2+} + 6e^- \qquad \text{(oxidation)}$$

$$2NO_3^- + 8H^+ + 6e^- \longrightarrow 2NO + 4H_2O \qquad \text{(reduction)}$$

The final balanced equation is

$$3Cu(s) + 2NO_3^-(aq) + 8H^+(aq) \longrightarrow 2NO(g) + 3Cu^{2+}(aq) + 4H_2O(l)$$

18-25 (a) The two half-reactions are

$$I^- \longrightarrow I_3^- \qquad \text{(oxidation)}$$

$$IO_4^- \longrightarrow IO_3^- \qquad \text{(reduction)}$$

The various steps are

$$3I^- \longrightarrow I_3^- \qquad \text{(oxidation)}$$

$$IO_4^- \longrightarrow IO_3^- \qquad \text{(reduction)}$$

$$3I^- \longrightarrow I_3^- \qquad \text{(oxidation)}$$

$$IO_4^- \longrightarrow IO_3^- + H_2O \qquad \text{(reduction)}$$

$$3I^- \longrightarrow I_3^- \qquad \text{(oxidation)}$$

$$IO_4^- + 2H_2O \longrightarrow IO_3^- + H_2O + 2OH^- \qquad \text{(reduction)}$$

$$3I^- \longrightarrow I_3^- + 2e^- \qquad \text{(oxidation)}$$

$$IO_4^- + H_2O + 2e^- \longrightarrow IO_3^- + 2OH^- \qquad \text{(reduction)}$$

The final balanced equation is

$$IO_4^-(aq) + 3I^-(aq) + H_2O(l) \longrightarrow IO_3^-(aq) + I_3^-(aq) + 2OH^-(aq)$$

(b) The two half-reactions are

$$Cr^{2+} \longrightarrow Cr^{3+} \qquad \text{(oxidation)}$$

$$H_2MoO_4 \longrightarrow Mo \qquad \text{(reduction)}$$

The various steps are

$$Cr^{2+} \longrightarrow Cr^{3+} \qquad \text{(oxidation)}$$

$$H_2MoO_4 \longrightarrow Mo + 4H_2O \qquad \text{(reduction)}$$

$$Cr^{2+} \longrightarrow Cr^{3+} \qquad \text{(oxidation)}$$

$$H_2MoO_4 + 6H^+ \longrightarrow Mo + 4H_2O \qquad \text{(reduction)}$$

$$Cr^{2+} \longrightarrow Cr^{3+} + e^- \qquad \text{(oxidation)}$$

$$H_2MoO_4 + 6H^+ + 6e^- \longrightarrow Mo + 4H_2O \qquad \text{(reduction)}$$

$$6Cr^{2+} \longrightarrow 6Cr^{3+} + 6e^- \qquad \text{(oxidation)}$$

$$H_2MoO_4 + 6H^+ + 6e^- \longrightarrow Mo + 4H_2O \qquad \text{(reduction)}$$

The final balanced equation is

$$H_2MoO_4(aq) + 6Cr^{2+}(aq) + 6H^+(aq) \longrightarrow Mo(s) + 6Cr^{3+}(aq) + 4H_2O(l)$$

18-27 (a) The two half-reactions are

$$Cl^- \longrightarrow ClO_2^- \qquad \text{(oxidation)}$$

$$CrO_4^{2-} \longrightarrow Cr^{3+} \qquad \text{(reduction)}$$

The various steps are

$$2H_2O + Cl^- \longrightarrow ClO_2^- \qquad \text{(oxidation)}$$

$$CrO_4^{2-} \longrightarrow Cr^{3+} + 4H_2O \qquad \text{(reduction)}$$

$$Cl^- + 2H_2O \longrightarrow ClO_2^- + 4H^+ \qquad \text{(oxidation)}$$

$$CrO_4^{2-} + 8H^+ \longrightarrow Cr^{3+} + 4H_2O \qquad \text{(reduction)}$$

$$Cl^- + 2H_2O \longrightarrow ClO_2^- + 4H^+ + 4e^- \qquad \text{(oxidation)}$$
$$CrO_4^{2-} + 8H^+ + 3e^- \longrightarrow Cr^{3+} + 4H_2O \qquad \text{(reduction)}$$

$$3Cl^- + 6H_2O \longrightarrow 3ClO_2^- + 12H^+ + 12e^- \qquad \text{(oxidation)}$$
$$4CrO_4^{2-} + 32H^+ + 12e^- \longrightarrow 4Cr^{3+} + 16H_2O \qquad \text{(reduction)}$$

The final balanced equation is

$$4CrO_4^{2-}(aq) + 3Cl^-(aq) + 20H^+(aq) \longrightarrow$$
$$3ClO_2^-(aq) + 4Cr^{3+}(aq) + 10H_2O(l)$$

(b) The two half-reactions are

$$S_2O_3^{2-} \longrightarrow S_4O_6^{2-} \qquad \text{(oxidation)}$$
$$Cu^{2+} \longrightarrow Cu^+ \qquad \text{(reduction)}$$

The various steps are

$$2S_2O_3^{2-} \longrightarrow S_4O_6^{2-} \qquad \text{(oxidation)}$$
$$Cu^{2+} \longrightarrow Cu^+ \qquad \text{(reduction)}$$

$$2S_2O_3^{2-} \longrightarrow S_4O_6^{2-} + 2e^- \qquad \text{(oxidation)}$$
$$Cu^{2+} + e^- \longrightarrow Cu^+ \qquad \text{(reduction)}$$

$$2S_2O_3^{2-} \longrightarrow S_4O_6^{2-} + 2e^- \qquad \text{(oxidation)}$$
$$2Cu^{2+} + 2e^- \longrightarrow 2Cu^+ \qquad \text{(reduction)}$$

Addition of the two half reaction equations yields

$$2S_2O_3^{2-}(aq) + 2Cu^{2+}(aq) \longrightarrow S_4O_6^{2-}(aq) + 2Cu^+(aq)$$

18-29 The two half-reactions are

$$CrI_3 \longrightarrow CrO_4^{2-} + IO_4^- \qquad \text{(oxidation)}$$
$$Cl_2 \longrightarrow Cl^- \qquad \text{(reduction)}$$

The various steps are

$$CrI_3 \longrightarrow CrO_4^{2-} + 3IO_4^- \qquad \text{(oxidation)}$$
$$Cl_2 \longrightarrow 2Cl^- \qquad \text{(reduction)}$$

$$CrI_3 + 16H_2O \longrightarrow CrO_4^{2-} + 3IO_4^- \qquad \text{(oxidation)}$$
$$Cl_2 \longrightarrow 2Cl^- \qquad \text{(reduction)}$$

$$CrI_3 + 16H_2O + 32OH^- \longrightarrow CrO_4^{2-} + 3IO_4^- + 32H_2O \qquad \text{(oxidation)}$$
$$Cl_2 \longrightarrow 2Cl^- \qquad \text{(reduction)}$$

$$CrI_3 + 32OH^- \longrightarrow CrO_4^{2-} + 3IO_4^- + 16H_2O + 27e^- \qquad \text{(oxidation)}$$

$$Cl_2 + 2e^- \longrightarrow 2Cl^- \qquad \text{(reduction)}$$

$$2CrI_3 + 64OH^- \longrightarrow 2CrO_4^{2-} + 6IO_4^- + 32H_2O + 54e^- \qquad \text{(oxidation)}$$

$$27Cl_2 + 54e^- \longrightarrow 54Cl^- \qquad \text{(reduction)}$$

The balanced equation is

$$2CrI_3(s) + 27Cl_2(g) + 64OH^-(aq) \longrightarrow$$
$$2CrO_4^{2-}(aq) + 6IO_4^-(aq) + 54Cl^-(aq) + 32H_2O(l)$$

18-31 We follow the first five steps given in Section 18-4.

(a) $Mo^{3+} \rightarrow MoO_2^{2+}$
$Mo^{3+} + 2H_2O \rightarrow MoO_2^{2+}$
$Mo^{3+} + 2H_2O \rightarrow MoO_2^{2+} + 4H^+$
$Mo^{3+} + 2H_2O \rightarrow MoO_2^{2+} + 4H^+ + 3e^-$
$Mo^{3+}(aq) + 2H_2O(l) \rightarrow MoO_2^{2+}(aq) + 4H^+(aq) + 3e^-$

(b) $P_4 \rightarrow H_3PO_4$
$P_4 \rightarrow 4H_3PO_4$
$P_4 + 16H_2O \rightarrow 4H_3PO_4$
$P_4 + 16H_2O \rightarrow 4H_3PO_4 + 20H^+$
$P_4 + 16H_2O \rightarrow 4H_3PO_4 + 20H^+ + 20e^-$
$P_4(s) + 16H_2O(l) \rightarrow 4H_3PO_4(aq) + 20H^+(aq) + 20e^-$

(c) $S_2O_8^{2-} \rightarrow HSO_4^-$
$S_2O_8^{2-} \rightarrow 2HSO_4^-$
$S_2O_8^{2-} + 2H^+ \rightarrow 2HSO_4^-$
$S_2O_8^{2-} + 2H^+ + 2e^- \rightarrow 2HSO_4^-$
$S_2O_8^{2-}(aq) + 2H^+(aq) + 2e^- \rightarrow 2HSO_4^-(aq)$

18-33 The steps are

(a) $2WO_3 \rightarrow W_2O_5$
$2WO_3 + 2H^+ \rightarrow W_2O_5 + H_2O$
$2WO_3(s) + 2H^+(aq) + 2e^- \rightarrow W_2O_5(s) + H_2O(l)$

(b) $U^{4+} + 2H_2O \rightarrow UO_2^+ + 4H^+$
$U^{4+}(aq) + 2H_2O(l) \rightarrow UO_2^+(aq) + 4H^+(aq) + e^-$

(c) $Zn + 4H_2O \rightarrow Zn(OH)_4^-$
$Zn + 4H_2O + 4OH^- \rightarrow Zn(OH)_4^{2-} + 4H_2O$
$Zn + 4OH^- \rightarrow Zn(OH)_4^{2-} + 2e^-$
$Zn(s) + 4OH^-(aq) \rightarrow Zn(OH)_4^{2-}(aq) + 2e^-$

18-35 The steps are

(a) $2SO_3^{2-} \rightarrow S_2O_4^{2-}$
$2SO_3^{2-} \rightarrow S_2O_4^{2-} + 2H_2O$
$2SO_3^{2-} + 4H_2O \rightarrow S_2O_4^{2-} + 2H_2O + 4OH^-$
$2SO_3^{2-} + 2H_2O + 2e^- \rightarrow S_2O_4^{2-} + 4OH^-$
$2SO_3^{2-}(aq) + 2H_2O(l) + 2e^- \rightarrow S_2O_4^{2-}(aq) + 4OH^-(aq)$

(b) $2Cu(OH)_2 \rightarrow Cu_2O$

$2Cu(OH)_2 \rightarrow Cu_2O + 3H_2O$

$2Cu(OH)_2 + 2H_2O \rightarrow Cu_2O + 3H_2O + 2OH^-$

$2Cu(OH)_2 + 2e^- \rightarrow Cu_2O + 2OH^- + H_2O$

$2Cu(OH)_2(s) + 2e^- \rightarrow Cu_2O(s) + 2OH^-(aq) + H_2O(l)$

(c) $2AgO \rightarrow Ag_2O$

$2AgO \rightarrow Ag_2O + H_2O$

$2AgO + 2H_2O \rightarrow Ag_2O + H_2O + 2OH^-$

$2AgO + H_2O + 2e^- \rightarrow Ag_2O + 2OH^-$

$2AgO(s) + H_2O(l) + 2e^- \rightarrow Ag_2O(s) + 2OH^-(aq)$

18-37 We must first balance the equation for the reaction. The steps are

$$Sb^{3+} \longrightarrow Sb^{5+} \qquad \text{(oxidation)}$$

$$BrO_3^- \longrightarrow Br^- \qquad \text{(reduction)}$$

$$Sb^{3+} \longrightarrow Sb^{5+} \qquad \text{(oxidation)}$$

$$BrO_3^- \longrightarrow Br^- + 3H_2O \qquad \text{(reduction)}$$

$$Sb^{3+} \longrightarrow Sb^{5+} \qquad \text{(oxidation)}$$

$$BrO_3^- + 6H^+ \longrightarrow Br^- + 3H_2O \qquad \text{(reduction)}$$

$$Sb^{3+} \longrightarrow Sb^{5+} + 2e^- \qquad \text{(oxidation)}$$

$$BrO_3^- + 6H^+ + 6e^- \longrightarrow Br^- + 3H_2O \qquad \text{(reduction)}$$

The complete balanced equation is

$$BrO_3^-(aq) + 6H^+(aq) + 3Sb^{3+}(aq) \longrightarrow Br^-(aq) + 3Sb^{5+}(aq) + 3H_2O(l)$$

The number of millimoles of BrO_3^- is

$$n = MV = (0.125 \text{ mmol} \cdot \text{mL}^{-1})(43.7 \text{ mL}) = 5.46 \text{ mmol}$$

The number of moles of antimony that reacts with 5.46 mmol of BrO_3^- is

$$\text{mol } Sb^{3+} = (5.46 \text{ mmol } BrO_3^-)\left(\frac{3 \text{ mol } Sb^{3+}}{1 \text{ mol } BrO_3^-}\right)$$

$$= 16.4 \text{ mmol}$$

The number of grams of antimony that reacts is

$$g\ Sb = (1.64 \times 10^{-2} \text{ mol})\left(\frac{121.8 \text{ g Sb}}{1 \text{ mol Sb}}\right) = 2.00 \text{ g}$$

$$\%\ \text{antimony} = \frac{2.00 \text{ g Sb}}{9.62 \text{ g ore}} \times 100 = 20.8\%$$

18-39 We must first balance the equation for the reaction. The steps are

$$Sn^{2+} \longrightarrow Sn^{4+} \qquad \text{(oxidation)}$$
$$I_3^- \longrightarrow 3I^- \qquad \text{(reduction)}$$

$$Sn^{2+} \longrightarrow Sn^{4+} + 2e^- \qquad \text{(oxidation)}$$
$$I_3^- + 2e^- \longrightarrow 3I^- \qquad \text{(reduction)}$$

Thus

$$I_3^-(aq) + Sn^{2+}(aq) \longrightarrow Sn^{4+}(aq) + 3I^-(aq)$$

The number of millimoles of $I_3^-(aq)$ used is

$$\text{mmol } I_3^- = (0.556 \text{ M})(34.6 \text{ mL}) = 19.2 \text{ mmol}$$

The number of millimoles of Sn^{2+} oxidized is

$$\text{mmol } Sn^{2+} = (19.2 \text{ mmol } I_3^-)\left(\frac{1 \text{ mmol } Sn^{2+}}{1 \text{ mmol } I_3^-}\right) = 19.2 \text{ mmol}$$

The mass of tin is

$$\text{mass of tin} = (19.2 \times 10^{-3} \text{ mol Sn})\left(\frac{118.7 \text{ g Sn}}{1 \text{ mol Sn}}\right) = 2.28 \text{ g}$$

The percentage of tin in the sample is

$$\% \text{ tin} = \frac{2.28 \text{ g Sn}}{10.0 \text{ g sample}} \times 100 = 22.8\%$$

18-41 We must first balance the equation for the reaction. The steps are

$$2S_2O_3^{2-} \longrightarrow S_4O_6^{2-} \qquad \text{(oxidation)}$$
$$I_3^- \longrightarrow 3I^- \qquad \text{(reduction)}$$

$$2S_2O_3^{2-} \longrightarrow S_4O_6^{2-} + 2e^- \qquad \text{(oxidation)}$$
$$I_3^- + 2e^- \longrightarrow 3I^- \qquad \text{(reduction)}$$

Thus

$$I_3^-(aq) + 2S_2O_3^{2-}(aq) \longrightarrow S_4O_6^{2-}(aq) + 3I^-(aq)$$

The number of millimoles of $Na_2S_2O_3$ used to titrate the I_3^- is

$$\text{mmol } Na_2S_2O_3 = (0.330 \text{ M})(36.4 \text{ mL}) = 12.0 \text{ mmol}$$

The number of millimoles of I_3^- is

$$\text{mmol } I_3^- = (12.0 \text{ mmol Na}_2\text{S}_2\text{O}_3)\left(\frac{1 \text{ mmol } I_3^-}{2 \text{ mmol Na}_2\text{S}_2\text{O}_3}\right) = 6.00 \text{ mmol}$$

The concentration of I_3^- is

$$M = \frac{6.00 \text{ mmol}}{15.0 \text{ mL}} = 0.400 \text{ M}$$

18-43 The reactants and products are given as

$$\text{P}_4 + \text{BaSO}_4 \longrightarrow \text{BaS} + \text{P}_4\text{O}_{10}$$

The two half-reactions are

$$\text{P}_4 \longrightarrow \text{P}_4\text{O}_{10}$$
$$\text{BaSO}_4 \longrightarrow \text{BaS}$$

The steps in balancing the first half-reaction are

$$\text{P}_4 + 10\text{H}_2\text{O} \longrightarrow \text{P}_4\text{O}_{10}$$
$$\text{P}_4 + 10\text{H}_2\text{O} \longrightarrow \text{P}_4\text{O}_{10} + 20\text{H}^+$$
$$\text{P}_4 + 10\text{H}_2\text{O} \longrightarrow \text{P}_4\text{O}_{10} + 20\text{H}^+ + 20e^-$$

The steps in balancing the second half-reaction are

$$\text{BaSO}_4 \longrightarrow \text{BaS} + 4\text{H}_2\text{O}$$
$$\text{BaSO}_4 + 8\text{H}^+ \longrightarrow \text{BaS} + 4\text{H}_2\text{O}$$
$$\text{BaSO}_4 + 8\text{H}^+ + 8e^- \longrightarrow \text{BaS} + 4\text{H}_2\text{O}$$

The complete, balanced equation is

$$8\text{P}_4(s) + 20\text{BaSO}_4(s) \longrightarrow 8\text{P}_4\text{O}_{10}(s) + 20\text{BaS}(s)$$

Upon dividing through by 4, we obtain

$$2\text{P}_4(s) + 5\text{BaSO}_4(s) \longrightarrow 2\text{P}_4\text{O}_{10}(s) + 5\text{BaS}(s)$$

The amount of phosphorus required to react with 2.16 g of $\text{BaSO}_4(s)$ is

$$\text{mass P}_4 = (2.16 \text{ g BaSO}_4)\left(\frac{1 \text{ mol BaSO}_4}{233.4 \text{ g BaSO}_4}\right)\left(\frac{2 \text{ mol P}_4}{5 \text{ mol BaSO}_4}\right)\left(\frac{123.9 \text{ g P}_4}{1 \text{ mol P}_4}\right)$$
$$= 0.459 \text{ g}$$

18-45   The two half-reactions are

$$MnO_4^- \longrightarrow MnO_2$$
$$H_2O \longrightarrow O_2$$

The steps in balancing the first half-reaction are

$$MnO_4^- \longrightarrow MnO_2 + 2H_2O$$
$$MnO_4^- + 4H_2O \longrightarrow MnO_2 + 2H_2O + 4OH^-$$
$$MnO_4^- + 2H_2O + 3e^- \longrightarrow MnO_2 + 4OH^-$$

The steps in balancing the second half-reaction are

$$2H_2O \longrightarrow O_2$$
$$2H_2O + 4OH^- \longrightarrow O_2 + 4H_2O$$
$$4OH^- \longrightarrow O_2 + 2H_2O + 4e^-$$

Multiply the first balanced half-reaction by 4 and the second by 3 and add to obtain

$$4MnO_4^-(aq) + 2H_2O(l) \longrightarrow 4MnO_2(s) + 3O_2(g) + 4OH^-(aq)$$

18-47   (a) The half-reactions are

$$Cr_2O_7^{2-} \longrightarrow Cr^{3+}$$
$$I^- \longrightarrow I_3^-$$

The steps in balancing the first half-reaction are

$$Cr_2O_7^{2-} \longrightarrow 2Cr^{3+}$$
$$Cr_2O_7^{2-} \longrightarrow 2Cr^{3+} + 7H_2O$$
$$Cr_2O_7^{2-} + 14H^+ \longrightarrow 2Cr^{3+} + 7H_2O$$
$$Cr_2O_7^{2-} + 14H^+ + 6e^- \longrightarrow 2Cr^{3+} + 7H_2O$$

and the steps in balancing the second half-reaction are

$$3I^- \longrightarrow I_3^-$$
$$3I^- \longrightarrow I_3^- + 2e^-$$

We multiply the second half-reaction by 3 and add the two half-reactions to obtain

$$Cr_2O_7^{2-}(aq) + 9I^-(aq) + 14H^+(aq) \longrightarrow 2Cr^{3+}(aq) + 3I_3^-(aq) + 7H_2O(l)$$

(b) The two half-reactions are

$$IO_4^- \longrightarrow I_3^-$$

$$I^- \longrightarrow I_3^-$$

The steps in balancing the first half-reaction are

$$3IO_4^- \longrightarrow I_3^-$$

$$3IO_4^- \longrightarrow I_3^- + 12H_2O$$

$$3IO_4^- + 24H^+ \longrightarrow I_3^- + 12H_2O$$

$$3IO_4^- + 24H^+ + 22e^- \longrightarrow I_3^- + 12H_2O$$

and those for the second half-reaction are

$$3I^- \longrightarrow I_3^-$$

$$3I^- \longrightarrow I_3^- + 2e^-$$

Multiply the second half-reaction by 11 and add to obtain

$$3IO_4^-(aq) + 33I^-(aq) + 24H^+(aq) \longrightarrow 12I_3^-(aq) + 12H_2O(l)$$

18-49   The two half-reactions are

$$Ag^{2+} \longrightarrow Ag^+$$

$$H_2O \longrightarrow O_2$$

The steps in balancing the first half-reaction are

$$Ag^{2+} + e^- \longrightarrow Ag^+$$

and those for the second half-reaction are

$$2H_2O \longrightarrow O_2$$

$$2H_2O \longrightarrow O_2 + 4H^+$$

$$2H_2O \longrightarrow O_2 + 4H^+ + 4e^-$$

Multiply the first half-reaction by 4 and add the two half-reactions to obtain

$$4Ag^{2+}(aq) + 2H_2O(l) \longrightarrow 4Ag^+(aq) + O_2(g) + 4H^+(aq)$$

18-51   (a) The two half-reactions are

$$Cr_2O_7^{2-} \longrightarrow Cr^{3+}$$

$$H_2O_2 \longrightarrow O_2$$

The steps in balancing the first half-reaction are

$$Cr_2O_7^{2-} \longrightarrow 2Cr^{3+}$$

$$Cr_2O_7^{2-} \longrightarrow 2Cr^{3+} + 7H_2O$$

$$Cr_2O_7^{2-} + 14H^+ \longrightarrow 2Cr^{3+} + 7H_2O$$

$$Cr_2O_7^{2-} + 14H^+ + 6e^- \longrightarrow 2Cr^{3+} + 7H_2O$$

and the steps in balancing the second half-reaction are

$$H_2O_2 \longrightarrow O_2 + 2H^+$$

$$H_2O_2 \longrightarrow O_2 + 2H^+ + 2e^-$$

Multiply the second half-reaction by 3 and add

$$Cr_2O_7^{2-}(aq) + 8H^+(aq) + 3H_2O_2(aq) \longrightarrow 2Cr^{3+}(aq) + 3O_2(g) + 7H_2O(l)$$

(b) The two half-reactions are

$$Cr^{3+} \longrightarrow Cr^{2+}$$

$$Zn \longrightarrow Zn^{2+}$$

Both are balanced by just adding electrons

$$Cr^{3+} + e^- \longrightarrow Cr^{2+}$$

$$Zn \longrightarrow Zn^{2+} + 2e^-$$

and the complete, balanced equation is

$$2Cr^{3+}(aq) + Zn(s) \longrightarrow 2Cr^{2+}(aq) + Zn^{2+}(aq)$$

18-53 (a) If H_2O_2 is acting as an oxidizing agent, then the oxygen is reduced and the product is H_2O. The half-reaction and the steps to balance it are

$$H_2O_2 \longrightarrow H_2O$$

$$H_2O_2 \longrightarrow 2H_2O$$

$$H_2O_2 + 2H^+ \longrightarrow 2H_2O$$

$$H_2O_2 + 2H^+ + 2e^- \longrightarrow 2H_2O$$

$$H_2O_2(aq) + 2H^+(aq) + 2e^- \longrightarrow 2H_2O(l)$$

(b) If H_2O_2 is acting as a reducing agent, then the oxygen is oxidized and the product is O_2. The half-reaction and the steps to balance it are

$$H_2O_2 \longrightarrow O_2$$

$$H_2O_2 \longrightarrow O_2 + 2H^+$$

$$H_2O_2 \longrightarrow O_2 + 2H^+ + 2e^-$$

$$H_2O_2(aq) \longrightarrow O_2(g) + 2H^+(aq) + 2e^-$$

The reaction in which H_2O_2 oxidizes and reduces itself (disproportionation) is obtained by adding the two half-reactions

$$2H_2O_2(aq) \longrightarrow 2H_2O(l) + O_2(g)$$

18-55 The equations for the reactions that take place are

$$H_2S(g) + Cd^{2+}(aq) \longrightarrow CdS(s) + 2H^+(aq)$$

$$CdS(s) + I_2(aq) \longrightarrow CdI_2(aq) + S(s)$$

$$I_2(aq) + 2Na_2S_2O_3(aq) \longrightarrow Na_2S_4O_6(aq) + 2NaI(aq)$$

The excess of I_2 added is given by

$$\text{excess mmol } I_2 = (0.0750 \text{ M})(7.65 \text{ mL})\left(\frac{1 \text{ mmol } I_2}{2 \text{ mmol } Na_2S_2O_3}\right)$$
$$= 0.287 \text{ mmol}$$

The total quantity of I_2 used is

$$\text{total mmol } I_2 = (0.0115 \text{ M})(30.00 \text{ mL}) = 0.345 \text{ mmol}$$

and the quantity of I_2 that reacts with the $CdS(s)$ is

$$\text{mmol } I_2 = 0.345 \text{ mmol} - 0.287 \text{ mmol} = 0.058 \text{ mmol}$$

According to the above chemical equations, this is equal to the mmol of $H_2S(g)$, and so the mass of H_2S in the air is

$$\text{mass } H_2S = (0.058 \text{ mmol})\left(\frac{10^{-3} \text{ mol}}{1 \text{ mmol}}\right)\left(\frac{34.08 \text{ g } H_2S}{1 \text{ mol } H_2S}\right)$$
$$= 1.98 \times 10^{-3} \text{ g}$$

and the mass percentage of H_2S in the air is

$$\% \ H_2S = \left(\frac{1.98 \times 10^{-3} \text{ g}}{10.75 \text{ g}}\right) \times 100 = 0.018\%$$

18-57 The quantity of H_2SO_4 neutralized is

$$\text{mol } H_2SO_4 = (0.00250 \text{ M})(0.01850 \text{ L})\left(\frac{1 \text{ mol } H_2SO_4}{2 \text{ mol } NaOH}\right)$$
$$= 2.31 \times 10^{-5} \text{ mol}$$

According to the equation for the reaction between $H_2O_2(aq)$ and $SO_2(g)$, this is also equal to the number of moles of SO_2. The mass of SO_2 is given by

$$\text{mass } SO_2 = (2.31 \times 10^{-5} \text{ mol}) \left(\frac{64.06 \text{ g } SO_2}{1 \text{ mol } SO_2} \right) = 1.48 \times 10^{-3} \text{ g}$$

and the mass percentage of $SO_2(g)$ in the air is

$$\% \text{ } SO_2 = \left(\frac{1.48 \times 10^{-3} \text{ g}}{812.1 \text{ g}} \right) \times 100 = 1.82 \times 10^{-4}\%$$

E   ANSWERS TO THE SELF-TEST

1	0	22	silver
2	+1	23	$AgNO_3(aq)$
3	+2	24	$Ni(s)$
4	−2	25	$Ni(s)$
5	+1	26	$AgNO_3(aq)$
6	true	27	iron
7	−1	28	cerium
8	−1	29	$CeCl_4(aq)$
9	−2	30	$FeCl_2(aq)$
10	−1	31	$Fe^{2+}(aq) \rightarrow Fe^{3+}(aq) + e^-$
11	+6	32	$Ce^{4+}(aq) + e^- \rightarrow Ce^{3+}(aq)$
12	false	33	$2NO_3^-(aq) \rightarrow N_2(g)$
13	true	34	$2NO_3^-(aq) \rightarrow N_2(g) + 6H_2O(l)$
14	fluorine	35	$2NO_3^-(aq) + 12H^+(aq) \rightarrow$ $N_2(g) + 6H_2O(l)$
15	−1	36	$2NO_3^-(aq) + 12H^+(aq) + 10e^- \rightarrow$ $N_2(g) + 6H_2O(l)$
16	+3	37	the number of electrons that are accepted in the reduction half-reaction
17	electrons		
18	increase	38	false
19	the element that is reduced	39	true
20	acceptor	40	large
21	nickel		

ENTROPY AND GIBBS FREE ENERGY

A   OUTLINE OF CHAPTER 19

19-1   Not all spontaneous reactions evolve energy.

Exothermic reactions are energetically downhill. (Figure 19-1)

Highly exothermic reactions are spontaneous.

$\Delta H_{rxn}^\circ < 0$ is not sufficient to guarantee reaction spontaneity.

19-2   The second law of thermodynamics places an additional restriction on energy transfers.

Entropy places additional restrictions on energy transfers.

Entropy is denoted by S.

When energy is transferred only as heat at constant temperature, the entropy change is given by

$$\Delta S = \frac{q}{T} \tag{19-1}$$

The units of entropy are $J \cdot K^{-1}$.

The second law of thermodynamics states that the total entropy change for spontaneous processes must always be positive.

19-3   Entropy is a measure of the amount of disorder or randomness in a system.

Entropy arises from positional disorder and thermal disorder.

The entropy of a perfect crystal is zero at absolute zero.

The entropy of a substance at fixed pressure increases as the temperature increases (Figure 19-4).

The greater the number of ways that the energy can be distributed among the energy levels of a substance, the greater is the entropy of the substance.

19-4   There is an increase in entropy on melting and vaporization.

The entropy of the liquid phase of a substance is greater than the entropy of the solid phase at a given temperature and pressure.

The molar entropy change upon fusion is given by

$$\Delta S_{fus} = \frac{\Delta H_{fus}}{T_m} \qquad (19\text{-}2)$$

The entropy of the gaseous phase of a substance is greater than the entropy of the liquid phase at a given temperature and pressure.

The molar entropy change upon vaporization is given by

$$\Delta S_{vap} = \frac{\Delta H_{vap}}{T_b} \qquad (19\text{-}3)$$

Gases are more disordered than liquids and liquids are more disordered than solids.

$$\Delta S_{vap} > \Delta S_{fus}$$

19-5   The molar entropy depends on molar mass and molecular structure.

The standard (1 atm) molar entropy is denoted by $S°$.

The units of $S°$ are $J \cdot mol^{-1} \cdot K^{-1}$.

Values of $S°$ for some compounds are given in Table 19-1.

Greater mass leads to a greater capacity to take up energy and thus to a higher entropy.

The more atoms of a given mass in a molecule, the higher is the entropy.

The more complex a molecule, the higher is the molar entropy.

19-6 $\Delta S_{rxn}°$ equals the entropy of the products minus the entropy of the reactants.

For the reaction represented by the chemical equation

$$a\text{A} + b\text{B} \longrightarrow y\text{Y} + z\text{Z}$$
$$\Delta S_{rxn}° = yS°[\text{Y}] + zS°[\text{Z}] - aS°[\text{A}] - bS°[\text{B}] \qquad (19\text{-}6)$$

where $\Delta S_{rxn}°$ is the standard entropy change.

If there are more moles of gaseous products than reactants, then $\Delta S_{rxn}° > 0$.

19-7   Nature acts to minimize the energy and to maximize the entropy of all processes.

Reactions with $\Delta S_{rxn} > 0$ are entropy driven and are said to be entropy favored.

Reactions with $\Delta H_{rxn} < 0$ are energy (enthalpy) favored.

If $\Delta H_{rxn} < 0$ and $\Delta S_{rxn} > 0$, then the reaction is spontaneous.

If $\Delta H_{rxn} > 0$ and $\Delta S_{rxn} < 0$, then the reaction is not spontaneous.

19-8   The sign of ΔG_{rxn} determines whether or not a reaction is spontaneous.

The Gibbs free energy change for a reaction that occurs at constant temperature is given by

$$\Delta G_{rxn} = \Delta H_{rxn} - T \, \Delta S_{rxn} \qquad (19\text{-}7)$$

Chemical reactions seek a compromise between energy minimization and entropy maximization.

The Gibbs criteria for reaction spontaneity are

if $\Delta G_{rxn} < 0$, then the reaction is spontaneous

if $\Delta G_{rxn} > 0$, then the reaction is not spontaneous

if $\Delta G_{rxn} = 0$, then the reaction is at equilibrium

The Gibbs free energy is minimized in a spontaneous process.

The relationship between ΔG_{rxn}, the reaction quotient, Q, and the equilibrium constant, K, is

$$\Delta G_{rxn} = 2.30RT \, \log\left(\frac{Q}{K}\right) \qquad (19\text{-}8)$$

If $Q/K < 1$, then $\Delta G_{rxn} < 0$.
If $Q/K > 1$, then $\Delta G_{rxn} > 0$.
If $Q/K = 1$, then $\Delta G_{rxn} = 0$.

Spontaneous is not synonymous with immediate.

For a reaction to occur, ΔG_{rxn} must be less than zero, but $\Delta G_{rxn} < 0$ does not guarantee that the reaction will occur at an appreciable rate.

19-9   It is the sign of ΔG_{rxn} and not ΔG°_{rxn} that determines reaction spontaneity.

The standard Gibbs free energy change, denoted by ΔG°_{rxn}, is equal to ΔG_{rxn} when the reactants and products are at standard conditions.

The value of ΔG°_{rxn} is given

$$\Delta G^{\circ}_{rxn} = \Delta H^{\circ}_{rxn} - T \, S^{\circ}_{rxn} \qquad (19\text{-}7)$$

The standard Gibbs free energy change for a reaction is related to the equilibrium constant by

$$\Delta G^{\circ}_{rxn} = -2.30RT \, \log K \qquad (19\text{-}10)$$

The sign of ΔG°_{rxn} determines reaction spontaneity only when all the products and reactants are at standard conditions.

19-10 ΔG°_{rxn} can be calculated from tabulated ΔG°_{f} values.

The standard Gibbs free energy of formation of a compound, denoted by ΔG°_{f}, is equal to the value of ΔG°_{rxn} for the reaction in which one mole of the compound at standard conditions is formed from its constituent elements at standard conditions.

For the reaction represented by the chemical equation

$$aA + bB \longrightarrow yY + zZ$$

$$\Delta G^\circ_{rxn} = y \, \Delta G^\circ_f \, [Y] + z \, \Delta G^\circ_f \, [Z] - a \, \Delta G^\circ_f [A] - b \, \Delta G^\circ_f \, [B] \qquad (19\text{-}13)$$

Values of ΔG°_f for some compounds are given in Table 19-1.

19-11 The van't Hoff equation governs the temperature dependence of equilibrium constants.

The van't Hoff equation is

$$\log\left(\frac{K_2}{K_1}\right) = \frac{\Delta H^\circ_{rxn}}{2.30R}\left(\frac{T_2 - T_1}{T_1 T_2}\right) \qquad (19\text{-}15)$$

where K_2 is the equilibrium constant at temperature T_2 and K_1 is the equilibrium constant at T_1.

The value of ΔH°_{rxn} is assumed to remain constant over the temperature range T_1 to T_2.

The value of K increases with increasing T for an endothermic reaction.

The value of K decreases with increasing T for an exothermic reaction.

The Fischer-Tropsch synthesis involves the production of straight-chain hydrocarbons and alcohols from $H_2(g)$, $CO(g)$, and $CO_2(g)$.

B   SELF-TEST

1   All exothermic processes are spontaneous processes. *True/False*

2   All processes that lead to an increase in entropy are spontaneous. *True/False*

3   Entropy arises from _____ disorder and _____ disorder.

4   The entropy of liquid water increases when the temperature is raised from 25°C to 50°C at constant pressure because _____

_____ .

5   The entropy of water vapor *(increases, decreases)* when the volume of the gas is increased from 0.50 L to 1.0 L at 200°C.

6   The entropy of a substance increases upon melting because _____

_____ .

7   The entropy of a substance increases upon vaporization because _____

_____ .

8   The value of the molar entropy change of fusion is given by $\Delta S_{fus} =$ _____

    _____.

9   The value of the molar entropy change of vaporization is given by $\Delta S_{vap} =$

    _____.

10 The molar entropy of $H_2O(l)$ is *(greater than, less than, the same as)* the molar entropy
    of $H_2O(g)$ at the same temperature and pressure.

11 The entropy of gaseous molecules at 25°C and 1 atm is greater the greater the
    _____ of the molecule and the larger the number of _____ in the molecule.

12 The molar entropy of $C_2H_2(g)$ is less than the molar entropy of $C_2H_6(g)$ at the same
    temperature and pressure because _____

    _____.

13 The standard entropy change of the equation $2H_2O(l) \longrightarrow 2H_2(g) + O_2(g)$ is *(positive, negative)*.

14 The standard molar entropy change of the equation $2H_2O(l) \longrightarrow 2H_2(g) + O_2(g)$
    in terms of the standard molar entropies of products and reactants is given by
    $\Delta S_{rxn}^\circ =$ _____.

15 Isothermal processes that lead to a decrease in the Gibbs free energy are spontaneous processes. *True/False*

16 If $\Delta G_{rxn} < 0$, then the reaction is _____.

17 If $\Delta G_{rxn} > 0$, then the reaction is _____.

18 If $\Delta G_{rxn} = 0$, then the reaction is _____.

19 If a spontaneous reaction is endothermic, then the change in entropy for the reaction must be *(positive, negative)*.

20 The value of the Gibbs free energy change of a reaction run at constant temperature
    is related to the changes in enthalpy and entropy of the reaction by the equation
    $\Delta G_{rxn} =$ _____.

21 A spontaneous endothermic reaction is _____ driven.

22 A spontaneous reaction for which the entropy change is negative is
    _____ driven.

23   If the value of ΔG_{rxn} is 123 kJ, then the reaction *(is, is not)* spontaneous.

24   All reactions with $\Delta H_{rxn} < 0$ and $\Delta S_{rxn} > 0$ are _____.

25   All reactions with $\Delta H_{rxn} > 0$ and $\Delta S_{rxn} < 0$ are _____.

26   The value of ΔG_{rxn} is independent of temperature. *True/False*

27   The maximum amount of work that can be obtained from a reaction is equal to

_____.

28   The relation between ΔG_{rxn} and Q/K is $\Delta G_{rxn} = $ _____.

29   A reaction for which $Q/K < 1$ *(is, is not)* spontaneous.

30   The standard Gibbs free energy change of a reaction is the Gibbs free energy change

of the reaction when _____ .

31   The standard Gibbs free energy change of a reaction is related to the equilibrium

constant of the reaction by the equation $\Delta G_{rxn}^{\circ} = $ _____

_____ .

32   The equilibrium constant at $25\,^{\circ}C$ for the dissociation of acetic acid is 1.7×10^{-5} M.
The dissociation reaction *(is, is not)* spontaneous when run under standard condi-
tions.

33   Tables of standard molar Gibbs free energies of formation of compounds can be
used to calculate values of ΔG_{rxn}°. *True/False*

34   The standard Gibbs free energy change of the chemical equation

$$2H_2O(l) \longrightarrow 2H_2(g) + O_2(g)$$

can be calculated by using tables of standard molar Gibbs free energies of formation
and the relationship $\Delta G_{rxn}^{\circ} = $ _____ .

35   The value of ΔG_{rxn}° for the dissociation of acetic acid is 27.1 kJ. The reaction is not
spontaneous under any conditions. *True/False*

36   The value of ΔG_{rxn} for a reaction is -342 kJ. The reaction must proceed rapidly
toward equilibrium. *True/False*

37   The value of ΔG_f° for $O_2(g)$ at $25\,^{\circ}C$ is 0 kJ$\cdot$mol^{-1}. *True/False*

38   The value of ΔH_f° for $O_2(g)$ at $25\,^{\circ}C$ is 0 kJ$\cdot$mol^{-1}. *True/False*

39   The value of S° for $O_2(g)$ at $25\,^{\circ}C$ is 0 J$\cdot$K$^{-1}\cdot$mol^{-1}. *True/False*

40 The value of the equilibrium constant for a reaction does not change when the temperature increases. *True/False*

41 The van't Hoff equation governs the temperature dependence of ΔH_{rxn}°. *True/False*

42 The van't Hoff equation is

43 For an exothermic reaction the value of the equilibrium constant *(increases, decreases)* with increasing temperature.

C   CALCULATIONS YOU SHOULD KNOW HOW TO DO

1 Calculate the values of ΔS_{fus} and ΔS_{vap} by using Equations (19-2) and (19-3). See Example 19-2 and Problems 19-1 through 19-5.

2 Calculate ΔS_{rxn}° from S° values of the reactants and products given in Table 19-1. See Example 19-4 and Problems 19-19 through 19-30.

3 Calculate ΔG_{rxn} by using the equation $\Delta G_{rxn} = \Delta H_{rxn} - T \Delta S_{rxn}$. See Problems 19-23 through 19-30.

4 Calculate ΔG_{rxn}° and ΔG_{rxn} given the equilibrium constant by using the equations $\Delta G_{rxn}^{\circ} = -2.30RT \log K$ and $\Delta G_{rxn} = 2.30RT \log(Q/K)$. See Examples 19-5, 19-6, and 19-7 and Problems 19-31 through 19-40.

5 Calculate ΔG_{rxn}° by using tabulated ΔG_{f}° values of the reactants and products given in Table 19-1. See Examples 19-8 and 19-9 and Problems 19-41 through 19-50.

6 Use the van't Hoff equation to calculate the value of the equilibrium constant at some other temperature. See Example 19-10 and Problems 19-55 and 19-56.

7 Use the van't Hoff equation to calculate the value of ΔH_{rxn}°. See Problems 19-51 through 19-54.

D   SOLUTIONS TO THE ODD-NUMBERED PROBLEMS

19-1   The values of ΔS_{fus} and ΔS_{vap} are given by

$$\Delta S_{fus} = \frac{\Delta H_{fus}}{T_m} \qquad \Delta S_{vap} = \frac{\Delta H_{vap}}{T_b}$$

where T_m and T_b are the melting and boiling points, respectively, on the Kelvin temperature scale. Thus we have for CH_4

$$\Delta S_{fus} = \frac{(0.9370 \text{ kJ}\cdot\text{mol}^{-1})(1000 \text{ J}\cdot\text{kJ}^{-1})}{90.7 \text{ K}} = 10.3 \text{ J}\cdot\text{K}^{-1}\cdot\text{mol}^{-1}$$

$$\Delta S_{vap} = \frac{8907 \text{ J}\cdot\text{mol}^{-1}}{109.2 \text{ K}} = 81.57 \text{ J}\cdot\text{K}^{-1}\cdot\text{mol}^{-1}$$

For C_2H_6

$$\Delta S_{fus} = \frac{2859 \text{ J}\cdot\text{mol}^{-1}}{89.9 \text{ K}} = 31.8 \text{ J}\cdot\text{K}^{-1}\cdot\text{mol}^{-1}$$

$$\Delta S_{vap} = \frac{15.65 \times 10^3 \text{ J}\cdot\text{mol}^{-1}}{184.6 \text{ K}} = 84.78 \text{ J}\cdot\text{K}^{-1}\cdot\text{mol}^{-1}$$

For C_3H_8

$$\Delta S_{fus} = \frac{3525 \text{ J}\cdot\text{mol}^{-1}}{91.5 \text{ K}} = 38.5 \text{ J}\cdot\text{K}^{-1}\cdot\text{mol}^{-1}$$

$$\Delta S_{vap} = \frac{20.13 \times 10^3 \text{ J}\cdot\text{mol}^{-1}}{231.1 \text{ K}} = 87.11 \text{ J}\cdot\text{K}^{-1}\cdot\text{mol}^{-1}$$

19-3 We calculate ΔS_{fus} by using the relationship

$$\Delta S_{fus} = \frac{\Delta H_{fus}}{T_m}$$

Using the values of T_m and ΔH_{fus} given, we have

$$CH_3OH \quad \Delta S_{fus} = \frac{3.177 \times 10^3 \text{ J}\cdot\text{mol}^{-1}}{175.4 \text{ K}} = 18.11 \text{ J}\cdot\text{K}^{-1}\cdot\text{mol}^{-1}$$

$$C_2H_5OH \quad \Delta S_{fus} = \frac{5.021 \times 10^3 \text{ J}\cdot\text{mol}^{-1}}{158.7 \text{ K}} = 31.64 \text{ J}\cdot\text{K}^{-1}\cdot\text{mol}^{-1}$$

$$C_3H_7OH \quad \Delta S_{fus} = \frac{5.195 \times 10^3 \text{ J}\cdot\text{mol}^{-1}}{147.1 \text{ K}} = 35.32 \text{ J}\cdot\text{K}^{-1}\cdot\text{mol}^{-1}$$

We calculate ΔS_{vap} by using the relationship

$$\Delta S_{vap} = \frac{\Delta H_{vap}}{T_b}$$

Using the values of T_b and ΔH_{fus} given, we have

$$CH_3OH \qquad \Delta S_{vap} = \frac{37.57 \times 10^3 \text{ J} \cdot \text{mol}^{-1}}{338.11 \text{ K}} = 111.1 \text{ J} \cdot \text{K}^{-1} \cdot \text{mol}^{-1}$$

$$C_2H_5OH \qquad \Delta S_{vap} = \frac{40.48 \times 10^3 \text{ J} \cdot \text{mol}^{-1}}{351.7 \text{ K}} = 115.1 \text{ J} \cdot \text{K}^{-1} \cdot \text{mol}^{-1}$$

$$C_3H_7OH \qquad \Delta S_{vap} = \frac{43.60 \times 10^3 \text{ J} \cdot \text{mol}^{-1}}{370.6 \text{ K}} = 117.7 \text{ J} \cdot \text{K}^{-1} \cdot \text{mol}^{-1}$$

19-5 $\qquad H_2S \qquad \Delta S_{fus} = \dfrac{\Delta H_{fus}}{T_m} = \dfrac{2.38 \times 10^3 \text{ J} \cdot \text{mol}^{-1}}{187.6 \text{ K}} = 12.7 \text{ J} \cdot \text{K}^{-1} \cdot \text{mol}^{-1}$

$$\Delta S_{vap} = \frac{\Delta H_{vap}}{T_b} = \frac{18.7 \times 10^3 \text{ J} \cdot \text{mol}^{-1}}{212.5 \text{ K}} = 88.0 \text{ J} \cdot \text{K}^{-1} \cdot \text{mol}^{-1}$$

From Example 19-2 we have for H_2O

$$\Delta S_{fus} = 22.1 \text{ J} \cdot \text{K}^{-1} \cdot \text{mol}^{-1}$$
$$\Delta S_{vap} = 109 \text{ J} \cdot \text{K}^{-1} \cdot \text{mol}^{-1}$$

The larger values of ΔS_{fus} and ΔS_{vap} for H_2O are a result of the breaking of hydrogen bonds in the processes solid $\rightarrow$ liquid and liquid $\rightarrow$ gas. The hydrogen bonds make for a higher degree of order and thus their breaking produces a greater increase in disorder.

19-7 (a) The mass of D_2O is greater than the mass of H_2O. Thus we predict for the standard molar entropies of the gases

$$S°(H_2O) < S°(D_2O)$$

(b) Because of its ring structure, ethylene oxide has less freedom of movement than ethanol. Thus we predict that

$$S°(\text{ethylene oxide}) < S°(\text{ethanol})$$

(c) Because of its ring structure, pyrrolidine has less freedom of movement than butyl amine. Thus we predict that

$$S°(\text{pyrrolidine}) < S°(\text{butyl amine})$$

19-9 The molecular masses are, approximately, for CH_3Cl, 50.5; for CH_4, 16.0; and for CH_3OH, 32. The structure and numbers of atoms are about the same; thus mass is the dominant factor, and we predict

$$S°(CH_4) < S°(CH_3OH) < S°(CH_3Cl)$$

19-11 The compound $Fe_3O_4(s)$ contains more atoms and has a greater mass than $Fe_2O_3(s)$. Thus we would expect that

$$S°(Fe_2O_3) < S°(Fe_3O_4)$$

19-13 Bromine molecules in $Br_2(l)$ are much more restricted in movement than bromine molecules in $Br_2(g)$, which are free to move through the gas. The positional disorder in the gaseous state is greater than in the liquid state; thus the entropy of bromine is greater in the gaseous state than in the liquid state at a given temperature and pressure.

19-15 (a) The argon atoms have a greater freedom of movement in the gaseous state. The entropy will increase.

(b) The oxygen atoms have a greater freedom of movement at lower pressure. The entropy will increase.

(c) Copper atoms have a greater thermal disorder at a higher temperature. The entropy will increase.

(d) The CO_2 molecules have a greater freedom of movement in the gaseous state. The entropy will decrease.

19-17 (a) We have the same number of moles of gaseous reactant and gaseous product ($\Delta n = 0$).

(b) We have two moles of gaseous reactants and no moles of gaseous products ($\Delta n = -2$).

(c) We have four moles of gaseous reactants and two moles of gaseous products ($\Delta n = -2$).

(d) We have one mole of gaseous reactant and two moles of gaseous products ($\Delta n = +1$).

The value of ΔS°_{rxn} increases as the net change in the number of moles of gas increases; thus

$$\Delta S^\circ_{rxn}(c) \approx \Delta S^\circ_{rxn}(b) < \Delta S^\circ_{rxn}(a) < \Delta S^\circ_{rxn}(d)$$

19-19 The value of ΔS°_{rxn} is given by

$$\Delta S^\circ_{rxn} = S^\circ(\text{products}) - S^\circ(\text{reactants})$$

(a) $\Delta S^\circ_{rxn} = 4S^\circ[NO_2(g)] + 6S^\circ[H_2O(g)] - 4S^\circ[NH_3(g)] - 7S^\circ[O_2(g)]$
$\Delta S^\circ_{rxn} = (4\ \text{mol})(240.4\ \text{J}\cdot\text{K}^{-1}\cdot\text{mol}^{-1}) + (6\ \text{mol})(188.7\ \text{J}\cdot\text{K}^{-1}\cdot\text{mol}^{-1})$
$\qquad - (4\ \text{mol})(192.5\ \text{J}\cdot\text{K}^{-1}\cdot\text{mol}^{-1}) - (7\ \text{mol})(205.0\ \text{J}\cdot\text{K}^{-1}\cdot\text{mol}^{-1})$
$\qquad = -111.2\ \text{J}\cdot\text{K}^{-1}$

(b) $\Delta S^\circ_{rxn} = S^\circ[CH_3OH(l)] - S^\circ[CO(g)] - 2S^\circ[H_2(g)]$
$\qquad = (1\ \text{mol})(126.9\ \text{J}\cdot\text{K}^{-1}\cdot\text{mol}^{-1}) - (1\ \text{mol})(197.8\ \text{J}\cdot\text{K}^{-1}\cdot\text{mol}^{-1})$
$\qquad - (2\ \text{mol})(130.6\ \text{J}\cdot\text{K}^{-1}\cdot\text{mol}^{-1})$
$\qquad = -332.1\ \text{J}\cdot\text{K}^{-1}$

(c) $\Delta S^\circ_{rxn} = S^\circ[CO(g)] + S^\circ[H_2(g)] - S^\circ[C(s)] - S^\circ[H_2O(g)]$
$\qquad = (1\ \text{mol})(197.8\ \text{J}\cdot\text{K}^{-1}\cdot\text{mol}^{-1}) + (1\ \text{mol})(130.6\ \text{J}\cdot\text{K}^{-1}\cdot\text{mol}^{-1})$
$\qquad - (1\ \text{mol})(5.74\ \text{J}\cdot\text{K}^{-1}\cdot\text{mol}^{-1}) - (1\ \text{mol})(188.7\ \text{J}\cdot\text{K}^{-1}\cdot\text{mol}^{-1})$
$\qquad = 134.0\ \text{J}\cdot\text{K}^{-1}$

The graphite form of $C(s)$ is used here.

(d) $\Delta S^\circ_{rxn} = 2S^\circ[CO_2(g)] - 2S^\circ[CO(g)] - S^\circ[O_2(g)]$

$= (2 \text{ mol})(213.6 \text{ J} \cdot \text{K}^{-1} \cdot \text{mol}^{-1}) - (2 \text{ mol})(197.8 \text{ J} \cdot \text{K}^{-1} \cdot \text{mol}^{-1})$

$- (1 \text{ mol})(205.0 \text{ J} \cdot \text{K}^{-1} \cdot \text{mol}^{-1})$

$= -173.4 \text{ J} \cdot \text{K}^{-1}$

19-21   The value of ΔS°_{rxn} is given by

$$\Delta S^\circ_{rxn} = S^\circ(\text{products}) - S^\circ(\text{reactants})$$

(a) $\Delta S^\circ_{rxn} = S^\circ[CO_2(g)] - S^\circ[C(s)] - S^\circ[O_2(g)]$

$= (1 \text{ mol})(213.6 \text{ J} \cdot \text{K}^{-1} \cdot \text{mol}^{-1}) - (1 \text{ mol})(5.74 \text{ J} \cdot \text{K}^{-1} \cdot \text{mol}^{-1})$

$- (1 \text{ mol})(205.0 \text{ J} \cdot \text{K}^{-1} \cdot \text{mol}^{-1})$

$= 2.9 \text{ J} \cdot \text{K}^{-1}$

(b) $\Delta S^\circ_{rxn} = 2S^\circ[SO_3(g)] - 2S^\circ[SO_2(g)] - S^\circ[O_2(g)]$

$= (2 \text{ mol})(256.3 \text{ J} \cdot \text{K}^{-1} \cdot \text{mol}^{-1}) - (2 \text{ mol})(248.4 \text{ J} \cdot \text{K}^{-1} \cdot \text{mol}^{-1})$

$- (1 \text{ mol})(205.0 \text{ J} \cdot \text{K}^{-1} \cdot \text{mol}^{-1})$

$= -189.2 \text{ J} \cdot \text{K}^{-1}$

(c) $\Delta S^\circ_{rxn} = S^\circ[CO_2(g)] + 2S^\circ[H_2O(l)] - S^\circ[CH_4(g)] - 2S^\circ[O_2(g)]$

$= (1 \text{ mol})(213.6 \text{ J} \cdot \text{K}^{-1} \cdot \text{mol}^{-1}) + (2 \text{ mol})(69.9 \text{ J} \cdot \text{K}^{-1} \cdot \text{mol}^{-1})$

$- (1 \text{ mol})(186.2 \text{ J} \cdot \text{K}^{-1} \cdot \text{mol}^{-1}) - (2 \text{ mol})(205.0 \text{ J} \cdot \text{K}^{-1} \cdot \text{mol}^{-1})$

$= -242.8 \text{ J} \cdot \text{K}^{-1}$

(d) $\Delta S^\circ_{rxn} = S^\circ[C_2H_4(g)] - S^\circ[C_2H_2(g)] - S^\circ[H_2(g)]$

$= (1 \text{ mol})(219.6 \text{ J} \cdot \text{K}^{-1} \cdot \text{mol}^{-1}) - (1 \text{ mol})(200.8 \text{ J} \cdot \text{K}^{-1} \cdot \text{mol}^{-1})$

$- (1 \text{ mol})(130.6 \text{ J} \cdot \text{K}^{-1} \cdot \text{mol}^{-1})$

$= -111.8 \text{ J} \cdot \text{K}^{-1}$

19-23   The reaction is spontaneous, because water spontaneously evaporates if the pressure of the water vapor is less than $P^\circ_{H_2O}$. Because the reaction is spontaneous, the sign of ΔG_{rxn} is negative. We learned in Chapter 5 that it requires energy to vaporize a liquid. Thus the sign of ΔH_{rxn} is positive; ΔS_{vap} is also positive (liquid $\rightarrow$ gas). Thus vaporization is entropy driven, because

$$\Delta H_{rxn} - T \Delta S_{rxn} < 0$$

and the negative $-T \Delta S_{rxn}$ term offsets the positive ΔH_{rxn} term.

19-25   The value of ΔS°_{rxn} is given by

$$\Delta S^\circ_{rxn} = S^\circ(\text{products}) - S^\circ(\text{reactants}) = S^\circ[C_6H_6(l)] - 3S^\circ[C_2H_2(g)]$$

$= (1 \text{ mol})(172.8 \text{ J} \cdot \text{K}^{-1} \cdot \text{mol}^{-1}) - (3 \text{ mol})(200.8 \text{ J} \cdot \text{K}^{-1} \cdot \text{mol}^{-1})$

$= -429.6 \text{ J} \cdot \text{K}^{-1}$

We can calculate ΔG°_{rxn} by using the relationship

$$\Delta G^\circ_{rxn} = \Delta H^\circ_{rxn} - T \Delta S^\circ_{rxn}$$

$$= -631 \text{ kJ} - (298 \text{ K})(-429.6 \text{ J} \cdot \text{K}^{-1})\left(\frac{1 \text{ kJ}}{1000 \text{ J}}\right) = -503 \text{ kJ}$$

The reaction is spontaneous in the direction

$$3C_2H_2(g) \longrightarrow C_6H_6(l)$$

when both $C_2H_2(g)$ and $C_6H_6(l)$ are at 1 atm and 25°C.

19-27 $\Delta S^\circ_{rxn} = 2S^\circ[CO_2(g)] + 2S^\circ[H_2O(g)] - S^\circ[C_2H_4(g)] - 3S^\circ[O_2(g)]$
$$= (2 \text{ mol})(213.6 \text{ J} \cdot \text{K}^{-1} \cdot \text{mol}^{-1}) + (2 \text{ mol})(188.7 \text{ J} \cdot \text{K}^{-1} \cdot \text{mol}^{-1})$$
$$- (1 \text{ mol})(219.6 \text{ J} \cdot \text{K}^{-1} \cdot \text{mol}^{-1}) - (3 \text{ mol})(205.0 \text{ J} \cdot \text{K}^{-1} \cdot \text{mol}^{-1})$$
$$= -30.0 \text{ J} \cdot \text{K}^{-1}$$

We calculate ΔG°_{rxn} by using

$$\Delta G^\circ_{rxn} = \Delta H^\circ_{rxn} - T\,\Delta S^\circ_{rxn}$$
$$= -1323 \text{ kJ} - (298 \text{ K})(-30.0 \text{ J} \cdot \text{K}^{-1})\left(\frac{1 \text{ kJ}}{1000 \text{ J}}\right) = -1314 \text{ kJ}$$

Thus when all the reactants and products are at standard conditions the reaction is spontaneous in the direction

$$C_2H_4(g) + 3O_2(g) \longrightarrow 2CO_2(g) + 2H_2O(g)$$

The value of ΔG_{rxn} is given by

$$\Delta G_{rxn} = \Delta G^\circ_{rxn} + 2.30RT \log Q$$

where

$$Q = \frac{P^2_{CO_2} P^2_{H_2O}}{P_{C_2H_4} P^3_{O_2}}$$

Thus

$$\Delta G_{rxn} = -1314 \text{ kJ} + \frac{(2.30)(8.314 \text{ J} \cdot \text{K}^{-1})(298.2 \text{ K})}{(1000 \text{ J} \cdot \text{kJ}^{-1})}$$
$$\times \log\left[\frac{(20 \text{ atm})^2(0.010 \text{ atm})^2}{(0.010 \text{ atm})(0.020 \text{ atm})^3}\right]$$
$$= -1314 \text{ kJ} + 32.4 \text{ kJ} = -1282 \text{ kJ}$$

The value of ΔG_{rxn} is negative and thus the reaction is spontaneous from left to right.

19-29 The relation between ΔG_{rxn} and ΔG°_{rxn} is

$$\Delta G_{rxn} = \Delta G^\circ_{rxn} + 2.30RT \log Q$$

For the equation

$$ATP(aq) + H_2O(l) \rightleftharpoons ADP(aq) + HPO_4^{2-}(aq)$$

we have

$$Q = \frac{[\text{ADP}][\text{HPO}_4^{2-}]}{[\text{ATP}]} = \frac{(0.50 \times 10^{-3} \text{ M})(5.0 \times 10^{-3} \text{ M})}{(5.0 \times 10^{-3} \text{ M})}$$
$$= 0.50 \times 10^{-3} \text{ M}$$

Thus

$$\Delta G_{rxn} = -30.5 \text{ kJ} + \frac{(2.30)(8.314 \text{ J} \cdot \text{K}^{-1})(310 \text{ K})}{(1000 \text{ J} \cdot \text{kJ}^{-1})} \log(0.50 \times 10^{-3})$$
$$= -30.5 \text{ kJ} - 19.6 \text{ kJ} = -50.1 \text{ kJ}$$

Because $\Delta G_{rxn} < 0$, the reaction is spontaneous from left to right at the stated conditions.

19-31   We have

$$\Delta G^{\circ}_{rxn} = -2.30RT \log K$$

At 250°C, we have

$$\Delta G^{\circ}_{rxn} = -(2.30)(8.314 \text{ J} \cdot \text{K}^{-1})(523 \text{ K}) \log(4.5 \times 10^{3})$$
$$= -36.5 \times 10^{3} \text{ J}$$

The reaction is spontaneous in the direction

$$\text{PCl}_5(g) \longrightarrow \text{PCl}_3(g) + \text{Cl}_2(g)$$

when PCl_5, PCl_3, and Cl_2 are at standard conditions. The value of ΔG_{rxn} at other conditions is given by

$$\Delta G_{rxn} = \Delta G^{\circ}_{rxn} + 2.30RT \log Q$$
$$= \Delta G^{\circ}_{rxn} + 2.30RT \log \frac{[\text{PCl}_3]_0[\text{Cl}_2]_0}{[\text{PCl}_5]_0}$$
$$= -36.5 \text{ kJ} + \left[\frac{(2.30)(8.314 \text{ J} \cdot \text{K}^{-1})(523 \text{ K})}{(1000 \text{ J} \cdot \text{kJ}^{-1})} \right] \log \left[\frac{(0.20)(0.80)}{1.0 \times 10^{-6}} \right]$$
$$= -36.5 \text{ kJ} + 52.0 \text{ kJ} = +15.5 \text{ kJ}$$

Because $\Delta G_{rxn} > 0$, the reaction to the right is not spontaneous under these conditions. The reaction from right to left is spontaneous.

19-33   The value of ΔG°_{rxn} is given by

$$\Delta G^{\circ}_{rxn} = -2.30RT \log K$$
$$= -(2.30)(8.314 \text{ J} \cdot \text{K}^{-1})(298 \text{ K}) \log(4.5 \times 10^{-4})$$
$$= 1.91 \times 10^{4} \text{ J} = 19.1 \text{ kJ}$$

Because $\Delta G_{rxn}^{\circ} > 0$, nitrous acid will not dissociate spontaneously when $[NO_2^-] = [H^+] = [HNO_2] = 1.00$ M (standard conditions). The value of ΔG_{rxn} at any other conditions is given by

$$\Delta G_{rxn} = 2.30RT \log\left(\frac{Q}{K}\right)$$

Thus

$$\Delta G_{rxn} = 2.30RT \log\left(\frac{\dfrac{[NO_2^-][H^+]}{[HNO_2]}}{K}\right)$$

$$= (2.30)(8.314 \text{ J}\cdot\text{K}^{-1})(298 \text{ K}) \log\left(\frac{\dfrac{(1.0 \times 10^{-5} \text{ M})(1.0 \times 10^{-5} \text{ M})}{(1.0 \text{ M})}}{(4.5 \times 10^{-4} \text{ M})}\right)$$

$$= -3.79 \times 10^4 \text{ J}$$

Because $\Delta G_{rxn} < 0$, nitrous acid will dissociate spontaneously under these conditions.

19-35   The value of ΔG_{rxn}° is given by

$$\begin{aligned}\Delta G_{rxn}^{\circ} &= -2.30RT \log K\\ &= -(2.30)(8.314 \text{ J}\cdot\text{K}^{-1})(298 \text{ K}) \log(1.35 \times 10^{-3})\\ &= 1.64 \times 10^4 \text{ J}\end{aligned}$$

Chloroacetic acid will not dissociate spontaneously when $[C_2H_2ClO_2^-] = [H^+] = [HC_2H_2ClO_2] = 1.0$ M. The value of ΔG_{rxn} at any other conditions is given by

$$\Delta G_{rxn} = 2.30RT \log\left(\frac{Q}{K}\right)$$

Thus

$$\Delta G_{rxn} = 2.30RT \log\left(\frac{\dfrac{[C_2H_2ClO_2^-][H^+]}{[HC_2H_2ClO_2]}}{K}\right)$$

$$= (2.30)(8.314 \text{ J}\cdot\text{K}^{-1})(298 \text{ K}) \log\left(\frac{\dfrac{(0.0010 \text{ M})(1.0 \times 10^{-5} \text{ M})}{(0.10 \text{ M})}}{(1.35 \times 10^{-3} \text{ M})}\right)$$

$$= -2.35 \times 10^4 \text{ J}$$

Chloroacetic acid will dissociate spontaneously under these conditions.

19-37   The value of ΔG_{rxn}° is given by

$$\Delta G_{rxn}^{\circ} = -2.30RT \log K$$

Thus

$$\Delta G^{\circ}_{rxn} = -(2.30)(8.314 \text{ J} \cdot \text{K}^{-1})(298 \text{ K}) \log(1.78 \times 10^{-10})$$
$$= 5.56 \times 10^4 \text{ J} = 55.6 \text{ kJ}$$

The reaction is spontaneous from right to left when $[Ag^+] = [Cl^-] = 1.0$ M (standard conditions). Therefore, it is not possible to prepare a solution that is 1.0 M in $Ag^+(aq)$ and $Cl^-(aq)$. Insoluble AgCl will precipitate out of the solution.

19-39   The value of ΔG°_{rxn} is given by

$$\Delta G^{\circ}_{rxn} = -2.30RT \log K$$

Thus

$$\Delta G^{\circ}_{rxn} = -(2.30)(8.314 \text{ J} \cdot \text{K}^{-1})(298 \text{ K}) \log(2.5 \times 10^3)$$
$$= -1.94 \times 10^4 \text{ J}$$

The reaction is spontaneous from left to right when $Ag^+(aq)$, $NH_3(aq)$, and $Ag(NH_3)_2^+(aq)$ are at standard conditions. The value of ΔG_{rxn} at any other condition is given by

$$\Delta G_{rxn} = 2.30RT \log\left(\frac{Q}{K}\right)$$

Thus

$$\Delta G_{rxn} = 2.30RT \log\left(\frac{\frac{[Ag(NH_3)_2^+]}{[Ag^+][NH_3]^2}}{K}\right)$$

$$= (2.30)(8.314 \text{ J} \cdot \text{K}^{-1})(298 \text{ K}) \log\left(\frac{\frac{(1.0 \times 10^{-3})}{(1.0 \times 10^{-3})(0.10)^2}}{(2.5 \times 10^3)}\right)$$

$$= -7.97 \times 10^3 \text{ J}$$

The reaction is spontaneous left to right.

19-41   The value of ΔG°_{rxn} is calculated by using the data in Table 19-1 and the relationship

$$\Delta G^{\circ}_{rxn} = \Delta G^{\circ}_f \text{ (products)} - \Delta G^{\circ}_f \text{ (reactants)}$$

(a) $\Delta G^{\circ}_{rxn} = \Delta G^{\circ}_f [CH_3OH(l)] - \Delta G^{\circ}_f [CO(g)] - 2 \Delta G^{\circ}_f [H_2(g)]$
$$= (1 \text{ mol})(-166.3 \text{ kJ} \cdot \text{mol}^{-1}) - (1 \text{ mol})(-137.2 \text{ kJ} \cdot \text{mol}^{-1})$$
$$- (2 \text{ mol})(0 \text{ kJ} \cdot \text{mol}^{-1})$$
$$= -29.1 \text{ kJ}$$

Using the relationship $\Delta G^\circ_{rxn} = -2.30RT \log K$, we have

$$\log K = -\frac{\Delta G^\circ_{rxn}}{2.30RT} = -\frac{(-29.1 \times 10^3 \text{ J})}{(2.30)(8.314 \text{ J} \cdot \text{K}^{-1})(298 \text{ K})} = 5.11$$

Thus

$$K = 1.29 \times 10^5 \text{ atm}^{-3}$$

(b) $\Delta G^\circ_{rxn} = \Delta G^\circ_f [\text{CO}(g)] + \Delta G^\circ_f [\text{H}_2(g)] - \Delta G^\circ_f [\text{C}(s)] - \Delta G^\circ_f [\text{H}_2\text{O}(g)]$
   $= (1 \text{ mol})(-137.2 \text{ kJ} \cdot \text{mol}^{-1}) + (1 \text{ mol})(0 \text{ kJ} \cdot \text{mol}^{-1})$
   $\quad - (1 \text{ mol})(0 \text{ kJ} \cdot \text{mol}^{-1}) - (1 \text{ mol})(-228.6 \text{ kJ} \cdot \text{mol}^{-1})$
   $= 91.4 \text{ kJ}$

From the relation $\Delta G^\circ_{rxn} = -2.30RT \log K$, we have

$$\log K = -\frac{\Delta G^\circ_{rxn}}{2.30RT} = -\frac{(91.4 \times 10^3 \text{ J})}{(2.30)(8.314 \text{ J} \cdot \text{K}^{-1})(298 \text{ K})} = -16.040$$

Thus

$$K = 9.12 \times 10^{-17} \text{ atm}$$

(c) $\Delta G^\circ_{rxn} = \Delta G^\circ_f [\text{CH}_4(g)] + \Delta G^\circ_f [\text{H}_2\text{O}(g)] - \Delta G^\circ_f [\text{CO}(g)] - 3 \Delta G^\circ_f [\text{H}_2(g)]$
   $= (1 \text{ mol})(-50.75 \text{ kJ} \cdot \text{mol}^{-1}) + (1 \text{ mol})(-228.6 \text{ kJ} \cdot \text{mol}^{-1})$
   $\quad - (1 \text{ mol})(-137.2 \text{ kJ} \cdot \text{mol}^{-1}) - (3 \text{ mol})(0 \text{ kJ} \cdot \text{mol}^{-1})$
   $= -142.2 \text{ kJ}$

From the relation $\Delta G^\circ_{rxn} = -2.30RT \log K$, we compute

$$\log K = -\frac{\Delta G^\circ_{rxn}}{2.30RT} = -\frac{(-142.2 \times 10^3 \text{ J})}{(2.30)(8.314 \text{ J} \cdot \text{K}^{-1})(298 \text{ K})} = 24.954$$
$$K = 8.99 \times 10^{24} \text{ atm}^{-2}$$

19-43 The value of ΔG°_{rxn} is given by

$$\Delta G^\circ_{rxn} = \Delta G^\circ_f (\text{products}) - \Delta G^\circ_f (\text{reactants})$$

Thus

$$\Delta G^\circ_{rxn} = 2 \Delta G^\circ_f [\text{HF}(g)] + \Delta G^\circ_f [\text{Cl}_2(g)] - 2 \Delta G^\circ_f [\text{HCl}(g)] - \Delta G^\circ_f [\text{F}_2(g)]$$
$$= (2 \text{ mol})(-273 \text{ kJ} \cdot \text{mol}^{-1}) + (1 \text{ mol})(0 \text{ kJ} \cdot \text{mol}^{-1})$$
$$\quad - (2 \text{ mol})(-95.30 \text{ kJ} \cdot \text{mol}^{-1}) - (1 \text{ mol})(0 \text{ kJ} \cdot \text{mol}^{-1})$$
$$= -355 \text{ kJ}$$

The value of ΔH_{rxn}° is given by

$$\Delta H_{rxn}^{\circ} = \Delta H_f^{\circ} \text{(products)} - \Delta H_f^{\circ} \text{(reactants)}$$

Thus

$$\begin{aligned}
\Delta H_{rxn}^{\circ} &= 2 \, \Delta H_f^{\circ}[HF(g)] + \Delta H_f^{\circ}[Cl_2(g)] - 2 \, \Delta H_f^{\circ}[HCl(g)] - \Delta H_f^{\circ}[F_2(g)] \\
&= (2 \text{ mol})(-271.1 \text{ kJ}\cdot\text{mol}^{-1}) + (1 \text{ mol})(0 \text{ kJ}\cdot\text{mol}^{-1}) \\
&\quad - (2 \text{ mol})(-92.31 \text{ kJ}\cdot\text{mol}^{-1}) - (1 \text{ mol})(0 \text{ kJ}\cdot\text{mol}^{-1}) \\
&= -357.6 \text{ kJ}
\end{aligned}$$

From the relation $\Delta G_{rxn}^{\circ} = -2.30RT \log K$ we have

$$\log K = -\frac{\Delta G_{rxn}^{\circ}}{2.30RT} = -\frac{(-355 \times 10^3 \text{ J})}{(2.30)(8.314 \text{ J}\cdot\text{K}^{-1})(298 \text{ K})} = 62.298$$

$$K = 2.0 \times 10^{62}$$

19-45 The value of ΔG_{rxn}° is given by

$$\begin{aligned}
\Delta G_{rxn}^{\circ} &= \Delta G_f^{\circ} \text{(products)} - \Delta G_f^{\circ} \text{(reactants)} \\
&= 2 \, \Delta G_f^{\circ}[SO_3(g)] - 2 \, \Delta G_f^{\circ}[SO_2(g)] - \Delta G_f^{\circ}[O_2(g)] \\
&= (2 \text{ mol})(-371.1 \text{ kJ}\cdot\text{mol}^{-1}) - (2 \text{ mol})(-300.2 \text{ kJ}\cdot\text{mol}^{-1}) \\
&\quad - (1 \text{ mol})(0 \text{ kJ}\cdot\text{mol}^{-1}) \\
&= -141.8 \text{ kJ}
\end{aligned}$$

The value of ΔH_{rxn}° is given by

$$\begin{aligned}
\Delta H_{rxn}^{\circ} &= \Delta H_f^{\circ} \text{(products)} - \Delta H_f^{\circ} \text{(reactants)} \\
&= 2 \, \Delta H_f^{\circ}[SO_3(g)] - 2 \, \Delta H_f^{\circ}[SO_2(g)] - \Delta H_f^{\circ}[O_2(g)] \\
&= (2 \text{ mol})(-395.7 \text{ kJ}\cdot\text{mol}^{-1}) - (2 \text{ mol})(-296.8 \text{ kJ}\cdot\text{mol}^{-1}) \\
&\quad - (1 \text{ mol})(0 \text{ kJ}\cdot\text{mol}^{-1}) \\
&= -197.8 \text{ kJ}
\end{aligned}$$

The value of $\log K$ is given by

$$\log K = -\frac{\Delta G_{rxn}^{\circ}}{2.30RT} = -\frac{(-141.8 \times 10^3 \text{ J})}{(2.30)(8.314 \text{ J}\cdot\text{K}^{-1})(298 \text{ K})} = 24.884$$

$$K = 7.66 \times 10^{24} \text{ atm}^{-1}$$

To estimate $K_{400^\circ C}$, we first calculate $\Delta G_{rxn(400^\circ C)}^{\circ}$. The value of ΔS_{rxn}° is given by

$$\begin{aligned}
\Delta S_{rxn}^{\circ} &= S^{\circ}\text{(products)} - S^{\circ}\text{(reactants)} \\
&= 2S^{\circ}[SO_3(g)] - 2S^{\circ}[SO_2(g)] - S^{\circ}[O_2(g)] \\
&= (2 \text{ mol})(256.3 \text{ J}\cdot\text{K}^{-1}\cdot\text{mol}^{-1}) - (2 \text{ mol})(248.4 \text{ J}\cdot\text{K}^{-1}\cdot\text{mol}^{-1}) \\
&\quad - (1 \text{ mol})(205.0 \text{ J}\cdot\text{K}^{-1}\cdot\text{mol}^{-1}) \\
&= -189.2 \text{ J}\cdot\text{K}^{-1}
\end{aligned}$$

We can find the value of ΔG°_{rxn} at some other temperature from

$$\Delta G^\circ_{rxn} = \Delta H^\circ_{rxn} - T\,\Delta S^\circ_{rxn}$$

Thus at 400°C

$$\Delta G^\circ_{rxn} = (-197.8 \text{ kJ}) - (673 \text{ K})(-0.1892 \text{ kJ} \cdot \text{K}^{-1}) = -70.5 \text{ kJ}$$

The value of the equilibrium constant at 400°C is given by

$$\log K = -\frac{\Delta G^\circ_{rxn}}{2.30RT} = -\frac{(-70.5 \times 10^3 \text{ J})}{(2.30)(8.314 \text{ J} \cdot \text{K}^{-1} \cdot \text{mol}^{-1})(673 \text{ K})} = 5.478$$

Therefore,

$$K = 3.01 \times 10^5 \text{ atm}^{-1}$$

19-47   The value of ΔG°_{rxn} is given by

$$\begin{aligned}
\Delta G^\circ_{rxn} &= \Delta G^\circ_f \text{ (products)} - \Delta G^\circ_f \text{ (reactants)} \\
&= \Delta G^\circ_f\,[H_2O(g)] + \Delta G^\circ_f\,[CO(g)] - \Delta G^\circ_f\,[H_2(g)] - \Delta G^\circ_f\,[CO_2(g)] \\
&= (1 \text{ mol})(-228.6 \text{ kJ} \cdot \text{mol}^{-1}) + (1 \text{ mol})(-137.2 \text{ kJ} \cdot \text{mol}^{-1}) \\
&\quad - (1 \text{ mol})(0 \text{ kJ} \cdot \text{mol}^{-1}) - (1 \text{ mol})(-394.4 \text{ kJ} \cdot \text{mol}^{-1}) \\
&= 28.6 \text{ kJ}
\end{aligned}$$

The value of ΔH°_{rxn} is given by

$$\Delta H^\circ_{rxn} = \Delta H^\circ_f \text{ (products)} - \Delta H^\circ_f \text{ (reactants)}$$

Thus

$$\begin{aligned}
\Delta H^\circ_{rxn} &= \Delta H^\circ_f\,[H_2O(g)] + \Delta H^\circ_f\,[CO(g)] - \Delta H^\circ_f\,[H_2(g)] - \Delta H^\circ_f\,[CO_2(g)] \\
&= (1 \text{ mol})(-241.8 \text{ kJ} \cdot \text{mol}^{-1}) + (1 \text{ mol})(-110.5 \text{ kJ} \cdot \text{mol}^{-1}) \\
&\quad - (1 \text{ mol})(0 \text{ kJ} \cdot \text{mol}^{-1}) - (1 \text{ mol})(-393.5 \text{ kJ} \cdot \text{mol}^{-1}) \\
&= 41.2 \text{ kJ}
\end{aligned}$$

The value of ΔS°_{rxn} is given by

$$\Delta S^\circ_{rxn} = S^\circ \text{(products)} - S^\circ \text{(reactants)}$$

Thus

$$\begin{aligned}
\Delta S^\circ_{rxn} &= S^\circ[H_2O(g)] + S^\circ[CO(g)] - S^\circ[H_2(g)] - S^\circ[CO_2(g)] \\
&= (1 \text{ mol})(188.7 \text{ J} \cdot \text{K}^{-1} \cdot \text{mol}^{-1}) + (1 \text{ mol})(197.8 \text{ J} \cdot \text{K}^{-1} \cdot \text{mol}^{-1}) \\
&\quad - (1 \text{ mol})(130.6 \text{ J} \cdot \text{K}^{-1} \cdot \text{mol}^{-1}) - (1 \text{ mol})(213.6 \text{ J} \cdot \text{K}^{-1} \cdot \text{mol}^{-1}) \\
&= 42.3 \text{ J} \cdot \text{K}^{-1}
\end{aligned}$$

Because $\Delta G_{rxn}^\circ = +28.6$ kJ the reaction is spontaneous right to left when all the reactants and all the products are at standard conditions. The reaction is enthalpy driven to the left.

19-49   The equation for the combustion of ethane is

$$C_2H_6(g) + \tfrac{7}{2}O_2(g) \longrightarrow 2CO_2(g) + 3H_2O(l)$$

The value of ΔG_{rxn}° is given by

$$\Delta G_{rxn}^\circ = \Delta G_f^\circ \text{ (products)} - \Delta G_f^\circ \text{ (reactants)}$$

Thus

$$\Delta G_{rxn}^\circ = 2\ \Delta G_f^\circ\ [CO_2(g)] + 3\ \Delta G_f^\circ\ [H_2O(l)] - \Delta G_f^\circ\ [C_2H_6(g)] - \tfrac{7}{2}\ \Delta G_f^\circ\ [O_2(g)]$$
$$= (2\ \text{mol})(-394.4\ \text{kJ}\cdot\text{mol}^{-1}) + (3\ \text{mol})(-237.2\ \text{kJ}\cdot\text{mol}^{-1})$$
$$-\ (1\ \text{mol})(-32.89\ \text{kJ}\cdot\text{mol}^{-1}) - (\tfrac{7}{2}\ \text{mol})(0\ \text{kJ}\cdot\text{mol}^{-1})$$
$$= -1468\ \text{kJ}$$

The maximum amount of work that can be obtained when $CO_2(g)$, $H_2O(l)$, $C_2H_6(g)$, and $O_2(g)$ are at standard conditions is 1468 kJ.

19-51   The van't Hoff equation is

$$\log \frac{K_2}{K_1} = \frac{\Delta H_{rxn}^\circ}{2.30R} \left(\frac{T_2 - T_1}{T_1 T_2} \right)$$

Substituting the values of the second and fourth sets of data, for example, we have

$$\log \left(\frac{16.9 \times 10^{-4}}{6.86 \times 10^{-4}} \right) = \frac{\Delta H_{rxn}^\circ (2300\ \text{K} - 2100\ \text{K})}{(2.30)(8.314\ \text{J}\cdot\text{K}^{-1})(2300\ \text{K})(2100\ \text{K})}$$
$$0.3916 = (2.165 \times 10^{-6}\ \text{J}^{-1})\Delta H_{rxn}^\circ$$
$$\Delta H_{rxn}^\circ = 1.81 \times 10^5\ \text{J} = 181\ \text{kJ}$$

19-53   The van't Hoff equation is

$$\log \frac{K_2}{K_1} = \frac{\Delta H_{rxn}^\circ}{2.30R} \left(\frac{T_2 - T_1}{T_1 T_2} \right)$$

Substituting the values of the last two sets of data, for example, we have

$$\log \left(\frac{1.77}{1.34} \right) = \frac{\Delta H_{rxn}^\circ (1273\ \text{K} - 1173\ \text{K})}{(2.30)(8.314\ \text{J}\cdot\text{K}^{-1})(1273\ \text{K})(1173\ \text{K})}$$
$$0.1209 = (3.502 \times 10^{-6}\ \text{J}^{-1})\Delta H_{rxn}^\circ$$

Thus

$$\Delta H_{rxn}^\circ = 3.45 \times 10^4\ \text{J} = 34.5\ \text{kJ}$$

19-55 The value of ΔH°_{rxn} is given by

$$\begin{aligned}
\Delta H^\circ_{rxn} &= \Delta H^\circ_f \, [PCl_5(g)] - \Delta H^\circ_f \, [PCl_3(g)] - \Delta H^\circ_f \, [Cl_2(g)] \\
&= (1 \text{ mol})(-375.0 \text{ kJ} \cdot \text{mol}^{-1}) - (1 \text{ mol})(-306.4 \text{ kJ} \cdot \text{mol}^{-1}) \\
&\quad - (1 \text{ mol})(0 \text{ kJ} \cdot \text{mol}^{-1}) \\
&= -68.6 \text{ kJ}
\end{aligned}$$

Using the van't Hoff equation, we have

$$\log\left(\frac{K_p}{0.562 \text{ atm}^{-1}}\right) = \frac{(-68.6 \times 10^3 \text{ J})(673 \text{ K} - 523 \text{ K})}{(2.30)(8.314 \text{ J} \cdot \text{K}^{-1})(673 \text{ K})(523 \text{ K})} = -1.5288$$

Thus

$$\frac{K_p}{0.562 \text{ atm}^{-1}} = 2.959 \times 10^{-2}$$

and

$$K_p = 0.0166 \text{ atm}^{-1} \text{ at } 400°C$$

19-57 We calculate ΔS_{fus} by using the relationship

$$\Delta S_{fus} = \frac{\Delta H_{fus}}{T_m}$$

Using the value of T_m and ΔH_{fus} given, we have

$$\text{Li} \quad \Delta S_{fus} = \frac{2.99 \times 10^3 \text{ J} \cdot \text{mol}^{-1}}{454 \text{ K}} = 6.59 \text{ J} \cdot \text{K}^{-1} \cdot \text{mol}^{-1}$$

$$\text{Na} \quad \Delta S_{fus} = \frac{2.60 \times 10^3 \text{ J} \cdot \text{mol}^{-1}}{371 \text{ K}} = 7.01 \text{ J} \cdot \text{K}^{-1} \cdot \text{mol}^{-1}$$

$$\text{K} \quad \Delta S_{fus} = \frac{2.33 \times 10^3 \text{ J} \cdot \text{mol}^{-1}}{336 \text{ K}} = 6.93 \text{ J} \cdot \text{K}^{-1} \cdot \text{mol}^{-1}$$

$$\text{Rb} \quad \Delta S_{fus} = \frac{2.34 \times 10^3 \text{ J} \cdot \text{mol}^{-1}}{312 \text{ K}} = 7.50 \text{ J} \cdot \text{K}^{-1} \cdot \text{mol}^{-1}$$

$$\text{Cs} \quad \Delta S_{fus} = \frac{2.10 \times 10^3 \text{ J} \cdot \text{mol}^{-1}}{302 \text{ K}} = 6.95 \text{ J} \cdot \text{K}^{-1} \cdot \text{mol}^{-1}$$

We calculate ΔS_{vap} by using the relationship

$$\Delta S_{vap} = \frac{\Delta H_{vap}}{T_b}$$

Using the values of T_b and ΔH_{vap} given, we have

$$\text{Li} \quad \Delta S_{vap} = \frac{134.7 \times 10^3 \text{ J} \cdot \text{mol}^{-1}}{1615 \text{ K}} = 83.41 \text{ J} \cdot \text{K}^{-1} \cdot \text{mol}^{-1}$$

$$\text{Na} \quad \Delta S_{vap} = \frac{89.6 \times 10^3 \text{ J} \cdot \text{mol}^{-1}}{1156 \text{ K}} = 77.5 \text{ J} \cdot \text{K}^{-1} \cdot \text{mol}^{-1}$$

$$\text{K} \quad \Delta S_{vap} = \frac{77.1 \times 10^3 \text{ J} \cdot \text{mol}^{-1}}{1033 \text{ J}} = 74.6 \text{ J} \cdot \text{K}^{-1} \cdot \text{mol}^{-1}$$

$$\text{Rb} \quad \Delta S_{vap} = \frac{69 \times 10^3 \text{ J} \cdot \text{mol}^{-1}}{956 \text{ K}} = 72 \text{ J} \cdot \text{K}^{-1} \cdot \text{mol}^{-1}$$

$$\text{Cs} \quad \Delta S_{vap} = \frac{66 \times 10^3 \text{ J} \cdot \text{mol}^{-1}}{942 \text{ K}} = 70 \text{ J} \cdot \text{K}^{-1} \cdot \text{mol}^{-1}$$

19-59 No, because if K is infinite, then ΔG°_{rxn} is negative infinite, and thus an infinite amount of work could be obtained from the reaction. If K is zero, then ΔG°_{rxn} is positive infinite, and thus an infinite amount of energy would be necessary to make the reaction take place.

19-61 The values of ΔG°_{rxn} for the equation

(1) $$\text{H}_2(g) + \text{O}_2(g) \rightleftharpoons \text{H}_2\text{O}_2(l)$$

is given by

$$\Delta G^\circ_{rxn} = \Delta G^\circ_f [\text{H}_2\text{O}_2(l)] - \Delta G^\circ_f [\text{H}_2(g)] - \Delta G^\circ_f [\text{O}_2(g)]$$
$$= (1 \text{ mol})(-120.4 \text{ kJ} \cdot \text{mol}^{-1}) - (1 \text{ mol})(0 \text{ kJ} \cdot \text{mol}^{-1}) - (1 \text{ mol})(0 \text{ kJ} \cdot \text{mol}^{-1})$$
$$= -120.4 \text{ kJ}$$

We must calculate ΔG°_{rxn} for the production of one mole of $\text{H}_2\text{O}_2(l)$. The equation is

(2) $$\text{H}_2\text{O}(l) + \tfrac{1}{2}\text{O}_2(g) \rightleftharpoons \text{H}_2\text{O}_2(l)$$

and ΔG°_{rxn} is given by

$$\Delta G^\circ_{rxn} = \Delta G^\circ_f [\text{H}_2\text{O}_2(l)] - \Delta G^\circ_f [\text{H}_2\text{O}(l)] - \tfrac{1}{2}\Delta G^\circ_f [\text{O}_2(g)]$$
$$= (1 \text{ mol})(-120.4 \text{ kJ} \cdot \text{mol}^{-1}) - (1 \text{ mol})(-237.2 \text{ kJ} \cdot \text{mol}^{-1})$$
$$\quad - (\tfrac{1}{2} \text{ mol})(0 \text{ kJ} \cdot \text{mol}^{-1})$$
$$= 116.8 \text{ kJ}$$

The reaction between hydrogen and oxygen is the more energy efficient because $\Delta G^\circ_{rxn}(1) < \Delta G^\circ_{rxn}(2)$.

19-63   Using the data in Problem 19-51, we have

$(1/T)/10^{-4}\ \text{K}^{-1}$	$\log K_p$
5.000	−3.3893
4.762	−3.1637
4.546	−2.9586
4.348	−2.7721
4.167	−2.6003

A plot of $\log K_p$ versus $1/T$ is a straight line (see plot). The equation for the straight line is

$$\log K = \left(\frac{-\Delta H^{\circ}_{rxn}}{2.30R}\right)\left(\frac{1}{T}\right) + b$$

The slope of the line is $-\Delta H^{\circ}_{rxn}/2.30R$. The slope can be calculated by using any

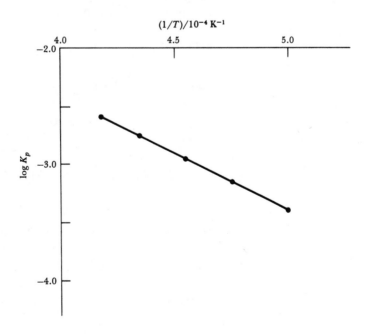

two points on the line; thus

$$\text{slope} = \frac{\log K_2 - \log K_1}{\left(\dfrac{1}{T_2} - \dfrac{1}{T_1}\right)}$$

$$= \frac{-3.1637 - (-3.3893)}{(4.762 - 5.000)(10^{-4}\ \text{K}^{-1})} = -9.4790 \times 10^3\ \text{K}$$

$$\text{slope} = \frac{-\Delta H^\circ_{rxn}}{2.30R} = -9.4790 \times 10^3\ \text{K}$$

$$\Delta H^\circ_{rxn} = -(-9.4790 \times 10^3\ \text{K})(2.30)(8.314\ \text{J}\cdot\text{K}^{-1})$$
$$= 181 \times 10^5\ \text{J} = 181\ \text{kJ}$$

19-65 Starting with $\Delta G^\circ_{rxn} = -2.30RT \log K$, we have at 25°C

$$\Delta G^\circ_{rxn} = -(2.30)(8.314\ \text{J}\cdot\text{K}^{-1})(298\ \text{K}) \log K$$
$$= -(5.70\ \text{kJ}) \log K$$

The difference in the values of ΔG°_{rxn} when there is a tenfold increase in K at 25°C is calculated as follows:

$$\Delta G^\circ_{rxn_2} - \Delta G^\circ_{rxn_1} = -(5.70\ \text{kJ}) \log K_2 + (5.70\ \text{kJ}) \log K_1$$
$$= (5.70\ \text{kJ}) \log\left(\frac{K_1}{K_2}\right)$$

where we have used the property of logarithms

$$\log a - \log b = \log\left(\frac{a}{b}\right)$$

We are given that $K_2 = 10K_1$; thus

$$\Delta G^\circ_{rxn_2} - \Delta G^\circ_{rxn_1} = (5.70\ \text{kJ}) \log\left(\frac{K_1}{10K_1}\right) = (5.70\ \text{kJ}) \log\left(\frac{1}{10}\right)$$
$$= -5.70\ \text{kJ}$$

A tenfold increase in K corresponds to a decrease of -5.70 kJ in ΔG°_{rxn}.

19-67 The gas solubility equilibrium is

$$X(g) \rightleftharpoons X(soln)$$

Thus

$$K = \frac{[X]_{soln}}{P_X}$$

If $[X]_{soln}$ decreases as T increases with P_X held constant, then K decreases as T increases. This means that ΔH°_{rxn} for the solubility equation is negative (Le Châtelier's principle).

19-69 The value of ΔH°_{rxn} for the equation

$$CO_2(aq) \rightleftharpoons CO_2(g)$$

can be calculated by using the data given and the van't Hoff equation, because the Henry's law constants given are equilibrium constants for the equation above. Thus

$$\log\left(\frac{K_2}{K_1}\right) = \frac{\Delta H^{\circ}_{rxn}}{2.30\ R}\left(\frac{T_2 - T_1}{T_1 T_2}\right)$$

and

$$\log\left(\frac{29.4}{13.2}\right) = \left(\frac{\Delta H^{\circ}_{rxn}}{2.30 \times 8.314\ \text{J} \cdot \text{K}^{-1}}\right)\left[\frac{25.0\ \text{K}}{(298\ \text{K})(273\ \text{K})}\right]$$

from which we obtain

$$\Delta H^{\circ}_{rxn} = +21.6\ \text{kJ}$$

19-71 The equation is

$$Mg(s) + 2HCl(aq) \rightleftharpoons H_2(g) + MgCl_2(aq)$$

The value of ΔH°_{rxn} is

$$\begin{aligned}\Delta H^{\circ}_{rxn} &= \Delta H^{\circ}_f[MgCl_2(aq)] + \Delta H^{\circ}_f[H_2(g)] - \Delta H^{\circ}_f[Mg(s)] - 2\,\Delta H^{\circ}_f[HCl(aq)]\\ &= (1\ \text{mol})(-801.2\ \text{kJ} \cdot \text{mol}^{-1}) + 0 - 0 - (2\ \text{mol})(-167.2\ \text{kJ} \cdot \text{mol}^{-1})\\ &= -466.8\ \text{kJ}\end{aligned}$$

The value of ΔS°_{rxn} is

$$\begin{aligned}
\Delta S^\circ_{rxn} &= S^\circ[MgCl_2(aq)] + S^\circ[H_2(g)] - S^\circ[Mg(s)] - 2S^\circ[HCl(aq)] \\
&= (1\ mol)(-25.1\ J \cdot K^{-1} \cdot mol^{-1}) + (1\ mol)(130.6\ J \cdot K^{-1} \cdot mol^{-1}) \\
&\quad - (1\ mol)(32.6\ J \cdot K^{-1} \cdot mol^{-1}) - (2\ mol)(56.5\ J \cdot K^{-1} \cdot mol^{-1}) \\
&= -40.4\ J \cdot K^{-1}
\end{aligned}$$

The value of ΔG°_{rxn} is given by

$$\Delta G^\circ_{rxn} = \Delta H^\circ_{rxn} - T\,\Delta S^\circ_{rxn}$$

Thus

$$\Delta G^\circ_{rxn} = -466.8\ kJ - \frac{(298.2\ K)(-40.4\ J \cdot K^{-1})}{(1000\ J \cdot kJ^{-1})} = -454.8\ kJ$$

E   ANSWERS TO THE SELF-TEST

1 false

2 false

3 positional . . . thermal

4 of the increased energy that is distributed among the molecules (increase in thermal disorder)

5 increases

6 of the increased positional disorder of the molecules

7 of the increased positional disorder of the molecules

8 $\Delta H_{fus}/T_m$

9 $\Delta H_{vap}/T_b$

10 less than

11 mass . . . atoms

12 of lower molecular mass, smaller number of atoms and less freedom of motion in C_2H_2

13 positive

14 $2S^\circ[H_2(g)] + S^\circ[O_2(g)] - 2S^\circ[H_2O(l)]$

15 true

16 spontaneous

17 not spontaneous

18 at equilibrium

19 positive

20 $\Delta H_{rxn} - T\,\Delta S_{rxn}$

21 entropy

22 energy (enthalpy)

23 is not

24 spontaneous

25 not spontaneous

26 false

27 the magnitude of ΔG_{rxn}

28 $2.30RT \log(Q/K)$

29 is

30 the reactants and products are at standard conditions

31 $-2.30RT \log K$

32 is not $[\Delta G^{\circ}_{rxn} = -(2.30)$
$(8.314 \text{ J} \cdot \text{K}^{-1})(298 \text{ K}) \log(1.7 \times$
$10^{-5})$ and $\Delta G^{\circ}_{rxn} > 0]$

33 true

34 $2 \Delta G^{\circ}_{f} [\text{H}_2(g)] + \Delta G^{\circ}_{f} [\text{O}_2(g)] -$
$2 \Delta G^{\circ}_{f} [\text{H}_2\text{O}(l)]$

35 false

36 false

37 true

38 true

39 false

40 false

41 false

42 $\log\left(\dfrac{K_2}{K_1}\right) = \dfrac{\Delta H^{\circ}_{rxn}}{2.30R}\left(\dfrac{T_2 - T_1}{T_1 T_2}\right)$

43 decreases

ELECTROCHEMISTRY

A   OUTLINE OF CHAPTER 20

20-1   Electrolysis is a chemical reaction that occurs as a result of the passage of an electric current through a solution.

A voltaic pile can produce an electric current that is capable of decomposing a variety of chemical substances (Figure 20-1).

Faraday discovered that the metal ions of many salts are deposited as the metal when an electric current is passed through the solution.

The unit of electric current is the ampere.

One ampere is a flow of one coulomb of charge per second.

$$\text{coulombs} = \text{amperes} \times \text{seconds}$$

In an equation,

$$Z = It \tag{20-1}$$

20-2   Electrolysis is described quantitatively by Faraday's laws.

Electrons combine with metal ions to form the metal during the passage of the electric current.

Faraday's laws are summarized as

$$\binom{\text{mass deposited as metal}}{\text{or evolved as gas}} = m = \left(\frac{It}{F}\right)\left(\frac{A}{n}\right) \tag{20-4}$$

where I is the current in amperes, t is the time in seconds, F is Faraday's constant, A is the molar mass, and n is the number of electrons involved in the equation for the reaction.

Faraday's constant, F, is the charge of one mole of electrons and is equal to 96,500 coulombs per mole.

Ions are the current carriers through the solution during electrolysis.

An electrode is a solid phase on the surface of which oxidation-reduction reactions occur.

Reduction occurs at the cathode.

Oxidation occurs at the anode.

Cations move toward the cathode.

Anions move toward the anode.

The decomposition voltage is the minimum voltage necessary to cause an electrolysis reaction to occur.

20-3 Many chemicals are produced on an industrial scale by electrolysis.

The chlor-alkali process involves the electrolysis of $NaCl(aq)$ to produce $Cl_2(g)$ and $NaOH(aq)$ (Figure 20-3).

The Hall process involves the electrolysis of $Al_2O_3(s)$ dissolved in cryolite, Na_3AlF_6, to produce aluminum metal (Figure 20-4).

The production of a layer of protective metal by electrochemical deposition is called electroplating (Figure 20-6).

20-4 An electrochemical cell produces electricity directly from a chemical reaction.

An electrochemical cell enables us to obtain an electric current from an oxidation-reduction reaction (Figure 20-8).

An electrochemical cell involves an oxidation half-reaction and a reduction half-reaction.

Electrodes are used to enable electrons to enter or leave an electrochemical cell. The electron transfer processes occur at the electrodes.

Salt bridges are used to separate two different electrolyte solutions in a cell. Current in the form of moving ions can pass through the salt bridge from one electrolyte solution to the other.

Current within the cell electrolyte(s) is carried by ions.

A cell must be designed so that the reducing agent and the oxidizing agent are physically separated.

Discharge denotes that current is drawn from the cell.

Electric current flows spontaneously through metallic conductors from a region of negative electric potential to a region of positive electric potential.

20-5 A cell diagram is used to represent an electrochemical cell.

By convention, the half-reaction of the left electrode of a cell is written as an oxidation half-reaction, and the half-reaction for the right electrode of a cell is written as a reduction half-reaction (oxidation at the left electrode, reduction at the right electrode).

The net cell reaction is given by the sum of the two electrode half-reactions adjusted so that the number of electrons is the same in both half-reactions.

20-6   The cell voltage depends on the concentrations of reactants and products of the cell reaction.

The cell voltage is a quantitative measure of the driving force of the cell reaction.

The effect of a change in the concentration of a reactant or product on the cell voltage can be predicted by applying Le Châtelier's principle.

The Nernst equation is

$$E = -\left(\frac{2.303RT}{nF}\right) \log\left(\frac{Q}{K}\right) \tag{20-6}$$

At 25°C, the Nernst equation is

$$E = -\left(\frac{0.0592 \text{ V}}{n}\right) \log\left(\frac{Q}{K}\right) \tag{20-8}$$

If $E_{cell} > 0$, then the cell reaction is spontaneous from left to right as written.
If $E_{cell} < 0$, then the cell reaction is spontaneous from right to left as written.
If $E_{cell} = 0$, then the cell reaction is at equilibrium.
The standard cell voltage, $E°$, is the voltage of the cell when $Q = 1$.
The relation between the standard cell voltage and the equilibrium constant for the cell reaction at 25°C is given by

$$E° = \left(\frac{0.0592 \text{ V}}{n}\right) \log K \tag{20-11}$$

Another form of the Nernst equation is

$$E = E° - \left(\frac{0.0592 \text{ V}}{n}\right) \log Q \tag{20-12}$$

A plot of E versus $\log Q$ is shown in Figure 20-10.

20-7 $E°$ values can be assigned to half-reaction equations.

A standard cell voltage is the difference in standard reduction voltages between the two cell electrodes:

$$E°_{cell} = E°_{red} + E°_{ox} \tag{20-14}$$

For a particular half-reaction

$$E°_{ox} = -E°_{red} \tag{20-15}$$

By convention, for the half-reaction

$$2H^+(aq, 1 \text{ M}) + 2e^- \longrightarrow H_2(g, 1 \text{ atm}) \qquad E° = 0 \text{ V}$$

Some standard electrode reduction voltages are given in Table 20-1.

The more positive the value of $E°$ for a half-reaction, the stronger is the oxidizing agent in the half-reaction.

The more negative the value of $E°$ value for a half-reaction, the stronger is the reducing agent in the half-reaction.

20-8   Electrochemical cells are used to determine concentrations of ions.

If $E°$ is known and if E is measured and if all the concentration terms in Q but one are known, then the unknown concentration can be calculated.

The pH of a solution can be determined by electrochemical cell measurements.

20-9   The value of ΔG_{rxn} is equal to the maximum amount of work that can be obtained from the reaction.

The Gibbs free energy change for an oxidation-reduction reaction is related to the cell voltage by

$$\Delta G_{rxn} = -nFE_{rxn} \qquad (20\text{-}19)$$

If ΔG_{rxn} is negative, then the magnitude of ΔG_{rxn} is equal to the maximum amount of work that can be obtained from the reaction.

If ΔG_{rxn} is positive, then ΔG_{rxn} is equal to the minimum amount of work that must be done to make the reaction occur.

20-10   A battery is an electrochemical cell or group of cells designed for use as a power source.

Primary batteries, such as the dry cell, are not rechargeable.

Secondary batteries, such as the lead storage battery, are rechargeable.

The dry cell, the lead storage battery, the nickel-cadmium battery, and the mercury battery are described.

B   SELF-TEST

1   Water can be decomposed by passing a current through a dilute aqueous solution of Na_2SO_4. *True/False*

2   In the electrolysis of water, electrons pass through the solution from the cathode to the anode. *True/False*

3   During electrolysis of a solution of $AgNO_3(aq)$, silver metal is deposited from solution at the *(anode, cathode)*.

4   The amount of silver deposited by the electrolysis of a $AgNO_3(aq)$ solution depends on the amount of charge that flows through the solution. *True/False*

5 The amount of charge that flows is related to the current by the relationship: charge = _____.

6 The amount of charge contained in one mole of electrons is _____.

7 Faraday's constant is _____.

8 The chlor-alkali process is used industrially to prepare _____ and _____ by the electrolysis of _____.

9 The Hall process is used industrially to prepare _____ by the electrolysis of _____.

10 An electric current can be obtained from an oxidation-reduction reaction. *True/ False*

11 In an electrochemical cell, the _____ reaction is separated from the _____ reaction.

12 In an electrochemical cell, electrons flow spontaneously in the external circuit from the (*positive, negative*) electrode to the (*positive, negative*) electrode.

13 The function of a salt bridge in an electrochemical cell is _____

_____

_____.

14 Consider the electrochemical cell whose cell diagram is

$$Cd(s)|Cd(NO_3)_2(aq)||Pb(NO_3)_2(aq)|Pb(s)$$

(a) Oxidation occurs at the _____ electrode.

(b) The oxidation half-reaction is _____.

(c) The reduction half-reaction is _____.

15 Consider the cell diagram

$$Zn(s)|ZnSO_4(aq)|Hg_2SO_4(s)|Hg(l)$$

(a) The electrolyte solution is _____.

(b) The substances in contact with $ZnSO_4(aq)$ are _____, _____, and _____.

(c) The salt bridge is _____.

16 The function of platinum in a hydrogen gas electrode is _____

_____.

17 The measured voltage of an electrochemical cell depends on the size of the electrodes. *True/False*

18 Consider the cell whose cell diagram is

$$Zn(s)|ZnSO_4(aq)||CuSO_4(aq)|Cu(s)$$

(a) The measured voltage _____ when the concentration of $ZnSO_4(aq)$ is increased.

(b) The measured voltage _____ when the concentration of $CuSO_4(aq)$ is increased.

(c) The measured voltage _____ when the amount of $Zn(s)$ is increased.

(d) The measured voltage _____ when the salt bridge is removed.

19 The sign of the cell voltage is _____ when the cell reaction is spontaneous left to right.

20 The equation for the relationship between the standard cell voltage, $E°$, and the equilibrium constant of a reaction at $25°C$ is given by $E° = $ _____.

21 The standard cell voltage is the measured cell voltage when _____

_____.

22 If $E°_{cell} = 0$, then $K = $ _____.

23 If $K < 1$, then $E°$ is *(less than, greater than)* zero.

24 The Nernst equation, which relates the cell voltage, E, and the reaction concentration quotient, Q, at $25°C$, is given by $E = $ _____.

25 The measured cell voltage is always equal to $E°$. *True/False*

26 The measured cell voltage when the cell reaction is at equilibrium is _____.

27 The standard voltage of a half-reaction is a directly measured quantity. *True/False*

28 The standard cell voltage is always a positive quantity. *True/False*

29 The standard reduction voltage of the hydrogen electrode is set equal to _____.

30 Standard electrode voltages are tabulated in the text for the *(oxidation, reduction)* half-reactions.

31 A large, positive standard electrode voltage for a reduction half reaction indicates a strong oxidizing agent in the half-reaction. *True/False*

32 The stronger the reducing agent, the more *(negative, positive)* is the half-reaction $E_{red}°$ value.

33 The standard cell voltage, $E_{cell}°$, for a reaction can be calculated from the standard electrode voltages of the half-reactions of the reaction. *True/False*

34 The value of $E_{cell}°$ is unchanged when the equation for the cell reaction is multiplied by a factor of 2. *True/False*

35 Measurement of the cell voltage can be used to calculate the concentration of a species in solution by using _____ equation.

36 The pH of a solution is related to the _____ of the hydrogen electrode.

37 The dry cell is a primary battery. *True/False*

38 The nickel-cadmium battery is a secondary battery. *True/False*

39 The maximum amount of work that can be obtained from a reaction is equal to

_____.

40 The value of ΔG_{rxn} for the combustion of a certain fuel is -2030 kJ. The maximum amount of work that can be obtained from the utilization of the fuel in a cell is

_____.

41 The Gibbs free energy change for an oxidation-reduction reaction is related to the corresponding cell voltage by the equation $\Delta G_{rxn} = $ _____.

42 The cell voltage for an oxidation-reduction reaction is 1.21 V. The reaction *(is, is not)* spontaneous.

43 Electrical energy can be used to drive a reaction for which ΔG_{rxn} is positive. *True/False*

C CALCULATIONS YOU SHOULD KNOW HOW TO DO

1 Calculate the current required to deposit a given amount of a metal or the amount of metal deposited during the passage of a given amount of current by using Equation (20-4). See Example 20-2 and Problems 20-1 through 20-10.

2 Write cell reactions and cell diagrams. See Example 20-4 and Problems 20-11 through 20-20.

3 Use the Nernst equation to calculate the value of $E°$ or the value of K, the equilibrium constant. See Examples 20-6 and 20-7 and Problems 20-29 through 20-36.

4 Use the values of the $E_{red}°$ for half-reactions given in Table 20-1 to calculate values of $E°$ for cell reactions. See Examples 20-8 and 20-10 and Problems 20-41 through 20-52.

5 Use the Nernst equation to determine the concentration of an ion in solution. See Examples 20-10 and 20-11 and Problems 20-37 through 20-40.

6 Calculate ΔG_{rxn} for reactions used in electrochemical cells by using Equation (20-19). See Example 20-12 and Problems 20-53 through 20-64.

D   SOLUTIONS TO THE ODD-NUMBERED PROBLEMS

20-1   We shall use Equation (20-4)

$$m = \left(\frac{It}{F}\right)\left(\frac{A}{n}\right)$$

The mass, m, of copper to be deposited is calculated as follows. The number of moles of copper in the solution is

$$n = MV = (0.150 \text{ M})(0.500 \text{ L}) = 0.0750 \text{ mol}$$

Thus the mass of the copper is

$$m = (0.0750 \text{ mol})(63.55 \text{ g} \cdot \text{mol}^{-1}) = 4.77 \text{ g}$$

The half-reaction for the deposition of $Cu(s)$ is

$$Cu^{2+}(aq) + 2e^- \longrightarrow Cu(s)$$

and therefore $n = 2$. The time required to deposit 4.77 g of $Cu(s)$ using a 1.25-A current is

$$t = \frac{mFn}{IA}$$

$$= \frac{(4.77 \text{ g})(96,500 \text{ C} \cdot \text{mol}^{-1})(2)}{(1.25 \text{ A})(63.55 \text{ g} \cdot \text{mol}^{-1})}$$

$$= 1.16 \times 10^4 \text{ s}$$

(In canceling units in the expression for t, recall that $1 \text{ A} = 1 \text{ C} \cdot \text{s}^{-1}$.)

20-3   The mass deposited is calculated by using Equation (20-4),

$$m = \left(\frac{It}{F}\right)\left(\frac{A}{n}\right)$$

The electrode reaction for the deposition of Cs(s) is

$$Cs^+(aq) + e^- \longrightarrow Cs(s)$$

and thus $n = 1$. Substituting the data given into Equation (20-4) yields

$$m = \frac{(0.500 \text{ A})(30 \text{ min})\left(\dfrac{60 \text{ s}}{1 \text{ min}}\right)\left(\dfrac{132.9 \text{ g Cs}}{1 \text{ mol Cs}}\right)}{(9.65 \times 10^4 \text{ C} \cdot \text{mol}^{-1})(1)}$$

$$= 1.24 \text{ g}$$

20-5 The mass of gas evolved is calculated by using Equation (20-4),

$$m = \left(\frac{It}{F}\right)\left(\frac{A}{n}\right)$$

The electrode reaction for the evolution of $F_2(g)$ is

$$2F^-(KF) \longrightarrow F_2(g) + 2e^-$$

and thus $n = 2$. Substitution of the data given into Equation (20-4) yields

$$m = \frac{(1500 \text{ A})(24 \text{ h})\left(\dfrac{3600 \text{ s}}{1 \text{ h}}\right)\left(\dfrac{38.00 \text{ g } F_2}{1 \text{ mol } F_2}\right)}{(9.65 \times 10^4 \text{ C} \cdot \text{mol}^{-1})(2)}$$

$$= 2.55 \times 10^4 \text{ g}$$

Liquid HF is not used in the commercial electrolysis because HF is a covalent compound and thus a poor conductor of electric current. Liquid HF is also very corrosive and very toxic.

20-7 The mass deposited is given by Equation (20-4),

$$m = \left(\frac{It}{F}\right)\left(\frac{A}{n}\right)$$

The electrode reaction for the deposition of Ga(s) is

$$Ga^{3+}(aq) + 3e^- \longrightarrow Ga(s)$$

and thus $n = 3$. Substitution of the data given into Equation (20-4) yields

$$m = \frac{(0.50 \text{ A})(30 \text{ min})\left(\dfrac{60 \text{ s}}{1 \text{ min}}\right)\left(\dfrac{69.72 \text{ g Ga}}{1 \text{ mol Ga}}\right)}{(9.65 \times 10^4 \text{ C} \cdot \text{mol}^{-1})(3)}$$

$$= 0.217 \text{ g}$$

20-9   The mass of gas evolved is calculated by using Equation (20-4),

$$m = \left(\frac{It}{F}\right)\left(\frac{A}{n}\right)$$

The electrode reaction for the evolution of $O_2(g)$ is

$$2H_2O(l) \longrightarrow O_2(g) + 4H^+(aq) + 4e^-$$

and thus $n = 4$. Substitution of the data given into Equation (20-4) yields

$$m = \frac{(30.35 \text{ A})(2.00 \text{ h})\left(\dfrac{3600 \text{ s}}{1 \text{ h}}\right)\left(\dfrac{32.00 \text{ g } O_2}{1 \text{ mol } O_2}\right)}{(9.65 \times 10^4 \text{ C} \cdot \text{mol}^{-1})(4)}$$

$$= 18.1 \text{ g}$$

The number of moles of $O_2(g)$ produced is

$$n = (18.1 \text{ g})\left(\frac{1 \text{ mol } O_2}{32.00 \text{ g } O_2}\right) = 0.566 \text{ mol}$$

The volume of $O_2(g)$ produced is calculated by using the ideal-gas equation,

$$V = \frac{nRT}{P}$$

$$= \frac{(0.566 \text{ mol})(0.0821 \text{ L} \cdot \text{atm} \cdot \text{K}^{-1} \cdot \text{mol}^{-1})(298 \text{ K})}{(1.00 \text{ atm})}$$

$$= 13.8 \text{ L}$$

20-11

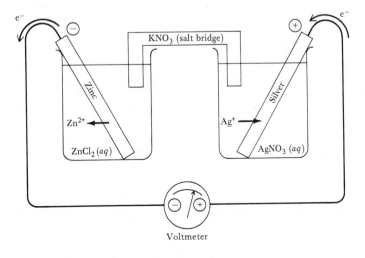

Voltmeter

Electrons flow from the negative electrode to the positive electrode in the external circuit. The reaction at the negative electrode is

$$Zn(s) \longrightarrow Zn^{2+}(aq) + 2e^-$$

Positive ions, $Zn^{2+}(aq)$, are produced at the negative electrode. The reaction at the positive electrode is

$$2Ag^+(aq) + 2e^- \longrightarrow 2Ag(s)$$

Positive ions, $Ag^+(aq)$, are consumed at the positive electrode. We write the cell diagram with the oxidation half-reaction occurring at the left electrode and the reduction half-reaction occurring at the right electrode. Thus the cell diagram is

$$Zn(s)|ZnCl_2(aq)||AgNO_3(aq)|Ag(s)$$

20-13   The reaction at the negative electrode is

$$V(s) \longrightarrow V^{2+}(aq) + 2e^-$$

The reaction at the positive electrode is

$$Cu^{2+}(aq) + 2e^- \longrightarrow Cu(s)$$

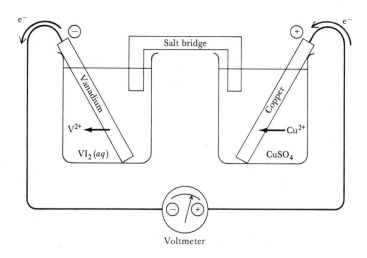

The cell diagram is

$$V(s)|VI_2(aq)||CuSO_4(aq)|Cu(s)$$

20-15   Oxidation takes place at the left electrode. Thus the half-reaction at the left electrode is

$$Pb(s) + 2I^-(aq) \longrightarrow PbI_2(s) + 2e^-$$

The reaction is not $Pb(s) \rightarrow Pb^{2+}(aq) + 2e^-$ because the oxidized lead is in the form of $PbI_2(s)$. The half-reaction at the right electrode is

$$2H^+(aq) + 2e^- \longrightarrow H_2(g)$$

The net cell reaction is

$$Pb(s) + 2HI(aq) \longrightarrow PbI_2(s) + H_2(g)$$

20-17 Oxidation takes place at the left electrode; thus

$$In(s) \longrightarrow In^{3+}(aq) + 3e^-$$

The reaction that occurs at the right electrode is

$$Re^{3+}(aq) + 3e^- \longrightarrow Re(s)$$

The net cell reaction is

$$In(s) + Re^{3+}(aq) \longrightarrow In^{3+}(aq) + Re(s)$$

A sketch of the cell is as follows.

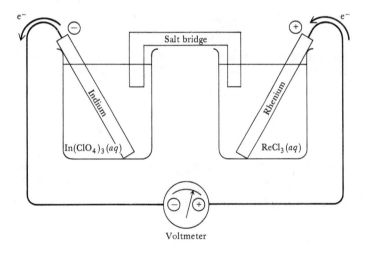

20-19 The half-reaction that occurs at the left electrode is

$$H_2(g) \longrightarrow 2H^+(aq) + 2e^- \qquad \text{(oxidation)}$$

Platinum is an inert electrode. The half-reaction that occurs at the right electrode is

$$Hg_2Cl_2(s) + 2e^- \longrightarrow 2Hg(l) + 2Cl^-(aq) \qquad \text{(reduction)}$$

The net cell reaction is

$$H_2(g) + Hg_2Cl_2(s) \longrightarrow 2Hg(l) + 2H^+(aq) + 2Cl^-(aq)$$

20-21 (a) An change in the amount of Ca(s) has no effect on the cell voltage.

(b) An increase in P_{H_2} corresponds to an increase in the concentration of $H_2(g)$, which drives the reaction from right to left. The cell voltage decreases.

(c) An increase in [HCl] drives the reaction from left to right. The cell voltage increases.

(d) Dissolution of $Ca(NO_3)_2$ in the $CaCl_2(aq)$ solution leads to an increase in $[Ca^{2+}]$. An increase in $[Ca^{2+}]$ drives the reaction from right to left. The cell voltage decreases.

20-23 (a) A change in the amount of $PbCl_2(s)$ has no effect on the cell voltage.

(b) Dilution of the cell solution decreases the value of [HCl]. A decrease in [HCl] increases the driving force of the reaction from left to right and thus increases the cell voltage.

(c) Addition of NaOH(s) to the cell solution decreases $[H^+]$ and thus increases the reaction driving force from left to right. The cell voltage increases.

(d) Addition of $HClO_4$ increases the concentration of $H^+(aq)$ and thus decreases the driving force of the reaction from left to right. The cell voltage decreases.

(e) A decrease in P_{H_2} decreases the driving force of the reaction from left to right and thus decreases the cell voltage.

(f) Because $\Delta H^\circ_{rxn} > 0$, an increase in temperature increases the driving force of the reaction from left to right. Thus the cell voltage increases.

20-25 (a) An increase in [HClO] drives the reaction from left to right. The cell voltage increases.

(b) The size of the electrode has no effect on the cell voltage.

(c) An increase in the pH corresponds to a decrease in $[H^+]$. A decrease in $[H^+]$ drives the reaction from right to left. The cell voltage decreases.

(d) Dissolving KCl(s) in the cell solution containing $Cl^-(aq)$ increases $[Cl^-]$. An increase in $[Cl^-]$ drives the reaction from right to left. The cell voltage decreases.

20-27 (a) Taking the oxygen half-reaction we have

$$2O_2(g) + 8H^+(aq) + 8e^- \longrightarrow 4H_2O(l)$$

Thus $n = 8$.

(b) Taking the zinc half-reaction we have

$$8OH^-(aq) + 2Zn(s) \longrightarrow 2Zn(OH)_4^{2-}(aq) + 4e^-$$

Thus $n = 4$.

20-29 The relation between $E°$ and K is

$$E° = \left(\frac{0.0592 \text{ V}}{n}\right) \log K$$

Solving for $\log K$, we have

$$\log K = \frac{nE°}{0.0592 \text{ V}}$$

The value of n for the reaction is 2, and thus

$$\log K = \frac{(2)(0.47 \text{ V})}{(0.0592 \text{ V})} = 15.9$$

or

$$K = 10^{15.9} = 7.6 \times 10^{15}$$

20-31 We first calculate $E°$ by using the Nernst equation:

$$E = E° - \left(\frac{0.0592 \text{ V}}{n}\right) \log Q$$

Thus, using the given equation for the reaction

$$E = E° - \left(\frac{0.0592 \text{ V}}{n}\right) \log\left(\frac{[Cd^{2+}]}{[Pb^{2+}]}\right)$$

For this reaction $n = 2$. Thus using the given concentrations, we have

$$0.293 \text{ V} = E° - \left(\frac{0.0592 \text{ V}}{2}\right) \log\left(\frac{0.0250 \text{ M}}{0.150 \text{ M}}\right)$$

$$0.293 \text{ V} = E° + 0.023 \text{ V}$$

$$E° = 0.293 \text{ V} - 0.023 \text{ V} = 0.270 \text{ V}$$

The relationship between $E°$ and K is

$$E° = \left(\frac{0.0592 \text{ V}}{n}\right) \log K$$

Thus

$$\log K = \frac{nE°}{0.0592 \text{ V}}$$

and using the above value of $E°$, we compute

$$\log K = \frac{(2)(0.270 \text{ V})}{(0.0592 \text{ V})} = 9.12$$

Thus

$$K = 10^{9.12} = 1.3 \times 10^9$$

20-33 Application of the Nernst equation to the cell reaction yields ($n = 3$)

$$E = E° - \left(\frac{0.0592 \text{ V}}{3}\right) \log\left(\frac{[\text{Al}^{3+}]}{[\text{Fe}^{3+}]}\right)$$

Thus

$$1.59 \text{ V} = E° - \left(\frac{0.0592 \text{ V}}{3}\right) \log\left(\frac{0.250 \text{ M}}{0.0050 \text{ M}}\right)$$

$$1.59 \text{ V} = E° - 0.0335 \text{ V}$$

and

$$E° = 1.59 \text{ V} + 0.034 \text{ V} = 1.62 \text{ V}$$

The relationship between $E°$ and K is

$$\log K = \frac{nE°}{0.0592 \text{ V}}$$

Thus

$$\log K = \frac{(3)(1.62 \text{ V})}{0.0592 \text{ V}} = 82.09$$

$$K = 10^{82.09} = 1.2 \times 10^{82}$$

20-35 The oxidation half-reaction is

$$\text{Zn}(s) \longrightarrow \text{Zn}^{2+}(aq) + 2e^-$$

The reduction half-reaction is

$$\text{Hg}_2\text{Cl}_2(s) + 2e^- \longrightarrow 2\text{Hg}(l) + 2\text{Cl}^-(aq)$$

The cell reaction is

$$\text{Zn}(s) + \text{Hg}_2\text{Cl}_2(s) \longrightarrow 2\text{Hg}(l) + \text{Zn}^{2+}(aq) + 2\text{Cl}^-(aq)$$

Application of the Nernst equation to the cell reaction ($n = 2$) yields

$$E = E° - \left(\frac{0.0592 \text{ V}}{2}\right) \log([Zn^{2+}][Cl^-]^2)$$

Thus

$$E = 1.03 \text{ V} - \left(\frac{0.0592 \text{ V}}{2}\right) \log[(0.040)(0.080)^2]$$

$$= 1.03 \text{ V} + 0.11 \text{ V} = 1.14 \text{ V}$$

20-37   Application of the Nernst equation to the cell reaction yields

$$E = E° - \left(\frac{0.0592 \text{ V}}{n}\right) \log([Zn^{2+}][Cl^-]^2)$$

The oxidation half-reaction is

$$Zn(s) \longrightarrow Zn^{2+}(aq) + 2e^-$$

and thus $n = 2$. The value of the cell voltage when $Q = 1.00$ is $E°$; thus

$$E° = 1.03 \text{ V}$$

Substitution of the data given into the Nernst equation yields

$$1.21 \text{ V} = 1.03 \text{ V} - \left(\frac{0.0592 \text{ V}}{2}\right) \log([Zn^{2+}](0.10)^2)$$

or

$$\log([Zn^{2+}](0.10)^2) = -\frac{2 (1.21 \text{ V} - 1.03 \text{ V})}{0.0592 \text{ V}} = -6.08$$

Therefore

$$[Zn^{2+}](0.10)^2 = 10^{-6.08} = 8.3 \times 10^{-7}$$

and

$$[Zn^{2+}] = 8.3 \times 10^{-5} \text{ M}$$

20-39   The cell diagram is

$$Pt(s)|H_2(g, 1.00 \text{ atm})|H^+(aq)\|Ag^+(1.00 \text{ M})|Ag(s)$$

Assuming oxidation at the left electrode, we have for the left electrode reaction

$$\tfrac{1}{2}H_2(g) \longrightarrow H^+(aq) + e^-$$

Reduction occurs at the right electrode.

$$Ag^+(aq) + e^- \longrightarrow Ag(s)$$

The net cell reaction is

$$\tfrac{1}{2}H_2(g) + Ag^+(aq) \rightleftharpoons H^+(aq) + Ag(s) \qquad n = 1$$

Application of the Nernst equation to the cell reaction yields

$$E = E° - \left(\frac{0.0592 \text{ V}}{1}\right) \log\left(\frac{[H^+]}{P_{H_2}^{1/2}[Ag^+]}\right)$$

Thus, using the data given, we have

$$0.900 \text{ V} = 0.800 \text{ V} - (0.0592 \text{ V}) \log\left[\frac{[H^+]}{(1.00 \text{ atm})^{1/2}(1.00 \text{ M})}\right]$$

$$= 0.800 \text{ V} - (0.0592 \text{ V}) \log[H^+]$$

and solving for $-\log[H^+] = pH$, we find

$$pH = -\log[H^+] = \frac{(0.900 \text{ V} - 0.800 \text{ V})}{(0.0592 \text{ V})} = 1.69$$

20-41   (a) The reduction half-reaction is

$$Fe(CN)_6^{3-}(aq) + e^- \longrightarrow Fe(CN)_6^{4-}(aq) \qquad E_{red}° = +0.36 \text{ V}$$

The oxidation half-reaction is

$$Cu(s) \longrightarrow Cu^+(aq) + e^- \qquad E_{ox}° = -E_{red}° = -0.52 \text{ V}$$

where the $E_{red}°$ values for the half-reactions are obtained from Table 20-1 and we used $E_{ox}° = -E_{red}°$ for a given half-reaction. The $E_{cell}°$ value for the equation

$$Cu(s) + Fe(CN)_6^{3-}(aq) \rightleftharpoons Cu^+(aq) + Fe(CN)_6^{4-}(aq)$$

is

$$E_{cell}° = E_{red}°[Fe(CN)_6^{3-}/Fe(CN)_6^{4-}] + E_{ox}°[Cu^+/Cu]$$

$$= 0.36 \text{ V} - 0.52 \text{ V} = -0.16 \text{ V}$$

(b) The reduction half-reaction is

$$Fe^{3+}(aq) + e^- \longrightarrow Fe^{2+}(aq) \qquad E_{red}° = +0.77 \text{ V}$$

The oxidation half-reaction is

$$Ag(s) \longrightarrow Ag^+(aq) + e^- \qquad E_{ox}° = -E_{red}° = -0.80 \text{ V}$$

The E_{cell}° value for the equation

$$Fe^{3+}(aq) + Ag(s) \longrightarrow Fe^{2+}(aq) + Ag^{+}(aq)$$

is

$$E_{cell}^{\circ} = E_{red}^{\circ}[Fe^{3+}/Fe^{2+}] + E_{ox}^{\circ}[Ag^{+}/Ag] = 0.77 \text{ V} - 0.80 \text{ V} = -0.03 \text{ V}$$

(c) The reduction half-reaction is

$$F_2(g) + 2e^- \longrightarrow 2F^-(aq) \qquad E_{red}^{\circ} = +2.87 \text{ V}$$

The oxidation half-reaction is

$$Zn(s) \longrightarrow Zn^{2+}(aq) + 2e^- \qquad E_{ox}^{\circ} = -E_{red}^{\circ} = +0.76 \text{ V}$$

The E_{cell}° value for the equation

$$Zn(s) + F_2(g) \longrightarrow Zn^{2+}(aq) + 2F^-(aq)$$

is

$$E_{cell}^{\circ} = E_{red}^{\circ}[2F^-/F_2] + E_{ox}^{\circ}[Zn^{2+}/Zn] = 2.87 \text{ V} + 0.76 \text{ V} = 3.63 \text{ V}$$

20-43   The oxidation half-reaction is

$$Cr^{2+}(aq) \longrightarrow Cr^{3+}(aq) + e^-$$

and the reduction half-reaction is

$$HClO(aq) + H^+(aq) + 2e^- \longrightarrow Cl^-(aq) + H_2O(l)$$

The E_{cell}° value for the complete cell is given by

$$E_{cell}^{\circ} = E_{red}^{\circ}[HClO/Cl^-] + E_{ox}^{\circ}[Cr^{3+}/Cr^{2+}]$$

From Table 20-1 we obtain

$$E_{red}^{\circ}[Cr^{3+}/Cr^{2+}] = -0.41 \text{ V}$$

Thus

$$E_{ox}^{\circ}[Cr^{3+}/Cr^{2+}] = -(-0.41 \text{ V}) = +0.41 \text{ V}$$

and

$$E_{cell}^{\circ} = 1.80 \text{ V} = E_{red}^{\circ}[HClO/Cl^-] + 0.41 \text{ V}$$
$$E_{red}^{\circ}[HClO/Cl^-] = 1.39 \text{ V}$$

20-45   The oxidation half-reaction is

$$Zn(s) \longrightarrow Zn^{2+}(aq) + 2e^-$$

and the reduction half-reaction is

$$Cd^{2+}(aq) + 2e^- \longrightarrow Cd(s)$$

The value of E°_{cell} for the complete cell reaction is given by

$$E^\circ_{cell} = E^\circ_{red}[Cd^{2+}/Cd] + E^\circ_{ox}[Zn^{2+}/Zn]$$

From Table 20-1 we obtain

$$E^\circ_{cell} = -0.40 \text{ V} + 0.76 \text{ V} = +0.36 \text{ V}$$

Thus the net reaction

$$Cd^{2+}(aq) + Zn(s) \longrightarrow Zn^{2+}(aq) + Cd(s)$$

occurs spontaneously at 1.00 M concentrations. Application of the Nernst equation to the cell reaction yields

$$E = 0.36 \text{ V} - \left(\frac{0.0592 \text{ V}}{2}\right) \log\left(\frac{[Zn^{2+}]}{[Cd^{2+}]}\right)$$

Thus at $[Zn^{2+}] = 1.00$ M and $[Cd^{2+}] = 0.0010$ M we have

$$E = 0.36 \text{ V} - \left(\frac{0.0592 \text{ V}}{2}\right) \log\left(\frac{1.00 \text{ M}}{0.0010 \text{ M}}\right)$$
$$= 0.36 \text{ V} - 0.09 \text{ V}$$
$$= 0.27 \text{ V} > 0$$

Because $E > 0$, the reaction is spontaneous under these conditions.

20-47   The reduction half-reaction is

$$H^+(aq) + e^- \longrightarrow \tfrac{1}{2}H_2(g)$$

and the oxidation half-reaction is

$$V^{2+}(aq) \longrightarrow V^{3+}(aq) + e^-$$

Thus we have for E°_{cell}

$$E^\circ_{cell} = E^\circ_{red}[H^+/H_2] + E^\circ_{ox}[V^{3+}/V^{2+}]$$

From Table 20-1 and the data given we have

$$E^\circ_{cell} = 0 + 0.24 \text{ V} = +0.24 \text{ V}$$

From the relation between $E°$ and K we have

$$\log K = \frac{nE°_{cell}}{0.0592 \text{ V}}$$

$$= \frac{(1)(0.24 \text{ V})}{0.0592 \text{ V}} = 4.05$$

$$K = 10^{4.05} = 1.12 \times 10^4 \text{ atm}^{1/2} \text{ M}^{-1}$$

Application of the Nernst equation to the cell reaction yields

$$E = 0.24 \text{ V} - (0.0592 \text{ V}) \log\left(\frac{[V^{3+}]P_{H_2}^{1/2}}{[V^{2+}][H^+]}\right)$$

Thus using the concentrations given, we obtain

$$E = 0.24 \text{ V} - (0.0592 \text{ V}) \log\left[\frac{(1.00 \times 10^{-4})(1.00)^{1/2}}{(1.0)(1.0)}\right]$$

$$= 0.48 \text{ V} > 0$$

Hence the reaction is spontaneous and $V^{2+}(aq)$ can liberate $H_2(g)$ under the given conditions.

20-49 The value of $E°_{cell}$ is given by

$$E°_{cell} = E°_{red}[O_2/H_2O] + E°_{ox}[Zn^{2+}/Zn]$$

From Table 20-1 we obtain

$$E°_{cell} = 1.23 \text{ V} - (-0.76 \text{ V}) = 1.99 \text{ V}$$

Application of the Nernst equation,

$$E = E° - \left(\frac{0.0592 \text{ V}}{n}\right) \log Q$$

to the cell reaction yields ($n = 4$)

$$E = E° - \left(\frac{0.0592 \text{ V}}{4}\right) \log\left(\frac{[Zn^{2+}]^2}{P_{O_2}[H^+]^4}\right)$$

Thus

$$E = 1.99 \text{ V} - \left(\frac{0.0592 \text{ V}}{4}\right) \log\left[\frac{(0.0010)^2}{(0.20)(0.20)^4}\right]$$

$$= 1.99 \text{ V} + 0.037 \text{ V} = 2.03 \text{ V}$$

20-51 The oxidation half-reaction in basic solution is

$$S_2O_3^{2-}(aq) + 6OH^-(aq) \longrightarrow 2SO_3^{2-}(aq) + 3H_2O(l) + 4e^-$$

The reduction half-reaction in basic solution is

$$O_2(g) + 2H_2O(l) + 4e^- \longrightarrow 4OH^-(aq)$$

From Table 20-1 we obtain

$$E_{red}^\circ[O_2/OH^-] = 0.40 \text{ V}$$

We can obtain the value of $E_{red}^\circ[SO_3^{2-}/S_2O_3^{2-}]$ from the value of E_{cell}°:

$$E_{cell}^\circ = E_{red}^\circ[O_2/OH^-] + E_{ox}^\circ[SO_3^{2-}/S_2O_3^{2-}]$$
$$= E_{red}^\circ[O_2/OH^-] - E_{red}^\circ[SO_3^{2-}/S_2O_3^{2-}]$$

Thus

$$0.98 \text{ V} = 0.40 \text{ V} - E_{red}^\circ[SO_3^{2-}/S_2O_3^{2-}]$$
$$E_{red}^\circ[SO_3^{2-}/S_2O_3^{2-}] = -0.98 \text{ V} + 0.40 \text{ V} = -0.58 \text{ V}$$

20-53 The reduction half-reaction is

$$Co^{3+}(aq) + e^- \longrightarrow Co^{2+}(aq) \qquad E_{red}^\circ = +1.81 \text{ V}$$

The oxidation half-reaction is

$$2H_2O(l) \longrightarrow O_2(g) + 4H^+(aq) + 4e^- \qquad \begin{aligned} E_{ox}^\circ &= -(+1.23 \text{ V}) \\ &= -1.23 \text{ V} \end{aligned}$$

The equation for the complete reaction is

$$4Co^{3+}(aq) + 2H_2O(l) \longrightarrow 4Co^{2+}(aq) + O_2(g) + 4H^+(aq)$$

and

$$E_{cell}^\circ = 1.81 \text{ V} - 1.23 \text{ V} = 0.58 \text{ V}$$

Application of the Nernst equation to the reaction yields ($n = 4$)

$$E = 0.58 \text{ V} - \left(\frac{0.0592 \text{ V}}{4}\right) \log\left(\frac{[Co^{2+}]^4 P_{O_2}[H^+]^4}{[Co^{3+}]^4}\right)$$

Substitution of the values given yields

$$E = 0.58 \text{ V} - \left(\frac{0.0592 \text{ V}}{4}\right) \log\left[\frac{(1.0 \times 10^{-4})^4(0.20)(0.30)^4}{(0.20)^4}\right]$$
$$= 0.58 \text{ V} + 0.24 \text{ V} = 0.82 \text{ V} > 0$$

The positive value of E means that the reaction is spontaneous under the stated conditions.

20-55 The reduction half-reaction is

$$Co^{3+}(aq) + e^- \longrightarrow Co^{2+}(aq) \qquad E^{\circ}_{red} = 1.81 \text{ V}$$

and the oxidation half-reaction is

$$2H_2O(l) \longrightarrow O_2(g) + 4H^+(aq) + 4e^- \qquad \begin{aligned} E^{\circ}_{ox} &= -(+1.23 \text{ V}) \\ &= -1.23 \text{ V} \end{aligned}$$

The equation for the complete reaction is

$$4Co^{3+}(aq) + 2H_2O(l) \longrightarrow 4Co^{2+}(aq) + O_2(g) + 4H^+(aq)$$

and

$$E^{\circ}_{cell} = 1.81 \text{ V} - 1.23 \text{ V} = 0.58 \text{ V}$$

Application of the Nernst equation to the cell reaction yields ($n = 4$)

$$E = 0.58 \text{ V} - \left(\frac{0.0592 \text{ V}}{4}\right) \log\left(\frac{[Co^{2+}]^4 P_{O_2}[H^+]^4}{[Co^{3+}]^4}\right)$$

If the solution is open to the atmosphere, the pressure of O_2 must be 1.00 atm for O_2 gas to be evolved from the solution. Thus we have, with $[Co^{3+}] = 0.010$ M, $[H^+] = 10^{-pH} = 10^{-1.0} = 1.0 \times 10^{-1}$ M,

$$E = 0.58 \text{ V} - \left(\frac{0.0592 \text{ V}}{4}\right) \log\left\{\frac{[Co^{2+}]^4 (1.00)(1.0 \times 10^{-1})^4}{(0.010)^4}\right\}$$

and

$$\begin{aligned} E &= 0.58 \text{ V} - 0.06 \text{ V} - (0.0592 \text{ V}) \log[Co^{2+}] \\ &= 0.52 \text{ V} - (0.0592 \text{ V}) \log[Co^{2+}] \end{aligned}$$

Thus the value of E will be positive for any possible value of $[Co^{2+}]$ when $[Co^{3+}] = 0.010$ M, and thus the oxidation of water by $Co^{3+}(aq)$ is a spontaneous process.

20-57 The value of ΔG_{rxn} is given by

$$\Delta G_{rxn} = -nFE$$

Two moles of electrons are transferred in this reaction; thus $n = 2$.

$$\begin{aligned} \Delta G_{rxn} &= -(2 \text{ mol})(96,500 \text{ C} \cdot \text{mol}^{-1})(1.05 \text{ V}) \\ &= -203,000 \text{ J} = -203 \text{ kJ} \end{aligned}$$

20-59 The value of ΔG°_{rxn} is given by

$$\Delta G^{\circ}_{rxn} = -nFE^{\circ}_{rxn}$$

In the reaction one mole of copper is oxidized from an oxidation state of zero to an oxidation state of $+2$. Thus the reaction requires two moles of electrons, and so $n = 2$.

$$\Delta G^{\circ}_{rxn} = -(2 \text{ mol})(96{,}500 \text{ C}\cdot\text{mol}^{-1})(0.65 \text{ V})$$
$$= -130{,}000 \text{ J} = -130 \text{ kJ}$$

20-61 (a) The oxidation half-reaction is

$$2\text{Ag}(s) \longrightarrow 2\text{Ag}^+(aq) + 2\text{e}^-$$

and the reduction half-reaction is

$$\text{F}_2(g) + 2\text{e}^- \longrightarrow 2\text{F}^-(aq)$$

The standard cell voltage, E°, is given by

$$E^{\circ} = E^{\circ}_{red}[\text{F}_2/\text{F}^-] + E^{\circ}_{ox}[\text{Ag}^+/\text{Ag}]$$
$$= 2.87 \text{ V} - (+0.80 \text{ V})$$
$$= 2.07 \text{ V}$$

The value of ΔG°_{rxn} is given by

$$\Delta G^{\circ}_{rxn} = -nFE^{\circ}$$

Two electrons are transferred in this reaction, thus

$$\Delta G^{\circ}_{rxn} = -(2 \text{ mol})(96{,}500 \text{ C}\cdot\text{mol}^{-1})(2.07 \text{ V})$$
$$= -400{,}000 \text{ J} = -400 \text{ kJ}$$

(b) The oxidation half-reaction is

$$\tfrac{1}{2}\text{H}_2(g) \longrightarrow \text{H}^+(aq) + \text{e}^-$$

and the reduction half-reaction is

$$\text{Fe}^{3+}(aq) + \text{e}^- \longrightarrow \text{Fe}^{2+}(aq)$$

The standard cell voltage, E°, is

$$E^{\circ} = E^{\circ}_{red}[\text{Fe}^{3+}/\text{Fe}^{2+}] + E^{\circ}_{ox}[\text{H}^+/\text{H}_2]$$
$$= 0.77 \text{ V} + 0 \text{ V} = 0.77 \text{ V}$$

The value of ΔG°_{rxn} is given by

$$\Delta G^{\circ}_{rxn} = -nFE^{\circ}$$

One electron is transferred in this reaction; thus $n = 1$.

$$\Delta G^{\circ}_{rxn} = -(1 \text{ mol})(96{,}500 \text{ C} \cdot \text{mol}^{-1})(0.77 \text{ V})$$
$$= -74{,}000 \text{ J} = -74 \text{ kJ}$$

20-63   The equation for the cell reaction is

$$\text{Zn}(s) + \text{Cd}^{2+}(aq) \longrightarrow \text{Zn}^{2+}(aq) + \text{Cd}(s)$$

The value of the standard cell voltage is

$$E^{\circ} = E^{\circ}_{red}[\text{Cd}^{2+}/\text{Cd}] + E^{\circ}_{ox}[\text{Zn}^{2+}/\text{Zn}]$$
$$= -0.40 \text{ V} - (-0.76 \text{ V}) = 0.36 \text{ V}$$

The value of ΔG°_{rxn} is

$$\Delta G^{\circ}_{rxn} = -nFE^{\circ}$$

In the reaction two moles of electrons are transferred from one mole of zinc to one mole of cadmium; thus $n = 2$.

$$\Delta G^{\circ}_{rxn} = -(2 \text{ mol})(96{,}500 \text{ C} \cdot \text{mol}^{-1})(0.36 \text{ V})$$
$$= -69{,}000 \text{ J} = -69 \text{ kJ}$$

The value of ΔG_{rxn} is given by

$$\Delta G_{rxn} = \Delta G^{\circ}_{rxn} + 2.30RT \log Q$$
$$= \Delta G^{\circ}_{rxn} + 2.30RT \log \left(\frac{[\text{Zn}^{2+}]}{[\text{Cd}^{2+}]} \right)$$
$$= -69 \text{ kJ} + (2.30)(8.314 \text{ J} \cdot \text{K}^{-1})(298 \text{ K}) \log \left(\frac{0.01 \text{ M}}{0.050 \text{ M}} \right)$$
$$= -69 \text{ kJ} - 3.98 \text{ kJ} = -73 \text{ kJ}$$

The value of E for the cell under the conditions given is

$$E = -\frac{\Delta G_{rxn}}{nF}$$
$$= -\frac{-73 \times 10^3 \text{ J}}{(2 \text{ mol})(96{,}500 \text{ C} \cdot \text{mol}^{-1})}$$
$$= 0.38 \text{ V}$$

20-65   The reaction that takes place in an ethane-oxygen cell is

$$\text{C}_2\text{H}_6(g) + \tfrac{7}{2}\text{O}_2(g) \rightleftharpoons 2\text{CO}_2(g) + 3\text{H}_2\text{O}(l)$$

The value of ΔG°_{rxn} is given by

$$\Delta G^{\circ}_{rxn} = 2 \, \Delta G^{\circ}_f [\text{CO}_2(g)] + 3 \, \Delta G^{\circ}_f [\text{H}_2\text{O}(l)] - \Delta G^{\circ}_f [\text{C}_2\text{H}_6(g)] - \tfrac{7}{2} \Delta G^{\circ}_f [\text{O}_2(g)]$$

Thus

$$\Delta G^\circ_{rxn} = (2 \text{ mol})(-394.4 \text{ kJ} \cdot \text{mol}^{-1}) + (3 \text{ mol})(-237.2 \text{ kJ} \cdot \text{mol}^{-1})$$
$$- (1 \text{ mol})(-32.89 \text{ kJ} \cdot \text{mol}^{-1}) - (\tfrac{7}{2} \text{ mol})(0 \text{ kJ} \cdot \text{mol}^{-1})$$
$$= -1467.5 \text{ kJ}$$

The value of the standard voltage of the cell is given by

$$E^\circ = -\frac{\Delta G^\circ_{rxn}}{nF}$$

The oxidation state of seven oxygen atoms is decreased from 0 to -2, thus 14 ($= 2 \times 7$) moles of electrons are involved and

$$E^\circ = -\frac{(-1467.5 \times 10^3 \text{ J})}{(14 \text{ mol})(96{,}500 \text{ C} \cdot \text{mol}^{-1})} = 1.086 \text{ V}$$

20-67 Replacing cadmium with iron in the nickel-cadmiun battery, we have

$$\ominus \text{steel} | \text{Fe}(s) | \text{Fe(OH)}_2(s) | \text{LiOH}(aq) | \text{NiOOH}(s), \text{Ni(OH)}_2(s) | \text{steel} \oplus$$

20-69 We assume oxidation at the left electrode; thus

$$\text{Mn}^{2+}(aq) \longrightarrow \text{MnO}_4^-(aq)$$

The balanced half-reaction is

$$4\text{H}_2\text{O}(l) + \text{Mn}^{2+}(aq) \longrightarrow \text{MnO}_4^-(aq) + 8\text{H}^+(aq) + 5e^-$$

The reduction half-reaction involves

$$\text{IO}_3^-(aq) \longrightarrow \text{I}^-(aq)$$

The balanced half-reaction is

$$6e^- + 6\text{H}^+(aq) + \text{IO}_3^-(aq) \longrightarrow \text{I}^-(aq) + 3\text{H}_2\text{O}(l)$$

The equation for the complete cell reaction is ($n = 6 \times 5 = 30$)

$$9\text{H}_2\text{O}(l) + 6\text{Mn}^{2+}(aq) + 5\text{IO}_3^-(aq) \longrightarrow 18\text{H}^+(aq) + 6\text{MnO}_4^-(aq) + 5\text{I}^-(aq)$$

20-71 The oxidation of lead in the presence of $O_2(g)$ and moisture is described by the equation.

$$2\text{H}_2\text{O}(g) + 2\text{Pb}(s) + \text{O}_2(g) \longrightarrow 2\text{Pb(OH)}_2(s)$$
$$\text{(white)}$$

20-73 The number of moles in one metric ton of copper is

$$\text{moles of Cu} = (1 \text{ metric ton})\left(\frac{1000 \text{ kg}}{1 \text{ metric ton}}\right)\left(\frac{1000 \text{ g}}{1 \text{ kg}}\right)\left(\frac{1 \text{ mol Cu}}{63.55 \text{ g Cu}}\right)$$

$$= 1.574 \times 10^4 \text{ mol}$$

The number of electrons required to deposit 1.574×10^4 mol of copper is

$$\text{moles of electrons} = (1.574 \times 10^4 \text{ mol Cu})\left(\frac{2 \text{ mol e}^-}{1 \text{ mol Cu}}\right)$$

$$= 3.148 \times 10^4 \text{ mol}$$

The charge that corresponds to 3.148×10^4 moles of electrons is

$$\text{charge} = (3.148 \times 10^4 \text{ mol})(96{,}500 \text{ C}\cdot\text{mol}^{-1}) = 3.038 \times 10^9 \text{ C}$$

One ampere-hour is a current of one ampere that flows for one hour. Thus the number of coulombs in $1\text{A}\cdot\text{h}$ is

$$1\text{A}\cdot\text{h} = (1 \text{ C}\cdot\text{s}^{-1})(1 \text{ h})\left(\frac{3600 \text{ s}}{1 \text{ h}}\right) = 3.600 \times 10^3 \text{ C}$$

The number of $\text{A}\cdot\text{h}$ in 3.038×10^9 C is

$$\frac{3.038 \times 10^9 \text{ C}}{3.600 \times 10^3 \text{ C}\cdot\text{A}^{-1}\cdot\text{h}^{-1}} = 8.44 \times 10^5 \text{ A}\cdot\text{h}$$

20-75 The mass of silver deposited is given by

$$m = \left(\frac{It}{F}\right)\left(\frac{A}{n}\right)$$

The half-reaction for the deposition of Ag(s) is

$$\text{Ag}^+(aq) + \text{e}^- \longrightarrow \text{Ag}(s)$$

and thus $n = 1$. Thus we have for the silver deposition

$$\frac{It}{F} = \frac{nm}{A} = \frac{(1)(0.876 \text{ g})}{(107.9 \text{ g}\cdot\text{mol}^{-1})} = 8.12 \times 10^{-3} \text{ mol}$$

The half-reaction for the deposition of Cd(s) is

$$\text{Cd}^{2+}(aq) + 2\text{e}^- \longrightarrow \text{Cd}(s)$$

and thus $n = 2$. Using the above value of It/F, we obtain for the mass of Cd(s) deposited

$$m = \left(\frac{It}{F}\right)\left(\frac{A}{n}\right) = (8.12 \times 10^{-3} \text{ mol})\left(\frac{112.4 \text{ g}\cdot\text{mol}^{-1}}{2}\right)$$

$$= 0.456 \text{ g}$$

20-77 Assuming that oxidation takes place at the left electrode, we have

$$Ag(s) + Br^-(aq) \longrightarrow AgBr(s) + e^-$$

Reduction occurs at the right electrode.

$$Ag^+(aq) + e^- \longrightarrow Ag(s)$$

The net cell reaction is

$$Ag^+(aq) + Br^-(aq) \rightleftharpoons AgBr(s)$$

and thus $n = 1$. Application of the Nernst equation to the cell reaction yields

$$E = E° - \left(\frac{0.0592 \text{ V}}{1}\right) \log\left(\frac{1}{[Ag^+][Br^-]}\right)$$

At equilibrium $E = 0$ and $[Ag^+][Br^-] = K_{sp}$; thus

$$0 = 0.728 \text{ V} - (0.0592 \text{ V}) \log\left(\frac{1}{K_{sp}}\right)$$

Thus

$$\log K_{sp} = \frac{-0.728 \text{ V}}{0.0592 \text{ V}} = -12.30$$

and

$$K_{sp} = 5.0 \times 10^{-13} \text{ M}^2$$

20-79 The oxidation half-reaction is

$$H_2(g) \longrightarrow 2H^+(aq) + 2e^-$$

and the reduction half-reaction is

$$Hg_2Cl_2(s) + 2e^- \longrightarrow 2Hg(l) + 2Cl^-(sat)$$

The equation for the cell reaction is

$$H_2(g) + Hg_2Cl_2(s) \rightleftharpoons 2H^+(aq) + 2Cl^-(sat) + 2Hg(l)$$

Because the concentration of $Cl^-(sat)$ is a constant, $[Cl^-]$ does not appear in the equilibrium constant expression for this equation, and so

$$K = \frac{[H^+]^2}{P_{H_2}}$$

If P_{H_2} is fixed at 1.00 atm, then

$$K = [H^+]^2$$

Thus

$$E = E° - \left(\frac{0.0592 \text{ V}}{n}\right) \log[H^+]^2$$

The value of $E°$ for the cell is 0.2415 V (you do not have to know this) and so

(1) $$E = 0.2415 \text{ V} - (0.0592 \text{ V}) \log[H^+]$$

For the reaction

$$HC_2H_3O_2(aq) \rightleftharpoons H^+(aq) + C_2H_3O_2^-(aq)$$

we have

(2) $$K_a = \frac{[H^+][C_2H_3O_2^-]}{[HC_2H_3O_2]}$$

In our discussion of the Henderson-Hasselbalch equation (Chapter 16) it was shown that in a solution containing an acid and its conjugate base

(3a) $$[HC_2H_3O_2]_{eq} \approx [HC_2H_3O_2]_0$$

(3b) $$[C_2H_3O_2^-]_{eq} \approx [C_2H_3O_2^-]_0$$

Thus from the measured value of E in combination with the relations (3), we can obtain a value for K_a by using the equation

$$E = 0.2415 \text{ V} - (0.0592 \text{ V}) \log \frac{K_a[HC_2H_3O_2]_0}{[C_2H_3O_2^-]_0}$$

20-81   The voltage measured between the $Zn(s)$ and $Cu(s)$ rods will be zero because the cell is short circuited. The reducing agent, $Zn(s)$, must be physically separated from the oxidizing agent, $CuSO_4(aq)$. In this case, the $Zn(s)$ rod is in the $Cu^{2+}(aq)$ solution.

20-83   We shall use the Nernst equation in the form

$$E = -\left(\frac{2.30RT}{nF}\right) \log\left(\frac{Q}{K}\right)$$

The cell reaction will take place until $Q = K$, which occurs when equilibrium has been reached:

$$E = -\left(\frac{2.30RT}{nF}\right) \log(1) = 0$$

20-85 The total charge is

$$\text{charge} = (0.600 \text{ C} \cdot \text{s}^{-1})(1 \text{ h})\left(\frac{60 \text{ min}}{1 \text{ h}}\right)\left(\frac{60 \text{ s}}{1 \text{ min}}\right)$$

$$= 2.16 \times 10^3 \text{ C}$$

The number of moles of electrons that corresponds to 2.16×10^3 C is

$$\text{moles of electrons} = \frac{2160 \text{ C}}{96,500 \text{ C} \cdot \text{mol}^{-1}} = 0.02238 \text{ mol}$$

The number of moles of metal deposited is ($n = 1$)

$$\text{moles of metal} = \text{moles of electrons} = 0.02238 \text{ mol}$$

We have the correspondence

$$2.42 \text{ g} \approxeq 0.02238 \text{ mol}$$

Dividing both sides by 0.02238, we have

$$108 \text{ g} \approxeq 1 \text{ mol}$$

The atomic mass of the metal is 108. The metal with an atomic mass of 108 is silver.

E ANSWERS TO THE SELF-TEST

1 true

2 false (The current in solution is carried by ions.)

3 cathode

4 true

5 current × time

6 96,500 coulombs or one Faraday

7 96,500 C·mol^{-1} (the charge on one mole of electrons)

8 chlorine, $Cl_2(g)$, sodium hydroxide, $NaOH(aq)$, and hydrogen, $H_2(g)$ . . . $NaCl(aq)$

9 aluminum metal . . . $Al_2O_3(s)$ dissolved in $Na_3AlF_6(l)$

10 true

11 oxidation half-reaction
. . . reduction half-reaction

12 negative . . . positive

13 to provide an ionic current path between the separated solutions

14 (a) left (negative)
(b) $Cd(s) \rightarrow Cd^{2+}(aq) + 2e^-$
(c) $Pb^{2+}(aq) + 2e^- \rightarrow Pb(s)$

15 (a) $ZnSO_4(aq)$
(b) $Zn(s)$ . . . $Hg_2SO_4(s)$ . . . $Hg(l)$
(c) There is no salt bridge in this cell.

16 to act as a metallic surface on which the electron transfer half-reaction $2H^+(aq) + 2e^- \rightleftharpoons H_2(g)$ can occur

17 false

18 (a) decreases   (b) increases
    (c) remains unchanged
    (d) becomes zero

19 positive

20 $\left(\dfrac{0.0592 \text{ V}}{n}\right) \log K$

21 $Q = 1$, that is, when all species are in their standard states

22 1

23 less than

24 $E^0 - \left(\dfrac{0.0592 \text{ V}}{n}\right) \log Q$

25 false

26 0 V

27 false (A reference half-reaction must be defined.)

28 false

29 0 V

30 reduction

31 true

32 negative

33 true

34 true

35 the Nernst

36 voltage

37 true

38 true

39 the magnitude of ΔG_{rxn}

40 2030 kJ

41 $-nFE_{rxn}$

42 is

43 true

NUCLEAR AND RADIOCHEMISTRY

A   OUTLINE OF CHAPTER 21

21-1   Many nuclei spontaneously emit small particles.

Nuclei consist of protons and neutrons, which are collectively called nucleons.

The number of protons is the atomic number, Z.

The number of nucleons is the mass number, A.

Atoms that contain the same number of protons but different numbers of neutrons are called isotopes.

An isotope is denoted by a symbol $_Z^A X$.

The spontaneous disintegration of a nucleus is called radioactivity; such a nucleus is radioactive.

A radioactive isotope is called a radioisotope.

Nuclear equations must be balanced with respect to charge and the number of nucleons.

21-2   There are several types of radioactive emissions.

The types of particles that are emitted in radioactive processes are listed in Table 21-1.

Radioactive decay is the process in which a nucleus emits a particle and transforms to another nucleus.

The proton-to-neutron ratio determines the stability of a nucleus.

The stable nuclei form a band of stability (Figure 21-2).

Nuclei that lie below the band of stability undergo β decay.

Nuclei that lie above the band of stability undergo positron emission.

All nuclei with $Z > 83$ are unstable.

Only a few stable nuclei have odd numbers of both protons and neutrons.

The number of stable nuclei with even and odd numbers of protons and neutrons are given in Table 21-3.

Nuclei that contain 2, 8, 28, 50, or 82 protons or neutrons (called the magic numbers) are particularly stable.

21-3 The rate of decay of a radioactive isotope is a first-order process.

Different radioisotopes have different half-lives.

The half-lives of some radioisotopes are listed in Table 21-4.

The number of nuclei remaining, N, after a decay time, t, is given by

$$\log\left(\frac{N_0}{N}\right) = \frac{0.301t}{t_{1/2}} \tag{21-1}$$

where N_0 is the initial number of nuclei and $t_{1/2}$ is the half-life of the radioisotope.

21-4 Radioactivity can be used to determine the age of rocks.

The age of a rock can be determined by its relative content of uranium-238 and lead-206. (Example 21-6).

21-5 Carbon-14 can be used to date certain archaeological objects.

Radiocarbon dating is useful for objects less than about 30,000 years old.

Living organisms contain a fixed percentage of carbon-14. The radiation due to carbon-14 in all living organisms is 15.3 disintegrations per minute per gram of total carbon.

The age of a carbon-containing object is given by

$$t = (1.90 \times 10^4 \text{ years}) \log\left(\frac{15.3}{R}\right) \tag{21-4}$$

where R is the number of disintegrations per minute per gram of carbon in the object.

21-6 Radioisotopes can be produced in the laboratory.

Radioisotopes that are not found in nature but are produced in the laboratory are called artificial radioisotopes.

Some of the many radioisotopes that are used in medicine are listed in Table 21-5.

Elements beyond uranium in the periodic table are produced artificially.

The elements beyond uranium in the periodic table are called the transuranium elements.

21-7 Nuclear chemistry can be used to detect extremely small quantities of the elements.

In neutron activation analysis the sample is irradiated by a beam of neutrons. The frequencies of the γ-rays emitted are characteristic of the isotopes present in the sample.

In a *PIXE* (*proton induced X-ray emission*) analysis the sample is irradiated by a beam of protons. The energies of the X-rays emitted are characteristic of the elements present in the sample.

21-8   Enormous amounts of energy accompany nuclear reactions.

Nuclear reactions are about a million times more energetic than chemical reactions.

The mass lost in a nuclear reaction is converted into energy.

The relation between mass lost and energy produced is given by

$$\Delta E = c^2 \, \Delta m \tag{21-6}$$

where c is the speed of light, 3.00×10^8 m·s^{-1}.

The energy required to break up a nucleus into its constituent protons and neutrons is called the binding energy.

The binding energy is calculated by calculating Δm for the formation of the nucleus from its constituent protons and neutrons and then using the equation $\Delta E = c^2 \, \Delta m$.

The graph of the binding energy per nucleon versus the mass number, called a binding energy curve, is shown in Figure 21-7.

21-9   Some nuclei fragment in nuclear reactions.

A nuclear reaction in which a nucleus splits into two smaller fragments is called a fission reaction.

Energy is released in the $^{235}_{92}\text{U}$ fission reaction.

21-10   The fission of uranium-235 can initiate a chain reaction.

A chain reaction occurs when uranium-235 undergoes a fission reaction after absorbing a neutron (Figure 21-9).

The smallest quantity of fissionable material that can support a chain reaction is called the critical mass.

21-11   A nuclear reactor utilizes a controlled chain reaction.

The chain reaction in a nuclear reactor is controlled by control rods, which are made out of substances that readily absorb neutrons.

The heat produced by a nuclear reaction in the core of the reactor is used to generate electricity (Figure 21-12).

21-12   A breeder reactor is designed to produce more fissionable material than it consumes.

Uranium-238 is converted to the fissionable material plutonium-239 in a breeder reactor.

21-13   Fusion reactions release more energy than fission reactions.

A nuclear reaction in which small nuclei join to form larger nuclei is called a fusion reaction.

The sun's energy is due to a nuclear reaction involving the fusion of four protons into a helium-4 nucleus and two positrons.

The hydrogen bomb utilizes a fusion reaction.

21-14   Exposure to radiation damages cells, tissues, and genes.

A measure of the activity of a radioactive substance is its specific activity.

The specific activity of a radioisotope is inversely proportional to its half-life, $t_{1/2}$.

The specific activity of a radioisotope is given by

$$\text{specific activity} = \left(\frac{4.2 \times 10^{23} \text{ disintegrations} \cdot \text{g}^{-1}}{M t_{1/2}} \right) \qquad (21\text{-}8)$$

where M is the atomic mass of the isotope and $t_{1/2}$ is the half-life in seconds.

The quantity 3.7×10^{10} disintegrations per second is called a curie and is designated by Ci.

The specific activities of some important radioisotopes are listed in Table 21-6.

The extent of the damage produced by radiation depends on the energy and type of radiation.

B   SELF-TEST

1   A radioisotope is _____.

2   Alpha particles are _____.

3   Beta particles are _____.

4   Gamma rays are _____.

5   Uranium-238 is an α-emitter. The nuclear equation for the disintegration of uranium-238 is $^{238}_{92}\text{U} \rightarrow$ _____.

6   Indium-116 is a β-emitter. The nuclear equation for the disintegration of indium-116 is $^{116}_{49}\text{In} \rightarrow$ _____.

7   Nuclei contain electrons as well as protons and neutrons. *True/False*

8 Potassium-38 is a positron emitter. The nuclear equation for the disintegration of potassium-38 is $^{38}_{19}\text{K} \rightarrow$ _____ .

9 Nuclei that lie above the band of stability emit _____ .

10 Nuclei that lie below the band of stability emit _____ .

11 All nuclei with $Z > 83$ are unstable. *True/False*

12 Elements with an odd number of protons usually have only one or two stable isotopes. *True/False*

13 A nucleus containing an even number of both protons and neutrons is likely to be unstable. *True/False*

14 Nuclei that contain a magic number of protons or neutrons are usually stable. *True/False*

15 All nuclei with $Z >$ _____ are radioactive.

16 All radioactive nuclei decay at the same rate. *True/False*

17 The rate of radioactive decay varies with temperature. *True/False*

18 Radioactive decay is a _____-order rate process.

19 The half-life of a radioactive sample is the time _____
_____ .

20 The age of a uranium-containing rock can be determined by measuring the masses of _____ and _____ in the rock sample.

21 Carbon-14 dating is used to determine the age of once-living material. *True/False*

22 All living organisms contain carbon-14. *True/False*

23 The rate of β-decay in living organisms is _____ disintegrations per minute per gram of carbon.

24 Objects of any age can be dated by the carbon-14 method. *True/False*

25 The atmospheric source of carbon-14 in living organisms is

_____ .

26 Radioisotopes that are made in the laboratory are called _____ .

27 Neutron activation analysis is used to measure trace quantities of elements. *True/False*

28   To carry out a neutron activation analysis, the sample is irradiated by a beam of

_____ .

29   In the PIXE analytical method, the sample is irradiated by a beam of

_____ .

30   The transuranium elements are laboratory made. _True/False_

31   The mass lost in a nuclear reaction is converted into _____ .

32   The relation between mass and energy is given by _____ .

33   The value of ΔE for a typical nuclear reaction is similar to that for a typical chemical reaction. _True/False_

34   Energy is _(absorbed, evolved)_ when a nucleus is broken up into its constituent protons and neutrons.

35   The binding energy per nucleon is the same for all nuclei. _True/False_

36   A binding energy curve is a plot of _____ versus

_____ .

37   In the uranium-235 fission reaction, when uranium-235 absorbs a neutron, the uranium-235 nucleus _____ .

38   The uranium-235 fission reaction can support a chain reaction because

_____ .

39   A quantity of uranium-235 less than the critical mass will not support a chain reaction. _True/False_

40   In a reactor the rate of the uranium-235 fission reactions can be controlled by inserting material that absorbs neutrons. _True/False_

41   The uranium-235 fission reaction can be used in a nuclear reactor to produce energy. _True/False_

42   A breeder reactor is designed to produce more fissionable material than is consumed. _True/False_

43   The major source of the sun's energy is the fusion of _____ into

_____ .

44   The specific activity of a radioactive substance is _____

_____ .

45   The specific activity of a radioisotope is related to the half-life and the atomic mass of the isotope by the equation: specific activity = _____ .

46   One curie is equal to _____ .

C   CALCULATIONS YOU SHOULD KNOW HOW TO DO

1   Complete and balance nuclear equations. See Examples 21-1 and 21-2 and Problems 21-1 through 21-4.

2   Calculate the quantity of a radioisotope that remains after a certain time. See Example 21-4, Problems 21-13 through 21-17 and Problems 21-19 and 21-22.

3   Calculate the time required for a radioisotope to decay to a certain level using Equation (21-1). See Problems 21-18 and 21-20 and 21-21.

4   Use Equation (21-4) to determine the ages of objects by radio-carbon dating. See Example 21-7 and Problems 21-23 through 21-28.

5   Determine the ages of rocks by uranium-lead dating. See Example 21-6 and Problems 21-29 and 21-30.

6   Calculate the binding energy and the binding energy per nucleon of a given nucleus. See Example 21-9 and Problems 21-31 through 21-34.

7   Calculate the energy released in nuclear reactions. See Problems 21-35 through 21-37 and 21-39 through 21-42.

8   Calculate the specific activity of a radioisotope from its half-life using Equation (21-8). See Section 21-14 and Problems 21-43 through 21-47.

D   SOLUTIONS TO THE ODD-NUMBERED PROBLEMS

21-1   (a) $^{72}_{30}\text{Zn} \rightarrow {}_{-1}^{0}\text{e} + {}^{72}_{31}\text{Ga}$

(b) $^{230}_{92}\text{U} \rightarrow {}^{4}_{2}\text{He} + {}^{226}_{90}\text{Th}$

(c) $^{136}_{57}\text{La} \rightarrow {}_{+1}^{0}\text{e} + {}^{136}_{56}\text{Ba}$

(d) $^{14}_{7}\text{N} + {}^{1}_{0}\text{n} \rightarrow {}^{1}_{1}\text{H} + {}^{14}_{6}\text{C}$

21-3   (a) $^{25}_{12}\text{Mg} + {}^{4}_{2}\text{He} \rightarrow {}^{28}_{13}\text{Al} + {}^{1}_{1}\text{H}$

(b) $^{27}_{13}\text{Al} + {}^{1}_{0}\text{n} \rightarrow {}^{4}_{2}\text{He} + {}^{24}_{11}\text{Na}$

(c) $^{17}_{8}\text{O} + {}^{1}_{1}\text{H} \rightarrow {}^{4}_{2}\text{He} + {}^{14}_{7}\text{N}$

(d) $^{63}_{29}\text{Cu} + {}^{1}_{1}\text{H} \rightarrow {}^{63}_{30}\text{Zn} + {}^{1}_{0}\text{n}$

21-5 The proton-to-neutron ratio in calcium-38 is $\frac{20}{18} = 1.11$, which lies above the band of stability. Thus calcium-38 is a positron emitter.

21-7 (a) The proton-to-neutron ratio in rubidium-76 is $(\frac{37}{39}) = 0.95$, which lies above the band of stability. Thus rubidium-76 is a positron emitter.

(b) The proton-to-neutron ratio in germanium-80 is $(\frac{32}{48}) = 0.67$, which lies below the band of stability. Thus germanium-80 is a β-emitter.

(c) The proton-to-neutron ratio in chlorine-32 is $(\frac{17}{15}) = 1.13$, which lies above the band of stability. Thus chlorine-32 is a positron emitter.

(d) The proton-to-neutron ratio in iron-62 is $(\frac{26}{36}) = 0.72$, which lies below the band of stability. Thus iron-62 is a β-emitter.

21-9 (a) The proton-to-neutron ratio in argon-35 is $(\frac{18}{17}) = 1.06$, which lies above the band of stability. Thus argon-35 decays by positron emission.

(b) Magnesium-24 has an even number of both protons and neutrons, and thus we predict that it is not radioactive.

(c) Calcium-40 has a magic number of both protons and neutrons, and thus we predict that it is not radioactive.

(d) Neon-20 has an even number of both protons and neutrons, and thus we predict that it is not radioactive.

21-11 (a) Sodium-24 has an odd number of both protons and neutrons. In addition, the proton-to-neutron ratio of sodium-24 is $(\frac{11}{13}) = 0.85$, which lies below the band of stability. Thus we predict that sodium-23 is a β-emitter.

(b) All elements with $Z > 83$ are radioactive.

(c) Tin-118 has a magic number of protons and an even number of neutrons. Thus we predict that tin-118 is not radioactive.

(d) All elements with $Z > 83$ are radioactive.

21-13 If we use Equation (21-1), then we have

$$\log \frac{N_0}{N} = \frac{0.301t}{t_{1/2}}$$

$$= \frac{(0.301)(1 \text{ day})\left(\dfrac{24 \text{ h}}{1 \text{ day}}\right)\left(\dfrac{60 \text{ min}}{1 \text{ h}}\right)}{110 \text{ min}} = 3.94$$

$$\frac{N_0}{N} = 8720$$

Inverting both sides gives the fraction remaining

$$\frac{N}{N_0} = 0.000115 = 1.15 \times 10^{-4}$$

21-15   According to Example 21-5, we can use Equation (21-1) with mass (m) replacing number of nuclei (N):

$$\log \frac{m_0}{m} = \log \frac{0.200 \text{ mg}}{m} = \frac{0.301t}{t_{1/2}} = \frac{(0.301)(182 \text{ days})}{(46.9 \text{ days})}$$

$$= 1.17$$

or

$$\frac{0.200 \text{ mg}}{m} = 10^{1.17} = 14.8$$

$$m = \frac{0.200 \text{ mg}}{14.7} = 0.0135 \text{ mg}$$

21-17   We use Equation (21-1).

$$\log \frac{N_0}{N} = \frac{0.301t}{t_{1/2}} = \frac{(0.301)(30 \text{ days})}{45 \text{ days}} = 0.20$$

$$\frac{N_0}{N} = 10^{0.20} = 1.6$$

$$\frac{N}{N_0} = 0.63$$

21-19   We use Equation (21-1)

$$\log \frac{N_0}{N} = \frac{0.301t}{t_{1/2}} = \frac{(0.301)(14 \text{ days})}{(14.3 \text{ days})} = 0.295$$

or

$$\frac{N_0}{N} = 10^{0.295} = 1.97$$

or

$$\frac{N}{N_0} = 0.507$$

21-21   We use Equation (21-1) with $N = 0.0010N_0$ (0.10% of the initial value). Thus we write

$$\log \frac{N_0}{N} = \log \frac{1}{0.0010} = \frac{0.301t}{t_{1/2}} = \frac{0.301t}{12.8 \text{ h}}$$

Solving for t gives

$$t = \left(\frac{12.8 \text{ h}}{0.301}\right) \log(1.0 \times 10^3) = 128 \text{ h} = 5.33 \text{ days}$$

21-23 We use Equation (21-4).

$$t = (1.90 \times 10^4 \text{ years}) \log \frac{15.3}{R}$$

$$= (1.90 \times 10^4 \text{ years}) \log \frac{15.3}{5.37} = 8640 \text{ years}$$

21-25 We use Equation (21-4) with $R = (0.145)(15.3 \text{ disintegrations} \cdot \text{min}^{-1} \cdot \text{g}^{-1}$ of carbon). Thus

$$t = (1.90 \times 10^4 \text{ years}) \log \frac{15.3}{R}$$

$$= (1.90 \times 10^4 \text{ years}) \log\left(\frac{1}{0.145}\right) = 15{,}900 \text{ years}$$

21-27 We use Equation (21-4), but first we must convert the decay rate to disintegrations $\cdot \text{min}^{-1} \cdot \text{g}^{-1}$.

$$R = (498 \text{ disintegrations} \cdot \text{h}^{-1} \cdot \text{g}^{-1})\left(\frac{1 \text{ h}}{60 \text{ min}}\right)$$

$$= 8.30 \text{ disintegrations} \cdot \text{min}^{-1} \cdot \text{g}^{-1}$$

Thus

$$t = (1.90 \times 10^4 \text{ years}) \log \frac{15.3}{R}$$

$$= (1.90 \times 10^4 \text{ years}) \log\left(\frac{15.3}{8.30}\right) = 5050 \text{ years}$$

21-29 The age of the uranite is given by

$$t = \frac{t_{1/2}}{0.301} \log \frac{N_0}{N} = \frac{(4.51 \times 10^9 \text{ years})}{0.301} \log \frac{N_0}{N}$$

where

$$\frac{N_0}{N} = \frac{\text{initial mass of } ^{238}_{92}\text{U}}{\text{present mass of } ^{238}_{92}\text{U}}$$

The initial mass of $^{238}_{92}U$ is the sum of the present mass and the mass that has decayed:

$$\frac{N_0}{N} = \frac{\text{mass of } ^{238}_{92}U \text{ that has decayed} + \text{present mass of } ^{238}_{92}U}{\text{present mass of } ^{238}_{92}U}$$

$$= \frac{\text{mass of } ^{238}_{92}U \text{ that has decayed}}{\text{present mass of } ^{238}_{92}U} + 1$$

The mass of lead resulting from the decay of uranium is

$$\text{mass of } ^{206}_{82}Pb = (\text{mass of } ^{238}_{92}U \text{ that has decayed})\left(\frac{1 \text{ mol } ^{238}_{92}U}{238 \text{ g } ^{238}_{92}U}\right)$$

$$\times \left(\frac{1 \text{ mol } ^{206}_{82}Pb}{1 \text{ mol } ^{238}_{92}U}\right)\left(\frac{206 \text{ g } ^{206}_{82}Pb}{1 \text{ mol } ^{206}_{82}Pb}\right)$$

$$= \left(\frac{206}{238}\right)(\text{mass of } ^{238}_{92}U \text{ that has decayed})$$

The mass ratio $^{206}_{82}Pb/^{238}_{92}U$ is given as

$$\text{mass ratio} = \frac{\text{mass of } ^{206}_{82}Pb}{\text{present mass of } ^{238}_{92}U} = 0.395$$

$$= \frac{\left(\dfrac{206}{238}\right)(\text{mass of } ^{238}_{92}U \text{ that has decayed})}{\text{present mass of } ^{238}_{92}U}$$

Therefore,

$$\frac{\text{mass of } ^{238}_{92}U \text{ that has decayed}}{\text{present mass of } ^{238}_{92}U} = \left(\frac{238}{206}\right)(0.395)$$

and

$$\frac{N_0}{N} = \left(\frac{238}{206}\right)(0.395) + 1 = 1.456$$

and the age of the uranite is

$$t = \frac{4.51 \times 10^9 \text{ years}}{0.301} \log 1.456$$

$$= 2.44 \times 10^9 \text{ years}$$

21-31 The mass difference between $^{206}_{82}Pb$ and its constituent nucleons is

$$\Delta m = (82 \times 1.0078 \text{ amu}) + (124 \times 1.0087 \text{ amu}) - 205.97446 \text{ amu}$$

$$= 1.7439 \text{ amu}$$

which corresponds to an energy of

$$\Delta E = c^2\, \Delta m = (3.00 \times 10^8 \text{ m} \cdot \text{s}^{-1})^2 (1.7439 \text{ amu})(1.66 \times 10^{-27} \text{ kg} \cdot \text{amu}^{-1})$$
$$= 2.61 \times 10^{-10} \text{ J}$$

The binding energy per nucleon is obtained by dividing this result by 206

$$\text{binding energy per nucleon} = \frac{2.61 \times 10^{-10} \text{ J}}{206 \text{ nucleon}}$$
$$= 1.26 \times 10^{-12} \text{ J} \cdot \text{nucleon}^{-1}$$

21-33 The mass difference between $^{35}_{17}\text{Cl}$ and its constituent particles is

$$\Delta m = (17 \times 1.0078 \text{ amu}) + (18 \times 1.0087 \text{ amu}) - 34.9689 \text{ amu}$$
$$= 0.3203 \text{ amu}$$

which corresponds to an energy

$$\Delta E = c^2\, \Delta m = (9.00 \times 10^{16} \text{ m}^2 \cdot \text{s}^{-2})(0.3203 \text{ amu})(1.66 \times 10^{-27} \text{ kg} \cdot \text{amu}^{-1})$$
$$= 4.79 \times 10^{-11} \text{ J}$$

The binding energy per nucleon is

$$\frac{4.79 \times 10^{-11} \text{ J}}{35 \text{ nucleons}} = 1.37 \times 10^{-12} \text{ J} \cdot \text{nucleon}^{-1}$$

21-35 The difference in mass between products and reactants is

$$\Delta m = 140.9137 \text{ amu} + 87.9142 \text{ amu} + (7 \times 1.0087 \text{ amu}) - 235.0439 \text{ amu}$$
$$- 1.0087 \text{ amu}$$
$$= -0.1638 \text{ amu}$$

which corresponds to an energy of

$$\Delta E = c^2\, \Delta m = (9.00 \times 10^{16} \text{ m}^2 \cdot \text{s}^{-2})(-0.1638 \text{ amu})(1.66 \times 10^{-27} \text{ kg} \cdot \text{amu}^{-1})$$
$$= -2.447 \times 10^{-11} \text{ J} \cdot \text{atom}^{-1} \text{ of } ^{235}_{92}\text{U}$$

The energy *released* per gram of $^{235}_{92}\text{U}$ is

$$\Delta E = (2.447 \times 10^{-11} \text{ J} \cdot \text{atom}^{-1})(6.022 \times 10^{23} \text{ atom} \cdot \text{mol}^{-1})$$
$$\times \left(\frac{1 \text{ mol } ^{235}_{92}\text{U}}{235.0439 \text{ g } ^{235}_{92}\text{U}} \right)$$
$$= 6.27 \times 10^{10} \text{ J} \cdot \text{g}^{-1}$$

The energy released in a 50-kiloton bomb is

$$\Delta E = (50 \text{ kton})\left(\frac{10^3 \text{ ton}}{1 \text{ kton}}\right)\left(\frac{10^3 \text{ kg}}{1 \text{ ton}}\right)(2.5 \times 10^6 \text{ J} \cdot \text{kg}^{-1})$$
$$= 1.25 \times 10^{14} \text{ J}$$

and

$$\text{mass of } {}^{235}_{92}\text{U consumed} = \frac{1.25 \times 10^{14} \text{ J}}{6.27 \times 10^{10} \text{ J} \cdot \text{g}^{-1}} = 1.99 \times 10^3 \text{ g}$$
$$= 1.99 \text{ kg}$$

21-37 The mass of an electron or a positron is 5.4858×10^{-4} amu. The loss of mass is

$$\Delta m = 2 \times 5.4858 \times 10^{-4} \text{ amu} = 1.0972 \times 10^{-3} \text{ amu}$$

The energy produced by the reaction is

$$\Delta E = c^2 \, \Delta m$$
$$= (9.00 \times 10^{16} \text{ m}^2 \cdot \text{s}^{-2})(1.0972 \times 10^{-3} \text{ amu})(1.66 \times 10^{-27} \text{ kg} \cdot \text{amu}^{-1})$$
$$= 1.64 \times 10^{-13} \text{ J}$$

The energy of each gamma ray is

$$E = \left(\frac{1}{2}\right)(1.64 \times 10^{-13} \text{ J}) = 8.196 \times 10^{-14} \text{ J}$$

Recall that the energy and frequency of electromagnetic radiation are related by (Equation (6-2))

$$E = h\nu$$

and so the frequency of each gamma ray is

$$\nu = \frac{E}{h} = \frac{8.196 \times 10^{-14} \text{ J}}{6.626 \times 10^{-34} \text{ J} \cdot \text{s}} = 1.24 \times 10^{20} \text{ Hz}$$

21-39 The mass of the products is

$$m_{\text{prod}} = 133.8969 \text{ amu} + 94.9125 \text{ amu} + 4.0026 \text{ amu} + 3(1.0087 \text{ amu})$$
$$= 235.8381 \text{ amu}$$

The mass of the reactants is

$$m_{\text{react}} = 235.0439 \text{ amu} + 1.0087 \text{ amu} = 236.0526 \text{ amu}$$

and the difference is

$$\Delta m = m_{\text{prod}} - m_{\text{react}} = -0.2145 \text{ amu}$$

This corresponds to an energy of

$$\Delta E = c^2 \, \Delta m = (3.00 \times 10^8 \text{ m} \cdot \text{s}^{-1})^2 (-0.2145 \text{ amu})(1.66 \times 10^{-27} \text{ kg} \cdot \text{amu}^{-1})$$
$$= -3.20 \times 10^{-11} \text{ J} = -1.93 \times 10^{13} \text{ J} \cdot \text{mol}^{-1}$$

The negative sign means that energy is released.

21-41   The number of moles of uranium-235 required to produce 3×10^{17} kJ is

$$\text{moles of } {}^{235}_{92}\text{U} = \frac{3 \times 10^{20} \text{ J}}{2 \times 10^{13} \text{ J} \cdot \text{mol}^{-1}} = 1.5 \times 10^7 \text{ mol}$$

$$\text{mass of } {}^{235}_{92}\text{U} = (1.5 \times 10^7 \text{ mol})\left(\frac{235 \text{ g } {}^{235}_{92}\text{U}}{1 \text{ mol } {}^{235}_{92}\text{U}}\right)\left(\frac{1 \text{ kg}}{1000 \text{ g}}\right)\left(\frac{1 \text{ ton}}{1000 \text{ kg}}\right)$$

$$= 3.5 \times 10^3 \text{ metric tons}$$

The mass of naturally occurring uranium needed to produce 3.5×10^3 metric tons of ^{235}U is

$$\text{mass of uranium} = \frac{3.5 \times 10^3 \text{ metric tons}}{0.007} = 5 \times 10^5 \text{ metric tons}$$

The time that the world supply would last is

$$\text{time} = \frac{10^6 \text{ metric tons}}{5 \times 10^5 \text{ metric tons} \cdot \text{y}^{-1}} = 2 \text{ y}$$

21-43   We use Equation (21-8).

$$\text{specific activity} = \frac{(4.2 \times 10^{23} \text{ disintegrations} \cdot \text{g}^{-1})}{M t_{1/2}}$$

$$= \frac{4.2 \times 10^{23} \text{ disintegrations} \cdot \text{g}^{-1}}{(18)(110 \text{ min})\left(\dfrac{60 \text{ s}}{1 \text{ min}}\right)}$$

$$= 3.5 \times 10^{18} \text{ disintegrations} \cdot \text{s}^{-1} \cdot \text{g}^{-1}$$

In units of curies we have

$$\text{specific activity} = (3.5 \times 10^{18} \text{ disintegrations} \cdot \text{s}^{-1} \cdot \text{g}^{-1})$$
$$\times \left(\frac{1 \text{ curie}}{3.7 \times 10^{10} \text{ disintegrations} \cdot \text{s}^{-1}}\right)$$
$$= 9.6 \times 10^7 \text{ Ci} \cdot \text{g}^{-1}$$

21-45   We first must convert the units of half-life to seconds:

$$t_{1/2} = (78 \text{ h})\left(\frac{60 \text{ min}}{1 \text{ h}}\right)\left(\frac{60 \text{ s}}{1 \text{ min}}\right) = 2.81 \times 10^5 \text{ s}$$

The specific activity of gallium-67 is

$$\text{specific activity} = \frac{4.2 \times 10^{23} \text{ disintegrations} \cdot \text{g}^{-1}}{(67)(2.81 \times 10^5 \text{ s})}$$
$$= 2.23 \times 10^{16} \text{ disintegrations} \cdot \text{s}^{-1} \cdot \text{g}^{-1}$$

The activity of the sample is

$$\text{activity} = (350 \text{ mCi})\left(\frac{1 \text{ Ci}}{1000 \text{ mCi}}\right)(3.7 \times 10^{10} \text{ disintegrations} \cdot \text{s}^{-1} \cdot \text{Ci}^{-1})$$
$$= 1.30 \times 10^{10} \text{ disintegrations} \cdot \text{s}^{-1}$$

The number of grams of gallium-67 required to produce this activity is

$$\text{mass of } {}^{67}_{31}\text{Ga} = \frac{1.30 \times 10^{10} \text{ disintegrations} \cdot \text{s}^{-1}}{2.23 \times 10^{16} \text{ disintegrations} \cdot \text{s}^{-1} \cdot \text{g}^{-1}}$$
$$= 5.81 \times 10^{-7} \text{ g}$$

The mass of ${}^{67}_{31}\text{GaCl}_3$ is

$$\text{mass} = (5.81 \times 10^{-7} \text{ g } {}^{67}_{31}\text{Ga})\left(\frac{1 \text{ mol } {}^{67}_{31}\text{Ga}}{67 \text{ g } {}^{67}_{31}\text{Ga}}\right)\left(\frac{1 \text{ mol } {}^{67}_{31}\text{GaCl}_3}{1 \text{ mol } {}^{67}_{31}\text{Ga}}\right)\left(\frac{173 \text{ g } {}^{67}_{31}\text{GaCl}_3}{1 \text{ mol } {}^{67}_{31}\text{GaCl}_3}\right)$$
$$= 1.5 \times 10^{-6} \text{ g} = 1.5 \text{ } \mu\text{g}$$

21-47 $\text{activity} = (6.5 \times 10^4 \text{ disintegrations} \cdot \text{min}^{-1})\left(\frac{1 \text{ min}}{60 \text{ s}}\right)$

$\qquad\qquad = 1.08 \times 10^3 \text{ disintegrations} \cdot \text{s}^{-1}$

$\qquad\qquad = (1.08 \times 10^3 \text{ disintegrations} \cdot \text{s}^{-1})\left(\frac{1 \text{ } \mu\text{Ci}}{3.7 \times 10^4 \text{ disintegrations} \cdot \text{s}^{-1}}\right)$

$\qquad\qquad = 0.029 \text{ } \mu\text{Ci}$

The specific activity of uranium-234 is given by Equation (21-8)

$$\text{specific activity} = \frac{(4.2 \times 10^{23} \text{ disintegrations} \cdot \text{g}^{-1})}{M t_{1/2}}$$

$$= \frac{(4.2 \times 10^{23} \text{ disintegrations} \cdot \text{g}^{-1})}{(234)(2.44 \times 10^5 \text{ y})\left(\dfrac{365 \text{ d}}{1 \text{ y}}\right)\left(\dfrac{24 \text{ h}}{1 \text{ d}}\right)\left(\dfrac{3600 \text{ s}}{1 \text{ h}}\right)}$$

$$= 2.33 \times 10^8 \text{ disintegrations} \cdot \text{s}^{-1} \cdot \text{g}^{-1}$$

$$= (2.33 \times 10^8 \text{ disintegrations} \cdot \text{s}^{-1} \cdot \text{g}^{-1})$$

$$\times \left(\frac{1 \text{ } \mu\text{Ci}}{3.7 \times 10^4 \text{ disintegrations} \cdot \text{s}^{-1}}\right)$$

$$= 6.30 \times 10^3 \text{ } \mu\text{Ci} \cdot \text{g}^{-1}$$

The mass of uranium-234 is obtained by dividing its activity by its specific activity

$$\text{mass of } ^{234}_{92}\text{U} = \frac{0.029\ \mu\text{Ci}}{6.30 \times 10^3\ \mu\text{Ci} \cdot \text{g}^{-1}} = 4.6 \times 10^{-6}\ \text{g} = 4.6\ \mu\text{g}$$

21-49 (a) $^{12}_{6}\text{C} + ^{1}_{1}\text{H} \rightarrow ^{13}_{7}\text{N} + \gamma$

(b) $^{13}_{7}\text{N} \rightarrow ^{13}_{6}\text{C} + ^{0}_{+1}\text{e}$

(c) $^{13}_{6}\text{C} + ^{1}_{1}\text{H} \rightarrow ^{14}_{7}\text{N} + \gamma$

(d) $^{14}_{7}\text{N} + ^{1}_{1}\text{H} \rightarrow ^{15}_{8}\text{O} + \gamma$

(e) $^{15}_{8}\text{O} \rightarrow ^{15}_{7}\text{N} + ^{0}_{+1}\text{e}$

(f) $^{15}_{7}\text{N} + ^{1}_{1}\text{H} \rightarrow ^{12}_{6}\text{C} + ^{4}_{2}\text{He}$

The net equation is

$$4^{1}_{1}\text{H} \rightarrow ^{4}_{2}\text{He} + 2\ ^{0}_{+1}\text{e} + 3\gamma$$

21-51 We have

$$\log \frac{N_0}{N} = \frac{0.301t}{t_{1/2}} = \frac{(0.301)(50.0\ \text{y})}{(12.3\ \text{y})} = 1.22$$

$$\frac{N_0}{N} = 16.6$$

$$\frac{N}{N_0} = 0.0602$$

The fraction remaining is 6.02×10^{-2}.

21-53 We have that

$$\log \frac{N_0}{N} = \frac{0.301t}{t_{1/2}}$$

$$= \frac{(0.301)(6\ \text{h})\left(\dfrac{60\ \text{min}}{1\ \text{h}}\right)}{25.0\ \text{min}} = 4.334$$

$$\frac{N_0}{N} = 21,600$$

or

$$\frac{N}{N_0} = 4.63 \times 10^{-5}$$

Recall that the rate of decay is proportional to the number of nuclei present; thus

$$\frac{N}{N_0} = \frac{\text{rate}}{\text{rate}_0}$$

and

$$\text{rate at 2 P.M.} = (4.63 \times 10^{-5})(10,000 \text{ disintegrations} \cdot \text{min}^{-1})$$
$$= 0.46 \text{ disintegrations} \cdot \text{min}^{-1}$$

or about one disintegration every two minutes.

21-55 The difference in mass between products and reactants is

$$\Delta m = 4.0026 \text{ amu} - (2 \times 2.0141 \text{ amu}) = -0.0256 \text{ amu}$$

The loss of mass corresponds to a *release* of energy of

$$\Delta E = c^2 \Delta m = (9.00 \times 10^{16} \text{ m}^2 \cdot \text{s}^{-2})(0.0256 \text{ amu})(1.66 \times 10^{-27} \text{ kg} \cdot \text{amu}^{-1})$$
$$= 3.82 \times 10^{-12} \text{ J per atom of helium}$$

The energy released per mole of helium is

$$\Delta E = (3.82 \times 10^{-12} \text{ J} \cdot \text{atom}^{-1})(6.022 \times 10^{23} \text{ atom} \cdot \text{mol}^{-1})$$
$$= 2.30 \times 10^{12} \text{ J} \cdot \text{mol}^{-1}$$

The energy released per gram of helium is

$$\Delta E = (2.30 \times 10^{12} \text{ J} \cdot \text{mol}^{-1})\left(\frac{1 \text{ mol } {}^{4}_{2}\text{He}}{4.0026 \text{ g } {}^{4}_{2}\text{He}}\right) = 5.75 \times 10^{11} \text{ J} \cdot \text{g}^{-1}$$

The number of moles of octane that must be burned to produce this amount of energy is

$$\text{moles of octane} = \frac{5.75 \times 10^{11} \text{ J}}{5.45 \times 10^6 \text{ J} \cdot \text{mol}^{-1}} = 1.06 \times 10^5 \text{ mol}$$

The mass of octane is

$$\text{mass of octane} = (1.06 \times 10^5 \text{ mol})\left(\frac{114.22 \text{ g } C_8H_{18}}{1 \text{ mol } C_8H_{18}}\right)$$
$$= 1.21 \times 10^7 \text{ g} = 1.21 \times 10^4 \text{ kg} = 12.1 \text{ metric ton}$$

21-57 The mass of ${}^{235}_{92}\text{U}$ in 1 kg of the uranium fuel is

$$\text{mass of } {}^{235}_{92}\text{U} = (0.03)(1 \text{ kg}) = 30 \text{ g}$$

The mass of ${}^{235}_{92}\text{U}$ that can be used is

$$\text{mass of } {}^{235}_{92}\text{U} \text{ that reacts} = \left(\frac{1}{3}\right)(30 \text{ g}) = 10 \text{ g}$$

The number of ${}^{235}_{92}\text{U}$ atoms in 10 g is

$$\text{number of } {}^{235}_{92}\text{U} = (10 \text{ g})\left(\frac{1 \text{ mol } {}^{235}_{92}\text{U}}{235 \text{ g } {}^{235}_{92}\text{U}}\right)(6.022 \times 10^{23} \text{ atom} \cdot \text{mol}^{-1})$$
$$= 2.56 \times 10^{22} \text{ atoms}$$

The energy released by the fission of 2.56×10^{22} atoms of ${}^{235}_{92}\text{U}$ is

$$\Delta E = (2.9 \times 10^{-14} \text{ kJ} \cdot \text{atom}^{-1})(2.56 \times 10^{22} \text{ atom})$$
$$= 7.4 \times 10^8 \text{ kJ} = 7.4 \times 10^{11} \text{ J}$$

The available energy per kilogram of the uranium fuel is

$$\Delta E = (0.30)(7.4 \times 10^{11} \text{ J}) = 2.2 \times 10^{11} \text{ J}$$

The energy produced by the power plant in one year is

$$\Delta E = (1000 \text{ megawatt})\left(\frac{10^6 \text{ W}}{1 \text{ MW}}\right)\left(\frac{1 \text{ J} \cdot \text{s}^{-1}}{1 \text{ W}}\right)\left(\frac{60 \text{ s}}{1 \text{ min}}\right)\left(\frac{60 \text{ min}}{1 \text{ h}}\right)$$
$$\times \left(\frac{24 \text{ h}}{1 \text{ d}}\right)\left(\frac{365 \text{ d}}{1 \text{ y}}\right)(1 \text{ y})$$

$$= 3.15 \times 10^{16} \text{ J}$$

The amount of the uranium fuel required is

$$\text{mass of uranium} = \frac{3.15 \times 10^{16} \text{ J}}{2.2 \times 10^{11} \text{ J} \cdot \text{kg}^{-1}}$$
$$= 1.4 \times 10^5 \text{ kg}$$

21-59 We use 6000 min^{-1} for R_0 and calculate $t_{1/2}$ for each subsequent time.

$$t_{1/2} = \frac{0.301t}{\log(6000/R)}$$

t/day	R/min^{-1}	$t_{1/2}$/day
10.0	4680	27.9
20.0	3650	27.9
30.0	2840	27.8
40.0	2200	27.6
50.0	1725	27.8
	average	27.8

The half-life of chromium-51 is 27.8 days.

21-61   The source of the water is

(a) 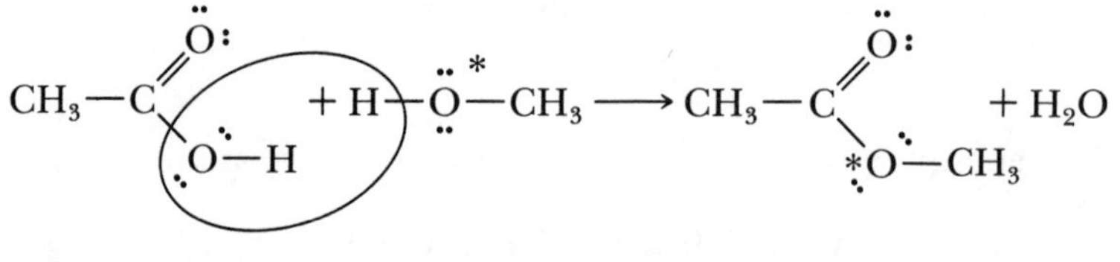 $CH_3-C\overset{\displaystyle \ddot{O}:}{\underset{\ddot{O}-H}{\Big\langle}} + H-\overset{*}{\underset{\cdot\cdot}{\ddot{O}}}-CH_3 \longrightarrow CH_3-C\overset{\displaystyle \ddot{O}:}{\underset{*\ddot{O}-CH_3}{\Big\langle}} + H_2O$

Thus if the oxygen atom in methanol is labeled with oxygen-18, all the oxygen-18 will appear in the ester. If acetic acid were labeled with oxygen-18, then oxygen-18 would appear in the H_2O *and* the ester because of the acid-dissociation reaction of acetic acid:

(b) 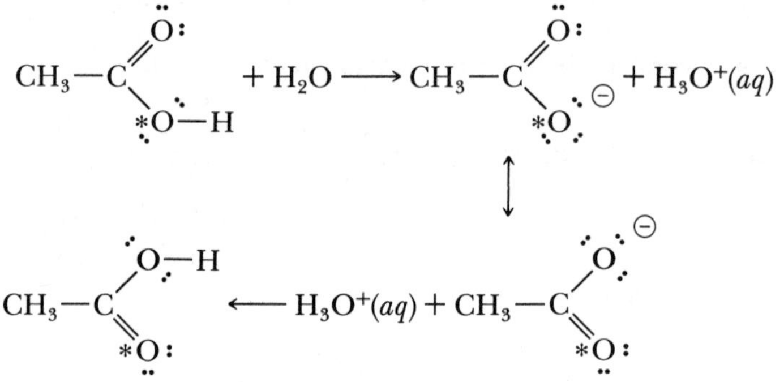 $CH_3-C\overset{\displaystyle \ddot{O}:}{\underset{*\ddot{O}-H}{\Big\langle}} + H_2O \longrightarrow CH_3-C\overset{\displaystyle \ddot{O}:}{\underset{*\ddot{O}:}{\Big\langle}}{}^{\ominus} + H_3O^+(aq)$

$\Big\updownarrow$

$CH_3-C\overset{\displaystyle \ddot{O}-H}{\underset{*\ddot{O}:}{\Big\langle}} \longleftarrow H_3O^+(aq) + CH_3-C\overset{\displaystyle \ddot{O}:}{\underset{*\ddot{O}:}{\Big\langle}}{}^{\ominus}$

$CH_3-C\overset{\displaystyle \ddot{O}:}{\underset{*\ddot{O}-H}{\Big\langle}} + H-\ddot{O}-CH_3 \longrightarrow CH_3-C\overset{\displaystyle \ddot{O}:}{\underset{\ddot{O}-CH_3}{\Big\langle}} + H_2O*$

$CH_3-C\overset{\displaystyle *\ddot{O}:}{\underset{\ddot{O}-H}{\Big\langle}} + H-\ddot{O}-CH_3 \longrightarrow CH_3-C\overset{\displaystyle *\ddot{O}:}{\underset{\ddot{O}-CH_3}{\Big\langle}} + H_2O$

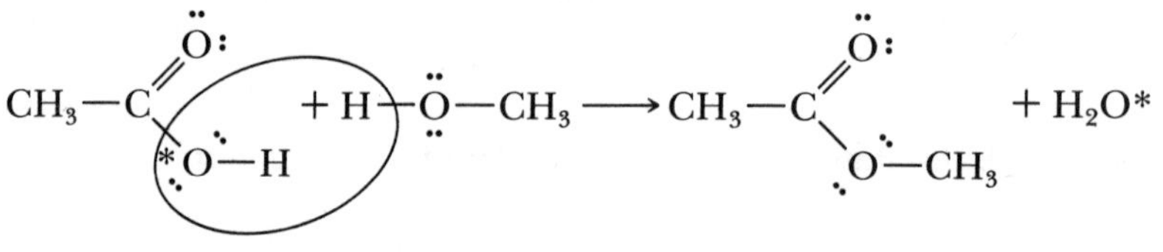

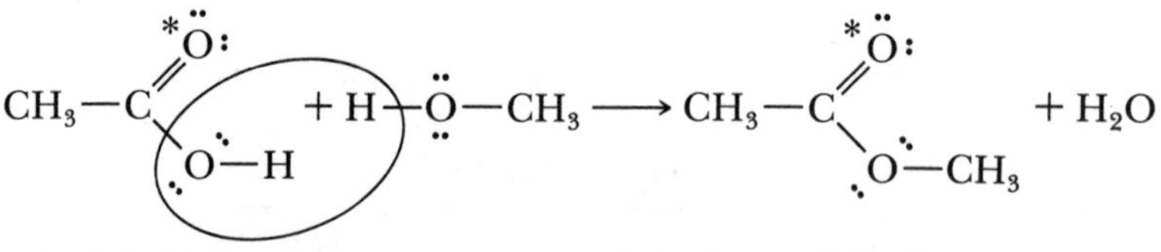

Thus the labelled oxygen atoms appear in water and in the ester.

21-63   The mass difference is

$$\Delta m = 4.0026 \text{ amu} + 1.0087 \text{ amu} - 2.0141 \text{ amu} - 3.0161 \text{ amu}$$
$$= -0.0189 \text{ amu}$$

and the energy *released* is

$$\Delta E = c^2\,\Delta m = (3.00 \times 10^8 \text{ m}\cdot\text{s}^{-1})^2(0.0189 \text{ amu})(1.66 \times 10^{-27} \text{ kg}\cdot\text{amu}^{-1})$$
$$= 2.82 \times 10^{-12} \text{ J} = 1.70 \times 10^{12} \text{ J}\cdot\text{mol}^{-1}$$

21-65   The mass difference is

$$\Delta m = 12.0000 \text{ amu} - 3(4.0026 \text{ amu}) = -0.0078 \text{ amu}$$

and the energy *released* is

$$\Delta E = c^2 \, \Delta m = (3.00 \times 10^8 \text{ m} \cdot \text{s}^{-1})^2 (0.0078 \text{ amu})(1.66 \times 10^{-27} \text{ kg} \cdot \text{amu}^{-1})$$
$$= 1.2 \times 10^{-12} \text{ J} = 7.0 \times 10^{11} \text{ J} \cdot \text{mol}^{-1}$$

21-67   One liter of water contains

$$\text{molecules } H_2O = (1000 \text{ g } H_2O)\left(\frac{1 \text{ mol } H_2O}{18.02 \text{ g } H_2O}\right)\left(\frac{6.022 \times 10^{23} \text{ molecule}}{1 \text{ mol}}\right)$$
$$= 3.34 \times 10^{25} \text{ molecules}$$

The number of hydrogen atoms is twice this result

$$\text{H atoms} = 6.68 \times 10^{25} \text{ atoms}$$

The number of deuterium atoms is given by

$$\text{D atoms} = (6.68 \times 10^{25} \text{ H atoms})\left(\frac{1 \text{ D atom}}{6700 \text{ H atoms}}\right)$$
$$= 9.97 \times 10^{21} \text{ D atoms}$$

The reaction for the fusion of two deuterium atoms into a helium atom is

$$2 \, {}^2_1\text{H} \longrightarrow {}^4_2\text{He}$$

and the associated energy is

$$\Delta E = c^2 \, \Delta m$$
$$= (3.00 \times 10^8 \text{ m} \cdot \text{s}^{-1})^2 [(4.0026 \text{ amu} - 2(2.0141 \text{ amu})]$$
$$\times (1.66 \times 10^{-27} \text{ kg} \cdot \text{amu}^{-1})$$
$$= -3.82 \times 10^{-12} \text{ J}$$

The number of such reactions is equal to one half of the total number of deuterium atoms in one kilogram of water, and so

$$\Delta E = (-3.82 \times 10^{-12} \text{ J})\left(\frac{9.97 \times 10^{21}}{2}\right)$$
$$= -1.91 \times 10^{10} \text{ J per kilogram water}$$

21-69   It requires large energies to overcome the Coulombic repulsion involved in a fusion nuclear reaction. We can estimate the energies involved by using Coulomb's law (Equation 7-3).

$$E = (2.31 \times 10^{-16} \, \text{J} \cdot \text{pm}) \frac{Z_1 Z_2}{d}$$

For two deuterium nuclei, $Z_1 = Z_2 = 1$, and d is the diameter of a deuterium nucleus, which is about 10^{-15} m, or 10^{-3} pm. Thus the Coulombic repulsion involved in bringing two deuterium nuclei together is about

$$E = 2 \times 10^{-13} \, \text{J}$$

For one mole of deuterium nuclei pairs we have

$$E = (2 \times 10^{-13} \, \text{J})(6.02 \times 10^{23} \, \text{mol}^{-1}) = 1 \times 10^{11} \, \text{J} \cdot \text{mol}^{-1}$$

If we assume that the deuterium nuclei are in thermal equilibrium, then their average kinetic energy is [Equation (4-16)]

$$E = \tfrac{3}{2} RT$$

The value of the temperature required to achieve a kinetic energy of 1×10^{11} $\text{J} \cdot \text{mol}^{-1}$ is

$$T = \frac{2E}{3R} = \frac{2 \times 10^{11} \, \text{J} \cdot \text{mol}^{-1}}{3 \times 8.314 \, \text{J} \cdot \text{mol}^{-1} \cdot \text{K}^{-1}} = 1 \times 10^{10} \, \text{K}$$

21-71 Assuming that the activity due to phosphorus-32 remains constant during the time of the experiment, we write

$$(\text{activity})_{\text{start}} = (\text{activity})_{\text{later}}$$

or

$$50{,}000 \text{ disintegrations} \cdot \text{min}^{-1} = (10.0 \text{ disintegrations} \cdot \text{min}^{-1} \cdot \text{mL}^{-1})$$
$$\times (\text{volume of blood})$$

Solving for the volume of blood, we find that

$$\text{volume of blood} = \frac{50{,}000 \text{ disintegrations} \cdot \text{min}^{-1}}{10.0 \text{ disintegrations} \cdot \text{min}^{-1} \cdot \text{mL}^{-1}}$$
$$= 5000 \text{ mL} = 5.0 \text{ L}$$

21-73 The number of grams of barium in the precipitate is

$$\text{mass of Ba}^{2+} = \frac{3270 \text{ disintegrations} \cdot \text{min}^{-1}}{7.6 \times 10^7 \text{ disintegrations} \cdot \text{min}^{-1} \cdot \text{g}^{-1}}$$
$$= 4.30 \times 10^{-5} \text{ g}$$

The number of moles of barium-131 is

$$\text{moles of } {}^{131}_{56}\text{Ba} = (4.30 \times 10^{-5} \text{ g}) \left(\frac{1 \text{ mol}}{131 \text{ g}} \right) = 3.28 \times 10^{-7} \text{ mol}$$

The number of moles of $SO_4^{2-}(aq)$ is

$$\text{moles of } SO_4^{2-}(aq) = \text{moles of } BaSO_4(s) = \text{moles of } {}^{131}_{56}Ba$$
$$= 3.28 \times 10^{-7} \text{ mol}$$

Assuming that essentially all the sulfate is precipitated (barium is in excess), we calculate the concentration of sulfate ion as

$$[SO_4^{2-}] = \frac{3.28 \times 10^{-7} \text{ mol}}{0.010 \text{ L}} = 3.3 \times 10^{-5} \text{ M}$$

21-75 The total activity of sulfur-35 is

$$\text{activity} = (14{,}000 \text{ disintegrations} \cdot \text{min}^{-1} \cdot \text{mL}^{-1})(75 \text{ mL})$$
$$= 1.05 \times 10^{6} \text{ disintegrations} \cdot \text{min}^{-1}$$

The total number of moles of $SO_4^{2-}(aq)$ is

$$\text{moles of } SO_4^{2-}(aq) = (0.010 \text{ M})(0.075 \text{ L}) = 7.50 \times 10^{-4} \text{ mol}$$

The molar activity of sulfur-35 is

$$\text{molar activity} = \frac{1.05 \times 10^{6} \text{ disintegrations} \cdot \text{min}^{-1}}{7.50 \times 10^{-4} \text{ mol}}$$
$$= 1.40 \times 10^{9} \text{ disintegrations} \cdot \text{min}^{-1} \cdot \text{mol}^{-1}$$

The total activity of sulfur-35 remaining in solution after the two solutions are mixed is

$$\text{activity} = (183 \text{ disintegrations} \cdot \text{min}^{-1} \cdot \text{mL}^{-1})(150 \text{ mL})$$
$$= 2.745 \times 10^{4} \text{ disintegrations} \cdot \text{min}^{-1}$$

The number of moles of $SO_4^{2-}(aq)$ in the solution is

$$\text{moles of } SO_4^{2-}(aq) = \frac{2.745 \times 10^{4} \text{ disintegrations} \cdot \text{min}^{-1}}{1.40 \times 10^{9} \text{ disintegrations} \cdot \text{min}^{-1} \cdot \text{mol}^{-1}}$$
$$= 1.96 \times 10^{-5} \text{ mol}$$

The concentration of sulfate ion is

$$[SO_4^{2-}] = \frac{1.96 \times 10^{-5} \text{ mol}}{0.150 \text{ L}} = 1.31 \times 10^{-4} \text{ M}$$

The solutions of $Pb(NO_3)_2(aq)$ and $Na_2SO_4(aq)$ are mixed on an equimolar basis, and so the concentration of $Pb^{2+}(aq)$ is

$$[Pb^{2+}] = [SO_4^{2-}] = 1.31 \times 10^{-4} \text{ M}$$

The solubility product of $PbSO_4$ is given by

$$K_{sp} = [Pb^{2+}][SO_4^{2-}]$$
$$= (1.31 \times 10^{-4} \text{ M})(1.31 \times 10^{-4} \text{ M})$$
$$= 1.7 \times 10^{-8} \text{ M}^2$$

E   ANSWERS TO THE SELF-TEST

1   a radioactive isotope

2   helium-4 nuclei that are emitted from radioactive nuclei

3   electrons that are emitted from radioactive nuclei

4   electromagnetic radiation of short wavelength or high frequency that is emitted from radioactive nuclei

5 $^4_2\text{He} + ^{234}_{90}\text{Th}$

6 $^{116}_{50}\text{Sn} + ^{0}_{-1}\text{e}$

7   false (There are no electrons in nuclei.)

8 $^{38}_{18}\text{Ar} + ^{0}_{+1}\text{e}$

9   positrons

10 β-particles

11   true

12   true

13   false

14   true

15   83

16   false

17   false

18   first

19   that is required for one half of the nuclei to decay

20   uranium-238 . . . lead-206

21   true

22   true

23   15.3

24   false

25   carbon dioxide, $^{14}\text{CO}_2$

26   artificial radioisotopes

27   true

28   neutrons

29   protons

30   true

31   energy

32 $\Delta E = c^2 \Delta m$ or $E = mc^2$

33   false (It is about 10^6 times larger.)

34   absorbed

35   false

36   binding energy per nucleon . . . number of nucleons (mass number)

37   splits into two roughly equal fragments

38   neutrons are produced when a uranium-235 nucleus undergoes fission

39   true

40   true

41   true

42   true

43   protons . . . helium-4 nuclei

44   the number of disintegrations per second per gram of material

45 $\left(\dfrac{4.2 \times 10^{23} \text{ disintegrations} \cdot \text{g}^{-1}}{M t_{1/2}} \right)$

46 3.7×10^{10} disintegrations$\cdot\text{s}^{-1}$

TRANSITION METAL COMPLEXES

A OUTLINE OF CHAPTER 22

22-1 There are 10 elements in each d transition metal series.

There are five d orbitals for each value of the principal quantum number, $n \geq 3$.

$l = 2$ and $m_l = 0, \pm 1$, or ± 2 for d orbitals.

The shapes and relative orientations of the five d orbitals are shown in Figure 22-2.

Sc to Zn form the 3d transition metal series.
Y to Cd form the 4d transition metal series.   (Figure 22-1)
Lu to Hg form the 5d transition metal series.

The electron configurations of the M(II) transition metal ions are strictly regular in the sense that the $n = 1$ level is filled first, then the $n = 2$ level is filled, then the $n = 3$ level is filled, and so on.

For the first d transition metal series

d^1	d^2	d^3	d^4	d^5
Sc(II)	Ti(II)	V(II)	Cr(II)	Mn(II)
21	22	23	24	25

d^6	d^7	d^8	d^9	d^{10}
Fe(II)	Co(II)	Ni(II)	Cu(II)	Zn(II)
26	27	28	29	30

Transition metal ions with x electrons in the outer d orbitals are called d^x ions.

The number of d electrons in the M(II) ion is the same as the position of the element within the d transition metal series. (d^1 is first, d^2 is second, and so on.)

Note that the second digit of the atomic number of the M(II) $3d$ transition metals is the same as x in d^x (except for Zn(II)).

22-2 Complexes consist of central metal atoms or ions that are bonded to ligands.

The complex ion $[Fe(CN)_6]^{4-}$ has an octahedral structure with six cyanide ions bonded to the central iron atom (Figure 22-3).

The complex ion $[Ni(CN)_4]^{2-}$ has a square-planar structure with four cyanide ions bonded to the central nickel atom (Figure 22-6).

The complex ion $[CoCl_4]^{2-}$ has a tetrahedral structure with four chloride ions bonded to the central cobalt atom (Figure 22-7).

The complex ion $[Ag(NH_3)_2]^+$ has a linear structure with two nitrogen atoms bonded to the central silver atom (Figure 22-8).

Some examples of complex ions are listed in Table 22-1.

22-3 Transition metal complexes have a systematic nomenclature.

The rules for naming transition metal complexes are given on pages 719 and 720 of the text.

The names of some common ligands are given in Table 22-2.

The chemical formula of a complex ion can be written when its name is given (see page 720 and Example 22-5).

22-4 Some octahedral and square-planar transition metal complexes can exist in isomeric forms.

Cis-trans isomers of square-planar and octahedral complexes exist (Figures 22-9 and 22-10).

The prefix *cis-* designates the structure in which the identical ligands are adjacent to each other.

The prefix *trans-* designates the structure in which identical ligands are opposite to each other.

22-5 Polydentate ligands bind to more than one coordination position around the metal ion.

Ligands that attach to a metal ion at more than one coordination position are called polydentate ligands or chelating agents.

The prefixes *bis-* and *tris-* are used in the nomenclature of complexes that contain chelating agents.

The oxalate ion (ox) and ethylenediamine (en) are examples of bidentate ligands. Ethylenediaminetetraacetate (EDTA) is a hexadentate ligand.

22-6 The five d orbitals of a transition metal ion in an octahedral complex are split into two groups by the ligands.

The five d orbitals are split into the two **sets:**

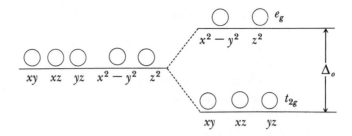

The magnitude of Δ_o depends on the central metal ion, its charge, and the ligands.

This splitting pattern arises from the orientation of the d orbitals relative to the ligands, as shown in Figure 22-11.

The colors of most transition metal complexes arise from electronic transitions within the metal d orbitals.

The energy difference, Δ_o, often corresponds to the visible region of the spectrum.

The visible absorption spectrum of the complex ion $[\text{Ti}(\text{H}_2\text{O})_6]^{3+}(aq)$ is shown in Figure 22-13.

The colors of many gemstones are due to electronic excitations of transition metal ions.

22-7 d-Orbital electron configuration is the key to understanding many properties of the d transition metal ions.

Molecules with no unpaired electrons cannot be magnetized by an external magnetic field and are called diamagnetic.

Molecules with unpaired electrons can be magnetized by an external magnetic field and are called paramagnetic.

Paramagnetic substances are drawn into a magnetic field (Figure 22-15).

Electrons are placed into the sets of d orbitals according to Hund's rule and the value of Δ_o.

Certain octahedral complexes can be either high spin or low spin.

The value of Δ_o and the ligands determine whether a d-electron configuration will be low spin or high spin.

If Δ_o is small, then the d electrons will occupy the e_g orbitals before they pair up in the t_{2g} orbitals (high spin).

If Δ_o is large, then the d electrons will fill the t_{2g} orbitals completely before occupying the higher-energy e_g orbitals (low spin).

The various possible ground-state d-electron configurations for octahedral ions are given in Figure 22-16.

22-8   Ligands can be ordered according to their ability to split the transition metal d orbitals.

The spectrochemical series orders ligands according to the magnitude of the splitting of the d orbitals that they cause (Figure 22-18).

The spectrochemical series can be used to predict whether a given complex will be low spin or high spin.

The value of Δ_o increases as the oxidation state of the metal increases.

The value of Δ_o increases as we move down a column in the periodic table for a given oxidation state.

With the exception of the metal halide complexes, all M(III) and higher oxidation state complex ions of the $4d$ and $5d$ transition metal series are low spin.

22-9   Transition metal complexes are classified as either inert or labile.

Taube's rules are used to predict whether a complex is inert or labile.

Taube's rules say that $t_{2g}^3 e_g^0$, $t_{2g}^4 e_g^0$, $t_{2g}^5 e_g^0$, and $t_{2g}^6 e_g^0$ octahedral complexes are inert, whereas all other octahedral complexes are labile.

22-10   The d-orbital splitting patterns in square-planar and tetrahedral complexes are different from those in octahedral complexes.

The splitting patterns for the d orbitals in square planar and tetrahedral complexes are

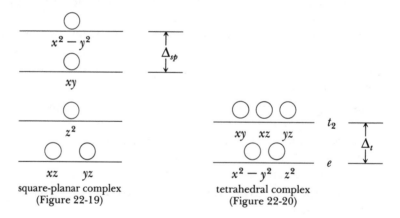

square-planar complex
(Figure 22-19)

tetrahedral complex
(Figure 22-20)

All d^8 square-planar complexes are low spin because Δ_{sp} is relatively large.

There are no low spin tetrahedral complexes because Δ_t is relatively small.

Magnetic studies can determine whether a complex is square planar or tetrahedral.

B SELF-TEST

1   There is a total of _____ metals in each d transition metal series.

2   Iron(II) is a d^6 ion; iron(II) has _____ d electrons.

3 Chromium(II) is a $d^{(\ )}$ ion.

4 Platinum(II) is a $d^{(\ )}$ ion.

5 Iron(III) is a $d^{(\ )}$ ion.

6 Transition metals often have more than one possible oxidation state. *True/False*

7 In the complex ion $[Fe(CN)_6]^{4-}$, the metal ion is _____ and the ligands are

_____ .

8 When the compound $K_4[Fe(CN)_6]$ is dissolved in water, the major species present are K^+ ions, Fe^{2+} ions, and CN^- ions. *True/False*

9 Most transition metal complexes are colored due to the electronic transitions of

_____ .

10 All nickel(II) complexes are the same color. *True/False*

11 The ligands NH_3 in $[Ni(NH_3)_6]^{2+}$ are arranged around the nickel atom in an

_____ structure.

12 The ligands CN^- in $[Pt(CN)_4]^{2-}$ are arranged around the platinum atom in a

_____ structure.

13 In any complex ion or complex molecule, name the _____ first

and then the _____ .

14 The name of the ligand NH_3 is _____ .

15 The name of the ligand CO is _____ .

16 The number of ligands of a particular type in a complex ion or complex molecule is

denoted by _____ .

17 The name tetrachlorocobaltate(II) indicates that the complex is an anion. *True/False*

18 The oxidation state of the metal atom in a complex is denoted by

_____ .

19 *cis*-diamminedichloroplatinum(II) is identical in physical properties to *trans*-diamminedichloroplatinum(II). *True/False*

20 The two Cl^- ligands in $[Pt(NH_3)_2Cl_2]$ in the *cis* isomer are located

_____ in the **square**-planar structure.

21 Geometrical isomers in MX_4Y_2 octahedral complexes may exist. *True/False*

22 A chelating ligand is a _____.

23 Ethylenediamine is an example of a bidentate ligand. *True/False*

24 The number of chelating ligands in a complex is indicated by _____

_____.

25 The five *d* orbitals in a metal ion without any attached ligands have the same energy. *True/False*

26 The five *d* orbitals in a metal ion with attached ligands have the same energy. *True/False*

27 The *d* orbitals of a transition metal ion in an octahedral complex are split into a lower set, called _____, and an upper set, called _____.

28 The t_{2g} set of orbitals can accommodate a maximum of _____ electrons.

29 The difference in energy between the t_{2g} and e_g orbitals is the same in all octahedral complexes. *True/False*

30 The difference in energy between the t_{2g} and e_g orbitals in an octahedral complex is denoted by _____.

31 If the value of Δ_o is small compared to the pairing energy, then the *d* electrons will pair up in the t_{2g} orbitals before occupying the e_g orbitals. *True/False*

32 The *d*-electron configuration of an octahedral complex is high spin when

_____.

33 If the value of Δ_o is small compared to the pairing energy, then the *d*-electron configuration is *(low, high)*-spin.

34 The value of Δ_o depends on the nature of the ligands in an octahedral complex. *True/False*

35 The value of Δ_o for the ligand Cl^- is *(greater than, less than)* that for the ligand CN^-.

36 The rate at which an octahedral complex exchanges its ligands depends on the *d*-electron configuration of the transition metal ion. *True/False*

37 A $t_{2g}^5 e_g^0$ octahedral complex is *(inert, labile)*.

38   The *d*-orbital splitting pattern for a square-planar transition metal complex is

39   The *d*-orbital splitting pattern for a tetrahedral transition metal complex is

40   A paramagnetic molecule behaves like a magnet in an externally applied magnetic field. *True/False*

41   A paramagnetic molecule contains *(paired, unpaired)* electrons.

42   A high-spin d^6 complex is *(paramagnetic, diamagnetic)*.

C   CALCULATIONS YOU SHOULD KNOW HOW TO DO

Although there are no numerical calculations in Chapter 22, here are some things that you should be able to do.

1   Determine electron configurations of transition metal ions. See Example 22-1 and Problems 22-1 through 22-4.

2   Determine the oxidation states of the metal atoms in complexes. See Example 22-3 and Problems 22-7 through 22-10.

3   Write the name of a complex from its chemical formula. See Example 22-4, Problems 22-15 through 22-18, and Problems 22-23 and 22-24.

4   Write the chemical formula of a complex from its name. See Examples 22-5 and 22-7, Problems 22-19 through 22-22, and Problems 22-25 and 22-26.

5   Draw structures of the geometrical isomers of complexes. See Example 22-6 and Problems 22-27 through 22-30.

6   Write d-orbital electron configurations of metals in octahedral ions. See Example 22-8 and Problems 22-31 and 22-32.

7   Using the spectrochemical series, predict whether a given complex is high spin or low spin. See Example 22-9 and Problems 22-33 through 22-36.

8   Using Taube's rules, predict whether a given complex is inert or labile. See Example 22-12 and Problems 22-43 through 22-46.

D   SOLUTIONS TO THE ODD-NUMBERED PROBLEMS

22-1   (a) $1s^2 2s^2 2p^6 3s^2 3p^6 3d^4$ or $[\text{Ar}]3d^4$

(b) $1s^2 2s^2 2p^6 3s^2 3p^6 3d^2$ or $[\text{Ar}]3d^2$

(c) $1s^2 2s^2 2p^6 3s^2 3p^6 3d^{10} 4s^2 4p^6 4d^6$ or $[\text{Kr}]4d^6$

(d) $1s^2 2s^2 2p^6 3s^2 3p^6 3d^{10} 4s^2 4p^6 4d^{10} 4f^{14} 5s^2 5p^6 5d^6$ or $[\text{Xe}]4f^{14}5d^6$

22-3   (a) Ag(I) has one more electron than Ag(II), and so it has ten $4d$ electrons.

(b) Pd(IV) has two less electrons than Pd(II), and so it has six $4d$ electrons.

(c) Ir(III) has one less electron than Ir(II), and so it has six $5d$ electrons.

(d) Co(II) has seven $3d$ electrons.

22-5   (a) The d^6 ions with a III oxidation state are those ions that are d^7 ions in a II oxidation state. Thus the answer is Co(III), Rh(III), and Ir(III).

(b) The d^4 ions with a IV oxidation state are those ions that are d^6 ions in a II oxidation state. Thus the answer is Fe(IV), Ru(IV), and Os(IV).

(c) The d^{10} ions with a (I) oxidation state are those ions that are d^9 ions in a II oxidation state. Thus the answer is Cu(I), Ag(I), and Au(I).

22-7   (a) $[\text{Os}(\text{NH}_3)_4\text{Cl}_2]^+$. The charge on the NH_3 ligand is 0 and that on the Cl^- is -1. The overall charge of the complex ion is $+1$, and so if x is the charge on Os, then

$$x + 4(0) + 2(-1) = +1$$
$$x = +3$$

(b) $[\text{CoCl}_6]^{3-}$. The charge on each Cl^- ligand is -1. The overall charge of the complex ion is -3, and so if x is the charge on Co, then

$$x + 6(-1) = -3$$
$$x = +3$$

(c) $[Fe(CN)_6]^{4-}$. The charge on each CN^- ligand is -1. The overall charge of the complex ion is -4, and so if x is the charge on Fe, then

$$x + 6(-1) = -4$$
$$x = +2$$

(d) $[Nb(NO_2)_6]^{3-}$. The charge on each NO_2^- ligand is -1. The overall charge of the complex ion is -3, and so if x is the charge on Nb, then

$$x + 6(-1) = -3$$
$$x = +3$$

22-9   (a) $[Cd(CN)_4]^{2-}$. The charge on each CN^- ligand is -1. The overall charge of the complex ion is -2, and so if x is the charge on Cd, then

$$x + 4(-1) = -2$$
$$x = +2$$

(b) $[Pt(NH_3)_6]^{2+}$. The charge on a NH_3 ligand is 0. The overall charge of the complex ion is $+2$, and so if x is the charge on Pt, then

$$x + 6(0) = +2$$
$$x = +2$$

(c) $[Pt(NH_3)_4Cl_2]$. The charge on a NH_3 ligand is 0 and that on a Cl^- ligand is -1. The overall charge of the complex ion is 0, and so if x is the charge on Pt, then

$$x + 4(0) + 2(-1) = 0$$
$$x = +2$$

(d) $[RhBr_6]^{3-}$. The charge on each Br^- ligand is -1. The overall charge of the complex ion is -3, and so if x is the charge on Rh, then

$$x + 6(-1) = -3$$
$$x = +3$$

22-11   (a) three moles of $K^+(aq)$ and one mole of $[Fe(CN)_6]^{3-}(aq)$

(b) one mole of $[Ir(NH_3)_6]^{3+}(aq)$ and three moles of $NO_3^-(aq)$

(c) one mole of $[Pt(NH_3)_4Cl_2]^{2+}(aq)$ and two moles of $Cl^-(aq)$

(d) one mole of $[Ru(NH_3)_6]^{3+}(aq)$ and three moles of $Br^-(aq)$

22-13   The key point is that only the chloride ions that exist in solution as $Cl^-(aq)$, and not the chloride ions that are complexed with the platinum ions, are precipitated by $Ag^+(aq)$ as $AgCl(s)$. Let's look at each case in turn.

$PtCl_4 \cdot 6NH_3$ Because all four chloride ions per formula unit are precipitated by $Ag^+(aq)$, all four chloride ions must exist in solution as $Cl^-(aq)$. The chemical formula of the complex salt must be $[Pt(NH_3)_6]Cl_4$.

$PtCl_4 \cdot 5NH_3$ One of the four chloride ions must be complexed to the platinum ion because it is not precipitated by $Ag^+(aq)$. The chemical formula of the complex salt must be $[Pt(NH_3)_5Cl]Cl_3$.

$PtCl_4 \cdot 4NH_3$ Two of the four chloride ions must be complexed to the platinum ion because they are not precipitated by $Ag^+(aq)$. The chemical formula of the complex salt must be $[Pt(NH_3)_4Cl_2]Cl_2$.

$PtCl_4 \cdot 3NH_3$ Three of the four chloride ions must be complexed to the platinum ion because they are not precipitated by $Ag^+(aq)$. The chemical formula of the complex salt must be $[Pt(NH_3)_3Cl_3]Cl$.

$PtCl_4 \cdot 2NH_3$ All four of the chloride ions must be complexed to the platinum ion because none are precipitated by $Ag^+(aq)$. The chemical formula of the complex must be $[Pt(NH_3)_2Cl_4]$.

22-15   (a) The complex ion is $[Cr(CN)_6]^{3-}$. If the oxidation state of Cr is denoted by x, then $x + 6(-1) = -3$, or $x = +3$. The name of the compound is potassium hexacyanochromate(III).

   (b) The complex ion is $[Cr(H_2O)_5Cl]^{2+}$. If x is the oxidation state of Cr, then $x + 5(0) + (-1) = +2$, or $x = +3$. The name of the compound is pentaaquachlorochromium(III) perchlorate.

   (c) The complex ion is $[Co(CO)_4Cl_2]^+$. If x is the oxidation state of Co, then $x + 4(0) + 2(-1) = +1$, or $x = +3$. The name of the compound is tetracarbonyldichlorocobalt(III) perchlorate.

   (d) The complex ion is $[Pt(NH_3)_4Br_2]^{2+}$. If x is the oxidation state of Pt, then $x + 4(0) + 2(-1) = +2$, or $x = +4$. The name of the compound is tetraamminedibromoplatinum(IV) chloride.

22-17   (a) The complex ion is $[Co(NO_2)_6]^{3-}$. Denoting the oxidation state of cobalt by x, we have $x + 6(-1) = -3$, or $x = +3$. The compound is called ammonium hexanitrocobaltate(III).

   (b) The complex ion is $[Ir(NH_3)_4Br_2]^+$. Denoting the oxidation state of iridium by x, we have $x + 4(0) + 2(-1) = +1$, or $x = +3$. The compound is called tetraamminedibromoiridium(III) bromide.

   (c) The complex ion is $[CuCl_4]^{2-}$. Denoting the oxidation state of copper by x, we have $x + 4(-1) = -2$, or $x = +2$. The compound is called potassium tetrachlorocuprate(II).

   (d) The complex is $[Ru(CO)_5]$. Denoting the oxidation state of ruthenium by x, we have $x + 5(0) = 0$, or $x = 0$. The molecule is called pentacarbonylruthenium(0).

22-19   (a) The complex consists of a central iron atom with five cyanide ions, CN^-, and one carbon monoxide, CO, as ligands. The oxidation state of the iron is $+2$, and so the charge on the complex ion is $+2 + 5(-1) + 0 = -3$. The formula of the compound is $Na_3[Fe(CN)_5CO]$.

(b) The complex ion consists of a central gold atom with two chloride ions and two iodide ions as ligands. The oxidation state of the gold is $+3$, and so the charge on the complex ion is $+3 + 2(-1) + 2(-1) = -1$. The formula of the compound is $trans\text{-}NH_4[AuCl_2I_2]$.

(c) The complex ion consists of a central cobalt atom with six cyanide ions as ligands. The oxidation state of the cobalt is $+3$, and so the charge on the complex is $+3 + 6(-1) = -3$. The formula of the compound is $K_3[Co(CN)_6]$.

(d) The complex ion consists of a central cobalt atom with six NO_2^- ions as ligands. The oxidation state of the cobalt is $+3$, and so the charge on the complex ion is $+3 + 6(-1) = -3$. The formula of the compound is $Ca_3[Co(NO_2)_6]_2$.

22-21 (a) The complex ion consists of a central platinum atom with a chloride ion and three ammonia molecules as ligands. The oxidation state of the platinum is $+2$, and so the charge on the complex ion is $+2 + (-1) + 3(0) = +1$. The formula of the compound is $[Pt(NH_3)_3Cl]NO_3$.

(b) The complex ion consists of a central copper atom with four fluoride ions as ligands. The oxidation state of the copper is $+2$, and so the charge on the complex ion is $+2 + 4(-1) = -2$. The formula of the compound is $Na_2[CuF_4]$.

(c) The complex ion consists of a central cobalt atom with six nitrite ions as ligands. The oxidation state of the cobalt is $+2$, and so the charge on the complex ion is $+2 + 6(-1) = -4$. The formula of the compound is $Li_4[Co(NO_2)_6]$.

(d) The complex ion consists of a central iron atom with six cyanide ions as ligands. The oxidation state of the iron is $+2$, and so the charge on the complex ion is $+2 + 6(-1) = -4$. The formula of the compound is $Ba_2[Fe(CN)_6]$.

22-23 (a) The complex ion is $[Os(NH_3)_2(en)_2]^{3+}$. If the oxidation state of Os is x, then $x + 2(0) + 2(0) = +3$, or $x = +3$. The name of the compound is diammine-*bis*(ethylenediamine)osmium(III) chloride.

(b) The complex ion is $[Co(NH_3)_3(en)Cl]^+$. If the oxidation state of Co is x, then $x + 3(0) + 0 + (-1) = +1$, or $x = +2$. The name of the compound is triamminechloroethylenediaminecobalt(II) nitrate.

(c) The complex ion is $[Fe(EDTA)]^{2-}$. If the oxidation state of Fe is x, then $x + (-4) = -2$, or $x = +2$. The name of the compound is ammonium ethylenediaminetetraacetatoferrate(II).

(d) The complex ion is $[Cr(C_2O_4)_3]^{3-}$. If the oxidation state of the Cr is x, then $x + 3(-2) = -3$, or $x = +3$. The name of the compound is potassium *tris*(oxalato)chromate(III).

22-25 (a) The complex ion consists of a central rhenium atom with three oxalate ions as ligands. The oxidation state of the rhenium is $+3$, and so the charge on the complex ion is $+3 + 3(-2) = -3$. The formula of the compound is $K_3[Re(C_2O_4)_3]$.

(b) The complex ion consists of a central cobalt atom with three ethylenediamine molecules as ligands. The oxidation state of the cobalt is $+2$, and so the charge on the complex ion is $+2 + 3(0) = +2$. The formula of the compound is $[Co(en)_3](C_2H_3O_2)_2$.

(c) The complex ion consists of a central chromium atom with an ethylenediaminetetraacetate ion as the ligand. The oxidation state of the chromium is $+2$, and so the charge on the complex ion is $+2 + (-4) = -2$. The formula of the compound is $Na_2[Cr(EDTA)]$.

(d) The complex ion consists of a central palladium atom with two chloride ions and two ethylenediamine molecules as ligands. The oxidation state of the palladium is $+4$, and so the charge on the complex ion is $+4 + 2(-1) + 2(0) = +2$. The formula of the compound is $[PdCl_2(en)_2](NO_3)_2$.

22-27   (a) The structure of the complex is octahedral. The possible arrangements of the ligands around the central cobalt ion are

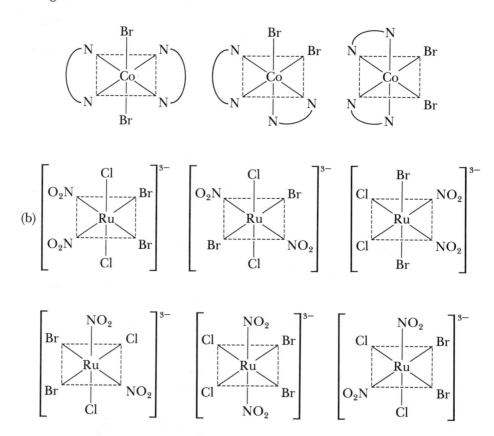

These structures are easier to visualize if you make a model of an octahedron as given in Appendix D of the text.

22-29 (a) The complex is square planar:

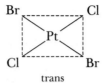

trans

(b) The complex ion is square planar:

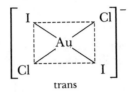

trans

(c) The complex is octahedral:

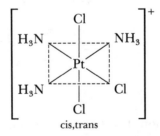

cis,cis

(d) The complex ion is octahedral:

$$\left[\begin{array}{c} H_3N \cdots \cdots \\ H_3N \end{array} \begin{array}{c} Cl \\ Pt \\ Cl \end{array} \begin{array}{c} NH_3 \\ Cl \end{array} \right]^{+}$$

cis,trans

22-31 (a) Niobium(III) is a d^2 ion. The d-orbital electron configuration of Nb^{3+} is

$$\underset{x^2-y^2 \quad z^2}{\bigcirc \quad \bigcirc} \quad e_g^0$$

$$\underset{xy \quad xz \quad yz}{\uparrow \quad \uparrow \quad \bigcirc} \quad t_{2g}^2$$

or simply t_{2g}^2.

(b) Molybdenum(II) is a d^4 ion. If Δ_o is greater than the energy that is required to pair electrons, then the d-orbital electron configuration of Mo^{2+} is

$$\frac{\bigcirc \quad \bigcirc}{x^2 - y^2 \quad z^2} \; e_g^0$$

$$\frac{\textcircled{\downuparrow} \quad \textcircled{\uparrow} \quad \textcircled{\uparrow}}{xy \quad xz \quad yz} \; t_{2g}^4$$

or t_{2g}^4.

(c) Manganese(II) is a d^5 ion. If Δ_o is less than the energy that is required to pair electrons, then the d-orbital electron configuration of Mn^{2+} is

$$\frac{\textcircled{\uparrow} \quad \textcircled{\uparrow}}{x^2 - y^2 \quad z^2} \; e_g^2$$

$$\frac{\textcircled{\uparrow} \quad \textcircled{\uparrow} \quad \textcircled{\uparrow}}{xy \quad xz \quad yz} \; t_{2g}^3$$

or $t_{2g}^3 e_g^2$.

(d) Gold(I) is a d^{10} ion. The d-orbital electron configuration of Au^+ is

$$\frac{\textcircled{\downuparrow} \quad \textcircled{\downuparrow}}{x^2 - y^2 \quad z^2} \; e_g^4$$

$$\frac{\textcircled{\downuparrow} \quad \textcircled{\downuparrow} \quad \textcircled{\downuparrow}}{xy \quad xz \quad yz} \; t_{2g}^6$$

or $t_{2g}^6 e_g^4$.

(e) Iridium(III) is a d^6 ion. The d-orbital electron configuration of a low-spin Ir^{3+} complex is

$$\frac{\bigcirc \quad \bigcirc}{x^2 - y^2 \quad z^2} \; e_g^0$$

$$\frac{\textcircled{\downuparrow} \quad \textcircled{\downuparrow} \quad \textcircled{\downuparrow}}{xy \quad xz \quad yz} \; t_{2g}^6$$

or $t_{2g}^6 e_g^0$.

22-33   We set up the following table

Ion	Oxidation state of central ion	x in d^x	Low-spin d-orbital electron configuration (number of unpaired electrons)	High-spin d-orbital electron configuration (number of unpaired electrons)
(a) $[Fe(CN)_6]^{4-}$	Fe(II)	6	$t_{2g}^6 e_g^0$ (0)	$t_{2g}^4 e_g^2$ (4)
(b) $[Fe(CN)_6]^{3-}$	Fe(III)	5	$t_{2g}^5 e_g^0$ (1)	$t_{2g}^3 e_g^2$ (5)
(c) $[Co(NH_3)_6]^{2+}$	Co(II)	7	$t_{2g}^6 e_g^1$ (1)	$t_{2g}^5 e_g^2$ (3)
(d) $[CoF_6]^{3-}$	Co(III)	6	$t_{2g}^6 e_g^0$ (0)	$t_{2g}^4 e_g^2$ (4)
(e) $[Mn(H_2O)_6]^{2+}$	Mn(II)	5	$t_{2g}^5 e_g^0$ (1)	$t_{2g}^3 e_g^2$ (5)

Thus we see that $[Fe(CN)_6]^{4-}$ is low-spin, $[Fe(CN)_6]^{3-}$ is low-spin, $[Co(NH_3)_6]^{2+}$ is high-spin, $[CoF_6]^{3-}$ is high-spin and $[Mn(H_2O)_6]^{2+}$ is high-spin.

22-35   (a) The complex involves iron(II), which is a d^6 ion. Referring to the spectrochemical series, we see that CN^- produces a relatively large Δ_o value. We predict that the complex is low spin with the d-electron configuration $t_{2g}^6 e_g^0$.

(b) The complex involves manganese(II), which is a d^5 ion. Because F^- produces a relatively small Δ_o value, we predict that the complex is high spin with the d-electron configuration $t_{2g}^3 e_g^2$.

(c) The complex involves cobalt(III), which is a d^6 ion. Because NO_2^- produces a relatively large Δ_o value, we predict that the complex is low spin with the d-electron configuration $t_{2g}^6 e_g^0$.

(d) The complex involves iron(III), which is a d^5 ion. Because there are no low spin tetrahedral complexes, we predict that the complex is high spin with the d-electron configuration $e^2 t_2^3$.

22-37   (a) The oxidation state of the vanadium atom in $[VCl_6]^{3-}$ is given by $x + 6(-1) = -3$, or $x = +3$. Vanadium(III) is a d^2 ion, and so there are two unpaired electrons in $[VCl_6]^{3-}$.

(b) The oxidation state of the cobalt atom in $[CoCl_4]^{2-}$ is given by $x + 4(-1) = -2$, or $x = +2$. Cobalt(II) is a d^7 ion. The d-electron configuration is $e^4 t_2^3$, and so there are three unpaired electrons in $[CoCl_4]^{2-}$.

(c) The oxidation state of the chromium atom in $[Cr(CO)_6]$ is given by $x + 6(0) = 0$, or $x = 0$. Chromium(0) is d^6 and CO gives rise to low spin complexes. Thus the d-electron configuration is $t_{2g}^6 e_g^0$, and so there are no unpaired electrons in $[Cr(CO)_6]$.

(d) The oxidation state, x, of the chromium ion in $[Cr(CN)_6]^{4-}$ is given by $x + 6(-1) = -4$, or $x = +2$. Chromium(II) is a d^4 ion and CN^- gives rise to low-spin complexes. Thus the d-electron configuration is $t_{2g}^4 e_g^0$, and so there are two unpaired electrons in the complex ion $[Cr(CN)_6]^{4-}$.

22-39 (a) Cobalt(III) is a d^6 ion. The d-electron configuration of low spin Co(III) is $t_{2g}^6 e_g^0$. There are no unpaired electrons; thus $[Co(en)_3]^{3+}$ is diamagnetic.

(b) Iron(II) is a d^6 ion. The CN^- ligand is a low spin ligand, and the d-electron configuration of low spin Fe(II) is $t_{2g}^6 e_g^0$. There are no unpaired electrons; thus $[Fe(CN)_6]^{4-}$ is diamagnetic.

(c) Nickel(II) is a d^8 ion. The d-electron configuration is

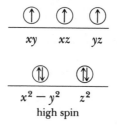

There are two unpaired electrons; thus $[NiF_4]^{2-}$ is paramagnetic.

(d) Cobalt(II) is a d^7 ion. The d-electron configuration is

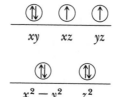

and so $[CoBr_4]^{2-}$ is paramagnetic.

22-41 Each complex ion could be either square planar or tetrahedral. Nickel(II) is a d^8 ion, and the two possible d-electron configurations of $[NiF_4]^{2-}$ are

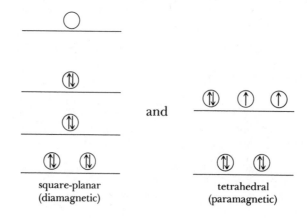

Because $[NiF_4]^{2-}$ is paramagnetic, we conclude that $[NiF_4]^{2-}$ is tetrahedral. The two possibilities for $[Ni(CN)_4]^{2-}$ are the same as shown above. Because $[Ni(CN)_4]^{2-}$ is diamagnetic, we predict that it is square planar.

22-43 (a) Titanium(III) has one d-electron. The d-electron configuration is $t_{2g}^1 e_g^0$, and so $[Ti(H_2O)_6]^{3+}$ is labile.

(b) The oxidation state of the vanadium atom in $[VF_6]^{3-}$ is given by $x + 6(-1) = -3$, or $x = +3$. Vanadium(III) is a d^2 ion, and so the d-electron configuration is $t_{2g}^2 e_g^0$ and $[VF_6]^{3-}$ is labile.

(c) The oxidation state of the chromium ion in $[Cr(NO_2)_6]^{3-}$ is given by $x + 6(-1) = -3$, or $x = +3$. Chromium(III) is a d^3 ion with a $t_{2g}^3 e_g^0$ d-electron configuration. Therefore $[Cr(NO_2)_6]^{3-}$ is inert.

(d) The oxidation state of the copper atom in $[CuCl_6]^{4-}$ is given by $x + 6(-1) = -4$, or $x = +2$. Copper(II) is a d^9 ion. The d-electron configuration is $t_{2g}^6 e_g^3$ and $[CuCl_6]^{4-}$ is labile.

22-45 (a) The oxidation state of the vanadium atom in $[V(H_2O)_6]^{3+}$ is given by $x + 6(0) = +3$, or $x = +3$. Vanadium(III) is a d^2 ion, and so the complex is labile.

(b) The oxidation state of the tungsten atom in $[WF_6]^{2-}$ is given by $x + 6(-1) = -2$, or $x = +4$. Tungsten(IV) is a d^2 ion, and so the complex is labile.

(c) The oxidation state of the chromium atom in $[Cr(CO)_6]$ is given by $x + 6(0) = 0$, or $x = 0$. Chromium(0) is low-spin d^6, and so the complex is inert.

(d) The oxidation state of the zinc atom in $[Zn(H_2O)_6]^{2+}$ is given by $x + 6(0) = +2$, or $x = +2$. Zn(II) is a d^{10} ion, and so the complex is labile.

22-47 (a) The charge on the complex ion is given by $+3 + 6(-1) = -3$. The formula is $[Co(NO_2)_6]^{3-}$.

(b) The charge on the complex ion is given by $+4 + 2(-1) + 2(0) = +2$. The formula is $trans$-$[PtCl_2(en)_2]^{2+}$.

(c) The charge on the complex ion is given by $+2 + 5(-1) + 0 = -3$. The formula is $[Fe(CN)_5CO]^{3-}$.

(d) The charge on the complex ion is given by $+3 + 2(-1) + 2(-1) = -1$. The formula is $trans$-$[AuCl_2I_2]^-$.

22-49 (a) The charge on the complex ion is given by $+3 + 3(-2) = -3$. The formula of the compound is $Li_3[Ru(C_2O_4)_3]$.

(b) The charge on the complex ion is given by $+2 + 4(-1) = -2$. The formula of the compound is $K_2[HgI_4]$.

(c) The charge on the complex ion is given by $+3 + 2(-1) = +1$. The formula of the compound is $[Cr(NH_3)_4Br_2]NO_3$.

(d) The charge on the complex ion is given by $+3 + 3(0) + 3(0) = +3$. The formula of the compound is $[Mo(H_2O)_3(CO)_3](C_2H_3O_2)_3$.

22-51   (a) The data indicate the number of chloride ions that are not bonded as ligands to the cobalt atom. Thus we have

$[Co(NH_3)_6]Cl_3$

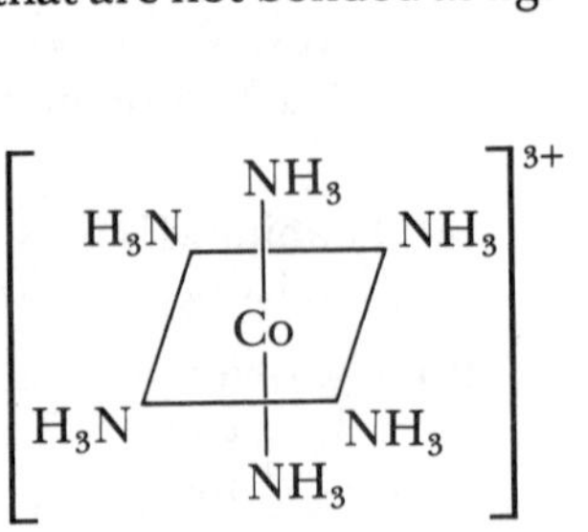

$[Co(NH_3)_5Cl]Cl_2$

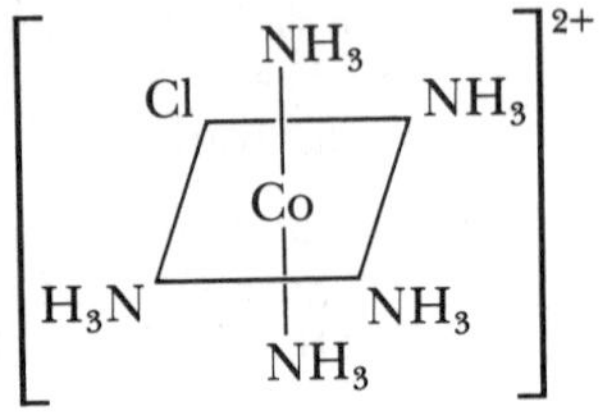

$[Co(NH_3)_4Cl_2]Cl$

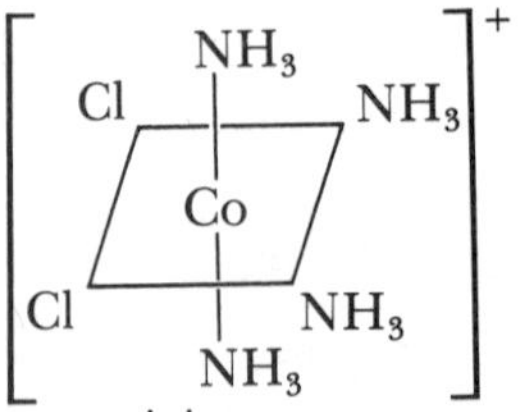

cis isomer

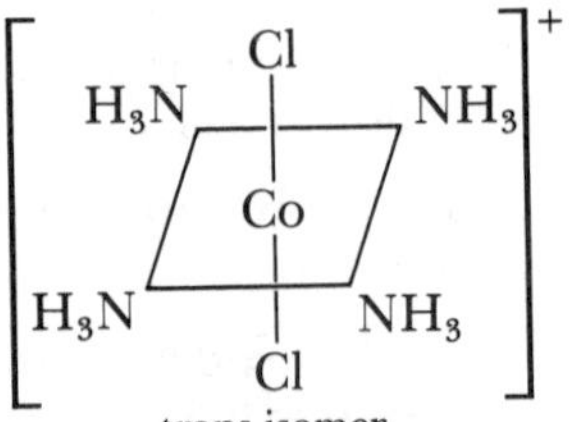

trans isomer

(b) There are cis and trans isomers of $[Co(NH_3)_4Cl_2]^+$ (as shown above) and hence two colors.

22-53   (a) The oxidation state of the cobalt atom in $[Co(CN)_6]^{3-}$ is given by $x + 6(-1) = -3$, or $x = +3$, and in $[CoCl_6]^{4-}$ it is given by $x + 6(-1) = -4$, or $x = +2$. Thus $[CoCl_6]^{4-}$ has more d-electrons and the statement is false.

(b) False [see part (a)].

(c) From part (a), we see that the cobalt atom in $[Co(CN)_6]^{3-}$ is d^6, while in $[CoF_6]^{4-}$ it is d^7. The CN^- causes the $[Co(CN)_6]^{3-}$ to be low spin, and so the d-electron configuration is $t_{2g}^6 e_g^0$. The F^- causes the $[CoF_6]^{4-}$ to be high spin, with a $t_{2g}^5 e_g^2$ d-electron configuration. Thus $[CoF_6]^{4-}$ is paramagnetic and $[Co(CN)_6]^{3-}$ is diamagnetic. Thus the statement of the problem is false.

(d) True [see part (c)].

22-55   (a) The oxidation state of the nickel atom in $[NiCl_4]^{2-}$ is given by $x + 4(-1) = -2$, or $x = +2$. Nickel(II) is a d^8 ion, and the d-electron configuration is $e^4 t_2^4$. Thus there are two unpaired electrons in $[NiCl_4]^{2-}$.

(b) The oxidation state of the cobalt atom in $[CoCl_4]^{2-}$ is given by $x + 4(-1) = -2$, or $x = +2$. Cobalt(II) is a d^7 ion, and the d-electron configuration is $e^4 t_2^3$. Thus there are three unpaired electrons in $[CoCl_4]^{2-}$.

(c) The oxidation state of the cobalt atom in $[Co(CO)_6]^{3+}$ is given by $x + 6(0) = +3$, or $x = +3$. Cobalt(III) is a d^6 ion, and the complex is low spin (due to CO). Thus the d-electron configuration is t_{2g}^6 and there are no unpaired electrons.

(d) The oxidation state of the iron atom in $[Fe(CN)_6]^{3-}$ is given by $x + 6(-1) = -3$, or $x = +3$. Iron(III) is a d^5 ion. The complex is low spin (due to CN^-) and the d-electron configuration is t_{2g}^5. Thus there is one unpaired electron in $[Fe(CN)_6]^{3-}$.

22-57 (a) Addition of $NaCN(s)$ adds $CN^-(aq)$ and thus shifts the equilibrium to the right.

(b) Addition of $AgCl(s)$ has no effect because it is a condensed phase.

(c) Because $\Delta H_{rxn}^{\circ} > 0$, a decrease in the temperature will shift the equilibrium to the left.

(d) The addition of $HNO_3(l)$ will decrease the concentration of $CN^-(aq)$ due to the reaction

$$H_3O^+(aq) + CN^-(aq) \rightleftharpoons HCN(aq) \qquad \left(K = \frac{1}{K_a} = 2.09 \times 10^9 \text{ M}^{-1} \right)$$

and so the equilibrium will shift to the left.

(e) The addition of $H_2O(l)$ will have no effect because there is an equal number of moles of solute species on each side of the equation.

(f) The addition of $NaCl(s)$ adds $Cl^-(aq)$ and thus shifts the equilibrium to the left.

22-59 The equation for the reaction is

(1) $\qquad Pb_2[Fe(CN)_6](s) + 4I^-(aq) \rightleftharpoons 2PbI_2(s) + [Fe(CN)_6]^{4-}(aq)$

and its equilibrium constant is

$$K_1 = \frac{[[Fe(CN)_6]^{4-}]}{[I^-]^4} = \frac{(0.11 \text{ M})}{(0.57 \text{ M})^4} = 1.04 \text{ M}^{-3}$$

The equations for the dissolution of both $Pb_2[Fe(CN)_6](s)$ and $PbI_2(s)$ are

(2) $\qquad Pb_2[Fe(CN)_6](s) \rightleftharpoons 2Pb^{2+}(aq) + [Fe(CN)_6]^{4-}(aq)$

(3) $\qquad PbI_2(s) \rightleftharpoons Pb^{2+}(aq) + 2I^-(aq)$

with

$$K_{sp(2)} = [Pb^{2+}]^2[[Fe(CN)_6]^{4-}]$$
$$K_{sp(3)} = [Pb^{2+}][I^-]^2$$

Note that

$$K_1 = \frac{K_{sp(2)}}{K_{sp(3)}^2}$$

and so

$$K_{sp(2)} = K_1 K_{sp(3)}^2 = (1.04 \text{ M}^{-3})(7.1 \times 10^{-9} \text{ M}^3)^2 = 5.3 \times 10^{-17} \text{ M}^3$$

E ANSWERS TO THE SELF-TEST

1 10

2 six

3 4

4 8

5 5

6 true

7 iron . . . the six cyanide ions

8 false

9 the d electrons of the metal ion

10 false

11 octahedral

12 square-planar

13 ligands . . . metal atom

14 ammine

15 carbonyl

16 a Greek prefix

17 true

18 a roman numeral in parentheses

19 false

20 on adjacent corners

21 true

22 polydentate ligand

23 true

24 a prefix such as *bis* or *tris*

25 true

26 false

27 t_{2g} . . . e_g

28 six

29 false

30 Δ_o

31 false

32 the value of Δ_o is less than the energy that is required to pair electrons

33 high

34 true

35 less than

36 true

37 inert

38

○
_____
$x^2 - y^2$

○
_____
xy

○
_____
z^2

○ ○
_____
xz xy

39

○ ○ ○ t_2
_____
xy xz yz

○ ○ e
_____
$x^2 - y^2$ z^2

40 true

41 unpaired

42 paramagnetic

ORGANIC CHEMISTRY

A   OUTLINE OF CHAPTER 23

23-1   Alkanes are hydrocarbons that contain only single bonds.

Hydrocarbons consist of only hydrogen and carbon.

The bonding in alkanes is described in terms of sp^3 hybrid orbitals on the carbon atoms.

Condensed structural formulas are more compact than Lewis formulas.

Additional hydrogen atoms cannot be bonded to carbon atoms in alkanes.

Alkanes are saturated hydrocarbons.

Rotation can occur about carbon-carbon single bonds.

Molecules that have the same chemical formula but different structures are called structural isomers.

Structural isomers have different chemical and physical properties.

The number of possible structural isomers increases with the number of carbon atoms in an alkane.

The principal sources of saturated hydrocarbons are petroleum and natural gas deposits.

Alkanes are relatively unreactive.

Alkanes react with oxygen in combustion reactions.

Alkane combustion reactions are highly exothermic.

The substitution reaction between an alkane and a halogen in the presence of ultraviolet light yields alkyl halides, or haloalkanes.

23-2   Alkanes and substituted alkanes can be named systematically according to IUPAC rules.

The IUPAC rules for naming alkanes and their derivatives are given on pages 746 and 747 in the text.

The names of some common groups are listed in Table 23-2.

The formula of a compound can be written from the IUPAC name of the compound (Example 23-3).

23-3 Hydrocarbons that contain double bonds are called alkenes.

In an unsaturated hydrocarbon not all the carbon atoms are bonded to four other atoms.

Alkenes are unsaturated hydrocarbons that contain one or more double bonds.

The double bond in an alkene forces the alkene to have a planar region about the double bond.

Cis-trans isomers of alkenes may exist.

The IUPAC nomenclature for alkenes and their derivatives is given on page 749 in the text.

Alkenes undergo combustion and substitution reactions.

Alkenes undergo these addition reactions:

   (a) addition of hydrogen in the presence of a catalyst and high temperature and pressure

   (b) addition of chlorine or bromine

   (c) addition of hydrogen chloride

   (d) addition of water in the presence of acid

Markovnikov's rule states that when HX adds to an alkene, the hydrogen atom becomes bonded to the carbon atom in the double bond already bearing the larger number of hydrogen atoms.

Markovnikov's rule is used to predict the primary products in addition reactions.

23-4 Hydrocarbons that contain a triple bond are called alkynes.

The IUPAC nomenclature for alkynes and their derivatives is given on page 752 in the text.

Alkynes undergo combustion reactions and the addition reactions that alkenes undergo.

23-5 Benzene belongs to a class of hydrocarbons called aromatic hydrocarbons.

Aromatic hydrocarbons have rings that are stabilized by π-electron delocalization.

Benzene is represented by the structure

A common way of naming disubstituted benzenes is the *ortho-*, *meta-*, and *para-* system (see page 754).

The benzene ring is stable and undergoes few reactions.

Benzene undergoes the substitution reactions that alkanes do.

23-6   Alcohols are organic compounds that contain an —OH group.

The IUPAC nomenclature for alcohols is given on page 755 in the text.

Low molecular mass alcohols form hydrogen bonds and are completely miscible with water.

High molecular mass alcohols have low solubilities in water.

Alcohols undergo some reactions analogous to water.

23-7   Aldehydes and ketones contain a carbon-oxygen double bond.

Aldehydes have the general formula RCHO.

The aldehyde group, —CHO, is planar.

A primary alcohol is an alcohol in which the —OH-bearing carbon atom is bonded to only one other carbon atom.

Aldehydes are obtained from the oxidation of primary alcohols.

A secondary alcohol is an alcohol in which the —OH-bearing carbon atom is bonded to two other carbon atoms.

Secondary alcohols are oxidized to ketones.

A ketone has the general formula

$$\begin{array}{c} R' \\ \diagdown \\ C=O \\ \diagup \\ R \end{array}$$

A tertiary alcohol is an alcohol in which the —OH-bearing carbon atom is bonded to three other carbon atoms.

Tertiary alcohols cannot be oxidized to a molecule containing a carbon-oxygen double bond.

23-8   Amines are organic derivatives of ammonia.

A primary amine has one hydrocarbon group and two hydrogen atoms bonded to a nitrogen atom.

A secondary amine has two hydrocarbon groups and one hydrogen atom bonded to a nitrogen atom.

A tertiary amine has three hydrocarbon groups bonded to a nitrogen atom.

Primary amines and secondary amines form hydrogen bond in the liquid state.

Amines can form hydrogen bonds with water.

Amines are weak bases.

23-9   The reaction of a carboxylic acid with an alcohol produces an ester.

An organic carboxylic acid can be obtained by the oxidation of an aldehyde or a primary alcohol.

Carboxylic acids produce $H_3O^+(aq)$ in water.

Carboxylic acids are neutralized by bases.

A carboxylate ion is the anion that results from the dissociation or neutralization of a carboxylic acid.

The carboxylate ion is stabilized by charge delocalization.

Esters are produced by the reaction of organic acids with alcohols. The yields of these reactions are often low.

The general formula of an ester is

$$\begin{array}{c} R \\ \diagdown \\ \quad\; C{=}O \\ \diagup \\ R'O \end{array}$$

where the R' group comes from the alcohol.

Esters are named by first naming the alkyl group from the alcohol and then designating the acid with the -ic ending changed to -ate.

B SELF-TEST

1 Alkanes contain carbon-carbon _____ bonds.

2 The bonding in alkanes can be described in terms of _____ hybrid orbitals on the carbon atoms.

3 Structural isomers have identical physical properties. *True/False*

4 The molecules whose formulas are

$$CH_3CH_2CH_3 \quad and \quad \begin{array}{c} CH_3CH_2 \\ | \\ CH_3 \end{array}$$

are structural isomers. *True/False*

5 Ethane, CH_3CH_3, is a planar molecule. *True/False*

6 The number of structural isomers of pentane is (*greater than, less than, the same as*) the number of structural isomers of heptane.

7 Alkanes undergo a great variety of reactions. *True/False*

8 Alkanes react with oxygen in a combustion reaction to form _____ and

_____ .

9 Hydrocarbons are used as fuels because _____

_____ .

10   The reaction between chlorine and an alkane is an **example** of a

_____ reaction.

11   The reaction between chlorine and an alkane requires _____ for the reaction to occur.

12   The reaction between chlorine and an alkane produces _____ .

13   In the IUPAC system for naming saturated hydrocarbons, the carbons in the main chain are numbered starting at the end that _____

_____ .

14   If two methyl groups are attached to the same carbon atom in an alkane, then only one number is necessary to designate the location of the methyl groups in the IUPAC name. _True/False_

15   Lewis formulas can be drawn if the IUPAC name is known. _True/False_

16   Alkenes are saturated hydrocarbons. _True/False_

17   Alkenes contain one or more carbon-carbon double bonds. (_True, False_)

18   The double bond in an alkene consists of a _____ bond and a

_____ bond.

19   The region around the double bond in an alkene has a _____

_____ geometry.

20   In the _cis_ isomer of 1,2-dichloroethene the two chlorine atoms lie _____

_____ .

21   Describe how alkenes are named.

22   The position of the double bond in an alkene must be designated. _True/False_

23   The reaction between hydrogen and an alkene is an example of an

_____ reaction.

24   The reaction between hydrogen and ethene in the presence of a catalyst produces

_____ .

25   The reaction between chlorine and ethene produces _____ .

26   The reaction between hydrogen chloride and ethene produces

_____ .

27 The reaction between water and ethene in the presence of acid produces
_____ .

28 _____ rule is used to predict the product of the addition of HCl(g) or
H$_2$O(l) to the double bond of an alkene.

29 Markovnikov's rule states that _____
_____
_____ .

30 Alkynes contain one or more carbon-carbon _____ bonds.

31 Alkynes undergo reactions similar to alkenes. *True/False*

32 Describe how alkynes are named.

33 The position of the triple bond in an alkyne must be designated by a number.
True/False

34 A compact way of writing the benzene structure is _____ .

35 Benzene contains three double bonds. *True/False*

36 Benzene undergoes the same reactions as an alkene. *True/False*

37 Derivatives of benzene are named by numbering the carbon atoms in benzene
according to _____ .

38 The designation *ortho-* in *o*-dichlorobenzene indicates that the two chlorine atoms
are in the _____ and _____ positions on the benzene ring.

39 The designation *para-* in *p*-dichlorobenzene indicates that the two chlorine atoms
are in the _____ and _____ positions on the benzene ring.

40 Aromatic hydrocarbons are stabilized by _____
_____ .

41 An alcohol contains the _____ group.

42 Describe how alcohols are named.

43 The position of the —OH group must be designated by a number in the IUPAC
name for an alcohol. *True/False*

44 Aldehydes have the general formula _____ .

45 Ketones have the general formula _____ .

46 Aldehydes and ketones contain a carbon-oxygen _____ bond.

47 The aldehyde group has a _____ shape.

48 Aldehydes are obtained from the oxidation of _____.

49 Ketones are obtained from the oxidation of _____.

50 An amine is an organic derivative of _____.

51 A secondary amine has *(one, two, three)* attached hydrocarbon groups.

52 Amines can form hydrogen bonds with water. *True/False*

53 Amines are weak *(acids, bases).*

54 Organic carboxylic acids have the general formula _____.

55 Carboxylic acids contain the _____ group.

56 Carboxylic acids can be obtained from the oxidation of _____ or

_____.

57 Carboxylic acids dissociate in water to produce _____ and

_____.

58 The two carbon-oxygen bonds in a carboxylate ion are identical. *True/False*

59 The two carbon-oxygen bonds in the carboxyl group are identical. *True/False*

60 The reaction between a carboxylic acid and a base yields a _____

and _____.

61 The reaction between a carboxylic acid and an alcohol yields an _____

and _____.

62 An ester has the general formula _____ where

_____.

C   CALCULATIONS YOU SHOULD KNOW HOW TO DO

There are no calculations in this chapter. You should know how to do the following:

1 Name organic compounds according to IUPAC rules
   (a) alkanes (See Examples 23-2 and Problems 23-7 through 23-12.)
   (b) alkynes (See Problem 23-23.)

(c) benzene derivatives (See Problem 23-30.)

(d) alcohols (See Problem 23-31.)

(e) aldehydes (See Problems 23-37.)

(f) carboxylic acids (See Problem 23-44.)

2   Write formulas from the IUPAC names of

(a) alkanes (See Example 23-3 and Problems 23-13 through 23-15.)

(b) alkenes (See Problem 23-16.)

(c) alkynes (See Problem 23-24.)

(d) alcohols (See Problem 23-32.)

(e) benzene derivatives (See Example 23-8 and Problem 23-29.)

(f) aldehydes (See Problem 23-38.)

(g) carboxylic acids (See Problem 23-43.)

3   Write chemical equations for the reactions involving

(a) alkanes (See Example 23-1 and Problems 23-1 and 23-2.)

(b) alkenes (See Examples 23-5 and 23-6 and Problems 23-17 through 23-22.)

(c) alkynes (See Example 23-7 and Problems 23-25 through 23-28.)

(d) aldehydes and ketones (See Example 23-9 and Problems 23-39 and 23-40.)

(e) amines (See Problems 23-41 and 23-42.)

(f) carboxylic acids (See Examples 23-10 and Problems 23-45, 23-46, 23-49, and 23-50.)

D   SOLUTIONS TO THE ODD-NUMBERED PROBLEMS

23-1   (a) $C_5H_{12}(g) + 8O_2(g) \rightarrow 5CO_2(g) + 6H_2O(l)$

(b) $C_2H_6(g) + Cl_2(g) \xrightarrow{\text{dark}} \text{N.R.}$

(c) $C_4H_{10}(g) + H_2SO_4(aq) \rightarrow \text{N.R.}$

(d) $CH_4(g) + Cl_2(g) \xrightarrow{\text{UV}} CH_3Cl(g) + HCl(g)$
            plus other chloromethanes such as $CH_2Cl_2(g)$

23-3   (a) The molecules are identical: One can be rotated 180° to superimpose upon the other.

(b) The molecules are identical. The chlorine atom is attached to the second carbon atom in each molecule.

(c) The molecules are different. They represent structural isomers because the chlorine atom is attached to a different carbon atom in each molecule.

(d) The molecules are identical. The groups in one molecule may be rotated around a carbon-carbon bond so that it is identical to the other molecule.

23-5 n-Hexane is

$$\begin{array}{c} \overset{H}{\underset{1}{|}} \quad \overset{H}{\underset{2}{|}} \quad \overset{H}{\underset{3}{|}} \quad \overset{H}{\underset{4}{|}} \quad \overset{H}{\underset{5}{|}} \quad \overset{H}{\underset{6}{|}} \\ H-C-C-C-C-C-C-H \\ \underset{H}{|} \quad \underset{H}{|} \quad \underset{H}{|} \quad \underset{H}{|} \quad \underset{H}{|} \quad \underset{H}{|} \end{array}$$

Different chloro isomers are obtained by attaching a chlorine atom to the first, second, or third carbon atoms in the chain. Therefore, you get three isomers of chlorohexane. Their IUPAC names are 1-chlorohexane, 2-chlorohexane, and 3-chlorohexane.

23-7   (a) The longest chain consists of four carbon atoms. The IUPAC name is 2-bromo-3-chlorobutane or 2-chloro-3-bromobutane.

(b) The longest chain consists of three carbon atoms. The IUPAC name is 2,2-dimethylpropane.

(c) The longest chain consists of three carbon atoms. The IUPAC name is 2-methyl-2-nitropropane.

(d) The longest chain consists of four carbon atoms. The IUPAC name is 1-amino-2-methylbutane.

23-9   (a) The name violates rule 3. The chain was not numbered to give the lowest number to the carbon atom that has an attached group. The correct IUPAC name is 2-methylpentane.

(b) The formula for 2-ethylbutane is

$$\begin{array}{c} CH_3CHCH_2CH_3 \\ | \\ CH_2 \\ | \\ CH_3 \end{array}$$

This name violates rule 2. The corret IUPAC name is 3-methylpentane.

(c) The formula for 2-propylhexane is

$$\begin{array}{c} CH_3-CH-CH_2-CH_2-CH_2-CH_3 \\ | \\ CH_2 \\ | \\ CH_2 \\ | \\ CH_3 \end{array}$$

This name violates rule 2. The correct IUPAC name is 4-methyloctane.

(d) One of the methyl groups has not been numbered (rule 6). The correct IUPAC name is 2,2-dimethylpropane.

23-11   (a) $CH_3-\underset{\underset{\displaystyle CH_3}{|}}{CH}-CH_2-CH_3$ 2-methylbutane

(b) $Cl-CH_2-CH_2-Br$ 1-bromo-2-chloroethane
                                        2-bromo-1-chloroethane

(c) $CH_3-\underset{\underset{\displaystyle Cl}{|}}{\overset{\overset{\displaystyle Cl}{|}}{C}}-\underset{\underset{\displaystyle Cl}{|}}{\overset{\overset{\displaystyle Cl}{|}}{C}}-Cl$ 1,1,1,2,2-pentachloropropane

(d) $CH_3-\underset{\underset{\displaystyle CH_3}{|}}{\overset{\overset{\displaystyle CH_3}{|}}{C}}-CH_3$ 2,2-dimethylpropane

23-13   (a) The parent alkane is butane. The name indicates that a methyl group is bonded to the second and third carbon atoms. Thus the structural formula is

$$CH_3-\underset{\underset{\displaystyle CH_3}{|}}{CH}-\underset{\underset{\displaystyle CH_3}{|}}{CH}-CH_3$$

(b) The parent alkane is butane. The name indicates that two methyl groups are bonded to the second carbon atom and one methyl group is bonded to the third carbon atom. The structural formula is

$$CH_3-\underset{\underset{\displaystyle CH_3}{|}}{\overset{\overset{\displaystyle CH_3}{|}}{C}}{-\!\!-\!\!-}\underset{\underset{\displaystyle CH_3}{|}}{CH}-CH_3$$

(c) The parent alkane is hexane. The name indicates that two methyl groups are bonded to the third carbon atom and an ethyl group is bonded to the fourth carbon atom. The structural formula is

$$CH_3-CH_2-\underset{\underset{\displaystyle CH_3}{|}}{\overset{\overset{\displaystyle CH_3}{|}}{C}}{-\!\!-\!\!-}\underset{\underset{\underset{\displaystyle CH_3}{|}}{\displaystyle CH_2}}{|}{CH}-CH_2-CH_3$$

(d) The parent alkane is octane. The name indicates that an isopropyl group is bonded to the fourth carbon atom. The structural formula is

$$CH_3-CH_2-CH_2-\underset{\underset{\displaystyle CH_3-CH-CH_3}{|}}{CH}-CH_2-CH_2-CH_2-CH_3$$

23-15 (a) The longest chain consists of four carbon atoms, and so we write

$$
\begin{array}{ccc}
& CH_3 & CH_3 \\
& | & | \\
H_3C-C & \rule{1cm}{0.4pt} & C-CH_3 \\
& | & | \\
& H & H
\end{array}
$$

(b) The longest chain consists of four carbon atoms, and so we write

$$
\begin{array}{ccc}
& NH_2 & CH_3 \\
& | & | \\
H_3C-C & \rule{1cm}{0.4pt} & C-CH_3 \\
& | & | \\
& H & H
\end{array}
$$

(c) The longest chain consists of five carbon atoms, and so we write

$$
\begin{array}{cccc}
& H & Cl & H \\
& | & | & | \\
H_3C-C & -C & \rule{0.6cm}{0.4pt} & C-CH_3 \\
& | & | & | \\
& H & CH_2 & H \\
& & | & \\
& & CH_3 &
\end{array}
$$

(d) The longest chain consists of three carbon atoms, and so we write

$$
\begin{array}{ccc}
Cl & Cl & Cl \\
| & | & | \\
H-C & -C & -C-H \\
| & | & | \\
H & H & H
\end{array}
$$

23-17 (a)
$$
\begin{array}{c}
H \\ \diagdown \\
\end{array}
C = C
\begin{array}{c}
CH_3 \\ \diagup \\
\end{array}
+ HCl \longrightarrow
\begin{array}{c}
Cl \\ | \\ H_3C-C-CH_3 \\ | \\ H
\end{array}
$$

2-chloropropane

(b)
$$
\begin{array}{c}
H_3C \\ \diagdown \\
\end{array}
C = C
\begin{array}{c}
CH_3 \\ \diagup \\
\end{array}
+ HBr \longrightarrow
\begin{array}{c}
H \quad Br \\ | \quad | \\ H_3C-C-C-CH_3 \\ | \quad | \\ H \quad H
\end{array}
$$

2-bromobutane

(c)
$$
\begin{array}{c}
H \\ \diagdown \\
\end{array}
C = C
\begin{array}{c}
CH_2CH_3 \\ \diagup \\
\end{array}
+ HCl \longrightarrow
\begin{array}{c}
H \quad Cl \quad H \quad H \\ | \quad | \quad | \quad | \\ H-C-C-C-C-H \\ | \quad | \quad | \quad | \\ H \quad H \quad H \quad H
\end{array}
$$

2-chlorobutane

(d) 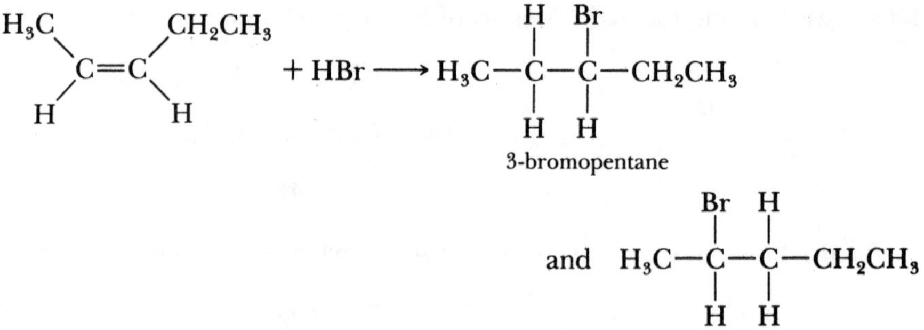 H_3C, CH_2CH_3 / $C=C$ / H, H $+ HBr \longrightarrow$ H₃C—C—C—CH₂CH₃ (with H and Br on carbons)

3-bromopentane

and   H₃C—C—C—CH₂CH₃ (with Br and H)

2-bromopentane

23-19 (a) 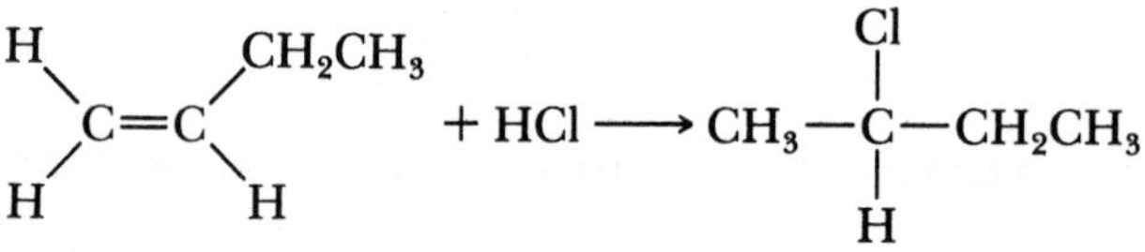 H, CH_2CH_3 / $C=C$ / H, H $+ HCl \longrightarrow$ CH₃—C—CH₂CH₃ (with Cl and H)

2-chlorobutane

(b) 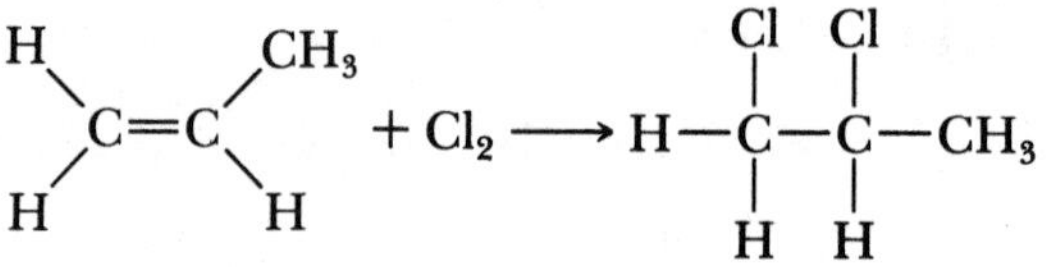 H, CH_3 / $C=C$ / H, H $+ Cl_2 \longrightarrow$ H—C—C—CH₃ (with Cl, Cl, H, H)

1,2-dichloropropane

(c) 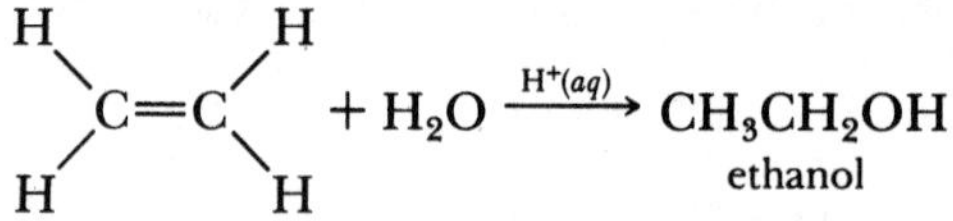 H, H / $C=C$ / H, H $+ H_2O \xrightarrow{H^+(aq)}$ CH₃CH₂OH

ethanol

(d) 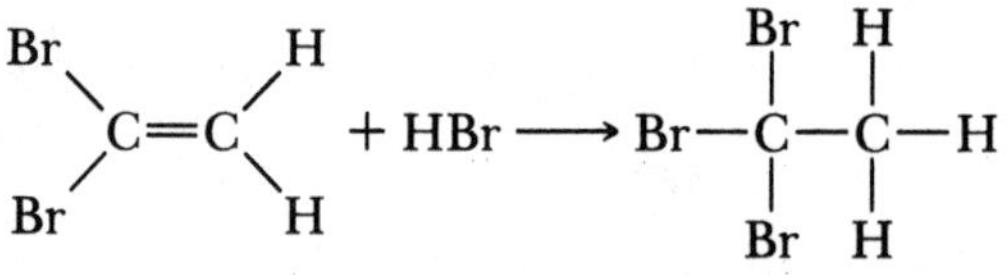 Br, H / $C=C$ / Br, H $+ HBr \longrightarrow$ Br—C—C—H (with Br, H, Br, H)

1,1,1-tribromoethane

23-21 (a) We shall react H_2O in the presence of an acid with an alkene in accord with Markovnikov's rule to obtain the desired alcohol. We use the alkenes

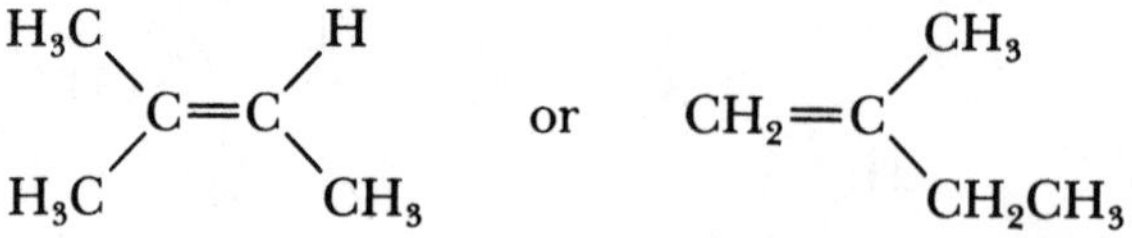

H_3C, H / $C=C$ / H_3C, CH_3 or $CH_2=C$ / CH_3, CH_2CH_3

(b) We react H_2O in the presence of an acid with an alkene in accord with Markovnikov's rule to obtain the desired alcohol. We use the alkene $CH_2=CHCH_3$.

(c) We react one mole of H_2 with the corresponding alkyne $CH_3C\equiv CCH_3$.

(d) We react HBr with an alkyne in accord with Markovnikov's rule to obtain the desired compound. We use $CH_3C\equiv CH$.

23-23 (a) propyne (b) 2-butyne

(c) 4,4-dimethyl-2-hexyne (d) 4-methyl-1-hexyne

23-25 We can break the reaction down into two steps. We shall use Markovnikov's rule to predict the product of each step. The first step is

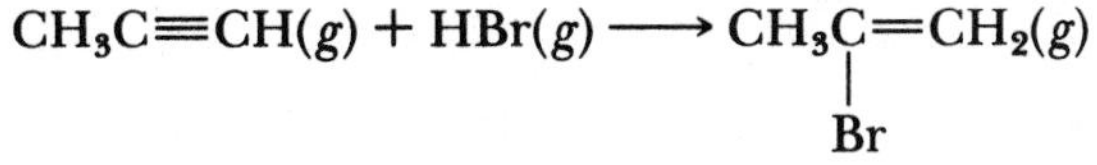

$$CH_3C\equiv CH(g) + HBr(g) \longrightarrow CH_3\underset{\underset{Br}{|}}{C}=CH_2(g)$$

The second step is

$$CH_3\underset{\underset{Br}{|}}{C}=CH_2(g) + HBr(g) \longrightarrow CH_3\overset{\overset{Br}{|}}{\underset{\underset{Br}{|}}{C}}CH_3(l)$$

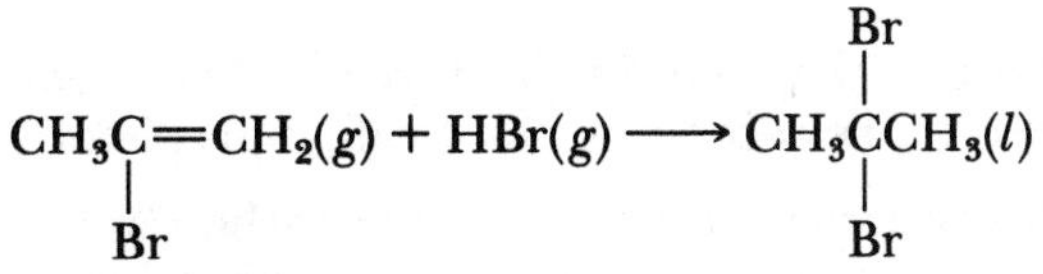

The product is 2,2-dibromopropane.

23-27 (a) $CH_3C\equiv CH(g) + 4O_2(g) \rightarrow 3CO_2(g) + 2H_2O(l)$

(b) This reaction can be broken down into two steps. We shall use Markovnikov's rule to predict the product in each step. The first step is

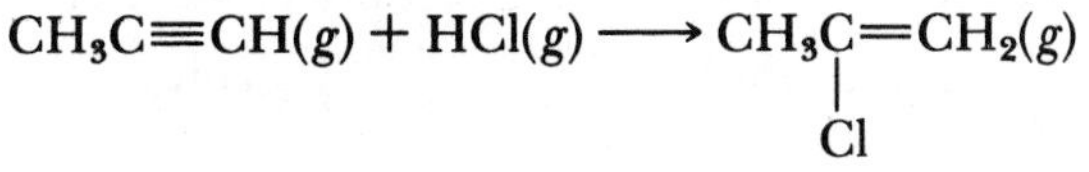

$$CH_3C\equiv CH(g) + HCl(g) \longrightarrow CH_3\underset{\underset{Cl}{|}}{C}=CH_2(g)$$

The second step is

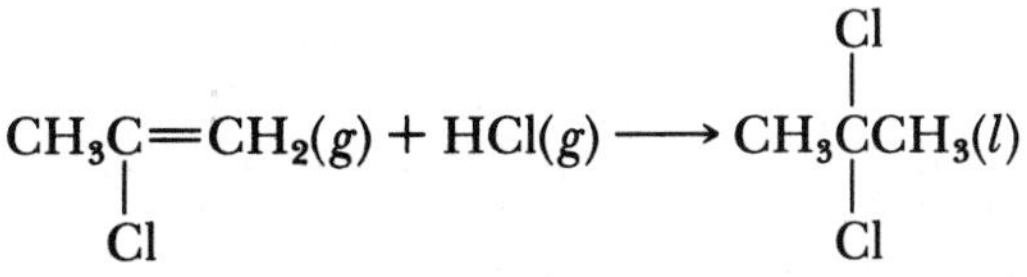

$$CH_3\underset{\underset{Cl}{|}}{C}=CH_2(g) + HCl(g) \longrightarrow CH_3\overset{\overset{Cl}{|}}{\underset{\underset{Cl}{|}}{C}}CH_3(l)$$

(c) $CH_3C\equiv CH(g) + 2Br_2(l) \longrightarrow CH_3\overset{\overset{Br}{|}}{\underset{\underset{Br}{|}}{C}}CHBr_2(l)$

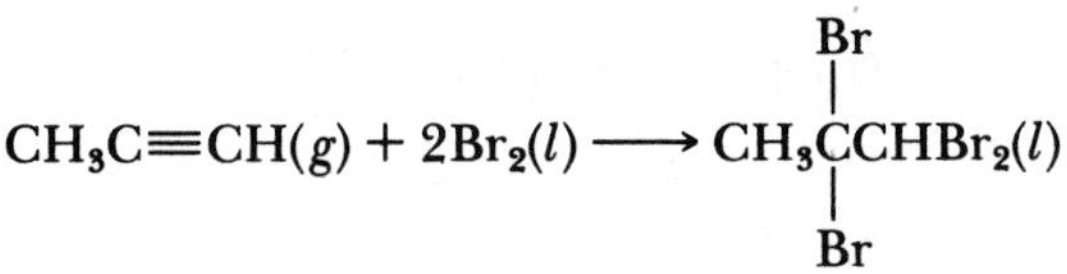

23-29 (a)

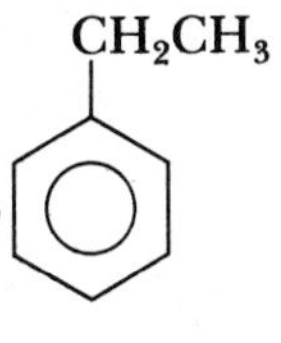

(b)

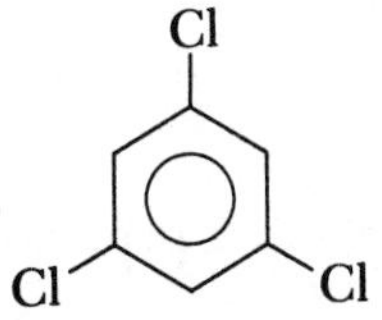

(c)

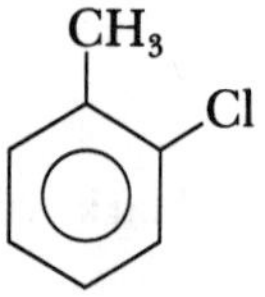

(d)

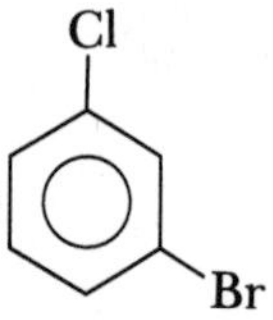

23-31   (a) The longest chain consists of three carbon atoms and the —OH group is attached to the second carbon atom, 2-propanol.

     (b) The longest chain consists of four carbon atoms and the —OH group is attached to the first carbon atom, 2,2-dimethyl-1-butanol.

     (c) The longest chain consists of three carbon atoms and the —OH group is attached to the second carbon atom, 1,3-dichloro-2-propanol.

     (d) The longest chain consists of four carbon atoms and the —OH group is attached to the second carbon atom, 2-butanol.

23-33   (a) a primary alcohol   (b) a secondary alcohol

     (c) a secondary alcohol   (d) a tertiary alcohol

23-35 $$2CH_3CH_2OH(l) + 2Na(s) \longrightarrow 2Na^+CH_3CH_2O^-(s) + H_2(g)$$

$$2CH_3CH_2CH_2OH(l) + 2Na(s) \longrightarrow 2Na^+CH_3CH_2CH_2O^-(s) + H_2(g)$$

23-37   (a) butanal   (b) 3-methylbutanal

     (c) methanal   (d) 3,4-dimethylpentanal

23-39   (a) The formula of diethyl ketone is

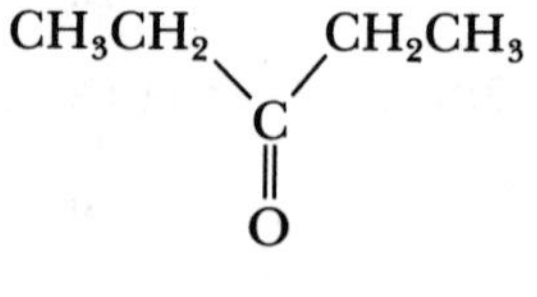

     The alcohol to use to prepare diethyl ketone is 3-pentanol.

     (b) The formula of methyl propyl ketone is

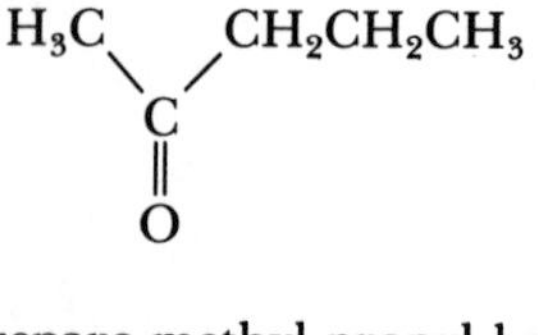

     The alcohol to use to prepare methyl propyl ketone is 2-pentanol.

(c) The formula of ethyl propyl ketone is

$$\underset{\displaystyle \overset{\displaystyle \underset{O}{\|}}{C}}{CH_3CH_2 \diagdown \diagup CH_2CH_2CH_3}$$

The alcohol to use to prepare ethyl propyl ketone is 3-hexanol.

23-41 (a) $C_2H_5NH_2(aq) + HBr(aq) \rightarrow C_2H_5NH_3^+Br^-(aq)$

(b) $2(CH_3)_2NH(aq) + H_2SO_4(aq) \rightarrow [(CH_3)_2NH_2^+]_2SO_4^{2-}(aq)$

(c) $\underset{}{\bigcirc}\!\!-NH_2$ $(aq) + HCl(aq) \longrightarrow$ $\underset{}{\bigcirc}\!\!-NH_3^+Cl^-$ (aq)

(d) $(C_2H_5)_3N(aq) + HCl(aq) \rightarrow (C_2H_5)_3NH^+Cl^-(aq)$

23-43 (a) CH_3CH_2COOH or $CH_3CH_2\overset{\displaystyle \overset{O}{\|}}{-C}-OH$

(b) $CH_3\underset{\displaystyle CH_3}{\underset{|}{CH}}COOH$ or $CH_3\underset{\displaystyle CH_3}{\underset{|}{CH}}-\overset{\displaystyle \overset{O}{\|}}{C}-OH$

(c) $CH_3\underset{\displaystyle CH_3}{\overset{\displaystyle CH_3}{\underset{|}{\overset{|}{C}}}}CH_2COOH$ or $CH_3\underset{\displaystyle CH_3}{\overset{\displaystyle CH_3}{\underset{|}{\overset{|}{C}}}}CH_2-\overset{\displaystyle \overset{O}{\|}}{C}-OH$

(d) $CH_3CH_2\underset{\displaystyle CH_3}{\underset{|}{CH}}CH_2COOH$ or $CH_3CH_2\underset{\displaystyle CH_3}{\underset{|}{CH}}CH_2-\overset{\displaystyle \overset{O}{\|}}{C}-OH$

23-45 (a) This is a neutralization reaction. The balanced equation is

$$HCOOH(aq) + NaOH(aq) \longrightarrow NaHCOO(aq) + H_2O(l)$$

(b) The reaction between an acid and an alcohol yields an ester. The balanced equation is

$$HCOOH(aq) + CH_3OH(aq) \xrightarrow{H^+(aq)} \underset{\displaystyle CH_3O}{\overset{\displaystyle H}{\diagdown \diagup}}C=O(aq) + H_2O(l)$$

(c) This is a neutralization reaction. The balanced equation is

$$2HCOOH(aq) + Ca(OH)_2(aq) \longrightarrow Ca(HCOO)_2(aq) + 2H_2O(l)$$

23-47 (a) $CH_3CH_2COOH(aq) + KOH(aq) \rightarrow KCH_3CH_2COO(aq) + H_2O(l)$
potassium propanoate

(b) $CH_3\overset{|}{\underset{CH_3}{CH}}COOH(aq) + KOH(aq) \rightarrow \quad KCH_3\overset{|}{\underset{CH_3}{CH}}COO(aq) \quad + H_2O(l)$
potassium 2-methylpropanoate

(c) $2Cl_2CHCOOH(aq) + Ca(OH)_2(aq) \rightarrow Ca(Cl_2CHCOO)_2(aq) + 2H_2O(l)$
calcium dichloroethanoate

23-49 Each of these reactions is the reaction between a carboxylic acid and an alcohol to yield an ester.

(a) benzoic acid + ethanol $\xrightarrow{H^+(aq)}$ ethyl benzoate $+ H_2O(l)$

(b) $\underset{\text{oxalic acid}}{HO-\overset{O}{\overset{\|}{C}}-\overset{O}{\overset{\|}{C}}-OH} + \underset{\text{1-propanol}}{2CH_3CH_2CH_2OH} \xrightarrow{H^+(aq)}$

$\underset{\text{propyl oxalate}}{CH_3CH_2CH_2O-\overset{O}{\overset{\|}{C}}-\overset{O}{\overset{\|}{C}}-OCH_2CH_2CH_3} + 2H_2O$

(c) $\underset{\text{acetic acid}}{CH_3-\overset{O}{\overset{\|}{C}}_{OH}} + \underset{\substack{\text{2-propanol}\\(\text{isopropyl}\\ \text{alcohol})}}{CH_3-\overset{|}{\underset{OH}{CH}}-CH_3} \xrightarrow{H^+(aq)} \underset{\substack{\text{isopropyl}\\ \text{acetate}}}{CH_3-\overset{O}{\overset{\|}{C}}_{O-\overset{CH_3}{\underset{CH_3}{CH}}}} + H_2O$

(d) $\underset{\substack{\text{trichloroacetic}\\ \text{acid}}}{Cl_3C-\overset{O}{\overset{\|}{C}}_{OH}} + \underset{\text{methanol}}{H-OCH_3} \xrightarrow{H^+(aq)} \underset{\substack{\text{methyl}\\ \text{trichloroacetate}}}{Cl_3C-\overset{O}{\overset{\|}{C}}_{OCH_3}} + H_2O$

23-51 1-chloropropane and "3-chloropropane" are the same molecule. One formula can be obtained from the other by just rotating it 180°.

23-53 The IUPAC names of the six alkanes are

1:	2,3-dimethylpentane	(a heptane)
2:	2,3,3-trimethylpentane	(an octane)
3:	3,4-dimethylhexane	(an octane)
4:	2,3-dimethylpentane	(a heptane)
5:	2-methylhexane	(a heptane)
6:	nonane	

(a) 1 and 4 are the same compound.

(b) 2 and 3 are isomers of octane.

(c) 3 and 5 are derivatives of hexane.

(d) 2 has the most methyl groups.

23-55 The stearate ion consists of a hydrophobic part (the long hydrocarbon chain) and a hydrophilic part (the carboxylate group). The hydrophobic parts of the stearate ions encapsulate a small grease particle and the hydrophilic parts keep the encapsulated entity in solution (see Figure K-4).

23-57 There is hydrogen bonding in 1-butanol, but none in diethyl ether or pentane.

23-59 The gas must be propene (C_3H_6).

propene   2-chloropropane

23-61 A tank of gasoline (75 L) corresponds to

$$\text{mass} = (75\ \text{L})(1000\ \text{mL} \cdot \text{L}^{-1})(0.80\ \text{g} \cdot \text{mL}^{-1}) = 6.0 \times 10^4\ \text{g}$$

Using octane as the gasoline, we have

$$\text{moles of octane} = (6.0 \times 10^4\ \text{g})\left(\frac{1\ \text{mol}\ C_8H_{18}}{114.2\ \text{g}\ C_8H_{18}}\right) = 525\ \text{mol}$$

The equation for the combustion of octane is

$$C_8H_{18}(l) + \frac{25}{2}O_2(g) \longrightarrow 8CO_2(g) + 9H_2O(l)$$

and so we have

$$\text{mol}\ O_2 = (525\ \text{mol}\ C_8H_{18})\left(\frac{\dfrac{25}{2}\text{mol}\ O_2}{1\ \text{mol}\ C_8H_{18}}\right) = 6.57 \times 10^3\ \text{mol}$$

The volume of $O_2(g)$ is

$$V = \frac{nRT}{P} = \frac{(6.57 \times 10^3 \text{ mol})(0.0821 \text{ L} \cdot \text{atm} \cdot \text{K}^{-1} \cdot \text{mol}^{-1})(293 \text{ K})}{1.0 \text{ atm}}$$
$$= 1.58 \times 10^5 \text{ L}$$

and the volume of air is

$$V_{air} = \frac{V_{O_2}}{0.21} = \frac{1.58 \times 10^5 \text{ L}}{0.21} = 7.5 \times 10^5 \text{ L}$$

which is about 10,000 times the volume of gasoline (75 L) burned.
    The energy produced is given by

$$\text{energy produced} = (6.0 \times 10^4 \text{ g C}_8\text{H}_{18})\left(\frac{48 \text{ kJ}}{1 \text{ g C}_8\text{H}_{18}}\right) = 2.9 \times 10^6 \text{ kJ}$$

23-63   Take a hundred-gram sample and write

$$81.71 \text{ g C} \approx 18.29 \text{ g H}$$

Divide each side by the respective atomic mass to obtain

$$6.803 \text{ mol C} \approx 18.14 \text{ mol H}$$

and divide through by 6.803 to obtain

$$1.000 \text{ mol C} \approx 2.667 \text{ mol H}$$

Thus the empirical formula of the hydrocarbon is C_3H_8. The formula mass of the hydrocarbon is determined from the gas data:

$$n = \frac{PV}{RT} = \frac{\left(\frac{750}{760}\text{atm}\right)(0.386 \text{ L})}{(0.0821 \text{ L} \cdot \text{atm} \cdot \text{mol}^{-1} \cdot \text{K}^{-1})(273 \text{ K})} = 0.0170 \text{ mol}$$

and so we have

$$0.0170 \text{ mol} \approx 0.75 \text{ g}$$

or

$$1.00 \text{ mol} \approx 44.1 \text{ g}$$

Thus the formula mass is 44.1, which corresponds closely with that of C_3H_8. The gas is propane.

23-65   The Lewis formula for 1-butene is

$$\underset{H}{\overset{H}{\diagdown}}C=C\underset{CH_2-CH_3}{\overset{H}{\diagup}}$$

(a) 1-butene + $Cl_2(g)$ ⟶ $Cl-CH_2-\underset{\underset{Cl}{|}}{CH}-CH_2-CH_3$

1,2-dichlorobutane

(b) We must use Markovnikov's rule in this case:

1-butene + $HCl(g)$ ⟶ $CH_3-\underset{\underset{Cl}{|}}{CH}-CH_2-CH_3$

2-chlorobutane

(c) We must use Markovnikov's rule in this case:

1-butene + $H_2O(l)$ $\xrightarrow{H^+(aq)}$ $CH_3-\underset{\underset{OH}{|}}{CH}-CH_2-CH_3$

2-butanol

(d) 1-butene + $H_2(g)$ $\xrightarrow{Pt}$ $CH_3-CH_2-CH_2-CH_3$

butane

23-67   (a) $\underset{H}{\overset{H}{\diagdown}}C=C\underset{H}{\overset{}{\diagup}}\underset{H}{\overset{H}{\diagdown}}C=C\underset{H}{\overset{H}{\diagup}}$ (g) + $2H_2(g)$ $\xrightarrow{Pt}$ $H-\overset{\overset{H}{|}}{\underset{\underset{H}{|}}{C}}-\overset{\overset{H}{|}}{\underset{\underset{H}{|}}{C}}-\overset{\overset{H}{|}}{\underset{\underset{H}{|}}{C}}-\overset{\overset{H}{|}}{\underset{\underset{H}{|}}{C}}-H$

(b) $\underset{H}{\overset{H}{\diagdown}}C=C\underset{H}{\overset{}{\diagup}}\underset{H}{\overset{H}{\diagdown}}C=C\underset{H}{\overset{H}{\diagup}}$ (g) + $2Cl_2(g)$ ⟶ $H-\overset{\overset{H}{|}}{\underset{\underset{Cl}{|}}{C}}-\overset{\overset{H}{|}}{\underset{\underset{Cl}{|}}{C}}-\overset{\overset{H}{|}}{\underset{\underset{Cl}{|}}{C}}-\overset{\overset{H}{|}}{\underset{\underset{Cl}{|}}{C}}-H$

(c) We must use Markovnikov's rule.

$\underset{H}{\overset{H}{\diagdown}}C=C\underset{H}{\overset{}{\diagup}}\underset{H}{\overset{H}{\diagdown}}C=C\underset{H}{\overset{H}{\diagup}}$ (g) + $2HCl(g)$ ⟶ $H-\overset{\overset{H}{|}}{\underset{\underset{H}{|}}{C}}-\overset{\overset{H}{|}}{\underset{\underset{Cl}{|}}{C}}-\overset{\overset{H}{|}}{\underset{\underset{Cl}{|}}{C}}-\overset{\overset{H}{|}}{\underset{\underset{H}{|}}{C}}-H$

23-69 We shall add HCl to each alkene according to Markovnikov's rule.

(a) $CH_2{=}CHCHCH_3 + HCl \rightarrow CH_3CHCHCH_3$
            | | |
            Cl   Cl Cl

(b) $BrCH_2CH{=}CHCH_3 + HCl \rightarrow BrCH_2CHCH_2CH_3$
                                     |
                                     Cl

and $BrCH_2CH_2CHCH_3$
                    |
                    Cl

(c)
                          Cl
                          |
$CH_2{=}CCH_3 + HCl \rightarrow CH_3CCH_3$
      | |
     CH_3   CH_3

(d) $ClCH{=}CHCH_3 + HCl \rightarrow ClCH_2CHCH_3$ and $Cl_2CHCH_2CH_3$
                                         |
                                         Cl

23-71 (a) The alcohol is $CH_3CH_2CH_2OH$. We would use propanal

$$CH_3CH_2C\overset{\displaystyle H}{\underset{\displaystyle O}{\diagup \atop \diagdown}}$$

(b) The alcohol is CH_3CHCH_2OH. We would use 2-methylpropanal
                                |
                              CH_3

$$CH_3CHC\overset{\displaystyle H}{\underset{\displaystyle O}{\diagup \atop \diagdown}}$$
     |
   CH_3

(c) The alcohol is
                  CH_3
                  |
$CH_3CH_2CCH_2OH$. We would use 2,2-dimethylbutanal
                  |
                  CH_3

$$CH_3CH_2\underset{\underset{\displaystyle CH_3}{\displaystyle |}}{\overset{\overset{\displaystyle CH_3}{\displaystyle |}}{C}}-C\overset{\displaystyle O}{\underset{\displaystyle H}{\diagup \atop \diagdown}}$$

E   ANSWERS TO THE SELF-TEST

1   single

2 sp^3

3   false

4   false

5   false (The bonding around each carbon atom is tetrahedral.)

6   less than

7   false (Alkanes are fairly unreactive.)

8 $CO_2(g)$ . . . $H_2O(l)$

9   their combustion reactions are highly exothermic

10   substitution

11   UV radiation

12   alkylchlorides or chloroalkanes

13   gives the lowest numbers to the carbon atoms that have attached groups

14   false (Each group must be designated with a number.)

15   true

16   false

17   true

18 σ . . . π

19   planar

20   on the same side of the double bond, or adjacent to one another

21   identify the longest consecutive carbon chain containing the double bond, drop the *-ane* from the name of the main chain and add *-ene*

22   true

23   addition

24   ethane

25   1,2-dichloroethane

26   chloroethane

27   ethanol (the alcohol CH_3CH_2OH)

28   Markovnikov's

29   when HX adds to an alkene, the hydrogen atom becomes bonded to the carbon atom in the double bond already bearing the larger number of hydrogen atoms

30   triple

31   true

32   identify the longest consecutive carbon chain containing the triple bond, drop the *-ane* from the corresponding alkane name and add *-yne*

33   true

34

35   false (All the carbon-carbon bonds are identical.)

36   false (Benzene is fairly unreactive.)

37

38   1 . . . 2

39   1 . . . 4

40 π-electron delocalization

41   —OH

42   identify the longest consecutive carbon chain containing the carbon atom bearing the —OH group, drop the *-e* from the

corresponding alkane name and
add -*ol*

43   true

44   RCHO

45
$$R' \atop R \diagdown\!\!\diagup C{=}O$$

46   double

47   planar or trigonal planar

48   primary alcohols

49   secondary alcohols

50   ammonia

51   two

52   true

53   bases

54   RCOOH

55   —COOH(carboxyl)

56   aldehydes . . . primary alcohols

57   carboxylate ions . . . hydronium
ions

58   true

59   false

60   salt . . . water

61   ester . . . water

62
$$R \atop R'O \diagdown\!\!\diagup C{=}O$$

where R′ is derived from the
alcohol

SYNTHETIC AND NATURAL POLYMERS

A   OUTLINE OF CHAPTER 24

24-1   Polymers are composed of many molecular subunits joined end to end.

Polymerization is the repeated addition of small molecules to form a long, continuous chain called a polymer.

The polymerization of ethylene, $H_2C{=}CH_2$, can be initiated by a free radical.

The monomers of polyethylene are ethylene.

Polyethylene can be written $+CH_2CH_2+_n$ where n is large.

Some common polymers are listed in Table 24-1.

24-2   Nylon and Dacron are made by condensation reactions.

In a condensation reaction, a small molecule, such as H_2O, is split out as each monomer is added to the polymer chain.

The condensation reaction to form nylon proceeds by the formation of an amide linkage between a carboxyl group and an amine group.

The condensation reaction to form Dacron proceeds by the formation of an ester linkage between a carboxyl group ($-COOH$) and an alcohol group ($-OH$).

24-3   Polymers with cross-linked chains are elastic.

At a given temperature, the longer the average length of the polymer chains, the less liquidlike the polymer is.

The polymer chains in a sample are coiled and intertangled with each other (Figure 24-2).

The relative movement of polymer chains that occurs when a sample is stretched can be decreased by connecting the chains through chemical bonds called cross-links.

Natural rubber is cross-linked by the formation of —S—S— bonds between the polyisoprene chains.

24-4   Amino acids have an amino group and a carboxyl group attached to a central carbon atom.

Proteins are polymers whose monomer units are amino acids.

Amino acids have the general formula

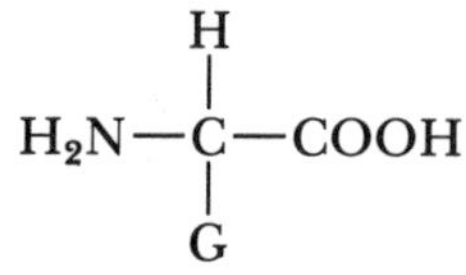

$$H_2N-\underset{\underset{G}{|}}{\overset{\overset{H}{|}}{C}}-COOH$$

where G is called the side group.

There is a total of 20 different amino acids commonly found in proteins.

The amino acids have optical isomers.

Optical isomers are nonsuperimposable mirror-image molecules (Figure 24-3).

The two optical isomers are distinguished by the letters D and L.

The L isomers of amino acids occur in proteins.

Biochemical reactions are stereospecific.

24-5   Amino acids are the monomers of proteins.

Proteins are formed by condensation reactions between the carboxyl group (—COOH) on one amino acid and the amino group (—NH₂) on another amino acid.

It is necessary to specify the order of the amino acids in a peptide.

Polypeptides are composed of long chains of amino acids joined together by peptide bonds.

The chain to which the amino acid side groups are attached is called the polypeptide backbone.

Proteins are naturally occurring polypeptides.

The order of the amino acid units in a polypeptide is called the primary structure of the polypeptide.

Three-letter designations for each amino acid are used to write abbreviated structures of peptides.

24-6   The shape of a protein molecule is called its tertiary structure.

The α-helix shape of certain proteins results from the formation of hydrogen bonds (Figure 24-6).

The structure within regions of a protein is called secondary structure (for example, α-helical structure).

Tertiary structure denotes the three-dimensional shape of a protein and is determined by X-ray analysis (Figure 24-7).

The shape of a protein depends on the nature and the order of the amino acid units making up the protein chain.

Tertiary structure plays a major role in protein function.

24-7 Normal hemoglobin and sickle-cell hemoglobin differ by 2 out of 574 amino acids.

Hemoglobin is the protein that transports oxygen in the bloodstream from the lungs to the tissues.

The shape and function of a protein depends in exacting detail on its amino acid sequence.

Hemoglobin has two sets of identical chains called α and β.

24-8 DNA is a double helix.

DNA stores and passes on genetic information.

DNA is a polynucleotide.

Nucleotides, the monomers of DNA and RNA, consist of a sugar portion, a phosphate group, and a nitrogen-containing ring compound called a base.

Deoxyribose and ribose are the sugars in the nucleotides of DNA and RNA, respectively.

DNA contains the four bases adenine (A), guanine (G), cytosine (C), and thymine (T).

RNA contains the four bases A, G, C, and U (uracil).

Nucleotides are joined by a condensation reaction between the phosphate group of one nucleotide and the 3-hydroxyl group on another nucleotide.

The DNA double helix consists of two polynucleotide chains intertwined in a helical fashion (Figure 24-11).

The two polynucleotide chains in the DNA double helix are held together by hydrogen bonding between base pairs: A and T bond together and G and C bond together (Figure 24-12).

The bases lie in the interior of the double helix; the sugar-phosphate backbone lies on the outside.

24-9 DNA can duplicate itself.

Each strand of the DNA double helix can act as a template for building a complementary strand.

The two new double helices are identical to the original double helix.

Genetic information is stored in a triplet code.

Each consecutive series of three bases along a DNA segment is a code for a particular amino acid.

A gene is a segment along a DNA molecule that codes the synthesis of one polypeptide.

DNA can have a molecular mass of over 10^9.

B   SELF-TEST

1 The repeated addition of small molecules to form a long, continuous chain is called

_____ .

2 The monomers of polyethylene are _____ .

3   The polymerization of nylon is an example of an addition polymerization reaction. *True/False*

4   The formation of Dacron is an example of a condensation polymerization reaction. *True/False*

5   In the condensation polymerization reaction to form nylon, water is split out during the reaction. *True/False*

6   Different polymers may consist of different numbers of monomers. *True/False*

7   The polymer chains in a sample are elongated to their maximum length. *True/False*

8   A cross-linked polymer can exhibit elastic behavior. *True/False*

9   Natural rubber is cross-linked by vulcanizing with sulfur. *True/False*

10   Amino acids are monomers from which _____ are built.

11   The general formula for an amino acid is

12   Amino acids can occur as _____ isomers.

13   Both isomers of an amino acid occur in biological systems. *True/False*

14   The amino acids in a polypeptide are linked by _____ bonds.

15   Two amino acids form a dipeptide when the _____ group of one amino acid reacts with the _____ group of the other amino acid to form a peptide bond.

16   The polypeptide backbone is the same for all tripeptides. *True/False*

17   The order of attachment of the amino acids to the polypeptide backbone is the same for all tripeptides. *True/False*

18   The primary structure of a protein is unique to that protein. *True/False*

19   All proteins contain the same number of amino acid units. *True/False*

20 A polypeptide may have a helical shape because of _____ bonds between _____.

21 The α-helix is an example of *(primary, secondary)* structure.

22 The three-dimensional shape of a protein is its _____ structure.

23 Nucleotides are the monomers from which the polymers ____ and ____ are built up.

24 Nucleotides consists of a _____ , _____ , and a _____ .

25 The sugar in DNA is _____ .

26 The sugar in RNA is _____ .

27 The four bases in DNA are _____ , _____ , _____ , and _____ .

28 Uracil is found in RNA but not in DNA. *True/False*

29 Two nucleotides can be joined by a condensation reaction between the _____ of one nucleotide and the _____ on another nucleotide.

30 The sugar-phosphate backbone is the same for all polynucleotides. *True/False*

31 The order of the attachment of the bases to the sugar-phosphate backbone is the same for all polynucleotides. *True/False*

32 The two polynucleotide chains in DNA are arranged as a _____ _____ .

33 In DNA, the amount of guanine is equal to the amount of _____ .

34 In DNA, adenine on one chain is always paired with _____ on the other chain.

35 The two chains in DNA are joined together by _____ bonds.

36 Each strand of DNA acts as a template for reproducing itself. *True/False*

37 Genetic information for the production of _____ is stored in DNA.

38 Each amino acid is coded by a sequence of _____ base pairs on the DNA segment.

C CALCULATIONS YOU SHOULD KNOW HOW TO DO

There are no new types of calculations in this chapter.

D SOLUTIONS TO THE ODD-NUMBERED PROBLEMS

24-1 In addition polymerization, monomers are joined to each other directly, without the formation of any small molecules as additional products. In condensation polymerization, monomers are joined together with the formation of small molecules as joint products. Usually condensation polymerization involves more than one kind of monomer, such as a diacid and a dialcohol. Teflon is an example of an addition polymer and Dacron is an example of a condensation polymer.

24-3 Both the dicarboxylic acid and diamine monomers of nylon 66 contain six carbon atoms (see page 772).

24-5 (a) No optical isomers. (The four substituents must be different.)

(b)

$$H_2N-\underset{COOH}{\overset{H}{\underset{|}{\overset{|}{C}}}}-CH_2OH \qquad HOH_2C-\underset{HOOC}{\overset{H}{\underset{|}{\overset{|}{C}}}}-NH_2$$

(c)

$$Br-\underset{COOH}{\overset{H}{\underset{|}{\overset{|}{C}}}}-Cl \qquad Cl-\underset{HOOC}{\overset{H}{\underset{|}{\overset{|}{C}}}}-Br$$

(d)

$$H_3CH_2C-\underset{Br}{\overset{CH_3}{\underset{|}{\overset{|}{Si}}}}-Cl \qquad Cl-\underset{Br}{\overset{CH_3}{\underset{|}{\overset{|}{Si}}}}-CH_2CH_3$$

24-7

$$H_2N-\overset{H}{\underset{CH_2}{\underset{|}{\overset{|}{C}}}}-COOH + H_2N-\overset{H}{\underset{CH}{\underset{|}{\overset{|}{C}}}}-COOH \longrightarrow H_2N-\overset{H}{\underset{CH_2}{\underset{|}{\overset{|}{C}}}}-\overset{O}{\overset{\|}{C}}-\overset{H}{\underset{|}{N}}-\overset{H}{\underset{CH}{\underset{|}{\overset{|}{C}}}}-COOH + H_2O$$

with benzene ring bearing OH (phenol) attached to CH₂ groups, and H₃C–CH–CH₃ (isopropyl) groups as shown.

or

$$H_2N-\underset{\underset{H_3C}{\overset{|}{\underset{CH}{\overset{|}{C}}}}CH_3}{\overset{\overset{H}{|}}{C}}-COOH + H_2N-\underset{\underset{}{\overset{|}{\underset{CH_2}{\overset{|}{C}}}}}{\overset{\overset{H}{|}}{C}}-COOH \longrightarrow H_2N-\overset{\overset{H}{|}}{\underset{\underset{H_3C}{\overset{|}{\underset{CH}{\overset{|}{C}}}}CH_3}{C}}-\overset{\overset{O}{\parallel}}{C}-\overset{\overset{H}{|}}{N}-\overset{\overset{H}{|}}{\underset{CH_2}{\overset{|}{C}}}-COOH + H_2O$$

24-9 Two different dipeptides result because we can form the peptide bond in two ways depending on which carboxyl and amino groups are linked:

$$H_2N-\overset{\overset{H}{|}}{\underset{\underset{gly}{H}}{C}}-\overset{\overset{\overset{\bullet\bullet}{O}\bullet}{\parallel}}{C}-\overset{\bullet\bullet}{\underset{H}{\overset{|}{N}}}-\overset{\overset{H}{|}}{\underset{\underset{ala}{CH_3}}{C}}-COOH$$

or

$$H_2N-\overset{\overset{H}{|}}{\underset{\underset{ala}{CH_3}}{C}}-\overset{\overset{\overset{\bullet\bullet}{O}\bullet}{\parallel}}{C}-\overset{\bullet\bullet}{\underset{H}{\overset{|}{N}}}-\overset{\overset{H}{|}}{\underset{\underset{gly}{H}}{C}}-COOH$$

24-11 We can form six different tripeptides from two different amino acids. If we represent the side groups of the two amino acids by G_1 and G_2, then the tripeptides are

$$H_2N-\overset{\overset{H}{|}}{\underset{G_1}{\overset{|}{C}}}-\overset{\overset{\overset{\bullet\bullet}{O}\bullet}{\parallel}}{C}-\overset{\bullet\bullet}{\underset{H}{\overset{|}{N}}}-\overset{\overset{H}{|}}{\underset{G_1}{\overset{|}{C}}}-\overset{\overset{\overset{\bullet\bullet}{O}\bullet}{\parallel}}{C}-\overset{\bullet\bullet}{\underset{H}{\overset{|}{N}}}-\overset{\overset{H}{|}}{\underset{G_2}{\overset{|}{C}}}-COOH$$

$$H_2N-\overset{\overset{H}{|}}{\underset{G_1}{\overset{|}{C}}}-\overset{\overset{\overset{\bullet\bullet}{O}\bullet}{\parallel}}{C}-\overset{\bullet\bullet}{\underset{H}{\overset{|}{N}}}-\overset{\overset{H}{|}}{\underset{G_2}{\overset{|}{C}}}-\overset{\overset{\overset{\bullet\bullet}{O}\bullet}{\parallel}}{C}-\overset{\bullet\bullet}{\underset{H}{\overset{|}{N}}}-\overset{\overset{H}{|}}{\underset{G_1}{\overset{|}{C}}}-COOH$$

$$H_2N-\underset{\underset{G_2}{|}}{\overset{\overset{H}{|}}{C}}-\overset{\overset{\cdot\cdot\overset{\cdot\cdot}{O}\cdot}{\|}}{C}-\underset{\underset{H}{|}}{\overset{}{\ddot{N}}}-\underset{\underset{G_1}{|}}{\overset{\overset{H}{|}}{C}}-\overset{\overset{\cdot\cdot\overset{\cdot\cdot}{O}\cdot}{\|}}{C}-\underset{\underset{H}{|}}{\overset{}{\ddot{N}}}-\underset{\underset{G_1}{|}}{\overset{\overset{H}{|}}{C}}-COOH$$

$$H_2N-\underset{\underset{G_2}{|}}{\overset{\overset{H}{|}}{C}}-\overset{\overset{\cdot\cdot\overset{\cdot\cdot}{O}\cdot}{\|}}{C}-\underset{\underset{H}{|}}{\overset{}{\ddot{N}}}-\underset{\underset{G_2}{|}}{\overset{\overset{H}{|}}{C}}-\overset{\overset{\cdot\cdot\overset{\cdot\cdot}{O}\cdot}{\|}}{C}-\underset{\underset{H}{|}}{\overset{}{\ddot{N}}}-\underset{\underset{G_1}{|}}{\overset{\overset{H}{|}}{C}}-COOH$$

$$H_2N-\underset{\underset{G_2}{|}}{\overset{\overset{H}{|}}{C}}-\overset{\overset{\cdot\cdot\overset{\cdot\cdot}{O}\cdot}{\|}}{C}-\underset{\underset{H}{|}}{\overset{}{\ddot{N}}}-\underset{\underset{G_1}{|}}{\overset{\overset{H}{|}}{C}}-\overset{\overset{\cdot\cdot\overset{\cdot\cdot}{O}\cdot}{\|}}{C}-\underset{\underset{H}{|}}{\overset{}{\ddot{N}}}-\underset{\underset{G_2}{|}}{\overset{\overset{H}{|}}{C}}-COOH$$

$$H_2N-\underset{\underset{G_1}{|}}{\overset{\overset{H}{|}}{C}}-\overset{\overset{\cdot\cdot\overset{\cdot\cdot}{O}\cdot}{\|}}{C}-\underset{\underset{H}{|}}{\overset{}{\ddot{N}}}-\underset{\underset{G_2}{|}}{\overset{\overset{H}{|}}{C}}-\overset{\overset{\cdot\cdot\overset{\cdot\cdot}{O}\cdot}{\|}}{C}-\underset{\underset{H}{|}}{\overset{}{\ddot{N}}}-\underset{\underset{G_2}{|}}{\overset{\overset{H}{|}}{C}}-COOH$$

24-13

24-15 (a) The sulfur atom forms only weak hydrogen bonds because the electronegativity of sulfur and hydrogen are about the same.

(b) There are none.

(c) The nitrogen atom can form a hydrogen bond to a hydrogen atom in H_2O.

(d) The two oxygen atoms can form hydrogen bonds to hydrogen atoms in H_2O.

24-17 The primary structure of a protein is the order of amino acid units in the protein.
The secondary structure is the structure within sections of the protein.
The tertiary structure is the overall three-dimensional shape of the protein.

24-19 The sugar in DNA polynucleotides is deoxyribose. The DNA triplet is deoxyguanosine-deoxyadenosine-deoxythymidine. The structures of the nucleotides are given in Section 24-8. The structural formula for the DNA triplet GAT is

24-21 The sugar in RNA is ribose. The RNA triplet UCU is uridine-cytidine-uridine.
The structural formula for the RNA triplet UCU is

[Chemical structure diagram of a nucleic acid segment with three nucleotides, showing phosphate groups, sugar rings, and nitrogenous bases]

24-23 The two sequences must be complementary to each other: A and T must be opposite to each other, and G and C must be opposite to each other. The other sequence must have the base sequence TTCAGAGCT.

24-25 We must have T and A opposite each other and G and C opposite each other. The complementary base sequence is

$$\underline{G \quad A \quad T \quad C \quad A \quad A \quad T}$$

24-27 The two strands come apart to give

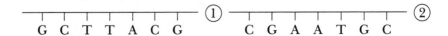

The complements to the two strands are

G	C	T	T	A	C	G	①	C	G	A	A	T	G	C	②
C	G	A	A	T	G	C		G	C	T	T	A	C	G	

24-29   There are two hydrogen bonds for each A—T pair and three hydrogen bonds for each G—C pair. The DNA sequence has four A—T pairs and two G—C pairs. The number of hydrogen bonds in the sequence is

$$\text{number of H bonds} = (4 \times 2) + (2 \times 3) = 14$$

Fourteen hydrogen bonds must be broken to separate the strands.

24-31   We learned in Chapter 19 that the maximum amount of work that can be obtained from a reaction that is run under standard conditions is equal to the value of ΔG°_{rxn}. Thus

$$\text{work} = \Delta G^{\circ}_{rxn} = (2.87 \times 10^3 \text{ kJ} \cdot \text{mol}^{-1})\left(\frac{1 \text{ mol glucose}}{180.16 \text{ g glucose}}\right)(1.0 \text{ g}) = 15.9 \text{ kJ}$$

24-33   We can obtain the equation for the combustion of sucrose from the three equations given:

$$\text{sucrose}(aq) + H_2O(l) \longrightarrow \text{glucose}(aq) + \text{fructose}(aq)$$
$$\Delta G^{\circ}_{rxn} = -29.3 \text{ kJ}$$
$$\text{fructose}(aq) \longrightarrow \text{glucose}(aq)$$
$$\Delta G^{\circ}_{rxn} = -1.6 \text{ kJ}$$
$$2 \text{ glucose}(aq) + 12O_2(g) \longrightarrow 12CO_2(g) + 12H_2O(l)$$
$$\Delta G^{\circ}_{rxn} = (2)(-2.87 \times 10^3 \text{ kJ}) = -5.74 \times 10^3 \text{ kJ}$$

If we add these three equations, then we have

$$\text{sucrose}(aq) + 12O_2(g) \longrightarrow 12CO_2(g) + 11H_2O(l)$$
$$\Delta G^{\circ}_{rxn} = -29.3 \text{ kJ} - 1.6 \text{ kJ} - 5.74 \times 10^3 \text{ kJ}$$
$$= -5.77 \times 10^3 \text{ kJ}$$

The value of ΔG°_{rxn} for one mole of sucrose is -5.77×10^3 kJ. The value of ΔG°_{rxn} for 1.0 g of sucrose is

$$\Delta G^{\circ}_{rxn} = (-5.77 \times 10^3 \text{ kJ} \cdot \text{mol}^{-1})\left(\frac{1 \text{ mol sucrose}}{342.3 \text{ g sucrose}}\right) = -16.9 \text{ kJ} \cdot \text{g}^{-1}$$

The maximum amount of work that can be obtained from the process is 16.9 kJ·g^{-1}.

24-35   The value of the equilibrium constant is given by

$$\log K = -\frac{\Delta G^{\circ}_{rxn}}{2.30RT}$$
$$= -\frac{-31 \times 10^3 \text{ J} \cdot \text{mol}^{-1}}{(2.30)(8.314 \text{ J} \cdot \text{mol}^{-1} \cdot \text{K}^{-1})(310 \text{ K})} = 5.23$$

or

$$K = 10^{5.23} = 1.7 \times 10^5 \text{ M}$$

24-37 The value of the equilibrium constant is given by

$$\log K = -\frac{\Delta G^{\circ}_{rxn}}{2.30RT}$$

$$= -\frac{-200 \times 10^3 \text{ J} \cdot \text{mol}^{-1}}{(2.30)(8.314 \text{ J} \cdot \text{mol}^{-1} \cdot \text{K}^{-1})(298 \text{ K})}$$

$$= 35.10$$

or

$$K = 10^{35.10} = 1.3 \times 10^{35} \text{ M}$$

E   ANSWERS TO THE SELF-TEST

1 polymerization

2 ethylene

3 false

4 true

5 true

6 true

7 false

8 true

9 true

10 polypeptides (proteins)

11

$$\begin{array}{c} \text{H} \\ | \\ \text{H}_2\text{N}-\text{C}-\text{COOH} \\ | \\ \text{G} \end{array}$$

12 optical

13 false

14 peptide

15 amino ($-NH_2$) . . . carboxyl ($-COOH$)

16 true

17 false

18 true

19 false

20 hydrogen . . . hydrogen and oxygen atoms in the peptide bonds

21 secondary

22 tertiary

23 RNA . . . DNA

24 sugar . . . phosphate group . . . base

25 deoxyribose

26 ribose

27 guanine . . . cytosine . . . adenine . . . thymine

28 true

29 phosphate group . . . 3-hydroxyl group

30 false (The sugar-phosphate backbone is the same in all DNA and the sugar-phosphate backbone is the same in all RNA. The sugars are not the same in DNA and RNA.)

31 false

32 double helix

33 cytosine

34 thymine

35 hydrogen

36 true

37 proteins

38 three

B-11 (a) $2Na(s) + O_2(g) \rightarrow Na_2O_2(s)$

(b) $2Na(s) + 2H_2O(l) \rightarrow 2NaOH(aq) + H_2(g)$

(c) $6Li(s) + N_2(g) \rightarrow 2Li_3N(s)$

(d) $NaH(s) + H_2O(l) \rightarrow NaOH(aq) + H_2(g)$

(e) $Li_3N(s) + 3H_2O(l) \rightarrow 3LiOH(aq) + NH_3(g)$

B-13 (a) $NaHCO_3$ (b) KOH

(c) $Ca(OH)_2$ (d) CsH

C-11 The equation for the reaction is

$$2Ca(s) + O_2(g) \longrightarrow 2CaO(s)$$

The number of moles of O_2 in 45.0 g of O_2 is

$$\text{mol of } O_2 = (45.0 \text{ g } O_2)\left(\frac{1 \text{ mol } O_2}{32.00 \text{ g } O_2}\right) = 1.41 \text{ mol}$$

The number of grams of Ca that reacts with 1.41 mol of O_2 is

$$\text{g of Ca} = (1.41 \text{ mol } O_2)\left(\frac{2 \text{ mol Ca}}{1 \text{ mol } O_2}\right)\left(\frac{40.08 \text{ g Ca}}{1 \text{ mol Ca}}\right)$$
$$= 113 \text{ g Ca}$$

The number of grams of CaO formed is given by

$$\text{g of CaO} = (1.41 \text{ mol } O_2)\left(\frac{2 \text{ mol CaO}}{1 \text{ mol } O_2}\right)\left(\frac{56.08 \text{ g CaO}}{1 \text{ mol CaO}}\right)$$
$$= 158 \text{ g CaO}$$

C-13 (a) mass lead $= (1.00 \text{ kg PbS})\left(\dfrac{\text{atomic mass Pb}}{\text{formula mass PbS}}\right)$

$$= (1.00 \text{ kg})\left(\frac{207.2}{239.3}\right) = 0.866 \text{ kg}$$

(b) mass lead $= (1.00 \text{ kg PbSO}_4)\left(\dfrac{\text{atomic mass Pb}}{\text{formula mass PbSO}_4}\right)$

$$= (1.00 \text{ kg})\left(\frac{207.2}{303.3}\right) = 0.683 \text{ kg}$$

(c) mass lead $= (1.00 \text{ kg PbCO}_3)\left(\dfrac{\text{atomic mass Pb}}{\text{formula mass PbCO}_3}\right)$

$$= (1.00 \text{ kg})\left(\frac{207.2}{267.2}\right) = 0.775 \text{ kg}$$

C-15 The equation for the neutralization reaction is

$$\text{CaO}(s) + 2\text{HCl}(aq) \longrightarrow \text{CaCl}_2(aq) + \text{H}_2\text{O}(l)$$

The number of moles of CaO(s) that corresponds to 20 g is

$$\text{mol CaO} = (20 \text{ g})\left(\frac{1 \text{ mol CaO}}{56.08 \text{ g CaO}}\right) = 0.36 \text{ mol}$$

The number of moles of HCl(aq) required is

$$\text{mol HCl} = (0.36 \text{ mol CaO})\left(\frac{2 \text{ mol HCl}}{1 \text{ mol CaO}}\right) = 0.72 \text{ mol}$$

and the number of mL of 0.10 M HCl(aq) is

$$V = \frac{n}{M} = \frac{0.72 \text{ mol}}{0.10 \text{ mol} \cdot \text{L}^{-1}} = 7.2 \text{ L} = 7200 \text{ mL}$$

D-19 The equation for the reaction is

$$\text{NaH}(s) + \text{H}_2\text{O}(l) \longrightarrow \text{NaOH}(aq) + \text{H}_2(g)$$

The number of moles of $\text{H}_2(g)$ produced is

$$\text{mol H}_2 = (0.450 \text{ g NaH})\left(\frac{1 \text{ mol NaH}}{24.00 \text{ g NaH}}\right)\left(\frac{1 \text{ mol H}_2}{1 \text{ mol NaH}}\right) = 0.0188 \text{ mol}$$

The volume of $\text{H}_2(g)$ produced is given by

$$V = \frac{nRT}{P} = \frac{(0.0188 \text{ mol})(0.0821 \text{ L} \cdot \text{atm} \cdot \text{mol}^{-1} \cdot \text{K}^{-1})(273 \text{ K})}{(1.00 \text{ atm})}$$

$$= 0.421 \text{ L}$$

D-21 The equation for the reaction is

$$2KClO_3(s) \longrightarrow 2KCl(s) + 3O_2(g)$$

The number of moles of $O_2(g)$ produced is

$$\text{mol } O_2(g) = (3.06 \text{ g KClO}_3)\left(\frac{1 \text{ mol KClO}_3}{122.6 \text{ g KClO}_3}\right)\left(\frac{3 \text{ mol } O_2}{2 \text{ mol KClO}_3}\right)$$

$$= 0.0374 \text{ mol}$$

The volume of $O_2(g)$ produced is

$$V = \frac{nRT}{P} = \frac{(0.0374 \text{ mol})(0.0821 \text{ L} \cdot \text{atm} \cdot \text{mol}^{-1} \cdot \text{K}^{-1})(288 \text{ K})}{\left(\dfrac{655}{760} \text{ atm}\right)}$$

$$= 1.03 \text{ L}$$

E-11 U.S. annual total per capita energy use is equivalent to 62 barrels of oil per person per year. Of this total, 20 percent is imported petroleum. There are about 230 million people in the United States; thus we have

$$\left(\begin{array}{c}\text{barrels of oil}\\\text{imported per day}\end{array}\right) = \left(62 \frac{\text{barrels}}{\text{person} \cdot \text{y}}\right)(0.20)(230 \times 10^6 \text{ person})\left(\frac{1 \text{ y}}{365 \text{ d}}\right)$$

$$= 7.8 \times 10^6 \text{ barrels} \cdot \text{d}^{-1}$$

E-13 In Section E-5 it is given that 354 kJ of energy is released per liter of $Na_2SO_4 \cdot 10H_2O(l)$ that crystallizes. Thus 354 kJ of energy can be stored per liter of $Na_2SO_4 \cdot 10H_2O$. The number of liters in 100 kg of the salt is given by

$$\text{volume} = \text{mass/density}$$

$$V = \frac{(100 \text{ kg})\left(\dfrac{1000 \text{ g}}{1 \text{ kg}}\right)}{\left(\dfrac{1.5 \text{ g}}{1 \text{ mL}}\right)\left(\dfrac{1000 \text{ mL}}{1 \text{ L}}\right)} = 67 \text{ L}$$

Thus

$$\text{energy stored} = (67 \text{ L})(354 \text{ kJ} \cdot \text{L}^{-1}) = 2 \cdot 4 \times 10^4 \text{ kJ}$$

E-15 From Section E-2 we have

(1) $\qquad C_2H_6(g) + \frac{1}{2}O_2(g) \longrightarrow C_2H_5OH(l) \qquad \Delta H^\circ_{rxn} = -193 \text{ kJ}$

For the equation

(2) $\qquad C_2H_6(g) + \frac{7}{2}O_2(g) \longrightarrow 2CO_2(g) + 3H_2O(l) \qquad \Delta H^\circ_{rxn} = -1427 \text{ kJ}$

Reversing Equation (1) and adding the result to Equation (2) yields

(3) $C_2H_5OH(l) + 3O_2(g) \longrightarrow 2CO_2(g) + 3H_2O(g)$

Thus

$$\Delta H^\circ_{rxn}(3) = \Delta H^\circ_{rxn}(2) - \Delta H^\circ_{rxn}(1)$$
$$= -1427 \text{ kJ} - (-193 \text{ kJ}) = -1234 \text{ kJ}$$

E-17 From Section E-5 we have $30 \text{ kW} \cdot \text{h} \cdot \text{d}^{-1}$ as the energy requirement of a typical U.S. home and $1 \text{ kW} \cdot \text{m}^{-2}$ as the power level of sunlight.
Assuming 8 h of sunlight per day, we have

$$(1 \text{ kW} \cdot \text{m}^{-2})(8 \text{ h} \cdot \text{day}^{-1}) = 8 \text{ kW} \cdot \text{h} \cdot \text{m}^{-2} \cdot \text{day}^{-1}$$

With a 12-m^2 collector area with a 30 percent efficiency we have

$$(8 \text{ kW} \cdot \text{h} \cdot \text{m}^{-2} \cdot \text{day}^{-1})(12 \text{ m}^2)(0.30) = 30 \text{ kW} \cdot \text{h} \cdot \text{day}^{-1}$$

F-13 An expression for the energy is obtained by substituting Equation (6-1) into Equation (6-2)

$$E = \frac{hc}{\lambda}$$
$$= \frac{(6.626 \times 10^{-34} \text{ J} \cdot \text{s})(3.00 \times 10^8 \text{ m} \cdot \text{s}^{-1})}{(240 \times 10^{-9} \text{ m})} = 8.28 \times 10^{-19} \text{ J} \cdot \text{photon}^{-1}$$

The energy per mole of photons is

$$E = (8.28 \times 10^{-19} \text{ J} \cdot \text{photon}^{-1})(6.022 \times 10^{23} \text{ photon} \cdot \text{mol}^{-1})$$
$$= 4.99 \times 10^5 \text{ J} \cdot \text{mol}^{-1} = 499 \text{ kJ} \cdot \text{mol}^{-1}$$

F-15 The equation for the reaction is

$$2C_8H_{18}(l) + 25O_2(g) \longrightarrow 16CO_2(g) + 18H_2O(l)$$

The number of moles of $C_8H_{18}(l)$ is

$$\text{mol } C_3H_8 = (16 \text{ gal})\left(\frac{4 \text{ qt}}{1 \text{ gal}}\right)\left(\frac{0.946 \text{ L}}{1 \text{ qt}}\right)\left(\frac{1000 \text{ mL}}{1 \text{ L}}\right)(0.80 \text{ g} \cdot \text{mL}^{-1})$$
$$\times \left(\frac{1 \text{ mol } C_8H_{18}}{114.22 \text{ g } C_8H_{18}}\right)$$
$$= 424 \text{ mol}$$

The mass of $CO_2(g)$ produced is given by

$$\text{mass } CO_2 = (424 \text{ mol } C_3H_8)\left(\frac{16 \text{ mol } CO_2}{2 \text{ mol } C_3H_8}\right)\left(\frac{44.01 \text{ g } CO_2}{1 \text{ mol } CO_2}\right)$$
$$= 1.49 \times 10^5 \text{ g} = 149 \text{ kg}$$

F-17 The equation for the reaction is

$$CaO(s) + SO_2(g) \longrightarrow CaSO_3(s)$$

Thus we write

$$mass\ CaO = (1.00 \times 10^6\ g\ SO_2)\left(\frac{1\ mol\ SO_2}{64.06\ g\ SO_2}\right)\left(\frac{1\ mol\ CaO}{1\ mol\ SO_2}\right)$$
$$\times \left(\frac{56.08\ g\ CaO}{1\ mol\ CaO}\right)$$
$$= 8.75 \times 10^5\ g = 875\ kg = 0.875\ metric\ tons$$

H-11 (a) Zircon contains SiO_4^{4-} ions.

(b) Enstatite is a silicate that contains long, straight-chain silicate polyanions (Figure H-4).

(c) Talc, like mica, contains two-dimensional polymeric silicate sheets (Figure H-5c).

H-13 For an n-type semiconductor, we can add small quantities of arsenic or antimony to silicon. For a p-type semiconductor, we can add gallium or indium.

H-15 Let the abundance of silicon-29 be denoted by x. Thus the abundance of silicon-30 will be given by

$$abundance\ of\ silicon\text{-}30 = 100 - 92.23 - x$$
$$= 7.77 - x$$

The atomic mass of naturally occurring silicon satisfies the equation

$$28.0855 = \left(\frac{92.23}{100}\right)(27.976927) + \left(\frac{x}{100}\right)(28.976495)$$
$$+ \left(\frac{7.77 - x}{100}\right)(29.973770)$$

or

$$28.0855 = 25.8031 + 0.28976495x + 2.3290 - 0.29973770x$$

Solving for x gives

$$x = 4.67$$

Thus the percentage of silicon-29 is 4.67 percent and that of silicon-30 is 3.10 percent.

H-17   The total mass of silicon in 500 metric tons of silicon dioxide is

$$\text{mass Si} = (\text{mass SiO}_2)\left(\frac{\text{atomic mass of Si}}{\text{formula mass of SiO}_2}\right)$$

$$= (500 \text{ tons})\left(\frac{28.09}{60.09}\right) = 234 \text{ tons}$$

Assuming a 75% yield gives

$$\text{mass Si obtained} = (0.75)(234 \text{ tons}) = 176 \text{ tons}$$

I-13   One milliliter of 33.1 percent by mass $NH_3(aq)$ contains

$$\text{mass NH}_3 = (0.331)(0.890 \text{ g}\cdot\text{mL}^{-1}) = 0.295 \text{ g}\cdot\text{mL}^{-1}$$

Thus the number of moles in NH_3 in one liter of solution is

$$\text{molarity} = (0.295 \text{ g}\cdot\text{mL}^{-1})\left(\frac{1000 \text{ mL}}{1 \text{ L}}\right)\left(\frac{1 \text{ mol NH}_3}{17.03 \text{ g NH}_3}\right) = 17.3 \text{ M}$$

I-15   The equations for the Ostwald process are given in the answer to Question I-7. From these equations we see that

$$1 \text{ mol NH}_3 \longrightarrow 1 \text{ mol HNO}_3$$

because the NO is recycled; thus we write

$$\text{mass HNO}_3 = (1.00 \times 10^6 \text{ g})\left(\frac{1 \text{ mol NH}_3}{17.03 \text{ g NH}_3}\right)\left(\frac{1 \text{ mol HNO}_3}{1 \text{ mol NH}_3}\right)$$
$$\times \left(\frac{63.02 \text{ g HNO}_3}{1 \text{ mol HNO}_3}\right)$$
$$= 3.70 \times 10^6 \text{ g} = 3.70 \text{ metric tons}$$

I-17   The equation for the reaction is

$$NH_4HS(s) \longrightarrow NH_3(g) + H_2S(g)$$

The total pressure is

$$P_{total} = P_{NH_3} + P_{H_2S} = 0.658 \text{ atm}$$

Using the fact that $P_{NH_3} = P_{H_2S}$ from the reaction stoichiometry, we find that

$$P_{NH_3} = P_{H_2S} = 0.329 \text{ atm}$$

Therefore

$$K_p = (P_{NH_2})(P_{H_2S}) = (0.329 \text{ atm})^2 = 0.108 \text{ atm}^2$$

and

$$K_c = [\text{NH}_3][\text{H}_2\text{S}] = \left(\frac{P_{\text{NH}_3}}{RT}\right)\left(\frac{P_{\text{H}_2\text{S}}}{RT}\right) = \frac{K_p}{(RT)^2}$$

$$= \frac{0.108 \text{ atm}^2}{[(0.0821 \text{ L}\cdot\text{atm}\cdot\text{mol}^{-1}\cdot\text{K}^{-1})(298 \text{ K})]^2} = 1.80 \times 10^{-4} \text{ M}^2$$

I-19 We use the equation [Equation (3-8)]

$$M_1V_1 = M_2V_2$$

to calculate

$$V_2 = \frac{M_1V_1}{M_2} = \frac{(6.00 \text{ M})(500 \text{ mL})}{(15.7 \text{ M})} = 191 \text{ mL}$$

Thus add 191 mL of the 15.7 M HNO_3 to enough water to make 500 mL of final solution.

J-13 For each case we treat the acid as a monoprotic acid and write

acid	+ $\text{H}_2\text{O}(l) \rightleftharpoons$ $\text{H}_3\text{O}^+(aq)$	+	conjugate base
0.250 M	~0		0
0.250 M − [H_3O^+]	[H_3O^+]		[B^-]

and because [H_3O^+] = [B^-], we have

$$\frac{[\text{H}_3\text{O}^+]^2}{0.250 \text{ M} - [\text{H}_3\text{O}^+]} = K_a$$

Using the pK_a values given in Interchapter J, we have for H_3PO_4

$$\frac{[\text{H}_3\text{O}^+]^2}{0.250 \text{ M} - [\text{H}_3\text{O}^+]} = 10^{-2.2} = 6.3 \times 10^{-3} \text{ M}$$

$$[\text{H}_3\text{O}^+] = 3.7 \times 10^{-2} \text{ M}$$

$$\text{pH} = 1.4$$

and for H_3PO_3

$$\frac{[\text{H}_3\text{O}^+]^2}{0.250 \text{ M} - [\text{H}_3\text{O}^+]} = 10^{-1.8} = 1.6 \times 10^{-2} \text{ M}$$

$$[\text{H}_3\text{O}^+] = 0.056 \text{ M}$$

$$\text{pH} = 1.3$$

J-15   We use the van't Hoff equation [Equation (14-7)]

$$\log \frac{K_2}{K_1} = \frac{\Delta H^\circ_{rxn}}{2.30R}\left(\frac{T_2 - T_1}{T_1 T_2}\right)$$

We write

$$\log \frac{K_c}{1.8 \text{ M}} = \frac{(92.9 \times 10^3 \text{ J} \cdot \text{mol}^{-1})}{(2.30)(8.314 \text{ J} \cdot \text{mol}^{-1} \cdot \text{K}^{-1})}\left[\frac{773 \text{ K} - 523 \text{ K}}{(523 \text{ K})(773 \text{ K})}\right]$$

$$= 3.00$$

or

$$K_c = 1.8 \times 10^3 \text{ M}$$

J-17   The equation for the reaction is

$$2Ca_3(PO_4)_2(s) + 6SiO_2(s) + 10C(s) \longrightarrow 6CaSiO_3(l) + 10CO(g) + P_4(g)$$

The maximum amount of $P_4(s)$ obtainable is given by

$$\text{mass } P_4 = (1.00 \text{ metric ton})\left(\frac{10^6 \text{ g}}{1 \text{ metric ton}}\right)\left[\frac{1 \text{ mol Ca}_3(PO_4)_2}{310.2 \text{ g Ca}_3(PO_4)_2}\right]$$

$$\times \left(\frac{1 \text{ mol } P_4}{2 \text{ mol Ca}_3(PO_4)_2}\right)\left(\frac{123.9 \text{ g } P_4}{1 \text{ mol } P_4}\right) = 2.00 \times 10^5 \text{ g}$$

$$= 0.200 \text{ metric ton}$$

J-19   The equation for the reaction is

$$Ca_3P_2(s) + 6D_2O(l) \longrightarrow 2PD_3(g) + 3Ca(OD)_2(aq)$$

The number of moles of $PD_3(g)$ produced is given by

$$\text{mol } PD_3 = (10.0 \text{ g } D_2O)\left(\frac{1 \text{ mol } D_2O}{20.03 \text{ g } D_2O}\right)\left(\frac{2 \text{ mol } PD_3}{6 \text{ mol } D_2O}\right) = 0.166 \text{ mol}$$

The volume is

$$V = \frac{nRT}{P} = \frac{(0.166 \text{ mol})(0.0821 \text{ L} \cdot \text{atm} \cdot \text{mol}^{-1} \cdot \text{K}^{-1})(273 \text{ K})}{\left(\dfrac{700}{760} \text{ atm}\right)}$$

$$= 4.04 \text{ L}$$

K-15   Using the data from Table K-2, we write

$$1 \times [Na^+] + 2 \times [Mg^{2+}] + 2 \times [Ca^{2+}] + 1 \times [K^+] + 2[Sr^{2+}]$$
$$- 1 \times [Cl^-] - 2 \times [SO_4^{2-}] - 1 \times [HCO_3^-] - 2 \times [CO_3^{2-}] - 1 \times [Br^-]$$
$$= 0.46 + 0.108 + 0.020 + 0.010 + 1.8 \times 10^{-4} - 0.55 - 0.056 - 0.0023$$
$$- 0.0006 - 0.00083$$
$$= -0.01 \quad \text{(or zero to within 1 percent accuracy)}$$

K-17 The ocean is buffered at a pH = 8.15. In contrast, most lakes and ponds are not buffered and thus undergo a drop in pH when acid rain falls into a lake or pond.

K-19 The equation for the reaction is

$$Cl_2(g) + 2Br^-(aq) \longrightarrow 2Cl^-(aq) + Br_2(l)$$

The number of moles of $Br^-(aq)$ in one billion liters of seawater is

$$mol\ Br^- = (8.3 \times 10^{-4}\ mol \cdot L^{-1})(1.0 \times 10^9\ L) = 8.3 \times 10^5\ mol$$

The quantity of $Cl_2(g)$ required is

$$g\ Cl_2 = (8.3 \times 10^5\ mol\ Br^-)\left(\frac{1\ mol\ Cl_2}{2\ mol\ Br^-}\right)\left(\frac{70.9\ g\ Cl_2}{1\ mol\ Cl_2}\right)$$

$$= 2.94 \times 10^7\ g = 29.4\ metric\ tons$$

L-11

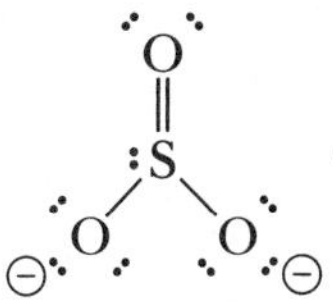

+ other resonance forms AX_3E trigonal pyramidal

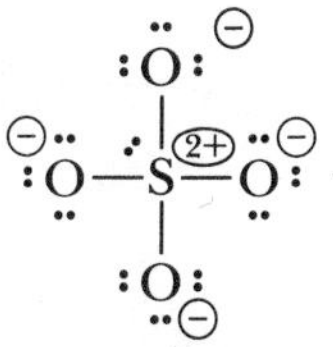

+ other resonance forms AX_4 tetrahedral

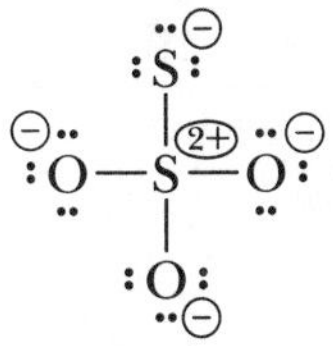

+ other resonance forms AX_4 tetrahedral

L-13

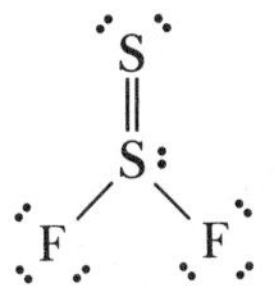

AX_3E trigonal pyramidal

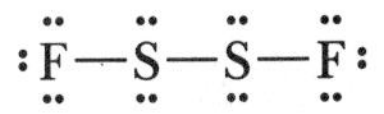

bent

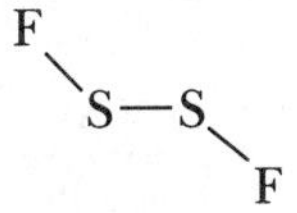

L-15 The salt $KHSO_4$ consists of a neutral cation ($K^+(aq)$) and an acidic anion ($HSO_4^-(aq)$). Table 15-5 gives $K_a = 1.20 \times 10^{-2}$ M for the equation

$$HSO_4^-(aq) + H_2O(l) \rightleftharpoons H_3O^+(aq) + SO_4^{2-}(aq)$$

Thus we set up the table

$HSO_4^-(aq) + H_2O(l) \rightleftharpoons H_3O^+(aq) + SO_4^{2-}(aq)$		
0.15 M	~0	0
$0.15\ M - [H_3O^+]$	$[H_3O^+]$	$[H_3O^+]$

and write

$$\frac{[H_3O^+]^2}{0.15\ M - [H_3O^+]} = 1.20 \times 10^{-2}\ M$$

$$[H_3O^+] = 0.037\ M$$

$$pH = 1.43$$

L-17 We use the van't Hoff equation (Equation (14-7))

$$\log \frac{K_2}{K_1} = \frac{\Delta H_{rxn}^\circ}{2.30R} \left(\frac{T_2 - T_1}{T_1 T_2} \right)$$

and write

$$\log \frac{K_2}{0.65\ \text{atm}^{-1/2}} = \frac{-190 \times 10^3\ \text{J} \cdot \text{mol}^{-1}}{(2.30)(8.314\ \text{J} \cdot \text{mol}^{-1} \cdot \text{K}^{-1})} \left(\frac{1123\ \text{K} - 1073\ \text{K}}{(1073\ \text{K})(1123\ \text{K})} \right)$$
$$= -0.412$$

or

$$\frac{K_2}{0.65\ \text{atm}^{-1/2}} = 10^{-0.412} = 0.387$$

$$K_2 = (0.387)(0.65\ \text{atm}^{-1/2}) = 0.25\ \text{atm}^{-1/2}$$

M-19 The equation that we shall use is Equation (20-11).

$$E^\circ = \left(\frac{0.0592\ \text{V}}{n} \right) \log K$$

The equation for the reaction in each case is

$$2Fe^{2+}(aq) + X_2 \rightleftharpoons 2Fe^{3+}(aq) + 2X^-(aq)$$

Note that $n = 2$ in Equation (20-11) in each case.

(a) $E° = +1.36 \text{ V} - 0.77 \text{ V} = 0.59 \text{ V}$

$$\log K = \left(\frac{n}{0.0592 \text{ V}}\right) E° = \left(\frac{2}{0.0592 \text{ V}}\right)(0.59 \text{ V}) = 19.9$$

$$K = 7.9 \times 10^{19}$$

(b) $E° = +1.07 \text{ V} - 0.77 \text{ V} = 0.30 \text{ V}$

$$\log K = \left(\frac{2}{0.0592 \text{ V}}\right)(0.30 \text{ V}) = 10.1$$

$$K = 1.3 \times 10^{10}$$

(c) $E° = +0.54 \text{ V} - 0.77 \text{ V} = -0.23 \text{ V}$

$$\log K = \left(\frac{2}{0.0592 \text{ V}}\right)(-0.23 \text{ V}) = -7.8$$

$$K = 1.6 \times 10^{-8}$$

Thus $Fe^{2+}(aq)$ can be oxidized to $Fe^{3+}(aq)$ by $Cl_2(g)$ and $Br_2(l)$, but not by $I_2(s)$.

M-21 The value of $E°$ for the reaction in question is given by

$$E° = +1.065 \text{ V} - 1.590 \text{ V} = -0.525 \text{ V}$$

The equilibrium constant is given by

$$\log K = \left(\frac{n}{0.0592 \text{ V}}\right) E° = \left(\frac{1}{0.0592 \text{ V}}\right)(-0.525 \text{ V}) = -8.868$$

$$K = 1.35 \times 10^{-9} \text{ M}^3$$

M-23 The equation for the titration of $I_3^-(aq)$ with $S_2O_3^{2-}(aq)$ is

$$2S_2O_3^{2-}(aq) + I_3^-(aq) \longrightarrow 3I^-(aq) + S_4O_6^{2-}(aq)$$

The number of moles of I_3^- produced by the reaction of $I^-(aq)$ with household bleach is

$$\text{mol } I_3^- = (0.2500 \text{ mol} \cdot \text{L}^{-1})(0.01855 \text{ L})\left(\frac{1 \text{ mol } I_3^-}{2 \text{ mol } S_2O_3^{2-}}\right) = 2.319 \times 10^{-3} \text{ mol}$$

The mass of NaOCl is given by

$$\text{mass NaOCl} = (2.319 \times 10^{-3} \text{ mol } I_3^-)\left(\frac{1 \text{ mol NaOCl}}{1 \text{ mol } I_3^-}\right)$$

$$\left(\frac{74.44 \text{ g NaOCl}}{1 \text{ mol NaOCl}}\right) = 0.1726 \text{ g}$$

and the mass percentage of NaOCl in the bleach is

$$\text{mass \%} = \left(\frac{0.1726 \text{ g}}{3.285 \text{ g}}\right) \times 100 = 5.254\%$$

N-15 (a) $x + 4(-2) = -1$, or $x = +7$

(b) $x + 4(-2) = -2$, or $x = +6$

(c) $x + 2(-2) = 0$, or $x = +4$

(d) $x + 2(-1) = 0$, or $x = +2$

(e) $x + 3(-1) = 0$, or $x = +3$

(f) $2x + 7(-2) = 0$, or $x = +7$

N-17

(a) $:\!\ddot{C}l\!-\!\underset{\underset{:\!\ddot{C}l\!:}{|}}{\overset{\overset{:\!\ddot{C}l\!:}{|}}{Ti}}\!-\!\ddot{C}l\!:$ AX_4 tetrahedral

(b) $^{\ominus}:\!\ddot{O}\!-\!\underset{\underset{\ominus\,:\!\ddot{O}\!:}{|}}{\overset{\overset{:\!\ddot{O}\!:\,\ominus}{|}}{\overset{+3}{Mn}}}\!-\!\ddot{O}\!:^{\ominus}$ plus other resonance forms AX_4 tetrahedral

(c) $:\!\overset{\ominus}{\ddot{C}l}\!-\!Ag\!-\!\ddot{C}l\!:$ AX_2 linear

N-19 The equilibrium constant for the equation

(1) $Ca^{2+}(aq) + CO_3^{2-}(aq) \rightleftharpoons CaCO_3(s)$

is

$$K = \frac{1}{K_{sp}} = 3.6 \times 10^8 \text{ M}^{-2}$$

We have for $HCO_3^-(aq)$

$$HCO_3^-(aq) + H_2O(l) \rightleftharpoons H_3O^+(aq) + CO_3^{2-}(aq)$$

Thus

$$K_a = 4.27 \times 10^{-11} \text{ M} = \frac{[H_3O^+][CO_3^{2-}]}{[HCO_3^-]}$$
$$= \frac{(10^{-8.15})[CO_3^{2-}]}{(2.3 \times 10^{-3} \text{ M})} = \frac{(7.08 \times 10^{-9} \text{ M})[CO_3^{2-}]}{(2.3 \times 10^{-3} \text{ M})}$$

and thus

$$[CO_3^{2-}] = 1.4 \times 10^{-5} \text{ M}$$

Thus the value of Q/K for Equation (1) is

$$\frac{Q}{K} = \frac{[1/(10.0 \times 10^{-3} \text{ M})(1.4 \times 10^{-5} \text{ M})]}{(3.6 \times 10^8 \text{ M}^{-2})} = 0.020$$

Because $Q/K < 1$, the reaction is spontaneous from left to right and the formation of $CaCO_3(s)$ is favored.

GLOSSARY

A

absolute alcohol (398): pure ethanol.

absolute temperature, T (131): the temperature given in the unit kelvin.

absolute temperature scale (132): the fundamental temperature scale. The absolute temperature scale is related to the more familiar Celsius scale. The temperature on the absolute temperature scale is found by adding 273.15°C to the temperature on the Celsuis scale. The unit of absolute temperature is the kelvin, K. The absolute temperature scale is also called the Kelvin scale.

absorption spectrum (209): the spectrum obtained when atoms or molecules absorb electromagnetic radiation and are raised to excited states.

acid (65): a compound that yields hydrogen ions when it it dissolved in water.

acid-base titration (111, 514): the exact neutralization of an acid by a base of known concentration, or of a base by an acid of known concentration.

acid dissociation constant, K_a (477): the equilibrium constant for the proton transfer reaction between an acid and water. For the general equation

$$HB(aq) + H_2O \rightleftharpoons B^-(aq) + H_3O^+(aq)$$

$$K_a = \frac{[B^-][H_3O^+]}{[HB]}$$

acid dissociation reaction (477): the proton transfer reaction between an acid and water. The general equation is

$$HB(aq) + H_2O(l) \rightleftharpoons B^-(aq) + H_3O^+(aq)$$

acid rain (243): rain that is more acidic than normal rain.

acidic anhydride (65): an oxide that yields an acid when it is dissolved in water.

acidic anion (491): an anion that reacts with water to produce $H_3O^+(aq)$ in aqueous solution.

acidic cation (491): a cation that reacts with water to form $H_3O^+(aq)$ in aqueous solution.

acidic hydrogen atom (65): a hydrogen atom in a species that dissociates in solution to become $H_3O^+(aq)$.

acidic proton (65): a dissociable hydrogen atom in a species.

acidic solution (73, 469): an aqueous solution in which $[H_3O^+] > [OH^-]$.

acidity (472): the concentration of $H_3O^+(aq)$ in an aqueous solution.

actinide series (51, 229): the inner transition series that is headed by actinium. The actinide series contains the elements actinium ($Z = 89$) through nobelium ($Z = 102$).

activation energy, E_a (418): the minimum energy necessary to cause a reaction between the colliding reactant molecules.

actual yield (106): the mass of a product that results from a reaction.

addition polymerization reaction (771): a reaction that involves a direct addition of monomer molecules to form a polymer chain.

addition reaction (749): a reaction in which atoms or molecules are added to a molecule.

alcohol (755): an organic compound that contains an —OH group attached to a hydrocarbon chain.

aldehyde (756): a class of organic compounds that has the general formula RCHO.

aldehyde group (756): the —CHO group.

alkali metal (47): any of the elements (lithium, sodium, potassium, rubidium, cesium, and francium) that constitute Group 1 of the periodic table.

alkaline (47): having the property of producing a basic solution.

alkaline earth metal (47): any of the elements (beryllium, magnesium, calcium, strontium, barium, and radium) that make up Group 2 of the periodic table.

alkaline manganese cell (650): a primary battery using the cell

$$^{\ominus}Zn(s)|Na_2ZnO_2(aq), NaOH(aq)|MnO_2(s),$$
$$Mn_2O_3 \cdot H_2O(s)|steel^{\oplus}$$

alkane (742): a hydrocarbon that contains only carbon-carbon single bonds. (See saturated hydrocarbon.)

alkene (748): a hydrocarbon that contains one or more carbon-carbon double bonds.

alkyl group (747): a group that is derived from an alkane by removing a hydrogen atom.

alkyl halide (745): a substance that is derived from an alkane by removing one or more hydrogen atoms and replacing them by halogen atoms. (See haloalkane.)

alkynes (751): the class of hydrocarbons that contain one or more carbon-carbon triple bonds.

allotrope (161, 503): a substance that can exist in different modifications in the same physical state; for example, graphite and diamond are allotropes of solid carbon.

allotropy (161, 503): a property wherein a substance has more than one possible molecular form.

alpha emitter (671): a radioisotope that decays by emitting α-particles.

α-helix (779): the helical shape of a polypeptide that results from the formation of hydrogen bonds between oxygen and hydrogen atoms in peptide bonds that are separated by three peptide units along the chain.

α-particle (16, 671): a helium-4 nucleus emitted in certain types of nuclear decay.

amalgam (629): a solution of a metal in mercury.

amines (758): a class of organic compounds that contain nitrogen. The general formulas for amines are RNH_2, $R-\overset{\cdot\cdot}{N}-H$,

$$\quad\quad\quad\quad\quad\quad | \atop R'$$

and $R-\overset{\cdot\cdot}{N}-R'$.

$$\quad\quad | \atop R''$$

amino acid (775): monomer from which proteins are built. The general formula for an amino acid is

$$\begin{array}{c} H \\ | \\ H_2N-C-COOH \\ | \\ G \end{array}$$

amino acid side group (775): the organic group —G that is attached to amino acids:

$$\begin{array}{c} H \\ | \\ H_2N-C-COOH \\ | \\ G \end{array}$$

amorphous (503): characteristic of a solid that does not have a definite crystal structure (e.g., glass).

ampere (625): the SI unit of current. One ampere is a flow of one coulomb of charge per second.

amphoteric (123, 555): soluble in both acids and bases.

amphoteric metal hydroxide (555): a metal hydroxide that is soluble in both acidic and basic solutions, but insoluble in neutral solutions.

analytical chemistry (308): the area of chemistry that deals with the chemical composition of substances.

anion (22, 250): a negatively charged ion.

anode (831): the electrode at which the oxidation occurs. During electrolysis, anions in solution move toward the anode.

antibonding orbital (336): a molecular orbital that has one or more nodes in the region between two nuclei.

antifreeze (391): a substance that is used to lower the freezing point of water.

apatite ore (503): phosphate rock that is used to produce phosphorus

aqueous solution (61): a solution in which a solute is dissolved in water. An aqueous solution is designated by (aq).

aromatic hydrocarbon (754): a class of hydrocarbons that have rings that are stabilized by π electron delocalization.

Arrhenius acid (468): a substance that produces $H^+(aq)$ in aqueous solution.

Arrhenius base (468): a substance that produces $OH^-(aq)$ in aqueous solution.

Arrhenius equation (419): the equation that describes the temperature dependence of a rate constant. The Arrhenius equation is

$$\log\left(\frac{k_2}{k_1}\right) = \frac{E_a}{2.30R}\left(\frac{T_2 - T_1}{T_1 T_2}\right)$$

where k_1 and k_2 are the rate constants at the absolute temperatures T_1 and T_2, respectively; E_a is the activation energy; and R is the gas constant.

artificial radioisotopes (680): radioactive isotopes that are produced by nuclear reactions in the laboratory and that are not found in nature.

asbestos (377): a mineral containing polymeric, cyclic polysilicate chains.

atom (6, 9): a basic component of matter.

atomic crystal (364): a crystal whose constituent particles are atoms.

atomic mass (10): the mass of an atom relative to the mass of an atom of carbon-12, which is assigned an atomic mass of exactly 12.

atomic mass unit (10): a unit based on the mass of carbon-12, which contains exactly 12 atomic mass units. The symbol for atomic mass unit is amu.

atomic number (17): the number of protons in the nucleus of an atom. The atomic number of an atom is designated by the symbol Z. Each element has a different atomic number.

atomic radius (229): the distance from the nucleus of an atom to the point where the electronic charge density is very small. Atoms do not have well-defined radii.

atomic spectroscopy (201): the study of the spectra of atoms.

atomic spectrum (201): a line spectrum due to the radiation emitted by gaseous, excited atoms or the radiation absorbed by gaseous atoms.

atomic substance (89): a substance that is composed of single atoms.

atomic theory (9): a theory that postulates that (1) matter is composed of small, indivisible particles called atoms; (2) the atoms of a given element all have the same mass and are identical in all respects, including chemical behavior; (3) the atoms of different elements differ in mass and in chemical behavior; (4) chemical compounds are composed of two or more different types of atoms joined together in simple fixed ratios. The particle that results when two or more atoms join together is called a molecule; (5) in a chemical reaction, the atoms involved are rearranged to form different molecules; no atoms are created or destroyed.

ATP (508): adenosine triphosphate, which supplies the energy requirements of biochemical reactions.

average kinetic energy (143): the average kinetic energy of one mole of a gas, E_{av}, is given by $E_{av} = \frac{3}{2}RT$, where T is the Kelvin temperature and R is the gas constant.

average speed (143): an average speed of a molecule in a gas of like molecules can be defined by the relationship $E_{av} = \frac{1}{2}M_{kg}v_{av}^2$, where E_{av} is the average kinetic energy per mole and M_{kg} is the mass in kilograms of one mole.

Avogadro's law (134): states that equal volumes of gases at the same pressure and temperature contain equal numbers of molecules.

Avogardro's number (91): the number of formula units contained in one mole of any substance. One mole of any substance contains 6.022×10^{23} formula units.

AX_mE_n (295): a general representation of a molecule or ion where A represents the central atom, X_m represents m ligands bonded to the central atom, and E_n represents n lone electron pairs (denoted by E) on the central atom.

axial vertex (293): one of the two vertices that lie above or below the equilateral-triangle midplane of a trigonal bipyramid. The two axial vertices are equivalent.

azeotrope (398): a solution that distills without change in composition.

azide (465): a compound that contains the azide ion, N_3^-.

azimuthal quantum number (213): the quantum number, l, that specifies the shape of an atomic orbital. The allowed values of l are 0, 1, 2, . . . , $n - 1$.

B

baking powder (506): a mixture of $Ca(H_2PO_4)_2(s)$ and $NaHCO_3(s)$ that is used to cause cakes and breads to rise.

balancing by inspection (46): a method of balancing chemical equations by trial and error.

balanced chemical equation (45): a chemical reaction, written in terms of chemical symbols, that has the same number of each type of atom on the reactant and the product sides of the equation.

balancing coefficient (45): the number placed in front of the chemical formula of a reactant or product in a chemical equation so that the chemical equation is balanced.

ball-and-stick molecular model (289): a model of a molecule that is constructed to display the angles between the bonds in the molecule.

Balmer series (208): the series of lines in the hydrogen atomic spectrum due to transitions from higher states ($n > 2$) to the $n = 2$ state.

band of stability (674): the region of stable nuclei in a plot of the number of protons versus the number of neutrons of all known stable nuclei.

barometer (128): a device used to measure the pressure of the atmosphere.

barometric pressure (129): the pressure exerted by the atmosphere.

base (64): a compound that yields hydroxide ions, $OH^-(aq)$, when it is dissolved in water. A base is a proton acceptor.

base (781): a nitrogen-containing ring compound that comprises a nucleotide. The five bases found in DNA or RNA are adenine, guanine, cytosine, uracil, and thymine.

base protonation constant, K_b (483): the equilibrium constant for the proton transfer reaction between a base and water: For the general equation

$$B^-(aq) + H_2O(l) \rightleftharpoons BH(aq) + OH^-(aq)$$

$$K_b = \frac{[BH][OH^-]}{[B^-]}$$

basic anhydride (64): an oxide that yields a base when it is dissolved in water.

basic anion (491): an anion that reacts with water to produce $OH^-(aq)$ in aqueous solution.

basic oxygen process (705): a process for making steel from pig iron in which hot, pure O_2 is blown through molten pig iron.

basic solution (74, 469): an aqueous solution in which $[OH^-] > [H_3O^+]$.

battery (649): an electrochemical cell or group of cells designed for use as a power source.

bent (296): the shape of a triatomic species in which the bond angle is less than $180°$; the shape of an AX_2E and an AX_2E_2 molecule.

beryl (120): a green mineral that is the chief source of beryllium and is used as a gem.

β-emitter (671): a radioisotope that emits electrons.

β-particle (16, 672): an electron emitted in certain types of nuclear decay.

bidentate (723): a chelating ligand that attaches to two metal coordination positions.

bifluoride ion (661): the $HF_2^-(aq)$ ion that is formed when hydrofluoric acid is dissolved in water.

$$2HF(aq) \rightleftharpoons H^+(aq) + HF_2^-(aq)$$

binary acid (66): an acid that consists of hydrogen and one other element.

binary compound (12): a compound that consists of two different elements.

binding energy (340): the energy with which an electron is bound in a molecule.

binding energy (nuclear) (685): the energy required to separate the nucleons in a nucleus.

binding energy curve (686): a plot of the binding energy per nucleon versus the mass number of a nucleus.

bismuthinite (124): a sulfide ore (Bi_2S_3) that is the most common source of bismuth.

blast furnace (705): a furnace in which Fe_2O_3 is reacted with coke at high temperatures to produce iron commercially.

body-centered cubic (362): describes the unit cell in which the components of the crystal are located at the corners and in the center of a cube.

boiler scale (539): deposit of metal carbonates from hard water.

boiling point elevation (389): the increase in the boiling point of a solution containing nonvolatile solutes over the boiling point of the pure solvent. The boiling point elevation is given by the equation $T_b - T_b^\circ = K_b m_c$, where T_b is the boiling point of the solution, T_b° is the boiling point of the pure solvent, m_c is the colligative molality of the solution, and K_b is the proportionality constant, called the boiling point elevation constant, for the solvent.

boiling point elevation constant (391): the proportionality constant between the boiling point elevation and the colligative molality of a solution. The value depends only on the solvent. The symbol is K_b and the units are $K \cdot m_c^{-1}$.

bomb calorimeter (178): a sealed reaction vessel that is used to measure the heat of combustion of a substance.

bond energy (174): bond enthalpy

bond enthalpy (174): the energy as heat required to break one mole of bonds between atom X and atom Y. The symbol for bond enthalpy is $H(X-Y)$.

bond length (264): the average distance between the nuclei of the two atoms that are joined by a covalent bond.

bond order (337): one half of the net number of bonding electrons in a diatomic molecule [see Equation (12-1)].

bonding orbital (335): a molecular orbital that is concentrated in a region between two nuclei.

bond polarity (282): the unequal sharing of the electrons in a covalent bond due to the difference in the electronegativities of the two atoms.

Born-Haber cycle (258): a closed sequence of thermodynamic steps used in calculating lattice energies of ionic compounds.

Boyle's law (131): states that the volume of a fixed mass of gas at constant temperature is inversely proportional to the pressure of the gas.

brass (708): an alloy of copper and zinc.

breeder reactor (690): a nuclear reactor that produces more fissionable material than is consumed.

Brønsted-Lowry acid (468): a proton donor.

Brønsted-Lowry base (468): a proton acceptor.

bronze (708): an alloy of copper and tin.

buffer (525): a solution that is resistant to changes in pH upon the addition of an acid or base.

buret (111): a precision-made piece of glassware that is used to measure accurately the volume of a solution that is added to another container.

C

calorie (179): the amount of energy as heat required to raise the temperature of one gram of water by one Celsius degree; 1 calorie = 4.184 J.

calorimeter (177): a device used to measure the amount of heat evolved or absorbed in a process.

carbohydrate (158): a compound composed of carbon, hydrogen, and oxygen with the general formula $C_x(H_2O)_y$.

carbon-14 dating (678): the determination of the age of formerly living materials from the rate of disintegration of carbon-14 in the sample.

carboxyl group (760): the —COOH group.

carboxylate ion (472): the anion that results from the dissociation or neutralization of a carboxylic acid. A carboxylate ion has the general formula $RCOO^-$ or

$$\left[R-C \begin{matrix} \diagup\!\!\!O \\ \diagdown\!\!\!O \end{matrix} \right]^-$$

carboxylic acid (471): a class of organic compounds that contain the —COOH group.

carrier gas (38): the inert gas used to carry a mixture of species through a gas chromatography column.

cassiterite (123): the mineral SnO_2, which is the primary ore of tin.

catalyst (103, 159, 420): a substance that increases the reaction rate but that is not a reactant. A catalyst acts by providing a different and faster reaction pathway (mechanism) than the reaction mechanism that would prevail in the absence of the catalyst.

cathode (628): the electrode at which reduction occurs. During electrolysis cations in solution move toward the cathode.

cation (22, 250): a positively charged ion.

caustic soda (85): sodium hydroxide, NaOH.

cell diagram (635): a notation used to represent an electrochemical cell. By convention, oxidation occurs at the left electrode and reduction occurs at the right electrode.

cell voltage (637): the voltage of an electrochemical cell.

centrifuge (560): an instrument that hastens the settling of a precipitate by centrifugation.

chain reaction (687): a self-sustaining reaction in which the products initiate further reaction; commonly applied to certain nuclear fission reactions in which neutrons that are produced by the fission process cause additional nuclei to fission, hence propagating the reaction.

charge delocalization (334): the distribution of the electronic charge over more than one atom in a polyatomic species.

Charles's law (132): states that the volume of a fixed mass of gas at constant pressure is directly proportional to the absolute temperature of the gas.

chelate (723): a complex that contains a metal ion and at least one chelating ligand.

chelating ligand (723): a ligand that attaches to a metal ion at more than one coordination position.

chemical equation (45): the representation of a chemical reaction by writing the chemical formulas of the reactants and products separated by an arrow.

chemical equilibrium (435): chemical equilibrium is attained when the rate of the forward reaction is equal to the rate of the reverse reaction. A true chemical equilibrium is approachable from either the reactant or the product side of the reaction. At equilibrium the reactant and product concentrations do not change with time.

chemical formula (12): the chemical notation for a compound. The relative numbers of atoms of each element in the compound are indicated by subscripts.

chemical nomenclature (12): the system of naming chemical compounds.

chemical reaction (44): the formation of new substances from other substances by a rearrangement of the constituent atoms.

chemical symbol (5): the abbreviation that is used to designate an element.

chlor-alkali process (629): a method of preparing chlorine, Cl_2, and sodium hydroxide, $NaOH(aq)$, by the electrolysis of an aqueous sodium chloride, $NaCl(aq)$, solution.

chromatogram (39): a recording of the results of a chromatographic separation.

chromatography (38): separation of the components of a solution by the different tendencies of adsorption on a condensed phase. The solution phase flows over the condensed (stationary) phase.

chromous bubbler (644): a device used to remove traces of oxygen from gases. It is prepared by reacting zinc metal with chromium(III) nitrate to form chromium(II).

cis- **(331):** on the same side.

cisplatin (722): cis-diamminedichloroplatinum(II), which is an anticancer drug.

cis-trans isomerism (331, 722): a form of geometric isomerism. The designation *cis* indicates that two identical ligands are adjacent to each other in some sense. The designation *trans* indicates that two identical ligands are directly opposite each other in some sense.

Clapeyron-Clausius equation (358): the equation that gives the temperature dependence of the equilibrium vapor pressure. The equation is

$$\log\left(\frac{P_2}{P_1}\right) = \frac{\Delta H_{vap}}{2.30R}\left(\frac{T_2 - T_1}{T_1 T_2}\right) \quad (11\text{-}3)$$

where P_2 is the equilibrium vapor pressure at the Kelvin temperature T_2, P_1 is the equilibrium vapor pressure at the Kelvin temperature T_1, ΔH_{vap} is the molar enthalpy of vaporization, and R is the molar gas constant, 8.314 $J \cdot K^{-1} \cdot mol^{-1}$.

Claus process (587): the production of sulfur from hydrogen sulfide that occurs in some deposits of natural gas. Hydrogen sulfide is burned in air to produce sulfur dioxide, which reacts with hydrogen sulfide to produce sulfur.

coal gasification (189): a process for producing combustible gaseous products from coal.

colligative molality (389): a concentration scale for solute particles in a solution. The colligative molality, m_c, is defined as

$$m_c = \frac{\text{moles of solute particles}}{\text{kilograms of solvent}}$$

The units of colligative molality are $\text{mol} \cdot \text{kg}^{-1}$.

colligative molarity (393): a concentration scale for solute particles in a solution. The colligative molarity, M_c, is defined as

$$M_c = \frac{\text{moles of solute particles}}{\text{liters of solution}}$$

The units of colligative molarity are $\text{mol} \cdot \text{L}^{-1}$.

colligative properties (388): the properties of a solution that depend on the ratio of the number of solute particles to the number of solvent particles. The major colligative properties are vapor pressure lowering, boiling point elevation, freezing point depression, and osmotic pressure.

collision frequency, z (146): the number of collisions that a molecule experiences in one second. The number of collisions per second can be estimated by using the relationship

$$z \approx \frac{v_{av}}{l}$$

where l is the mean free path and v_{av} is the average speed of the molecules.

collision theory (417): the postulate that two molecules must collide with sufficient energy in order to react.

combination reaction (61): a reaction between two different substances in which a single product is formed.

combustion (101): the burning of a substance in oxygen.

combustion analysis (101): a determination of the mass percent composition of a compound from the amounts of CO_2 and H_2O formed by combustion of the compound.

combustion reaction (62, 159): a reaction in which a substance is burned in oxygen.

common ion (550): the same ionic constituent of two or more salts, usually in aqueous solution.

common-ion effect (550): the decrease in the solubility of an ionic solid caused by the presence in the solution of one of its constituent ions due to another salt..

complementary base pairs (784): the base pairs adenine and thymine (A−T) and guanine and cytosine (G−C), which are always opposite each other on the two polynucleotide chains in a DNA double helix.

complex ion (550): a charged chemical species containing a metal ion with one or more attached ligands.

complexation reaction (550): a reaction in which a complex ion is formed.

components (382): the species of a solution.

compound (4): a pure substance that can be broken down into simpler substances. A compound is composed of two or more different kinds of atoms.

compound unit (27): a unit of measurement that is expressed in terms of two or more units.

compressibility (127): the extent to which a substance changes its volume with increasing pressure.

concentration (108): the quantity of solute dissolved in a given quantity of solvent or solution.

concentration quotient, Q_{sp}, (557): An expression that has the same algebraic form as the K_{sp} expression (see solubility product constant) but into which arbitrary (nonequilibrium) values of the ionic concentrations can be substituted.

condensation polymerization reaction (772): the formation of a polymer from two different monomer molecules by splitting out a small molecule such as water.

condenser (38): a component of a distillation apparatus in which the vapors are cooled and thereby converted to liquid.

conduction band (368): a densely packed set of orbitals that extend throughout a crystal and that are analogous to antibonding orbitals in a molecule. Electrons move through a metal by means of the conduction band.

conduction electrons (368): electrons in the conduction band.

conjugate acid (487): an acid that is formed when a base accepts a proton from another species.

conjugate acid-base pair (487): two species that are coupled by means of a proton transfer reaction.

conjugate base (487): a base that is formed when an acid transfers a proton to another species.

conservation of energy (164): the law describing the concept that the total energy of a system never changes. Energy cannot be created or destroyed.

conservation of orbitals (325): the principle that states that when atomic orbitals are combined, the total number of new hybrid atomic orbitals is equal to the number of orbitals used to make them.

contact process (103): a method for the production of sulfuric acid, H_2SO_4, in which sulfur is oxidized to sulfur trioxide, which is then combined with water.

continuous spectrum (200): electromagnetic radiation that contains radiation of all the wavelengths in some region.

control rod (688): one of the cadmium or boron rods used to control the rate of the reaction in a nuclear reactor by absorbing neutrons.

coordinate covalent bond (276): a covalent bond that is formed when one species contributes both electrons to the bond.

coulomb (30): the SI unit of charge.

Coulomb's law (255): gives the energy change involved when two infinitely separated ions are brought to a separation distance, d, as

$$E = (2.31 \times 10^{-16} \, J \cdot pm) \frac{Z_1 Z_2}{d}$$

where Z_1 and Z_2 are the ionic charges of the two ions. When d is expressed in picometers, the energy is given in joules.

covalent bond (263): the bond formed between two atoms by a shared electron pair.

covalent network crystal (366): a crystal in which the constituent particles are held together by covalent bonds.

criteria of reaction spontaneity (607): the value of a quantity associated with a reaction, such as ΔG_{rxn} or Q/K, that can be used to predict whether a reaction is spontaneous or not.

critical mass (687): the minimum mass that will support a nuclear chain reaction.

critical point (360): the point in the phase diagram of a substance at which the liquid-gas curve abruptly terminates.

critical temperature (360): the minimum temperature above which a gas cannot be liquefied, no matter what its pressure; the temperature at the critical point.

crystallographic radius (229): an atomic radius that has been determined from X-ray analysis of a crystal containing the atoms of interest.

curie (692): a measure of the radioactivity of a sample; $1 \, Ci = 3.7 \times 10^{10}$ disintegrations per second.

cylindrically symmetric (215): characteristic of a function that depends only on the distance from an axis. A cylindrically symmetric function has a circular cross section.

D

d orbital (213, 714): an orbital for which $l = 2$. There are five d orbitals for each value of $n \geq 3$.

d transition metal series (714): the d transition metal series are as follows:

$3d$ series: $Z = 21$ to $Z = 30$ (Sc to Zn)

$4d$ series: $Z = 39$ to $Z = 48$ (Y to Cd)

$5d$ series: $Z = 71$ to $Z = 80$ (Lu to Hg)

dsp^3 (324): one of the five hybrid atomic orbitals obtained by combining a $3s$ orbital, three $3p$ orbitals, and one $3d$ orbital on the same atom. The dsp^2 orbitals have trigonal bipyramidal symmetry.

d^2sp^3 (325): one of the six equivalent hybrid atomic orbitals obtained by combining a $3s$ orbital, three $3p$ orbitals, and two $3d$ orbitals on the same atom. The d^2sp^3 orbitals point to the vertices of a regular octahedron.

d^x ion (715): a transition metal ion that has x electrons in its outer d orbitals.

$d_{xy}, d_{xz}, d_{yz}, d_{x^2-y^2}, d_{z^2}$ orbitals (714): the set of five d orbitals.

Dalton's law of partial pressure (140): states that the total pressure exerted by a mixture of gases is the sum of the partial pressures of each of the gases. For a mixture of two gases

$$P_{total} = P_1 + P_2$$

Each gaseous component exerts a pressure independent of the other gases.

d-orbital splitting pattern (724, 734): the five d orbitals of a transition metal ion in a complex are split into groups of orbitals of differing energies by the ligands in the complex.

de Broglie wavelength (205): the wavelength associated with a moving particle. The wavelength is given by $\lambda = h/mv$, where h is Planck's constant, m is the mass of the particle, and v is the speed of the particle.

decomposition reaction (66): a reaction in which a substance is broken up into two or more simpler substances.

decomposition voltage (629): the minimum voltage that is necessary to decompose a substance electrochemically.

deionize (539): to remove the ions in water by means of ion-exchange resins.

deionized water (539): water from which all cations and anions have been removed.

delocalized orbitals (334): π orbitals in a molecule that are not associated with a particular pair of atoms.

Δ_o (724): the magnitude of the splitting of the two sets of d orbitals, t_{2g} and e_g, on a metal ion in an octahedral complex.

Δ_{sp} (734): the magnitude of the splitting of the two highest-energy d orbitals, d_{xz} and $d_{x^2-y^2}$, on a metal ion in a square-planar complex.

Δ_t (734): the magnitude of the splitting of the two set of d orbitals, e and t_2, on a metal ion in a tetrahedral complex.

ΔG_f° (612): the standard molar Gibbs free energy of formation of a substance.

ΔG_{rxn} (607): the Gibbs free energy change of a reaction. The value of ΔG_{rxn} for a reaction run at a constant temperature is given by $\Delta G_{rxn} = \Delta H_{rxn} - T \Delta S_{rxn}$, where ΔH_{rxn} is the enthalpy change of the reaction, ΔS_{rxn} is the entropy change of the reaction and T is the temperature in kelvins. The value of ΔG_{rxn} is the maximum amount of work that can be obtained from the reaction under the stated conditions.

ΔG_{rxn}° (610): the standard Gibbs free energy

change for a reaction, which is the Gibbs free energy change for the reaction run under standard conditions.

ΔH_f° (167): the standard molar enthalpy of formation of a compound.

ΔH_{rxn} (165): the heat, q_P, absorbed or evolved by a reaction when the reaction occurs at constant pressure.

ΔS_{fus}° (601): the standard molar entropy change upon fusion. The value of ΔS_{fus}° is given by $\Delta S_{fus}^\circ = \Delta H_{fus}^\circ/T_m$, where ΔH_{fus}° is the molar enthalpy of fusion and T_m is the melting point in kelvins at one atmosphere.

ΔS_{rxn} (599): the entropy change of a reaction at conditions other than standard conditions.

ΔS_{rxn}° (605): the entropy change of a reaction when the reactants and products are at standard conditions. The value of ΔS_{rxn}° is given by $\Delta S_{rxn}^\circ = S_{products}^\circ - S_{reactants}^\circ$, where $S_{products}^\circ$ is the total entropy of all the product species and $S_{reactants}^\circ$ is the total entropy of all the reactant species.

ΔS_{vap}° (601): the standard molar entropy change upon vaporization. The value of ΔS_{vap}° is given by $\Delta S_{vap}^\circ = \Delta H_{vap}^\circ/T_b$, where ΔH_{vap}° is the standard molar enthalpy of vaporization and T_b is the boiling point in kelvins at one atmosphere.

ΔU_{rxn} (165): the heat, q_V, absorbed or evolved during a reaction that occurs at constant volume.

density (27): the mass per unit volume of a substance.

desalination (537): the process of removing dissolved solids from seawater.

deuterium (18, 156): the isotope of hydrogen that has a mass number of 2.

deviation from ideality (146): the behavior of a gas such that for one mole of the gas, the ratio PV/RT is not equal to 1.

dew point (357): the air temperature at which the relative humidity is 100 percent; depends on the partial pressure of water vapor in the air.

Dewar flask (177): an insulated vessel that heat cannot readily leave or enter. A thermos bottle is an example of Dewar flask.

diamagnetic (728): not magnetized by an external magnetic field. Diamagnetic molecules contain no unpaired electrons.

diatomic molecule (6): a molecule that is composed of two atoms.

dilution (110): a decrease in the concentration of a solution obtained by adding solvent.

dimer (772): a pair of identical molecules bonded together into a single unit.

dipeptide (777): a molecule composed of two amino acids joined by a peptide bond.

dipole-dipole attraction (350): the attraction between polar molecules.

dipole moment (281): a measure of the polarity of a bond. The dipole moment has both magnitude and direction. The direction of the dipole moment is represented as an arrow ($\leftrightarrow$) pointing from the positive charge to the negative charge.

diprotic acid (485): an acid that has two dissociable protons.

direction of reaction spontaneity (452): the direction (left to right or right to left) in which a reaction proceeds toward equilibrium.

discharge (633): the production of an electric current from an electrochemical cell.

disproportionation (709): chemical reaction in which a single species acts as both oxidizing and reducing agent.

distillation (38): a process by which a substance is separated from a liquid phase by volatilization upon heating. The vapor is then condensed to liquid by cooling.

disubstituted (745): replaced two hydrogen atoms in a compound by two other atoms or groups of atoms.

disulfide bond (774): the bond formed between two cysteine side groups on the same or neighboring polypeptide chains. The disulfide bond is of the type $-CH_2-S-S-CH_2-$.

DNA (781): deoxyribonucleic acid, the substance that contains the genetic information in cells. DNA is a polynucleotide composed of the sugar deoxyribose, the phosphate group, and the four bases adenine, thymine, guanine, and cytosine.

donor-acceptor complex (276): the product of the formation of a coordinate covalent bond between two species.

doping (375): addition of selected impurity atoms to a pure semiconductor.

double bond (271): the bond formed between two atoms by two shared electron pairs.

double helix (784): the shape of DNA — two polynucleotide chains intertwined in a helical fashion.

double replacement reaction (71): a reaction of the type $AB + CB \rightarrow AD + BC$ in which the cations in each compound exchange anionic partners.

dry cell (650): a primary battery utilizing the cell

$$^{\ominus}Zn(s)|ZnCl_2 \cdot 2NH_3(s)|NH_4Cl(aq)|MnO_2(s),$$
$$Mn_2O_3 \cdot H_2O(s)|C(s)^{\oplus}$$

dynamic equilibrium (355, 383, 435): a state of balance between forward and reverse processes such that no net change in the system takes place.

E

e_g **(724):** the set of d orbitals of higher energy on a metal ion in an octahedral complex.

e **orbitals (734):** the set of d orbitals of lower energy on a metal ion in a tetrahedral complex. The e orbitals consist of the $d_{x^2-y^2}$ and d_{z^2} orbitals.

effusion (144): the process whereby a gas exits through a very small hole in a container.

18-electron outer configuration (251): the relatively stable outer electron configuration $ns^2np^6nd^{10}$.

elastomer (774): a polymeric substance that can be stretched and that returns to its original shape when the stretching force is released.

electrochemical cell (632): an experimental setup by which an electric current can be obtained from a chemical reaction.

electrochemistry (624): the study of the chemical processes involved when an electric current is passed through materials.

electrode (628): a metal conductor used to establish electrical contact with an electrolyte solution. The electron transfers occur across the metal-electrolyte interface.

electrolysis (83, 624): a chemical reaction that occurs as a result of the passage of an electric current through a solution.

electrolyte (248): a substance that dissolves in water to produce solutions that conduct an electric current.

electromagnetic spectrum (199, 200): the range of wavelengths or frequencies of electromagnetic radiation.

electron (15): a subatomic particle that has a negative charge and a mass that is $\frac{1}{1837}$ that of a hydrogen atom.

electron acceptor (572): the reactant that gains electrons in an electron transfer reaction. The electron acceptor is reduced in an oxidation-reduction reaction.

electron affinity, *EA* (254): the energy released in the process of adding an electron to an atom. The equation for this process is

$$\text{atom}(g) + \text{electron} \longrightarrow \text{ion}(g) + EA$$

electron configuration (221): the assignment of electrons to orbitals according to the Pauli exclusion principle.

electron deficiency or **electron-deficient compound (276):** a condition or a compound in which one or more of the atoms other than hydrogen have less than eight valence electrons; such a compound violates the octet rule.

electron diffraction (205): the scattering of a beam of electrons in a definite manner by a substance.

electron donor (572): the reactant that loses electrons in an electron transfer reaction. An electron donor is oxidized in an oxidation-reduction reaction.

electron microscope (205): an instrument that uses the wavelike property of electrons to investigate subcellular and molecular structures.

electron-pair acceptor (494): an electron-deficient species that can act as a Lewis acid.

electron-pair donor (494): a species with a lone pair of electrons that can act as a Lewis base.

electron pairing energy (730): the energy required to pair up two electrons in the *d* orbitals of a metal in a complex.

electron transfer reaction (571): a reaction in which one species is oxidized and another species is reduced.

electronegativity (280): a measure of the force with which an atom attracts the electrons that it is sharing in a covalent bond.

electronic structure (195): the arrangement of the electrons within an atom.

electroplating (631): the production of a layer of protective metal by electrochemical deposition.

electrostatic attraction (255): the Coulombic attraction between oppositely charged ions.

element (4): a substance that contains only one kind of atom. There are over 100 known elements.

elementary process (415): a chemical reaction that occurs in a single step—the reactants go directly to the products without the involvement of intermediates.

emf series (644): electromotive force series; an arrangement of half-reactions in the order of their $E°$ values.

emission spectrum (209): spectrum obtained when gaseous excited atoms or molecules return to the ground state with the emission of light of characteristic wavelengths.

empirical formula (94): the simplest chemical formula of a substance. (See simplest formula.)

end point (514): the point in a titration at which the indicator changes color.

endothermic reaction (166): a reaction that absorbs energy as heat ($\Delta H_{rxn} > 0$).

energy change (165): difference in energy of a system before and after a process has occurred. The change in energy of a reaction is given the symbol ΔU_{rxn}, where $\Delta U_{rxn} = U_{products} - U_{reactants}$ denotes the change in energy of a reaction.

energy-favored reaction (606): a reaction for which $\Delta U_{rxn} < 0$.

energy state (207): one of the discrete set of energies that an atom or molecule can have.

enthalpy, *H* (165): a defined quantity given by the equation $H = U + PV$, where U is the energy, P is the pressure, and V is the volume of a system.

enthalpy change, ΔH_{rxn} (165): the energy evolved or absorbed as heat during a reaction when the reaction takes place at constant pressure. The enthalpy change is given as

$$\Delta H_{rxn} = H_{products} - H_{reactants}$$

for a reaction.

enthalpy of formation (170): the enthalpy change for the reaction in which one mole of a compound is formed from its elements.

entropy (598): a quantitative measure of the amount of disorder in a substance. The symbol for entropy is S. The SI unit of entropy is joules per kelvin, $J \cdot K^{-1}$.

entropy change, ΔS_{rxn} (599): the difference in the entropy of the reaction products and the reactants.

entropy-driven reaction (606): a spontaneous reaction for which $\Delta S_{rxn} > 0$ and $\Delta H_{rxn} \geqslant 0$.

entropy-favored reaction (606): a reaction for which $\Delta S_{rxn} > 0$.

enzyme (422): a protein that catalyzes a chemical reaction in biological systems.

equatorial vertex (293): one of the three vertices of the equilateral triangle that forms the shared base of a trigonal bipyramid. The three equatorial vertices are equivalent.

equilibrium (354): a state characterized by the equality of forward and reverse rates for a process.

equilibrium concentration (436): the value of the concentration of a reactant or of a product when the reaction has attained equilibrium.

equilibrium constant (424, 439): the algebraic relationship between reactant and product concentrations that exists at equilibrium. The form of the equilibrium constant expression for a chemical reaction is obtained by applying the law of concentration action to the balanced chemical equation.

equilibrium constant expression (424, 439): the expression for the equilibrium constant for a chemical reaction that is given by the law of concentration action. For the balanced chemical equation

$$a\text{A}(g) + b\text{B}(soln) + c\text{C}(s) \rightleftharpoons$$
$$x\text{X}(g) + y\text{Y}(soln) + z\text{Z}(l)$$

the equilibrium constant expression is given by

$$K_c = \frac{[\text{X}]^x[\text{Y}]^y}{[\text{A}]^a[\text{B}]^b}$$

equilibrium shift (446): the response of an equilibrium chemical reaction to a displacement from equilibrium produced by a change in conditions that affect the reaction equilibrium.

equilibrium state (424): state in which the forward reaction rate is equal to the reverse reaction rate.

equilibrium vapor pressure (355): the pressure of a vapor in equilibrium with its liquid.

equivalence point (514): the pH or point in a titration at which all the acid or base initially present is just neutralized.

escaping tendency (392): the tendency of a substance to leave a solution. The higher the vapor pressure of a substance, the higher the escaping tendency. The lower the colligative molality of the solute, the higher the escaping tendency of the solvent.

ester (760): a class of organic compounds that result from the reaction between a carboxylic acid and an alcohol.

esterification reaction (761): a reaction between an organic acid and an alcohol to produce an ester.

eutrophication (507): depletion of the oxygen in a body of water by decaying organisms such as algae.

excess reactant (104): the reactant that is present in larger quantity than is necessary to react with the other reactants in a reaction.

excited state (207, 224): an energy state that is higher than the ground state.

exothermic reaction (166): a reaction that evolves energy as heat ($\Delta H_{rxn} < 0$).

expanded valence shell (277): the idea that elements beyond the second row of the periodic table can accommodate more than eight electrons by using d orbitals. Such elements (P, S, Cl) need not obey the octet rule.

external circuit (632): the part of an electrical circuit involving an electrochemical cell that does not include the electrochemical cell.

F

f orbital (213): an orbital for which $l = 3$. There are seven f orbitals for each value of $n \geqslant 4$.

face-centered cubic unit cell (362): the unit cell in which the components of the crystal are located at the corners of the cube and in the centers of the six faces of the cube.

faraday (627): the value of Faraday's constant, $9.65 \times 10^4 \text{ C} \cdot \text{mol}^{-1}$.

Faraday's constant (627): the charge on one mole of electrons. Faraday's constant, F, is equal to $96{,}500 \text{ C} \cdot \text{mol}^{-1}$.

Faraday's laws (626): the first law states that the extent of an electrochemical reaction depends solely on the quantity of electricity that is passed through a solution. The second law states that the mass of a substance that is deposited as a metal or evolved as a gas by the passage of a given quantity of electricity is directly proportional to the molar mass of the substance divided by the number of electrons consumed or produced per formula unit. Faraday's laws are expressed quantitatively by the equation

$$\left(\begin{array}{c}\text{mass deposited as}\\ \text{metal or evolved gas}\end{array}\right) = m = \left(\frac{It}{F}\right)\left(\frac{A}{n}\right)$$

where I is the current in amperes, t is the time in seconds, F is Faraday's constant, A is the molar mass of the metal or gas, and n is the number of electrons required to produce one formula unit of metal or gas.

filtration (38): the process of separating a liquid phase from a solid phase by the use of a material, such as special papers, through which the liquid phase can pass.

first electron affinity, EA_1, (254): the energy associated with the process of adding an electron to an isolated atom.

first excited state (207): the first energy state above the ground state.

first ionization energy (195): the minimum energy required to remove an electron from a neutral atom, A, to produce the A^+ ion.

first law of thermodynamics (164): the law of conservation of energy.

first-order rate law (409): a rate law in which the reaction rate is proportional to the first power of the concentration of a reactant. The rate law is of the form rate = k[A].

first-order reaction (409): a reaction whose rate law is a first-order rate law.

Fisher-Tropsch process (synthesis) (156, 190): syntheses involving reactions of hydrogen with carbon monoxide to produce straight-chain hydrocarbons and alcohols with up to 10 carbon atoms. For example,

$$CO(g) + 2H_2(g) \xrightarrow{\text{catalyst}} CH_3OH(l)$$

fission (686): a nuclear reaction in which a nucleus splits into two smaller, roughly equal-sized fragments.

flocculent (556): fluffy; a precipitate that does not settle readily.

formal charge (268): the assignment of a charge to an atom in a molecule or ion by a set of rules. The formal charge of an atom is found by the relationship

$$\begin{aligned}\begin{array}{c}\text{formal}\\ \text{charge}\end{array} &= \left(\begin{array}{c}\text{number of valence}\\ \text{electrons in the atom}\end{array}\right)\\ &\quad - \left(\begin{array}{c}\text{total number of}\\ \text{lone pair electrons}\end{array}\right)\\ &\quad - \frac{1}{2}\left(\begin{array}{c}\text{total number of}\\ \text{shared electrons}\end{array}\right)\end{aligned}$$

formula mass (90): the relative mass of a formula unit. The formula mass is the sum of the atomic masses of all the atoms that make up the formula unit.

formula unit (59, 90): the simplest component of a substance. The formula unit may be an atom, a molecule, or a group of ions. A formula unit is defined by the chemical formula. Thus NaCl (one Na^+ and one Cl^-) is the formula unit of sodium chloride.

forward rate (435): the rate of the forward reaction.

forward reaction (424): the formation of the reaction products from the reactants, or the reaction that proceeds left to right for the equation as written.

forward reaction rate (424): the reaction rate for the reaction that takes place left to right as written.

fossil fuel (188): oil, coal, or natural gas.

fountain effect (462): a demonstration of the solubility of ammonia in water.

4d transition-metal series (227): the second transition-metal series, which involves the sequential filing of the 4d orbitals.

fractional distillation (397): a distillation that involves a long distillation column in which the vapor is continuously condensed and revaporized.

Frasch process (586): a process for extracting sulfur from underground deposits by using hot (180°C) high-pressure water to melt the sulfur.

free radical (275): a species with one or more unpaired electrons. All species with an odd number of electrons are free radicals.

free radical reaction (745): a reaction involving free radicals, which are species with unpaired electrons.

freezing point depression (391): the decrease in the freezing point of a solution below the freezing point of the pure solvent. The freezing point depression is given by the equation $T_f^\circ - T_f = K_f m_c$, where T_f° is the freezing point of the pure solvent, T_f is the freezing point of the solution, m_c is the colligative molality of the solution, and K_f is a proportionality constant, called the freezing point depression constant, of the solvent.

freezing point depression constant (391): the proportionality constant between the freezing point depression and the colligative molality of a solution. The value depends only on the solvent. The symbol is K_f and the units are $K \cdot m_c^{-1}$.

frequency, ν (199): the number of maxima or minima of a wave that pass a given point per second. The symbol of frequency is ν and the units of frequency are cycles per second, s^{-1}, or hertz, Hz (1 Hz = 1 cycle $\cdot s^{-1}$).

fuel (166): a substance that can be used in a chemical reaction to provide energy for the performance of tasks.

fuel rod (688): one of the rods in a nuclear reactor that contain the isotope that undergoes fission.

fuming sulfuric acid (590): $H_2S_2O_7$ (35% in H_2SO_4), which is obtained by absorbing SO_3 into nearly pure sulfuric acid.

fusion (690): the process by which a nucleus is produced from smaller nuclei.

G

galena (123): the ore PbS.

γ-ray (16): a high energy electromagnetic wave emitted in certain types of nuclear decay.

gas (127): the physical state of matter having the properties of occupying the entire volume and assuming the shape of its container and having a large compressibility.

gas constant (135): the constant, R, in the ideal-gas equation. Its value depends on the units of P, V, and T:

$$R = 0.0821 \text{ L} \cdot \text{atm} \cdot \text{mol}^{-1} \cdot \text{K}^{-1}$$
$$= 8.314 \text{ J} \cdot \text{mol}^{-1} \cdot \text{K}^{-1}$$

gas electrode (636): an electrode involving a gaseous species.

gas-liquid chromatography (38): an analytical technique used to separate mixtures of gases or volatile liquids by flowing the vapor mixture over a liquid phase in which the vapor components have different solubilities.

gasohol (189): a mixture of gasoline and ethyl alcohol.

gas thermometer (132): a thermometer that uses the volume of a fixed mass of a gas to measure the temperature.

Gay-Lussac's law of combining volumes (133): the volumes of gases that combine to form reaction products are in the ratio of small whole numbers. The volumes must be measured at the same temperature and pressure.

gene (787): a segment along a DNA molecule that codes the synthesis of a particular polypeptide.

geometrical isomers (289): molecules that have the same chemical formula but different geometrical arrangements of the atoms. Geometrical isomers have different chemical and physical properties.

Gibbs criteria (of reaction spontaneity) (607): criteria used to predict whether a process is spontaneous or not. The Gibbs criteria are

1. $\Delta G_{rxn} < 0$; the reaction is spontaneous;

2. $\Delta G_{rxn} > 0$; the reaction is not spontaneous—product formation requires energy input;

3. $\Delta G_{rxn} = 0$; the reaction is at equilibrium.

Gibbs free energy (607): a quantity that serves as a compromise function between enthalpy and entropy. For a reaction run at constant temperature, the Gibbs free energy change is given by $\Delta G_{rxn} = \Delta H_{rxn} - T \Delta S_{rxn}$.

Gibbs free energy change, ΔG_{rxn} (607): the change in Gibbs free energy for a reaction. ΔG_{rxn} is given by

$$\Delta G_{rxn} = G(\text{products}) - G(\text{reactants})$$

The value of ΔG_{rxn} determines the reaction spontaneity.

Glauber's salt (191): the chemical $Na_2SO_4 \cdot 10H_2O(s)$.

Graham's law of effusion (145): the relation between the rates of effusion of two gases, which is given by

$$\frac{\text{rate}_A}{\text{rate}_B} = \left(\frac{M_B}{M_A}\right)^{1/2}$$

where M_A and M_B are the molecular masses of gas A and of gas B, respectively.

greenhouse effect (241): the increase in temperature of the troposphere resulting from absorption of infrared radiation by atmospheric carbon dioxide and water.

ground electronic state (221): the state of lowest energy. The ground electronic state is obtained by filling up the atomic orbitals of lowest energy according to the Pauli exclusion principle and Hund's rule.

ground state (207): the lowest possible energy state of an atom or molecule.

ground-state wave function (317): the wave function for the lowest energy state of a species.

group (52): the collection of elements that are in the same column in the periodic table. A group of elements is also called a family of elements.

Group 1 metals (50): the elements that appear in the first column of the periodic table. The Group 1 metals are called the alkali metals.

Group 2 metals (50): the elements that appear in the second column of the periodic table. The Group 2 metals are called the alkaline earth metals.

Guggenheim notation (28): a notation used to label table headings and graph axes that yields dimensionless numbers for tabulation and graphing.

H

Haber process (156, 450): the method by which ammonia is produced commer-

cially from nitrogen and hydrogen. The reaction

$$N_2(g) + 3H_2(g) \rightleftharpoons 2NH_3(g)$$

is carried out on a commercial scale at 500°C and 300 atm, with the aid of a catalyst.

half-life (414, 675): the time it takes for one half of a sample to undergo reaction; denoted by $t_{1/2}$.

half-reaction (572): one part of an electron transfer reaction representing either the loss of electrons or the gain of electrons by a reactant.

halide (48): a binary compound consisting of a halogen and another element.

Hall process (630): the industrial method of preparing aluminum by the electrolysis of a solution of aluminum oxide, Al_2O_3, dissolved in molten cryolite, $Na_3AlF_6(l)$.

haloalkane (745): a substance derived from an alkane in which one or more hydrogen atoms of the alkane are replaced by halogen atoms (also called alkyl halide).

halogen (48): a member of the group of elements fluorine, chlorine, bromine, iodine, and astatine, which are the Group 7 elements in the periodic table.

hard water (538): water that contains appreciable amounts of divalent cations, such as Ca^{2+}, Mg^{2+}, and Fe^{2+}, together with the anions HCO_3^- and/or SO_4^{2-}.

heat, q (165): a mode of energy transfer that occurs as a result of a temperature difference.

heat capacity, c_P (175): the heat required to raise the temperature of a substance by one Kelvin degree. The SI unit of heat capacity is joules per kelvin, $J \cdot K^{-1}$.

heat of formation (170): standard molar enthalpy of formation.

heat of reaction (166): the amount of energy evolved or absorbed as heat when a chemical reaction occurs.

heating curve (346): a plot of how the temperature of a substance varies with time if it is heated at a constant rate.

heavy water (18, 156): water that is composed of deuterium and oxygen, D_2O.

Heisenberg uncertainty principle (210): states that it is not possible to measure accurately both the position and the momentum of a particle simultaneously.

Henderson-Hasselbalch equation (527): an equation that relates the pH of a buffer solution to the stoichiometric concentrations of a conjugate acid-base pair.

Henry's law (384): states that the solubility of a gas in a liquid is directly proportional to the equilibrium partial pressure of the gas over the solution. The equation is $P_{gas} = k_h M_{gas}$, where P_{gas} is the equilibrium gas pressure over the solution, M_{gas} is the concentration of the gas in the solution, and k_h is the proportionality constant, called Henry's law constant, for the gas.

Henry's law constant (384): the proportionality constant between the solubility of a gas in a liquid and the equilibrium pressure of the gas over the solution. The symbol is k_h and the units are $atm \cdot M^{-1}$.

hertz, Hz (199): the SI unit of frequency. One hertz is equal to one cycle per second.

Hess's law (168): states that if two or more chemical equations are added together, then the value of ΔH_{rxn} for the resulting equation is equal to the sum of the ΔH_{rxn} values for the separate equations.

heterogeneous (37): not uniform in chemical composition, for example, a mixture of salt and sugar.

heterogeneous catalysis (422): catalysis in which the catalyst is in a different phase from the reactants.

heterogeneous catalyst (422): a solid catalyst that catalyzes a gas- or solution-phase reaction.

heterogeneous mixture (37): a mixture in which the components are not uniform from point to point.

heteronuclear diatomic molecule (339): a molecule that consists of two different nuclei.

high-spin configuration (728): a d electron configuration of a complex in which the d electrons occupy a higher-energy set of d orbitals before they pair up in the lower-energy set of d orbitals.

homogeneous (108, 382): having uniform properties throughout.

homonuclear diatomic molecule (335): a molecule that consists of two atoms of the same element.

Hund's rule (223, 339): states that for any set of orbitals of the same energy, the ground-state electron configuration is obtained by placing the electrons in different orbitals of this set with parallel spins until each of the orbitals has one electron, before pairing up any of the electrons.

hybrid atomic orbital (320): an orbital on an atom that is the result of combining different atomic orbitals on the same atom according to a procedure of quantum mechanics.

hydrated salt (hydrate) (101): A salt that forms crystals containing a definite percentage by mass of water; for example, $CuSO_4 \cdot 5H_2O$.

hydrocarbon (98, 159, 742): a class of organic compounds that consist of only hydrogen and carbon.

hydrogen bonding (351): a special type of dipole-dipole attraction that involves the electrostatic interaction of a hydrogen atom in one species with an electronegative atom in another species.

hydrogen electrode (641): an electrode consisting of a platinum electrode and hydrogen gas, $H_2(g)$, at 1 atm pressure. By convention, the standard reduction voltage of the hydrogen electrode is zero.

hydrogen ion, $H^+(aq)$ (65): a proton that occurs when a hydrogen atom has lost its electron. In aqueous solution the hydrogen ion, designated by $H^+(aq)$, exists primarily as the $H_3O^+(aq)$ ion.

hydrogen molecular ion (335): the species H_2^+, which consists of two protons and one electron.

hydrogenation (750): addition of hydrogen to a molecule.

hydrohalic acid (660): a binary acid that contains hydrogen and a halogen.

hydronium ion (65, 468): the species, $H_3O^+(aq)$, that is the dominant form of the hydrogen ion in aqueous solution.

hypothesis (3): a proposition put forth as a possible explanation for the occurrence of a phenomenon, which serves as a guide to further investigation.

I

ideal gas (135): a gas that obeys the ideal-gas law.

ideal-gas equation (135): the equation $PV = nRT$, where P is the pressure, V is the volume, T is the temperature, and n is the number of moles of the gas; R is the gas constant.

ideal-gas law (135): the combination of Charles's law, Boyle's law, and Avogadro's law. The ideal-gas law equation is $PV = nRT$.

ideal solution (387): a solution in which the solute molecules and the solvent molecules are randomly distributed throughout the solution.

indicator (511): a substance that is used to signal, by a color change, the end point in a titration.

inert complex (733): a complex that exchanges its ligands slowly with other available ligands.

infrared spectrum (309): a plot of the infrared radiation energy absorbed versus the wavelength of the radiation for a species.

inner transition metals (54, 228): the two 14-member series of metals that involve the sequential filling of the f orbitals. These series are called the lanthanides and the actinides, respectively.

intercept (396, 412, 798): the value of y at which a straight line crosses the y axis. The intercept is b in the equation for a straight line, $y = mx + b$.

interhalogen compound (300): a compound in which a central halogen atom is bonded to one or more atoms of a more electronegative halogen.

intermediate (416): a species that is formed from the reactants and is involved in the conversion of reactants to products but that does not appear as a reactant or product in the overall reaction.

intrinsic electron spin (217): a characteristic property of an electron due to the spin of the electron around its axis in one of two directions.

ion (21): a species that has either a deficiency of electrons (in which case the ion is positively charged) or an excess of electron(s) (in which case the ion is negatively charged).

ion-exchange resin (539): an organic polymer containing acidic and/or basic groups that can remove cations (via the acid groups) or anions (via the basic groups) by means of an ion-exchange reaction.

ion pair (252): a positive and negative ion held together by electrostatic attraction.

ion product constant of water (469): the equilibrium constant for the equation

$$H_2O(l) + H_2O(l) \rightleftharpoons$$
$$H_3O^+(aq) + OH^-(aq)$$

The ion product constant is given by $K_w = [H_3O^+][OH^-]$. The value of K_w is $1.00 \times 10^{-14} \ M^2$ at 25°C.

ionic bond (250): the electrostatic attraction that holds oppositely charged ions together.

ionic charge (59): the positive or negative charge on an ion.

ionic compound (22, 59, 250): a compound that is composed of positive and negative ions. An ionic compound has no net charge.

ionic crystal (364): an ordered array of negatively and positively charged ions.

ionic equation (72): a chemical equation that shows directly only the ions involved in a reaction.

ionic radius (253): the radius of an ion that is obtained from X-ray crystallographic measurements.

ionization energy (195): the minimum energy that is required to remove an electron completely from a gaseous atom or ion.

ionosphere (239): the outermost region of the atmosphere that contains ions and electrons produced by solar radiation.

isoelectronic (22): possessing the same number of electrons as another species (iso- means the same).

isotope (18): an atom of an element that has a particular mass number. Isotopes of an element have the same number of protons but different numbers of neutrons.

IUPAC nomenclature (746): the system of naming organic compounds that has been recommended by the International Union of Pure and Applied Chemistry.

J

joule (143): the SI unit of energy: $1 \ J = 1 \ kg \cdot m^2 \cdot s^{-2}$.

K

K_c (439): the equilibrium constant expressed in terms of concentrations of the products and reactants.

karat (701): a unit for expressing the amount of gold in alloys. Pure gold is 24 karat.

kelvin (132): the unit of temperature on the absolute temperature scale.

ketone (757): a class of organic compounds that has the general formula RCR'.

$$\overset{\parallel}{\text{O}}$$

kilowatt (188): a unit of power. One kilowatt is 1000 joules per second.

kilowatt-hour (191): a unit of energy. One kilowatt-hour is the energy produced by a one-kilowatt power source operating for one hour.

kinetic energy (143): the energy of a body due to its motion. The SI unit of kinetic energy is the joule, J. The formula relating the kinetic energy to the speed of the body is $E = \frac{1}{2}mv^2$, where m is the mass of the body and v is its speed.

kinetic theory of gases (143): a molecular theory of gases. A gas is considered as mostly empty space. The gas molecules are viewed as tiny spheres in constant motion. The molecules are traveling about at high speeds and are continually colliding with each other and with the walls of the container. The pressure of a gas is due to the collisions of the molecules of the gas with the walls of the container.

K_p **(440):** an equilibrium constant expressed in terms of equilibrium partial pressures of products and/or reactants.

L

labile complex (733): a complex that exchanges its ligands rapidly with other available ligands.

lanthanide series (51, 228): the inner transition metal series that is headed by lanthanum. The lanthanide series contains the elements lanthanum ($Z = 57$) through ytterbium ($Z = 70$).

lattice energy (257): the energy released when isolated negative ions and isolated positive ions combine to form an ionic crystal.

laughing gas (465): nitrous oxide, $N_2O(g)$.

law of concentration action (438): states that the equilibrium constant expression for an equation is given by the ratio of product equilibrium concentrations to reactant equilibrium concentrations, with each concentration factor raised to a power equal to the stoichiometric coeffi-

cient of that species in the balanced equation. Pure liquids and solids, whose concentrations cannot be varied, do not appear in the equilibrium constant expression.

law of conservation of mass (7): states that in an ordinary chemical reaction, the total mass of the reacting substances is equal to the total mass of the products formed.

law of constant composition (8): states that the mass percentage of each element in a compound is always the same, regardless of the source of the compound or of how the compound is prepared.

Le Châtelier's principle (446): if a chemical reaction at equilibrium is subjected to a change in conditions that displaces the reaction from equilibrium, then the direction in which the reaction proceeds toward a new equilibrium state will be such as to at least partially offset the change in conditions.

lead storage battery (649): a group of the following cells arranged in series:

$$\ominus Pb(s)|PbSO_4(s)|H_2SO_4(aq)|PbO_2(s),$$
$$PbSO_4(s)|Pb(s)\oplus$$

The 12-V lead storage battery has six of these cells in series.

Lewis acid (494): an electron-pair acceptor.

Lewis base (494): an electron-pair donor.

Lewis electron-dot formula (198): a pictorial representation of an atom. The nucleus and inner-core electrons are indicated by the chemical symbol of the atom and the outer electrons are indicated by dots placed around the chemical symbol.

Lewis formula (263): the formula for a molecule or other species in which covalent bonds are indicated by lines and lone pairs by dots.

ligand (295, 716): an anion or a neutral molecule that binds to metal ions to form a complex ion. Also, an atom that is bonded to a central atom in a molecule or ion.

ligand-substitution reaction (717): a reaction involving a change in ligands attached to the central metal ion in a complex.

ligating atoms (723): the atoms of a ligand that attach to a metal ion in a complex species.

limiting reactant (104): the reactant that is consumed completely in a reaction in which nonstoichiometric amounts of reactants are allowed to react.

line spectrum (201): the resolution of the components of electromagnetic radiation that contains radiation of only a few discrete wavelengths. The spectrum consists of a few lines corresponding to these wavelengths.

linear molecule (282): a molecule in which all the atoms lie on a straight line.

liquid (127): the physical state of matter having the properties of fixed volume, assumption of the shape of its container, and very small compressibility.

liquid-solid chromatography (40): a means of separating compounds in solution by passing the solution through a column packed with a pulverized solid compound.

litmus (74): a material obtained from lichens, which is red in acidic solutions and blue in basic solutions.

litmus paper (74): a paper impregnated with litmus, a vegetable substance that is red in acidic solutions and blue in basic solutions.

localized bond orbital (318): the orbital that describes the bonding electrons in a covalent bond between two atoms. The bonding electrons are concentrated primarily in the region between the two atoms joined by the covalent bond.

lock-and-key theory (423): the postulate that an enzyme acts as a specific template to one of the reactants to catalyze the chemical reaction.

logarithm (793): the power to which 10 must be raised to attain a number. The logarithm of a number a is $\log a = x$ such that $a = 10^x$.

London fog (243): a fog that is polluted with oxides of sulfur.

London force (353): the attractive force between nonpolar molecules and atoms arising from the correlation of the electron distributions.

lone electron pair or lone pair (264): a pair of valence electrons that are not shared between two atoms in a molecule.

lone pair (264): a lone electron pair.

low-spin configuration (728): a d electron configuration in a complex in which the d electrons pair up in the lower-energy d orbitals before they occupy the higher-energy set of d orbitals.

LOX (190): liquid oxygen.

Lyman series (208): the series of lines in the hydrogen atomic spectrum due to transitions from higher states ($n > 1$) to the ground state ($n = 1$).

M

macromolecules (770): molecules that contain thousands of atoms. Polymers are macromolecules.

magic numbers (674): the numbers 2, 8, 20, 28, 50, and 82. Nuclei that contain a magic number of protons or neutrons are particularly stable and abundant in nature.

magnetic quantum number (215): the quantum number, m_l, that determines the spatial orientation of an orbital. The allowed values of m_l are $-l, \ldots, -1, 0, +1, \ldots, +l$ or $-l \leq m_l \leq l$.

main-group elements (53): the elements in groups headed by the numbers 1 through 8 in the periodic table.

malleable (16): able to be rolled into thin sheets.

manganese nodules (536): porous chunks of metallic oxides that form spontaneously in the vicinity of vent holes in the ocean floor.

manometer (128): a device used to measure the pressure of a gas. It consists of a U-shaped tube partially filled with mercury. One end of the tube is evacuated and sealed. The other end is attached to the vessel containing the gas. (See Figure 4-3 in the text.)

Markovnikov's rule (750): states that when HX adds to an unsaturated hydrocarbon, the hydrogen atom becomes bonded to the carbon atom in the double or triple bond already bearing the larger number of hydrogen atoms.

mass (8): the inherent amount of material in an object.

mass number (17): the total number of protons and neutrons in an atom. The mass number is designated by the symbol A.

mass spectrometer (21): an instrument used to measure the relative masses and amounts of atoms and molecules present in a sample.

mass spectrometry (315): the study of the fragmentation patterns of molecular ions produced in a mass spectrometer. Mass spectra often are used to identify compounds.

mass spectrum (314): a plot of the relative numbers of ions of various masses versus the mass of the ions; obtained from a mass spectrometer.

mean free path, l (145): the average distance a gas molecule travels between collisions. The mean free path depends on the pressure, the temperature, and the size of the molecule.

melting point curve (360): a plot of the pressure at which the solid and liquid phases of a substance are in equilibrium versus the temperature.

mercaptans (593): organic compounds that contain the —SH group.

mercury battery (650): a battery using the cell

$$^{\ominus}\text{steel}|\text{Zn}(s)|\text{ZnO}(s)|\text{KOH}(aq, 40\%)$$
$$|\text{HgO}(s)|\text{Hg}(l)|\text{steel}^{\oplus}$$

mesosphere (239): the region above the stratosphere wherein the temperature decreases with altitude.

meta (754): designation for disubstituted benzenes with substituents at the 1 and 3 positions.

metal (5): a substance that has the following properties: it has a characteristic luster; it can be rolled into sheets; it can be drawn into wires; it can be melted and cast into various shapes; and it is a good conductor of electricity and heat. About three fourths of the elements are metals. All the metals except mercury are solids at 20°C.

metallic crystal (367): the crystalline form of a metal, in which the lattice sites are occupied by ions and the valence electrons are delocalized.

method of half-reactions (573): a system of balancing oxidation-reduction equations in which the oxidation half-reaction and the reduction half-reaction are balanced separately.

method of initial rates (408): a means of obtaining the rate law from a determination of the reaction rate at the start of the reaction during which time the concentrations of the reactants do not change appreciably.

method of successive approximations (480, 797): a method of solving a quadratic equation.

metric system (25): a system of scientific units of measurement based on the meter, the kilogram, and the second as the base units of length, mass, and time, respectively.

metric ton (103): a mass of 1000 kg or 2205 lb.

mica (377): a mineral containing two-dimensional polymeric sheets with the composition $Si_2O_5^{2-}$.

micelles (541): small droplets that are soluble in water as a result of the polar groups on the surface.

midpoint (520): the point on the titration curve that is halfway between the starting point and the equivalence point.

mixture (36): a composition of two or more substances that may be separated into various pure components.

mol (90): the symbol for the unit mole.

molality (388): a concentration scale for a solute in a solution. The molality, m, is defined as

$$m = \frac{\text{moles of solute}}{\text{kilograms of solvent}}$$

The units of molality are $mol \cdot kg^{-1}$.

molar (108): pertaining to one mole.

molar bond enthalpy, H(bond) (174): the enthalpy change associated with the dissociation of one mole of a given type of bond. The units are joules per mole, $J \cdot mol^{-1}$, or kilojoules per mole, $kJ \cdot mol^{-1}$.

molar enthalpy of fusion (346): the energy that is required to melt one mole of a substance. It is denoted by ΔH_{fus}. The SI units are $kJ \cdot mol^{-1}$.

molar enthalpy of sublimation (349): the energy that is required to sublime one mole of a substance. It is denoted by ΔH_{sub}. The SI units are $kJ \cdot mol^{-1}$.

molar enthalpy of vaporization (347): the energy that is required to vaporize one mole of a substance. It is denoted by ΔH_{vap}. The SI units are $kJ \cdot mol^{-1}$.

molar entropy of fusion, ΔS_{fus} (601): the entropy change that occurs upon melting of one mole of a substance. The value of ΔS_{fus} is given by

$$\Delta S_{fus} = \frac{\Delta H_{fus}}{T_m}$$

where ΔH_{fus} is the molar enthalpy of fusion and T_m is the melting point in kelvins.

molar entropy of vaporization, ΔS_{vap} (601): the entropy change upon vaporization of one mole of a substance. The value of ΔS_{vap} is given by

$$\Delta S_{vap} = \frac{\Delta H_{vap}}{T_b}$$

where ΔH_{vap} is the molar enthalpy of vaporization and T_b is the boiling point in kelvins.

molar heat capacity, C_p (176): the heat capacity per mole of a substance. The SI unit of molar heat capacity is $J \cdot K^{-1} \cdot mol^{-1}$.

molar heat of formation, ΔH_f° (170): the enthalpy change at $25\,^\circ C$ for the reaction in which one mole of a substance at 1 atm is formed from the elements at 1 atm.

molar mass (90, 138): the mass in grams of one mole of a substance. The units of molar mass are $g \cdot mol^{-1}$.

molar volume (135): the volume occupied by one mole of a substance. At $0\,^\circ C$ and 1.00 atm the molar volume of an ideal gas is equal to 22.4 L.

molarity (108): the concentration of a solution expressed as the number of moles of solute per liter of solution. The units of molarity are $mol \cdot L^{-1}$ and the symbol of molarity is M.

mole (90): the quantity of a substance that is equal to its formula mass in grams. The official SI definition of the mole is the amount of substance of a system that contains as many elementary entities as there are atoms in exactly 0.012 kg of carbon-12. The symbol for a mole is mol.

mole fraction (140): an expression for the concentration of a solution. In a solution containing n_1 moles of solvent and n_2 moles of solute, the mole fraction of the solvent is defined as

$$X_1 = \frac{n_1}{n_1 + n_2}$$

The mole fraction is a unitless quantity.

molecular compound (63): a compound composed of molecules; such compounds generally have low melting and low boiling points.

molecular crystal (264, 365): a three-dimensional ordered array of molecules.

molecular diameter, σ (145): the experimentally determined diameter of a molecule.

molecular formula (97): the chemical formula of a molecular compound which gives the number of atoms of each element that makes up one formula unit of the compound.

molecular ion (313): an ion produced by the loss or gain of electrons by a molecule.

molecular mass (14): the mass of a molecule relative to the atomic mass of carbon-12. The molecular mass is the sum of the atomic masses of the atoms that make up the molecule.

molecular orbital (317): a wave function that describes an electron in a molecule.

molecular orbital theory (335): a theory of bonding based on orbitals that extend over two or more atoms.

molecular substance (89): a substance that is composed of molecules.

molecular vibrations (309): vibrational (back and forth) motions of the atoms in a molecule.

molecule (6, 9): an entity in which two or more atoms are joined together.

monoclinic (589): in the text, a crystalline form of sulfur.

monomers (770): small molecules that are joined together to form a polymer.

muriatic acid (665): hydrochloric acid, $HCl(aq)$.

N

natural abundance (19): the percentage of an isotope of an element that is present in the naturally occurring element.

natural law (3): a concise summary of experimental observations regarding some aspects of the behavior of matter in nature.

negative deviation (397): a deviation from Raoult's law by a nonideal solution whose vapor pressure is less than that calculated by Raoult's law.

Nernst equation (638): the quantitative relationship between the cell voltage, E, and the value of Q. At $25\,^\circ C$ the Nernst equation is given by

$$E = E° - \left(\frac{0.0592 \text{ V}}{n}\right) \log Q$$

where $E°$ is the standard cell voltage and n is the number of moles of electrons transferred in the cell reaction as written.

net ionic equation (72): an ionic equation written with the omission of the spectator ions.

neutral anion (491): an anion that does not react with water in aqueous solution to produce either $H_3O^+(aq)$ or $OH^-(aq)$.

neutral cation (491): a cation that does not react with water in aqueous solution to produce either $H_3O^+(aq)$ or $OH^-(aq)$.

neutral solution (469): an aqueous solution in which $[H_3O^+] = [OH^-]$.

neutralized (73): the condition attained on complete reaction of an acid with a base or *vice versa*.

neutralization reaction (73): a reaction between an acid and a base.

neutron (17): a subatomic particle that has almost the same mass as a proton and has no charge.

neutron activation analysis (682): an analytical method to measure trace quantities of elements. The sample is irradiated by a beam of neutrons; the nuclear products emit γ-rays of energies that are characteristic of each isotope.

nickel-cadmium battery (650): a battery utilizing the cell

$$\ominus \text{steel}|Cd(s)|Cd(OH)_2(s)|LiOH(aq)$$
$$|NiOOH(s), Ni(OH)_2(s)|\text{steel}\oplus$$

nitride (461): a compound that contains the nitride ion, N^{3-}.

nitrogen fixation (460): a process whereby $N_2(g)$ is converted into nitrogen-containing compounds.

noble-gas outer electron configuration (250): the outer electron configuration ns^2np^6. Metal atoms may attain a noble-gas outer electron configuration by losing electrons. Nonmetal atoms attain a noble-gas outer electron configuration by gaining electrons.

NMR spectrum (311): the spectrum of a molecule obtained from a nuclear magnetic resonance spectrometer.

noble gases (50): the elements that appear in the extreme right-hand column of the periodic table. The noble gases are helium, neon, argon, krypton, xenon, and radon. The noble gases are relatively unreactive and were once called the inert gases.

nodal surface (214): a surface over which the value of an orbital is zero.

nonelectrolyte (248): a substance that dissolves in water to produce solutions that do not conduct an electric current.

nonmetal (5): a substance that does not have the properties of a metal. The nonmetals are not uniform in their physical appearance or chemical properties.

nonpolar bond (280): a pure covalent bond.

nonpolar molecule (282, 304): a molecule that has no net dipole moment.

normal boiling point (356): the temperature at which the equilibrium vapor pressure of a liquid equals exactly 1 atm.

normal sublimation point (361): the temperature at which the equilibrium vapor pressure of a solid is exactly 1 atm.

n-type semiconductor (375): a semiconductor produced when atoms with five valence electrons are added in minute amounts to silicon or germanium; n stands for negative.

nuclear equation (671): an equation representing a nuclear reaction.

nuclear magnetic resonance (NMR) (311): absorption of radio-wave region electromagnetic energy by a sample in a magnetic field.

nuclear reactor (688): a device using a controlled chain reaction to produce thermal energy to power a heat engine.

nucleon (671): a proton or a neutron in a nucleus.

nucleotide (781): a monomer of DNA or RNA that consists of a sugar, a phosphate group, and a nitrogen-containing ring compound called a base.

nucleus (16): that (central) part of an atom in which are concentrated essentially all the mass and all the positive charge of the atom.

O

octahedral (296): shaped like an octahedron; the shape of an AX_6 molecule.

octahedron (293): a regular solid body that has six vertices and eight faces, each of which is an identical equilateral triangle. All six vertices are equivalent.

octet rule (264): states that many elements form covalent bonds so as to end up with eight electrons in their outer shells. The octet rule is particularly useful for compounds that contain carbon, nitrogen, oxygen, and fluorine.

oleum (590): fuming sulfuric acid, $H_2S_2O_7$ (35% in H_2SO_4).

opposite spins (220): spins in opposite directions. Two electrons that have opposite spins have different values of m_s.

optical isomer (776): nonsuperimposable isomers that are mirror images of each other.

orbital (211): a one-electron wave function.

organic acid (759): an organic compound that contains dissociable protons.

organic compound (742): a compound that contains carbon atoms.

ortho (754): designation for disubstituted benzenes with substituents at the 1 and 2 positions.

orthosilicate ion (376): the simplest silicate anion, SiO_4^{4-}.

osmosis (393): the spontaneous passage of a solvent (usually water) from a dilute solution to a more concentrated solution through a semipermeable membrane.

osmotic pressure (393): the hydrostatic pressure produced in the process of the passage of a solvent through a rigid semipermeable membrane from a dilute solution to a more concentrated solution. The osmotic pressure, π, is given by the equation $\pi = RTM_c$, where R is the gas constant, T is the absolute temperature, and M_c is the colligative molarity of the solution.

Ostwald process (463): the conversion of ammonia to nitric acid involving the oxidation of NH_3 to NO_2 and the dissolution of NO_2 in water.

outer electron (197): an electron in the shell with the highest value of the principal quantum number, n.

overlap (319): the combining of an orbital of one atom with an orbital of another atom.

oxidation (62, 571): a process that involves an increase in the oxidation state of an atom. Oxidation involves a loss of electrons.

oxidation half-reaction (572): the half-reaction in which electrons appear on the right-hand side.

oxidation state (568): a number assigned to an atom in a chemical species by a set of rules based on the number of electrons and on the electronegativities of the various atoms in the species.

oxidation-reduction reaction (62, 568): a chemical reaction involving a transfer of electrons from one species to another.

oxidized (62, 571): transferred electrons or increased oxidation state.

oxidizing agent (572): the reactant that contains the atom that is reduced in an electron transfer reaction.

oxyacid (66, 667): an inorganic acid that contains oxygen atoms.

oxyhalogen (667): a compound that contains oxygen and a halogen.

ozone layer (245): the region between 15 and 30 km in altitude in the atmosphere that contains ozone, O_3, produced photochemically by the action of solar ultraviolet light on oxygen.

P

p orbital (213): an orbital for which $l = 1$. All p orbitals are cylindrically symmetric. There are three p orbitals for each value of $n \geq 2$.

paper-chromatography (39): an analytical technique for separating compounds in solution using treated porous paper that is dipped in a liquid which is allowed to wick along the paper, thus separating the compounds.

para (754): designation for disubstituted benzenes with substituents at the 1 and 4 positions.

parallel spins (223): spins in the same direction. Electrons that have parallel spins have the same value of m_s.

paramagnetic (339): magnetized by an external magnetic field and consequently attracted to the region between the poles of a magnet. Paramagnetic molecules contain at least one unpaired electron.

partial pressure (140): the pressure exerted by one component in a mixture of gases.

pascal (129): the SI unit of pressure. A pascal, Pa, is equal to 1 newton per square meter, $1 \ N \cdot m^{-2}$; 1 kilopascal corresponds to about $\frac{1}{100}$ of an atmosphere.

Pauli exclusion principle (218): the principle that no two electrons in the same atom can have the same set of four quantum numbers.

peptide bond (777): the bond formed when the amino group on one amino acid reacts with the carboxylic acid group on another amino acid. The peptide bond is

$$-\overset{\overset{\displaystyle\cdot\cdot}{\|}}{\underset{\displaystyle\cdot\text{O}\cdot}{C}}-\overset{\displaystyle\cdot\cdot}{\underset{\displaystyle H}{N}}-$$

percent dissociation (476): the percentage of an acid in aqueous solution that has transferred a proton to water.

percentage yield (106): the ratio of the actual yield to the theoretical yield times 100.

period (52): a horizontal row of the periodic table.

periodic table of the elements (49): an arrangement of the elements according to increasing atomic number such that elements that have similar properties appear in the same column of the table.

peroxide (83, 160): a compound with an oxygen-oxygen single bond ($-O-O-$). The peroxide ion is O_2^{2-}.

pH (472): a measure of the acidity of an aqueous solution. The pH is defined as $pH = -\log[H_3O^+]$.

pH meter (474): an instrument used to determine pH by means of electrochemical measurements.

pH transition range of an indicator (512): the pH region in which the acid form and the base form of an indicator are present simultaneously in similar amounts. The pH range is equal to $pK_{ai} \pm 1$, where K_{ai} is the acid dissociation constant of the indicator.

phase diagram (359): a simultaneous plot of the equilibrium vapor pressure curve, the equilibrium sublimation pressure curve, and the solid-liquid equilibrium curve (melting point curve) of a substance.

phosphate rock (504): ores containing the phosphate group PO_4^{3-}.

photochemical (243): light induced.

photochemical smog (244): an especially irritating smog produced by the action of sunlight on a mixture of oxides of nitrogen, oxygen, and hydrocarbons in the atmosphere.

photochromic glass (378): glass that contains small dispersed amounts of silver chloride.

photodissociation (244): the dissociation of a molecule produced by light absorption.

photoelectric effect (202): the phenomenon in which electrons are ejected from the surface of a metal if the surface is irradiated with certain ultraviolet radiation.

photoelectron spectroscopy (341): the measurement of the photon energies required to eject electrons from gaseous molecules.

photoelectron spectrum (341): a plot of the photon energies required to eject electrons from a gaseous molecule.

photon (202): packet of energy that constitutes electromagnetic energy. The energy of one photon is given by $E = h\nu$.

photosynthesis (158): the conversion of CO_2 and H_2O into carbohydrates and O_2 in plants, a process that is driven by the energy of absorbed sunlight.

π bond (330): the result of two electrons occupying a π orbital.

π orbital (330): a localized bond orbital that is the result of combining p atomic orbitals from different atoms. The cross section of a π orbital is similar to that of an atomic p orbital.

π^* orbital (337): designation for an antibonding π orbital.

pig iron (705): iron obtained directly from a blast furnace.

PIXE (particle-induced X-ray emission) (683): an analytical method that is used to measure quantities of elements in very small samples. A sample that is irradiated with a beam of protons yields nuclear products that emit X-rays of energies that are characteristic of each isotope.

pK_a (478): a measure of the strength of an acid. The value of pK_a is given by $pK_a = -\log K_a$.

pK_b (483): a measure of the strength of a base. The value of pK_b is given by $pK_b = -\log K_b$.

planar (289): two-dimensional; flat.

planar molecule (275): a molecule in which all the atoms lie in a plane.

Planck's constant (202): the proportionality constant, h, that relates the energy, E, and frequency, ν, of electromagnetic radiation. The equation is $E = h\nu$, where $h = 6.626 \times 10^{-34}$ J·s.

plastic sulfur (589): a rubbery form of sulfur that occurs when liquid sulfur is quenched.

pOH (474): by definition pOH $\equiv$ $-\log[OH^-]$.

polar bond (280): a covalent bond in which the electron pair is not shared equally by each atom. The electron pair is more likely to be found near the more electronegative atom.

polar molecule (283, 304): a molecule that has a dipole moment.

polyatomic ion (63): an ion that consists of more than one atom.

polyatomic molecule (318): a molecule composed of three or more atoms.

polydentate ligand (723): a ligand that attaches to a metal ion at more than one coordination position.

polymer (377, 770): a long chainlike molecule that is formed by joining together many small molecules called monomers.

polymerization (770): a reaction in which monomers combine to form a polymer.

polynucleotide (781): a polymer made up of nucleotides.

polypeptide (778): a molecule composed of a chain of amino acids joined together by peptide bonds.

polypeptide backbone (778): the chain in a polypeptide to which the amino acid side groups are attached.

polyprotic acid (485): an acid that can donate more than one proton per acid molecule.

positional disorder (599): the distribution of the particles of a substance over positions in space.

positive deviation (Raoult's law) (397): deviation from Raoult's law by a nonideal solution whose vapor pressure is greater than that calculated by Raoult's law.

positron (672): a particle that has the same mass as an electron but a positive charge.

power (188): the rate of production or utilization of energy.

precipitate (71): an insoluble product of a reaction that occurs in solution.

precipitation reaction (71): a double replacement reaction involving the formation of a precipitate.

pressure (128): force per unit area. Gas pressure is the force exerted by a gas per unit area on the wall of its container. Common units of pressure are the torr and the standard atmosphere, atm. The SI unit of pressure is the pascal, Pa (1 atm = 760 torr = 101.3 kPa = 14.7 psi).

primary alcohol (757): an alcohol in which the —OH group is attached to a carbon atom that is attached to only one other carbon atom, as in RCH_2OH.

primary battery (649): a nonrechargeable battery.

primary structure (778): the order of the amino acid units in a polypeptide.

principal of maximum overlap (319): an explanation of bonding in molecules that views a covalent bond as the result of maximizing the overlap of orbitals on the two atoms joined by a chemical bond.

principal quantum number (211): the integer, n, that specifies the energy of the electron in the hydrogen atom. The principal quantum number can take on the values 1, 2, 3, ...

probability density (211): the probability that an electron will be found in a small volume, ΔV, surrounding the point (x, y, z). The probability density is given by $\psi^2 \Delta V$, where ψ^2 is the square of the wave function.

product (45): a substance that is formed in a chemical reaction.

proof (alcohol) (398): twice the percentage by volume of alcohol in an alcohol-water solution.

protein (775, 778): a naturally occurring polypeptide.

proton (17): a subatomic particle that has a positive charge equal in magnitude but opposite in sign to that of an electron, and a mass almost equal to that of a hydrogen atom.

proton acceptor (468): a species capable of accepting a proton from an acid.

proton donor (468): a species capable of donating a proton to a base.

proton transfer reaction (468): a reaction in which a proton is transmitted from one species to another. It is also called a protonation reaction.

protonation reaction (468): a reaction involving the transfer of a proton from one species to another. It is also called a proton transfer reaction.

p-type semiconductor (375): a semiconductor produced when atoms with three valence electrons are added in minute amounts to silicon or germanium; p stands for positive.

pure covalent bond (280): a bond in which the electron pair is shared equally by each atom joined by the covalent bond.

pure ionic bond (281): an electrostatic bond formed when one electron from one atom is transferred completely to another atom.

Q

Q_c (451): the reaction quotient expressed in terms of concentrations of reactants and products.

Q_p (451): the reaction quotient expressed in terms of pressures of reactants and products.

Q/K (452): the value of the ratio of the reaction quotient to the equilibrium constant of a chemical reaction. The numerical value of Q/K indicates the direction in which a nonequilibrium reaction system spontaneously proceeds toward equilibrium.

quadratic equation (442): an algebraic equation that can be put in the form $ax^2 + bx + c = 0$, where a, b, and c are known and x is unknown.

quadratic formula (442): the solution to a quadratic equation. The two roots of a quadratic equation are given by

$$x = \frac{-b \pm \sqrt{b^2 - 4ac}}{2a}$$

qualitative analysis (559): the determination of the species present in a sample.

qualitative observation (7): expression of the result of an observation or experiment as general (nonnumerical) characteristics.

quanta (202): discrete units of electromagnetic energy.

quantitative analysis (559): the determination of the amount of each species in a sample.

quantitative measurement (6): expression of the result of an observation or experiment as a number.

quantitative reaction (578): a chemical reaction whose equilibrium constant is very large.

quantization of energy (204): restriction of energy to certain, discrete values.

quantized (207): restricted to certain fixed values.

quantum condition (206): the relationship between the radius of the orbit of an electron around hydrogen nucleus and the wavelength of the electron. In an equation, $2\pi r = n\lambda$ $n = 1, 2, 3, \ldots$.

quantum number (211): an integer or half-integer that, in sets of four, characterizes the energy states of atoms.

quantum theory (204): the theory that predicts the quantized energies of particles.

quenching (589): quickly placing a heated substance into cold water.

R

radioactive (15, 671): decompose spontaneously by the emission of a small particle such as an alpha particle or a beta particle.

radioactive decay (672): the process in which a radioactive nucleus emits a particle and transforms to another nucleus.

radioactivity (15, 671): property of certain nuclei that spontaneously emit small particles such as alpha particles or beta particles.

radiocarbon dating (678): carbon-14 dating.

radioisotope (671): a radioactive isotope.

Raoult's law (386): states that the equilibrium vapor pressure of a solvent over a solution is proportional to the mole fraction of the solvent. The equation is $P_1 = X_1 P_1^\circ$, where P_1 is the equilibrium vapor pressure of the solution, P_1° is the equilibrium vapor pressure of the pure solvent at the same temperature as the solution, and X_1 is the mole fraction of the solvent.

rare-earth element (54): any member of the lanthanides, or the series of elements lanthanum ($Z = 57$) through ytterbium ($Z = 70$). The rare earths occur because of the sequential filling of the $4f$ orbitals.

Raschig synthesis (464): the formation of hydrazine, N_2H_4, via the reaction of ammonia, NH_3, with sodium hypochlorite, $NaClO$.

rate constant (409): the proportionality constant between the reaction rate and the concentrations of the reactants that appear in the rate law.

rate-determining step (416): the step in a reaction mechanism that controls the overall reaction rate. The rate-determining step is much slower than any other step in the reaction mechanism.

rate law (408): the rate of a reaction expressed in terms of the concentrations of the species that affect the reaction rate.

rate of crystallization (383): the number of moles of solute that crystallize from a solution per second.

rate of solution (383): the number of moles of solute that dissolve per second.

reactant (45): a substance consumed in a chemical reaction; it appears on the left side of the chemical equation.

reaction mechanism (416): the sequence of elementary processes by which reactants are converted to products.

reaction quotient, *Q* (451): the ratio of arbitrary or initial product concentrations to arbitrary or initial reactant concentrations, with each concentration factor raised to a power equal to the stoichiometric coefficient of that species in the balanced equation. Pure liquids and solids do not appear in the reaction quotient expression. For the balanced chemical equation

$$aA(g) + bB(soln) + cC(s) \rightleftharpoons$$
$$xX(g) + yY(soln) + zZ(l)$$

the reaction quotient is given by

$$Q = \frac{[X]_0^x[Y]_0^y}{[A]_0^a[B]_0^b}$$

reaction rate (405): the rate at which a reactant, A, is consumed or a product, P, is produced. The rate is defined as

$$\text{rate} = \frac{-\Delta[A]}{\Delta t} = \frac{\Delta[P]}{\Delta t}$$

Units of the reaction rate are $M \cdot s^{-1}$ (moles per liter per second).

reactivity series (69): an ordering of the metals according to their chemical reactivity.

red phosphorus (503): an allotrope of phosphorus, which is less reactive than the white form.

redox reaction (568): an oxidation-reduction or electron-transfer reaction.

reduced (62, 571): decreased oxidation state of a species; gained electrons.

reducing agent (572): the reactant that contains the atom that is oxidized in an electron transfer reaction.

reduction (62, 571): a process that involves a decrease in the oxidation state of an atom. Reduction involves a gain of electrons.

reduction half-reaction (572): the half-reaction in which electrons appear on the left-hand side.

relative humidity (356): the ratio of the partial pressure of the water vapor in the atmosphere to the equilibrium vapor pressure of water at the same temperature times 100:

$$\text{relative humidity} = \frac{P_{H_2O}}{P^\circ_{H_2O}} \times 100$$

resonance (272): the procedure of superimposing each of the possible Lewis formulas for a molecule or ion to obtain a more accurate picture of the electron distribution.

resonance form (272): one of the possible Lewis formulas that can be written for a molecule or an ion without altering the positions of the nuclei.

resonance hybrid (273): a superimposed formula of a species for which it is possible to write more than one satisfactory Lewis formula.

resonance stabilization (275): the stability of a species ascribed to the fact that the energy of the species represented by a superposition of Lewis formulas is lower than the energy of any of its individual Lewis formulas.

reverse osmosis (394): the process in which the solvent (usually water) passes through a rigid semipermeable membrane from a solution to the pure solvent as a result of applying to the solution a pressure in excess of the osmotic pressure.

reverse rate (435): the rate of the reverse (right to left) reaction.

reverse reaction (424, 435): the formation of the reactants from the reaction products, or the reaction that proceeds right to left for the equation as written.

reverse reaction rate (424): the rate of the reaction that occurs right to left as the equation is written.

rhombic (588): in the text, a crystalline form of sulfur.

RNA (781): ribonucleic acid. RNA is a polynucleotide composed of the sugar ribose, the phosphate group, and the four bases adenine, uracil, guanine, and cytosine.

roasting (of an ore) (587): heating an ore in the presence of oxygen.

S

s orbital (213): an orbital for which $l = 0$. All s orbitals are spherically symmetric.

sacrificial anode (711): a reactive piece of metal that is electrically connected to a less active metal and that is preferentially oxidized, thereby protecting the less active metal against corrosion.

salt (73): an ionic compound formed in a neutralization reaction or in the reaction of a metal and a nonmetal.

salt bridge (632): a concentrated electrolyte solution suspended in a gel that is used to make electrical contact between two different electrolyte solutions that are part of an electrochemical cell.

saturated hydrocarbon (743): a hydrocarbon in which the bonding about each carbon atom is tetrahedral. No more hydrogen atoms can be added to any carbon atom. (See alkane.)

saturated solution (384): a solution in which no more solute can be dissolved.

Schrödinger equation (211): the central equation of quantum theory, which takes into account the wave nature of electrons and yields the discrete energy levels of atoms and molecules.

scientific law (3): a concise summary of a large body of experimental results.

scientific method (2): the use of carefully controlled experiments to answer certain questions.

scientific theory (3): an explanation of a scientific law and an aid in making predictions that lead to new knowledge.

scrubber (243): a device that is used to remove SO_2 from the effluent gases produced by fossil fuel combustion.

second electron affinity, EA_2 (255): the energy associated with the process of adding an electron to a singly charged negative ion according to

$$X^-(g) + e^- \longrightarrow X^{2-}(g)$$

second excited state (207): the second available energy state above the ground state.

second ionization energy (195): the minimum energy required to remove an electron from an A^+ ion to produce the A^{2+} ion.

second-order rate law (411): a rate law in which the reaction rate is proportional to the second power of the concentration of a reactant. The rate law is of the form rate $= k[A]^2$ or rate $= k[A][B]$.

second-order reaction (411): a reaction whose rate law is a second-order rate law.

secondary alcohol (757): an alcohol in which the —OH group is attached to a carbon atom that is attached to two other carbon atoms, as in

$$RCH_2CHCH_3 \atop | \atop OH$$

secondary battery (649): a battery that is rechargeable.

secondary structure (780): the coiled helical portion in different regions of a protein chain.

second law of thermodynamics (599): states that the total entropy change for a spontaneous process must always be positive. The entropy of the universe is constantly increasing.

seesaw (296): the shape of a AX_4E class molecule or ion.

semiconductor (53): a semimetal. A semimetal conducts electricity and heat less well than metals but better than nonmetals.

semimetal (53): an element that has properties intermediate to metals and nonmetals.

semipermeable membrane (392): a membrane that allows the passage of only certain species, for example, water molecules.

shell (197): the energy level designated by the principal quantum number, n. The $n = 1$ shell is called the K shell; the $n = 2$ shell, the L shell; the $n = 3$ shell, the M shell; and so forth.

side group (775): the group —G in the amino acid

$$H_2N - \underset{\underset{G}{|}}{\overset{\overset{H}{|}}{C}} - COOH$$

σ bond (320): a bond that occurs when a σ orbital is occupied by one electron or two electrons of opposite spin.

σ-bond framework (329): all the σ bonds that are formed in a molecule or ion.

σ orbital (320): a molecular orbital that is cylindrically symmetric when viewed along a line drawn between the two nuclei joined by the covalent bond.

σ^* orbital (337): designation for an antibonding σ orbital.

significant figures (23): the precision of a measured quantity as indicated by the number of digits used to express the result.

silicate polyanion (polysilicate ion) (377): an anionic polymer composed of silicon and oxygen.

simple cubic unit cell (362): the unit cell in which the components of the crystal are located at the corners of a cube.

simplest formula (94): the formula of a substance derived from an analysis of the composition of the compound. It gives the relative number of atoms in the formula unit. (See molecular formula.)

single replacement reaction (67): a reaction in which one element in a compound is replaced by another element.

slag (705): a molten calcium silicate byproduct of the production of iron in a blast furnace.

slope (396, 412, 798): the ratio of the change in the vertical coordinate to the change in the horizontal coordinate, $\Delta y / \Delta x$.

soda ash (85): sodium carbonate, Na_2CO_3.

softened water (539): water from which divalent cations have been removed.

solid (126): the physical state of matter having the properties of fixed volume, fixed shape, and very small compressibility.

solubility (384, 543): the maximum quantity of solute that can be dissolved in a given quantity of solvent in ordinary circumstances.

solubility product constant (544): the equilibrium constant expression obtained by applying the law of concentration action to the equilibrium between an ionic solid and its constituent ions in solution. The symbol is K_{sp}.

solubility rules (543): a set of guidelines that can be used to predict whether an ionic compound is soluble or insoluble in water.

solute (108, 382): a substance that is dissolved in another substance to form a solution.

solution (107, 382): a mixture of two or more substances that is uniform and homogeneous at the molecular level.

solvated electrons (84): a species that results when, for example, sodium metal is dissolved in liquid ammonia:

$$Na(s) \xrightarrow[NH_3(l)]{} Na^+(NH_3) + e^-(NH_3)$$

Solvay process (85): the commercial process used to manufacture $NaHCO_3(s)$ and $Na_2CO_3(s)$.

solvent (108, 382): the substance in which a solute is dissolved to form a solution. The solvent is generally present in greater quantity than the solute.

sp orbital (319): one of the two equivalent hybrid orbitals obtained by the combination of an ns orbital and one np orbital on the same atom. The two sp orbitals point 180° from each other.

sp^2 orbital (322): one of the three equivalent hybrid orbitals obtained by the combination of an ns orbital and two np orbitals on the same atom. The three sp^2 orbitals point to the vertices of an equilateral triangle.

sp^3 orbital (323): one of the four equivalent hybrid atomic orbitals obtained by the combination of an ns orbital and the three np orbitals on the same atom. The four sp^3 orbitals point to the vertices of a tetrahedron.

space-filling molecular model (289): a model of a molecule that is constructed to represent the relative sizes of the atoms in the molecule and the angles between bonds.

specific activity (691): a measure of the activity of a radioactive substance; the number of nuclei that disintegrate per second per gram of radioactive isotope. [See Equation 21-8].

specific heat, c_{sp} (176): the heat capacity per gram of substance. The SI unit of specific heat is joules per kelvin per gram, $J \cdot K^{-1} \cdot g^{-1}$.

spectator ion (72): an ion present in a solution that does not participate directly in a reaction.

spectrochemical series (732): an arrangement of ligands in order of increasing ability of the ligands to split the metal d orbitals: $Cl^- < F^- < H_2O < NH_3 < NO_2^- < CN^- < CO$.

spectroscopic method (310): any of a number of analytical methods that employ spectra to identify or measure the amounts of compounds.

spectrum (309): a plot of the electromagnetic energy absorbed versus the wavelength of the energy for a species.

speed of light (199): light travels with a speed of 3.00×10^8 m $\cdot$ s^{-1}. It is denoted by the symbol c.

spherically symmetric (211): characteristic of a function that depends only on the distance from a center and not on its direction in space.

spin down (219): the state in which the spin quantum number, m_s, is $-\frac{1}{2}$.

spin quantum number (217): the quantum number, m_s, that designates the spin state of an electron. The allowed values of m_s are $+\frac{1}{2}$ or $-\frac{1}{2}$.

spin up (219): the state in which the spin quantum number, m_s, is $+\frac{1}{2}$.

spontaneous (608): proceeding without external input.

square planar (296): the shape of an AX_4E_2 molecule.

square pyramidal (296): shaped like a pyramid with a square base; the shape of an AX_5E molecule.

standard atmosphere (atm) (129): a unit of pressure. One atmosphere is equal to 760 torr.

standard cell voltage (639): the voltage of an electrochemical cell when Q for the cell reaction is equal to 1. The standard cell voltage, $E°$, is related to the equilibrium constant for the reaction by the equation

$$E° = \left(\frac{0.0592 \text{ V}}{n} \right) \log K \text{ at } 25°C$$

where n is the number of moles of electrons transferred in the equation as written.

standard enthalpy change, $\Delta H°_{rxn}$ (167): the amount of energy absorbed or evolved as heat when all gases are at 1 atm and all solution species are at 1 M.

standard entropy, $S°$ (602): the entropy of a substance at 1 atm. If the substance is a solute, then its concentration is 1 M.

standard entropy change, $\Delta S°_{rxn}$ (605): the value of the entropy change for a reaction when all gases, solids, and liquids are at 1 atm and all solutes are at 1 M.

standard Gibbs free energy change, $\Delta G°_{rxn}$ (610): the value of ΔG_{rxn} at 25°C when all gases are at one atm and all solution species are at one molar.

standard molar enthalpy of formation, $\Delta H°_f$ (170): the enthalpy change for the reaction in which one mole of substance at 1 atm and 25°C is formed from the elements at 1 atm and 25°C.

standard molar Gibbs free energy of formation $\Delta G°_f$ (612): the Gibbs free energy change for the formation of a substance at 25°C from its constituent elements all at standard conditions.

standard reduction voltage (641): the standard voltage, $E°$, for a half-reaction based on the assignment of $E° = 0$ for the electrode reaction

$$2H^+(aq, 1 \text{ M}) + 2e^- \longrightarrow H_2(g, 1 \text{ atm})$$

The standard cell voltage, $E°_{cell}$, is given by

$$E°_{cell} = E°_{red} - E°_{ox}$$

where $E°_{red}$ is the standard reduction voltage of the right electrode in an electrochemical cell and $E°_{ox}$ ($-E°_{red}$) is the standard oxidation voltage of the left electrode in an electrochemical cell.

stationary state (207): one of the allowed energy states of an atom or a molecule.

steam reforming reaction (156): a large-scale process of producing hydrogen from natural gas and steam according to the reaction

$$CH_4(g) + H_2O(g) \xrightarrow[30 \text{ atm}]{1000°C} CO(g) + 3H_2(g)$$

steel (705): an alloy composed primarily of iron with variable amounts of carbon and other substances added to produce special properties.

stereoisomers (331): molecules with the same atom-to-atom bonding but different spatial arrangements of the atoms.

stereospecific reaction (777): a reaction in which the relative orientations of the groups attached to a specific atom are unchanged.

stoichiometric coefficient (98): a numerical coefficient of a reactant or product species in a balanced chemical equation; a balancing coefficient.

stoichiometrically equivalent to ⇌ (94): a symbol that denotes a stoichiometric correspondence between two quantities.

stoichiometry (93): the procedures for the calculations of the quantities of elements or compounds involved in chemical reactions.

stratosphere (239): the region of the atmosphere from 10 to 50 km in altitude that lies above the troposphere.

strong acid (469): an acid that is completely dissociated in aqueous solution.

strong base (470): a base that produces concentration of $OH^-(aq)$ in aqueous solution equal to the concentration of the base.

strong electrolyte (248): an electrolyte that is 100 percent or near 100 percent dissociated into ions in solutions.

structural chemistry (290): the area of chemistry in which the shapes and sizes of molecules are studied.

structural formula (742): a formula that indicates the various attachments of the atoms in a molecule.

structural isomers (743): compounds that have the same molecular formula but different arrangements of the atoms.

subatomic particle (15): one of the particles of which atoms are composed; a proton, neutron, or electron.

subcritical mass (688): a mass of a spontaneously fissionable substance that is insufficient to sustain a nuclear chain reaction.

sublimation (349): the process whereby a solid is converted directly to a gas.

sublimation pressure curve (360): a plot of the pressure of a vapor in equilibrium with its solid versus the temperature.

subshell (211): the group of orbitals designated by a particular l value within a shell.

substitution reaction (67, 744): a single replacement reaction.

substrate (423): the reactant that binds to the enzyme in an enzyme-catalyzed reaction.

sugar-phosphate backbone (783): the chain in a polynucleotide to which the bases are attached. The nucleotides are joined by bonds with the oxygen atom at the five-carbon position on one nucleotide through a phosphate group to the three-carbon position on a second nucleotide.

supercritical mass (688): a mass of a spontaneously fissionable substance that exceeds the mass necessary to sustain a nuclear chain reaction.

supernatant (560): the solution that remains after a substance has been precipitated from the original solution.

superoxide (83, 160): a substance that contains the ion O_2^-, which is called the superoxide ion.

superphosphate (504): water-soluble $Ca(H_2PO_4)_2$, which is an important fertilizer.

symmetry (302): exact correspondence of type and number of atoms on opposite sides of a dividing line or plane or about a center or axis.

synthesis gas (190): a mixture of $CO(g)$ and $H_2(g)$.

T

t_2 orbitals (734): the set of d orbitals of higher energy on a metal ion in a tetrahedral complex. The t_2 orbitals consist of d_{xy}, d_{xz}, and d_{yz}.

t_{2g} (724): the set of d orbitals of lower energy on a metal ion in an octahedral complex. The t_{2g} orbitals consist of $d_{x^2-y^2}$ and d_{z^2}.

talc (377): a mineral that contains two-dimensional silicate sheets with the overall composition $Si_2O_5^{2-}$.

termination reaction (770): a reaction that stops the growth of a polymer chain.

tertiary alcohol (758): an alcohol in which the —OH group is attached to a carbon atom that is attached to three other carbon atoms, as in

$$\begin{array}{c} CH_3 \\ | \\ CH_3CCH_3 \\ | \\ OH \end{array}$$

tertiary structure (780): the three-dimensional shape of a protein.

tetrahedral bond angle (290): the angle between two bonds formed by an atom whose bonds are directed toward the vertices of a tetrahedron. The tetrahedral bond angle is 109.5°.

tetrahedron (289): a regular solid body that has four equivalent vertices and four equivalent faces, each of which is an equilateral triangle.

tetravalent (290): bonded to four other atoms.

theoretical yield (106): the mass of a particular product that is calculated to result if all of the limiting reactant in a balanced chemical equation is converted to products.

theory (3): an explanation of a scientific law.

thermal decomposition (67): a decomposition reaction that occurs when the temperature of a substance is increased.

thermal disorder (599): the distribution of the available energy among the particles of a substance.

thermite reaction (105): a reaction between aluminum metal and a metal oxide that yields Al_2O_3 and the free metal.

thermochemistry (166): the study of the heat evolved or absorbed in chemical reactions.

thermodynamics (164): the study of energy transfers.

thin-layer chromatography (39): see paper-chromatography.

3d transition metal series (226): the series of ten elements with atomic numbers 21 through 30.

threshold frequency (202): the minimum frequency of ultraviolet radiation for electrons to be ejected from a particular metal. The threshold frequency is denoted by ν_0.

tin disease (123): the conversion of white tin to gray tin.

tincture of iodine (664): an alcohol solution of iodine, formerly used as an antiseptic.

titrant (514): the solution of acid (base) that is added to a solution of base (acid) during a titration.

titration (111, 514): the neutralization of a given volume of a basic (acidic) solution by slowly adding an acidic (basic) solution of known concentration until the base (acid) has been completely neutralized.

titration curve (514): a plot of the pH of the solution that results when an acid solution is titrated with a base solution (or when a base solution is titrated with an

acid solution) as a function of the volume of the added solution.

torr (128): a convenient unit of pressure. The pressure of a gas is expressed as the height of a column of mercury that is supported by the pressure of the gas. One torr is one millimeter of mercury.

trans- (331): across from.

trans-cis isomerism (331, 722): geometric isomerism.

transition metal (53, 700): an element in the groups that are not headed by a number in the periodic table. They serve as a transition between the reactive Group 1 and Group 2 metals and the nonmetals.

transuranium element (229, 682): an element of atomic number greater than that of uranium ($Z > 92$).

tridentate (723): a chelating ligand that attaches to three metal coordination positions.

trigonal bipyramid (293, 296): a solid body that has five vertices and six equilateral triangular faces. A trigonal bipyramid has the shape of two triangular pyramids that share an equilateral triangular base.

trigonal planar (292, 296): the shape of a molecule in which the three atoms bonded to a central atom lie at the vertices of an equilateral triangle with the central atom in the center of the triangle. All four atoms lie in the same two-dimensional surface.

trigonal pyramid (294, 296): a solid body that has four vertices and four triangular faces. Three of the four faces are identical. The unique face serves as a triangular base for the pyramid.

triple bond (271): the bond formed between two atoms by three shared electron pairs.

triple point (360): a point on a phase diagram at which three phases of a substance coexist in equilibrium.

triplet code (786): the sequence of three bases or nucleotides along a DNA segment that codes for a particular amino acid.

triprotic acid (485): an acid that has three dissociable protons.

tritium (156): the isotope of hydrogen containing one proton and two neutrons.

trona (85): a mineral with the composition $Na_2CO_3 \cdot NaHCO_3 \cdot 2H_2O(s)$, which yields sodium carbonate when heated.

troposphere (239): the lowest region of the atmosphere, from 0 to 10 km above sea level. Accounts for 80 percent of the mass and contains essentially all of the earth's weather.

T-shaped (296): the shape of an AX_3E_2 molecule.

U

unit cell (362): the smallest subunit of a crystal lattice that contains all the structural information about the crystal.

unit conversion factor (25): an expression that is used to convert a physical quantity from one unit to another. It has the value of unity.

unsaturated hydrocarbon (748): a hydrocarbon that contains carbon atoms that are bonded to each other by double or triple bonds. Hydrogen atoms may be added to unsaturated hydrocarbons.

unsaturated solution (384): a solution in which more of the same solute can be dissolved.

uranium-lead dating (677): the determination of the age of a rock sample from the masses of uranium-238 and lead-206 in the sample.

V

valence band (368): the set of bonding orbitals that extend throughout a crystal and that are analogous to bonding orbitals in a molecule.

valence-bond theory (318): a theory of chemical bonding that involves localized bond orbitals and possibly delocalized bond orbitals.

valence electron (198, 263): an electron in the outer shell of an atom.

valence-shell electron-pair repulsion (VSEPR) theory (290): the theory that the shape of a molecule is determined by the mutual repulsion of the electron pairs in the valence shell of the central atom.

valence-shell electrons (198, 263): the electrons that are located in the outermost occupied shell of an atom.

van der Waals constants (147): the two constants, a and b, that appear in the van der Waals equation. The values of a and b depend on the particular gas.

van der Waals equation (147): an equation that describes the behavior of a nonideal gas. The equation is

$$\left(P + \frac{n^2 a}{V^2}\right)(V - nb) = nRT$$

where a and b are van der Waals constants, whose values depend on the particular gas.

van der Waals forces (353): a general term for the attractive forces between molecules; van der Waals forces include dipole-dipole forces and London forces.

van't Hoff equation (449): the equation that governs the temperature dependence of the equilibrium constant. The van't Hoff equation is

$$\log\left(\frac{K_2}{K_1}\right) = \frac{\Delta H^{\circ}_{rxn}}{2.30R}\left(\frac{T_2 - T_1}{T_1 T_2}\right) \text{(19-15)}$$

where ΔH°_{rxn} is the standard enthalpy of reaction and R is the gas constant.

vapor pressure curve (356): a plot of the equilibrium vapor pressure of a liquid versus temperature.

vapor pressure lowering (387): the amount by which the equilibrium vapor pressure of a solution is less than the equilibrium vapor pressure of the pure solvent.

vector (282): a quantity that has both magnitude and direction.

visible region (200): the region of the electromagnetic spectrum from 400 to 700 nm.

volt (629): the SI unit of voltage.

volatile (38): readily converted from a liquid to a gas; a substance with a relatively high equilibrium vapor pressure.

voltaic pile (624): a device, consisting of alternate discs of dissimilar metals, each separated by an electrolyte layer, that is used to produce a voltage.

volumetric flask (109): a precision-made piece of glassware that can be used to prepare a precise liquid volume.

vulcanization (774): the formation of —S—S— cross-links between polyisoprene chains by reaction with sulfur.

W

water-gas reaction (156, 167, 190): the reaction in which steam is passed over hot carbon to produce a mixture of carbon monoxide and hydrogen:

$$C(s) + H_2O(g) \longrightarrow CO(g) + H_2(g)$$

water-gas shift reaction (190): a reaction in which some of the $CO(g)$ in synthesis gas is converted to $CO_2(g)$ according to

$$CO(g) + H_2O(g) \longrightarrow CO_2(g) + H_2(g)$$

water glass (376): sodium silicate dissolved in water, $Na_4SiO_4(aq)$.

watt (188): the SI unit of power. One watt is one joule per second.

wave function (211): a function that describes the positions of the electrons in an atom or a molecule. A wave function is denoted by ψ, and has the physical interpretation that $\psi^2 \, \Delta V$ is the probability that an electron is to be located in the little volume ΔV.

wave-particle duality (204): the concept that both light and matter appear to be particlelike under certain conditions and to be wavelike under other conditions.

wavelength, λ (198): the distance between successive maxima or minima of a wave. The symbol for wavelength is λ and a unit of wavelength is meters.

weak acid (470): an acid that is incompletely dissociated in aqueous solution or that reacts only partially with water.

weak base (470): a base that reacts only partially with water.

weak electrolyte (248): a substance that dissolves in water to produce solutions that conduct an electric current poorly.

white phosphorus (503): an allotrope of phosphorus, which is very reactive chemically, and which consists of tetrahedral P_4 molecules.

work, w (164): energy transferred when a force acts to cause a displacement of the boundaries of a system.

work function (203): the minimum energy required to remove an electron from the surface of a metal. The work function is denoted by Φ.

X

X-ray crystallography (366): determination of the positions of the atoms in the unit cell of a crystal by X-ray diffraction studies.

X-ray diffraction (205): the scattering of X-rays in a definite pattern by a crystalline substance.

X-ray diffraction pattern (361): the array of spots on an X-ray film that results when X-rays pass through a crystal.

Y

yield (106): the percent conversion of reactants to products in a chemical reaction.

Z

zone refining (375): a recrystallization method involving a moving melted zone that is used to prepare very high-purity crystals.

Physical Constants

Constant	Symbol	Value
atomic mass unit	amu	1.66056×10^{-27} kg
Avogadro's number	N	6.02205×10^{23} mol^{-1}
Bohr radius	a_0	5.292×10^{-11} m
Boltzmann constant	k	1.38066×10^{-23} J$\cdot$K^{-1}
charge of a proton	e	1.60219×10^{-19} C
Faraday constant	F	$96{,}485$ C$\cdot$mol^{-1}
gas constant	R	8.31441 J$\cdot$K$^{-1}\cdot$mol^{-1}
		0.08206 L$\cdot$atm$\cdot$K$^{-1}\cdot$mol^{-1}
mass of an electron	m_e	9.10953×10^{-31} kg
		5.48580×10^{-4} amu
mass of a neutron	m_n	1.67495×10^{-27} kg
		1.00866 amu
mass of a proton	m_p	1.67265×10^{-27} kg
		1.00728 amu
Planck's constant	h	6.62618×10^{-34} J$\cdot$s
speed of light	c	2.997925×10^8 m$\cdot$s^{-1}

SI Prefixes

Prefix	Multiple	Symbol	Prefix	Multiple	Symbol
tera	10^{12}	T	deci	10^{-1}	d
giga	10^9	G	centi	10^{-2}	c
mega	10^6	M	milli	10^{-3}	m
kilo	10^3	k	micro	10^{-6}	μ
			nano	10^{-9}	n
			pico	10^{-12}	p
			femto	10^{-15}	f
			atto	10^{-18}	a